INTRODUCTION TO GENERAL TOPOLOGY

Introduction to
General Topology

HELEN F. CULLEN *University of Massachusetts*

D. C. HEATH AND COMPANY
BOSTON

LIBRARY OF CONGRESS CATALOG CARD NUMBER: 67-16908

PRINTED JULY 1967

PREFACE

The book contains an introduction to general topology suitable for beginning graduate and advanced undergraduate students. The text grew out of a course given to such students at the University of Massachusetts over the past fifteen years. It is hoped that the book will serve to increase the student's understanding of calculus and to prepare the student for modern analysis and further study in topology.

The text starts with the (ϵ, δ)—definition of continuity found in beginning calculus books and builds the topological structure on the generalization of this definition. The book is intended to be self-contained for good post-calculus students and can be studied concurrently with an advanced calculus course. The student needs a small amount of elementary set theory and a good definition of the real number system.

There are many ways to choose a course from the book, depending—as usual—on the maturity of the students in the class, the preferences of the instructor and the time allowed for the course. The basic unit in the book is the section; there are 36 sections. In general, at least after Chapter 1, the first parts of the sections tend to contain the basic material on the particular topic under study. The subheadings throughout each section cut the sections into subunits which may be taken up or skipped at the instructor's discretion. For example, in the middle of section 26 in the chapter on connectedness, a subsection labeled "Quasi-components" is included. This location seems to be reasonable from the point of view of the mathematics but "quasi-components" may not be regarded by all instructors in a one-semester course as being as basic or essential as the material at the beginning of some of the later sections on compactness. These subheadings are intended to help the instructor tell at a glance how much of the section is appropriate for his particular course.

Chapter 1 develops gradually the general topological structure through the concepts of basic neighborhood relation, open set, closed set, derived set, closure, base, subbase, first and second countability, homeomorphism, topological invariant, net, filter, and convergence. The term basic neighborhood is used to describe Hausdorff's original neighborhoods. All common ways of defining a topological space are investigated but the now standard "set and topology" definition is used throughout after its introduction toward the end of section 3.

As a result of this developmental approach, however, the first three sections of chapter 1 may seem to some to proceed at too slow a pace. To compensate for this, an abbreviated summary is included at the end of section 3 which restates the basic definitions of topology. This summary could, with a few back looks, be used more or less as a starting point for an instructor who decided that his class could omit some of the developmental and motivational material in the sections which precede it. Lastly, in chapter 1 only, all functions are "onto." Since every function is "onto" its range, this is no restriction for the topics discussed in chapter 1.

Chapter 2 contains a discussion of the lattice of all topologies on a set and a study of the important methods for generating spaces. The relative topology, the weak and strong topologies, defined by functions, are all introduced, as are product spaces and quotient spaces. With the introduction of the relative topology, "into" for functions is defined and then used throughout the rest of the book.

Chapter 3 contains a study of the separation axioms starting with the T_0-axiom and progressing through T_1, T_2, regular, completely regular, and normal spaces. The category of Hausdorff spaces is introduced. Separation of points and sets by functions into the space E^1 of real numbers is introduced, and the Urysohn lemma and Tietze extension theorems are proved. The chapter ends with the introduction of the ring $C(X)$ of continuous functions from a completely regular space X into E^1. The ring is proved to be a topological invariant up to isomorphisms and introduces the student to the idea of an algebraic topological invariant.

Chapter 4 begins with a study of metrics and metrizable spaces. It is established soon thereafter that every metrizable space is normal and first countable. Further it is shown that separability and second countability are equivalent for metrizable spaces. Products of metrizable spaces are studied. Every normal, second countable space is proved to be metrizable in the Urysohn imbedding theorem. Important examples of metrizable spaces are studied, including the Euclidean spaces, Hilbert space and certain function spaces. Uniform convergence is introduced. Metric spaces are defined. Completeness is introduced and every metric space is imbedded isometrically in a complete metric space. Every complete metric space is shown to be of the second category and the fixed point theorem for contraction mappings on complete metric spaces is included. Lastly, uniform continuity, uniform structures, uniformizable spaces and the topology of uniform convergence are introduced. Hausdorff uniformizable spaces are characterized as completely regular spaces. Uniform spaces are introduced and every Hausdorff uniform space is imbedded in a complete Hausdorff uniform space by a homeomorphism which is uniformly continuous both ways.

Chapter 5 contains an introduction to the topological property of connectedness. The basic concepts defined in terms of connectedness, namely, cut point, local connectedness, pathwise connectedness, components and q-components, are introduced. Connected subsets of E^1 are studied and the intermediate value theorem and the fixed point theorem for the real interval $[a, b]$ are proved.

Chapter 6 contains an introduction to the topological property of compactness. The related concepts of countable compactness, local compactness, compactification and paracompactness are also studied. Equivalent definitions of compactness in terms of closed sets, filters and nets are included. A countably compact but not compact space is introduced. Any product of compact spaces is proved to be compact. The combinations "compact and connected," "compact and Hausdorff," "compact and metric" and "compact and uniform" are studied in some detail. The basic Stone-Weierstrass theorem is proved. The one-point and the Stone-Čech compactifications are introduced. Curves are introduced, and the arc, the simple closed curve and the Peano space are all characterized. Arcwise connectedness and pathwise connectedness are proved to be equivalent in Hausdorff spaces. The last section of the chapter introduces paracompactness. Dieudonné's proof that every paracompact space is normal and A. H. Stone's proof that every metric space is paracompact are both included. Lastly Smirnov's metrization theorem is proved as well as the Smirnov-Dieudonné theorem that a locally metrizable, Hausdorff space is metrizable if and only if it is paracompact. Partitions of unity are also introduced.

Chapter 7, the last chapter in the book, contains an introduction to homotopy. The basic homotopy equivalence for functions and the basic homotopy equivalence for spaces, as a generalization of the topological equivalence for spaces, are introduced. Then, again to acquaint the student with the idea of an algebraic topological invariant, the fundamental groupoid and the fundamental group are introduced. Hurewicz's elementary proof, that the fundamental group of the circumference space, S^1, is not trivial, is included. Finally, path spaces, the higher homotopy groups and H-spaces are introduced and the higher homotopy groups are proved to be abelian.

Problems have been included throughout the text at appropriate points to emphasize a concept or a theorem. Examples are included to illustrate each concept and property. Definitions, lemmas, theorems, corollaries, and examples are numbered, first with a section number and then with a position number relative to that section; e. g., "15.10 Theorem" is the 10th item in section 15. The Halmos symbol ▮ is used to signal the end of a proof.

A partial list of definitions and symbols is included at the end of the text.

HELEN CULLEN
University of Massachusetts

ACKNOWLEDGMENTS

The author wishes to acknowledge both the direct and indirect contributions of many persons: her teachers; her students; her two colleagues at the University of Massachusetts, Dr. Robert Wagner who urged her to undertake the writing of the book in the first place and Dr. Lorraine Lavallee who used part of the manuscript in a one-semester course and made several good suggestions. The author also wishes to acknowledge the contribution of her colleague, Dr. Richard Palais at Brandeis University, who read the entire manuscript thoroughly and made many comments which have resulted, without question, in improving the presentation in many places.

Lastly, the author acknowledges, with thanks, the patient and scholarly attitude of Dr. Richard T. Wareham of D. C. Heath and Company.

H. F. C.

CONTENTS

INTRODUCTION TO GENERAL TOPOLOGY

CHAPTER 1

The General Topological Structure

1. BASIC HAUSDORFF NEIGHBORHOOD RELATIONS ON SETS.

The structure called a topological space is the most general structure on which continuous functions can be usefully defined. Hence the topological space is the modern answer to the question, "With a set of elements X, a set of elements Y and a function f from X onto Y, what structure is needed on X and/or Y before it can be decided whether such a function f is continuous?" Consequently, our study begins with the definition of continuity found in a beginning calculus book.

Let f be a function which has the set of all real numbers as its domain and range. Such a function is said to be continuous at a point p if and only if for any real number $\epsilon > 0$, there exists a real number $\delta > 0$, such that if "$|x - p| < \delta$" is true, then "$|f(x) - f(p)| < \epsilon$" is true. $f(x)$ and $f(p)$ denote the images of x and p respectively. The geometric interpretation indicates that δ and ϵ serve merely to identify subsets (intervals) A and B of real numbers that are "close to" p and $f(p)$, respectively. Continuity then requires that for any "such" set B there exists another "such" set A that is mapped by f into B, i.e., for x in A, $f(x)$ is in B.

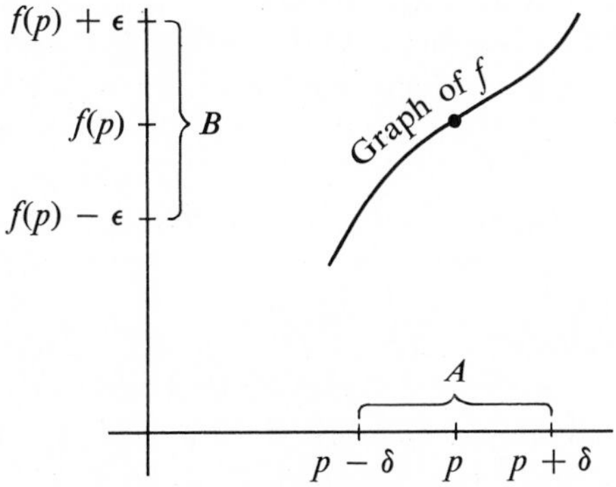

FIGURE 1

Thus continuity in calculus is defined in terms of certain sets associated with individual points in the domain and range. The first objective then is to define a collection of such sets for any set X. It is this assignment of A to p and of B to $f(p)$ which must be generalized; hence, the basic relevant properties of this assignment must be observed and recorded.

One of the first questions which arises is "Can $\{p\}$ serve as a set A and $\{f(p)\}$ serve as a set B?" The answer to this question will change as the theory develops. However, for the present, let us consider what the effect on continuity would be if either or both of these situations occurred. If $\{p\}$ could be A, then every function f would be continuous at every point of its domain, since $A = \{p\}$ would always be mapped into any set B containing $f(p)$. If $\{f(p)\}$ could be B, while A had to be a usual δ-interval, then no function would be continuous at a point p unless it was constant throughout some interval containing p. Neither of these results seems desirable, so the sets associated with points ought to have the properties of the interiors of intervals; i.e., the set of points between the end points should, it appears, be non-empty.

Another question which arises is whether the end points play any significant role. In other words, would the definition "for each $\epsilon > 0$, there exists a $\delta > 0$ such that $|x - p| \leq \delta$ implies that $|f(x) - f(p)| \leq \epsilon$" yield the same "continuity" as the usual definition? To settle this question, let $A^* = \{x \mid a \leq x \leq b\}$ and assume $f[A] \subseteq B$. If $A = \{x \mid a < x < b\}$, $f[A] \subseteq B$ also. Conversely, if $I = \{x \mid a < x < b\}$ and $f[I] \subseteq B$, then for $I^* = \{x \mid a + (b - a)/4 \leq x \leq b - (b - a)/4\}$, $f[I^*] \subseteq B$ also. Thus any function that is continuous according to one definition is continuous by the other definition also. Hence the definitions are equivalent.

The above considerations lead then to the following conclusions: the end points of the intervals are not significant, i.e., they may or may not be included, but the so-called interiors of the intervals are essential. The properties of these interiors and their relation to their midpoints are described in the "*basic neighborhood axioms*" for a topological space *due to Hausdorff*.

The first three of Hausdorff's original axioms constitute the start of our study of the general topological structure called a topological space. The term "basic neighborhood" is used throughout the book in place of Hausdorff's term "neighborhood" for two reasons—(1) the unqualified term "neighborhood" is used today with a larger meaning than that with which Hausdorff originally used it (definition 1.3 and lemma 1.4), and (2) the word "basic" is justified by theorem 3.46.

$P(S)$ will always denote the set of all subsets of the set S—the so-called *power set* of S.

1.1 Definition. A *basic neighborhood relation* R for a set S is a relation whose domain is S, whose range is contained in $P(S)$ and which satisfies the following three conditions (the first three *Hausdorff neighborhood axioms*):

Axiom BN-I: (p, V) in R implies that p is in V;

Axiom BN-II: (p, V) and (p, W) in R implies that there exists G in $P(S)$ such that $G \subseteq V \cap W$ and (p, G) is in R;

Axiom BN-III: (p, V) in R and q in V imply that there exists W in $P(S)$ such that $W \subseteq V$ and (q, W) is in R.

1.2 Definition. A set V of $P(S)$ is called a *basic neighborhood* of a point p relative to a basic neighborhood relation R for S if and only if (p, V) is in R.

Thus a basic neighborhood relation is a collection of elements (p, V) in $S \times P(S)$. Axiom BN-I says that every basic neighborhood of a point contains the point. Axiom BN-II says that two basic neighborhoods of a point p contain in their intersection a basic neighborhood of p. Axiom BN-III says that any basic neighborhood contains a basic neighborhood for each of its points.

EXERCISE 1. Let S denote the set of real numbers. Let $R = \{(p, V_p^\epsilon) \mid V_p^\epsilon = \{x \mid |x - p| < \epsilon \text{ for } \epsilon > 0\}\}$. Prove that R is a basic neighborhood relation for S and hence that axioms BN-I, BN-II and BN-III do describe properties of the relation that assigns the "interiors" of intervals of real numbers to their midpoints. This is the usual basic neighborhood relation for the real numbers.

EXERCISE 2. Let S denote the set of all ordered pairs of real numbers. Prove that the relation $R = \{((a, b), U_{(a,b)}^\epsilon) \mid U_{(a,b)}^\epsilon = \{(x, y) \mid |x - a| < \epsilon \text{ and } |y - b| < \epsilon \text{ for } \epsilon > 0\}\}$ is a basic neighborhood relation for S. This relation is one of the usual basic neighborhood relations for the number plane, Euclidean 2-space.

EXERCISE 3. Let S denote the set of real numbers. Prove that the relation $R = \{(p, V_p) \mid V_p = \{x \mid x \geq p\}\}$ is a basic neighborhood relation for S.

EXERCISE 4. Let S denote the set of all ordered pairs of real numbers. Let $R = \{((a, b), U_{(a,b)}^\epsilon) \mid U_{(a,b)}^\epsilon = \{(x, y) \mid x = a \text{ and } |y - b| < \epsilon \text{ for } \epsilon > 0\}\}$. Prove that R is a basic neighborhood relation for S.

EXERCISE 5. Let S denote the set of natural numbers. Let $R = \{(k, U_k) \mid U_k = \{j \mid j \text{ divides } k\}\}$. Prove that R is a basic neighborhood relation for S.

EXERCISE 6. Let S be a set. Let $R = \{(x, S) \mid x \in S\}$. Prove that R is a basic neighborhood relation for S.

EXERCISE 7. Let S denote the set of real numbers. Let $R = \{(x, U) \mid x \text{ is real and } U = \{x\}\}$. Prove that R is a basic neighborhood relation for S.

This last exercise appears to introduce a contradiction to some previous remarks, i.e., that the set $\{p\}$ could not be a basic neighborhood of p in defining continuity for calculus. Thus it must be decided whether to add to the axioms in order to exclude a basic neighborhood relation formed from all pairs, $(p, \{p\})$, or to go on with the three axioms which do describe the basic neighborhood relation of calculus but which also describe other new and maybe even "weird" structures. The reason that any particular set of axioms is chosen anywhere in mathematics is that the content of the axioms is general enough to describe many different models and yet specific enough to yield some results by deduction. If there are too many axioms in the set, the structure described is too special to have many applications; if there are too few axioms in the set, nothing much can be deduced. However, at the beginning it is better to err on the side of generality, since restrictions can always be made later on. Thus, the axioms will be kept as they are, temporarily, and as much theory as possible will be deduced from them.

The basic neighborhood is the analogue of the so-called "interior" of an interval of real numbers. It is these basic neighborhoods for real numbers that the ϵ and δ of calculus identify. Since it has been shown previously that continuity can be defined in terms of intervals with one, both or no end points included, a concept analogous to such an interval is defined and called a neighborhood.

1.3 Definition. Let p be a point of a set S and let R be a basic neighborhood relation for S. A subset M of S is called a *neighborhood* of p if and only if there exists a basic neighborhood V of p such that $V \subseteq M$.

1.4 Lemma. *Every basic neighborhood of a point p is a neighborhood of p but not every neighborhood of p is necessarily a basic neighborhood of p.*

Proof: Exercise.

1.5 Example. Let S denote the number (x, y)-plane consisting of the set of all ordered pairs of real numbers. Let the interiors of squares be assigned as basic neighborhoods as in previous exercise 2. $N = \{(x, y) \mid x = y$ or $|x| \leq 1$ and $|y| \leq 1\}$ is a neighborhood of $(0, 0)$ but is not a basic neighborhood of $(0, 0)$.

Now that the terms basic neighborhood and neighborhood have been established, we test the structure consisting of a set and a basic neighborhood relation to see whether continuity can be defined.

REMARK: Any function is a function *onto* its range. In chapter 1 only, all functions are "onto." In section 9, at the beginning of chapter 2, "into" functions are introduced.

1.6 Definition. Let f be a function from a set S onto a set T; let R_1, R_2 be basic neighborhood relations for S and T, respectively. f is said to be *continuous* at the point a of S if and only if for each basic neighborhood V of $f(a)$ assigned by R_2, there exists a basic neighborhood U of a assigned by R_1 such that $f[U] \subseteq V$.

Thus basic neighborhood relations appear to make possible the definition of continuity.

Analogous to the definition of continuity for a function from the set of all reals onto the set of all reals, in terms of intervals containing their end points is the following alternate definition of continuity.

1.7 Definition. Let f be a function from a set S onto a set T; let R_1, R_2 be basic neighborhood relations for S and T respectively. f is said to be *continuous* at the point x_0 of S if and only if for each neighborhood N of $f(x_0)$ determined by R_2, there exists a neighborhood M of x_0 determined by R_1 such that $f[M] \subseteq N$.

EXERCISE 8. Show that the above definitions for continuity of functions are equivalent.

EXERCISE 9. Let X be the set of all real numbers with $R_1 = \{(a, U_a) \mid U_a = \{x \mid x \leq a\}\}$. Let Y be the set of all real numbers with $R_2 = \{(b, V_b^\epsilon) \mid V_b^\epsilon = \{y \mid |y - b| < \epsilon, \epsilon > 0\}\}$. Let f be the function from X onto Y such that $f(x) = x$. Show that f is not continuous. Is f^{-1} continuous?

EXERCISE 10. Again let X be the set of all real numbers with $R = \{(a, U_a^\epsilon) \mid U_a^\epsilon = \{x \mid x < a + \epsilon, \epsilon > 0\}\}$. Let Y with R_2 be as in the previous exercise. Let f be the function from X onto Y such that $f(x) = x$. Show that f is not continuous but that f^{-1} is continuous.

A detailed study of general continuity for functions will be undertaken and the properties it shares with continuity from calculus will be observed. However, first this new pair, a set and a basic neighborhood relation, which has been called into being by continuity will be examined closely to determine what other fundamental concepts have been defined implicitly by the three basic (Hausdorff) neighborhood axioms BN-I, BN-II, BN-III. Also questions such as "Can two different basic neighborhood relations for a set S be essentially the same," "What significant types of these pairs, i.e., a set and a basic neighborhood relation, are there," "What kinds of properties do these pairs have," will be considered, as well as other questions which will be introduced by the theory as it develops. As the next section will show, this pair, consisting of a set and a basic neighborhood relation, is not the final continuity structure.

2. EQUIVALENT BASIC NEIGHBORHOOD RELATIONS. NEIGHBORHOOD RELATIONS. DERIVED SET.

Equivalent Basic Neighborhood Relations

We now consider whether different basic neighborhood relations for a set, S, always determine different sets of continuous functions. A hint, as to what the answer is, comes again from the calculus books where continuity of a so-called "real-valued function f of two real variables" is defined. Let the domain of this function be the (x, y)-plane, i.e., the set of all ordered pairs of real numbers;

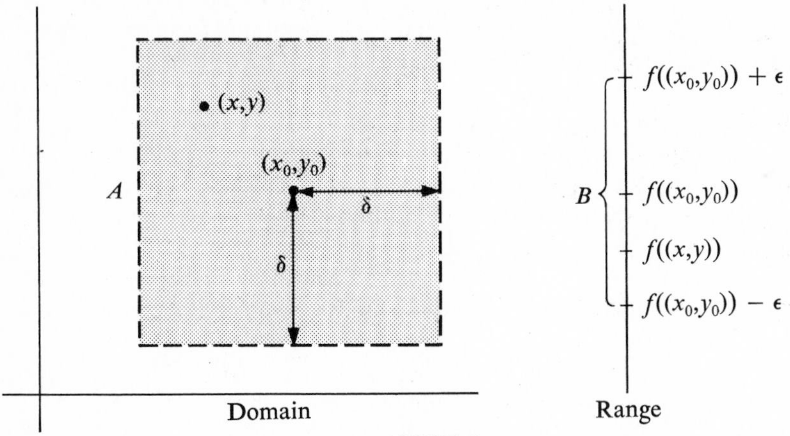

FIGURE 2

let the range be the set of all real numbers. In one of these books such a function f is said to be continuous at a point (x_0, y_0) in the domain if and only if for each $\epsilon > 0$, there exists a $\delta > 0$ such that if $|x - x_0| < \delta$ and $|y - y_0| < \delta$, then $|f((x, y)) - f((x_0, y_0))| < \epsilon$ in the range, where again $f((x, y))$ and $f((x_0, y_0))$ represent, respectively, images in the range of f of the points (x, y) and (x_0, y_0) in the domain of f. Interpreting this geometrically, we find that ϵ again identifies an interval B about the real number $f((x_0, y_0))$ on a straight line representing the real numbers, that δ identifies a square, A, about (x_0, y_0) in the (x, y)-plane and that continuity implies that for each such set B, there is a square A mapped into it by the function f. However, in another of these calculus books a real-valued function f of two real variables is said to be continuous at a point (x_0, y_0) in the domain if and only if for each $\epsilon > 0$, there exists a $\delta > 0$ such that

$$|f((x, y)) - f((x_0, y_0))| < \epsilon \quad \text{if} \quad \sqrt{(x - x_0)^2 + (y - y_0)^2} < \delta.$$

Interpreting this geometrically we find that ϵ identifies, as before, an interval of real numbers near $f((x_0, y_0))$ in the range of f but that δ now identifies a disc of radius δ about (x_0, y_0) in the domain and that continuity implies that for each interval B about $f((x_0, y_0))$, there exists a disc A about (x_0, y_0) that is mapped by f into B.

Now a function f from the plane onto the line which is continuous in the "disc" sense is also continuous in the "square" sense and conversely. The proof of this fact is based on the property that if there exists a square, containing the point (x_0, y_0), which is mapped into an interval about $f((x_0, y_0))$, then there can be shown to exist, inside the square and containing (x_0, y_0), a disc which then is also mapped into the interval in the range of f. Conversely, for each disc we can find a square, etc. Thus, we are forced to define equivalent basic neighborhood relations for a set. Equivalent basic neighborhood relations, of course, ought to define the same "continuity" structure on the set. Thus, as was stated

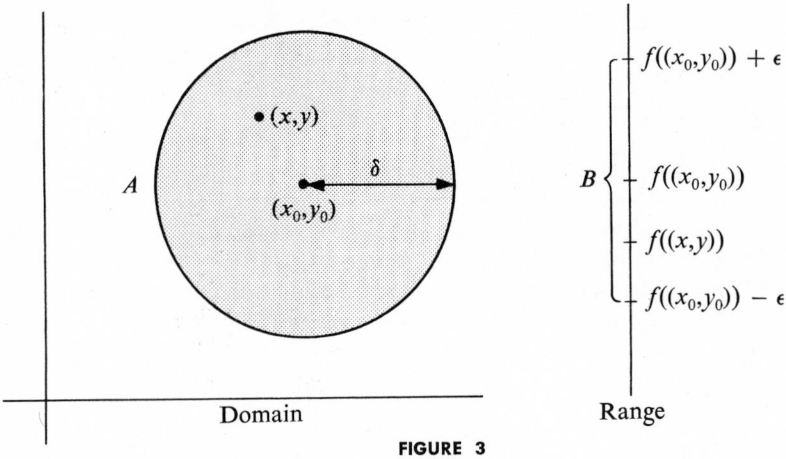

FIGURE 3

previously, the basic neighborhood relation with which we started is not after all our final goal. The equivalent basic neighborhood relations will be combined into an equivalence class to define our desired structure.

2.1 Definition. Two basic neighborhood relations R_1, R_2 defined on a set S are said to be *equivalent basic neighborhood relations* if and only if for each (r, U_1) in R_1, there exists (r, U_2) in R_2 such that $U_2 \subseteq U_1$ and conversely, for each (r, V_2) in R_2, there exists (r, V_1) in R_1 such that $V_1 \subseteq V_2$. This is a standard equivalence relation and identifies, for any given set S, equivalence classes of basic neighborhood relations. These equivalence classes are subsets of $P(S \times P(S))$.

EXERCISE 1. Prove that the assignment of "interiors" of circles in the plane to their centers and the assignment of "interiors" of squares in the plane to their centers are equivalent basic neighborhood relations for the set of points in the plane. (Assume $\sqrt{(a-c)^2 + (b-d)^2} + \sqrt{(c-e)^2 + (d-f)^2} \geq \sqrt{(a-e)^2 + (b-f)^2}$.)

EXERCISE 2. Find a third basic neighborhood relation for the points in the plane that is equivalent to the "circles" and "squares" relations of the previous exercise.

2.2 Theorem. *If S is any set and if R_1 and R_2 are equivalent basic neighborhood relations for S, then the set of neighborhoods for each point in S determined by R_1 is exactly the same as the set determined by R_2.*

Proof: By definition 1.3, a subset M of S is a neighborhood of a point q of S determined by R_1 if and only if there is a basic neighborhood V of q such that (q, V) is in R_1 and $V \subseteq M$. Let M be such a neighborhood of q. Since R_1 and R_2 are equivalent, there is a basic neighborhood W of q such that $W \subseteq V$ and (q, W) is in R_2. Hence $W \subseteq M$ and M is a neighborhood of q determined by R_2. Similarly any neighborhood of q determined by R_2 will also be determined by R_1. ▮

2.3 Corollary. *Let R_1 and R_2 be basic neighborhood relations for S and T, respectively, and let R_1^* and R_2^* be basic neighborhood relations for S and T, respectively, such that R_1 is equivalent to R_1^* and R_2 is equivalent to R_2^*. Then R_1 and R_2 determine the same class of continuous functions from S onto T as do R_1^* and R_2^*.*

Proof: The corollary follows from theorem 2.2 and definition 1.7. ▮

Thus, continuity for a function goes with an equivalence class of basic neighborhood relations for the domain and range rather than with the individual basic neighborhood relations. This fact leads to the definition of a new structure—a pair consisting of a set and an equivalence class of basic neighborhood relations. This latter structure (definition 2.7, below) will be the first fundamental continuity structure to be discussed. First, however, some properties of neighborhoods are established.

Neighborhood Relations

Theorem 2.2 implies that a unique relation, one which assigns neighborhoods to points, is determined by any class of equivalent basic neighborhood relations for a set S. The characteristic properties of this relation are established in the next theorem. This new relation is called, naturally, the neighborhood relation for the structure, i.e., for the set S and any equivalence class of basic neighborhood relations for S.

2.4 Theorem. *Let R_ν denote a basic neighborhood relation for a set S. Let R^+ denote the relation $\{(p, N) \mid p$ is a point in S and N is a neighborhood of p determined by $R_\nu\}$. Let $\{N_p\}$ denote the set of images of p assigned by R^+. Then the following are true:*

(*a*) *if $S \supseteq M \supseteq N$, for N in $\{N_p\}$, then M is in $\{N_p\}$;*
(*b*) *the intersection of two sets in $\{N_p\}$ belongs to $\{N_p\}$;*
(*c*) *p belongs to every set in $\{N_p\}$;*
(*d*) *if (p, M) belongs to R^+, there exists a set $V \subseteq M$ such that (p, V) is in R^+ and for every y in V, (y, V) is in R^+;*
(*e*) *$R_\nu \subseteq R^+$.*

Proof:

(*a*) By definition of a neighborhood of a point, N contains a basic neighborhood of p assigned by R_ν; hence, M contains a basic neighborhood of p assigned by R_ν.
(*b*) Let N_p^1 and N_p^2 denote two neighborhoods in $\{N_p\}$. $N_p^1 \supseteq U$ and $N_p^2 \supseteq V$, say, where U and V are basic neighborhoods of p assigned by R_ν. Hence, $(U \cap V) \subseteq N_p^1 \cap N_p^2$. Axiom BN-II then implies that $N_p^1 \cap N_p^2$ is a neighborhood of p.
(*c*) By definition of the collection $\{N_p\}$, p belongs to every N_p.

(*d*) Let M be any neighborhood of p. M contains V, a basic neighborhood of p assigned by R_ν. Let q be in V. By Axiom BN-III, V contains a basic neighborhood U of q assigned by R_ν. Hence, (q, V) is in R^+.
(*e*) R_ν and R^+ are both subsets of $S \times P(S)$ and since $U \subseteq U$, (x, U) in R_ν implies that (x, U) is in R^+. ▮

Thus, a set, S, and a basic neighborhood relation, R_ν, for S determine a class $\{R_\nu\}$ of equivalent basic neighborhood relations for S and a new relation R^+ for S called a *neighborhood relation.*

2.5 Definition. Let S be a set. A relation R^+, whose domain is S and whose range is in $P(S)$, is called *a neighborhood relation* for S if and only if

Axiom N-I: (p, N) in R^+ implies p is in N;

Axiom N-II: (p, N) in R^+ and $M \supseteq N$ imply that (p, M) is in R^+;

Axiom N-III: if (p, N^1) and (p, N^2) are in R^+, then $(p, N^1 \cap N^2)$ belongs to R^+;

Axiom N-IV: if (p, N) belongs to R^+, then there exists $V \subseteq N$ such that (p, V) is in R^+ and, for q in V, (q, V) belongs to R^+.

The images assigned to p by R^+ are called *neighborhoods* of p.

The next theorem establishes that every neighborhood relation on a set S is determined by a basic neighborhood relation in the sense of theorem 2.4.

2.6 Theorem. *Let S be a set, and let R^+ be a neighborhood relation for S. The relation $R = \{(p, V) \mid (p, V)$ is in R^+ and, for q in V, (q, V) is in $R^+\}$ is a basic neighborhood relation for S. Further, R^+ is the neighborhood relation for S determined by R.*

Proof:

A. For each (p, V) in R, p is in V since (p, V) is in R^+. Thus axiom BN-I is satisfied. Further, for any p in S, there exists such a (p, V) by definition of a neighborhood relation. Hence, the domain of R is S.

B. If (p, V) and (p, W) are both in R, then (p, V) and (p, W) are both in R^+. Hence, $(p, V \cap W)$ is in R^+. By axiom N-IV, there exists G, $G \subseteq V \cap W$, (p, G) is in R^+ and if q is in G, (q, G) is in R^+. Hence, (p, G) is in R and axiom BN-II is satisfied.

C. Let (p, V) belong to R and let q be in V. By definition of R, (q, V) is in R. Since $V \supseteq V$, axiom BN-III is satisfied.

Axioms BN-I, BN-II and BN-III are satisfied and so R is a basic neighborhood relation for S. R in turn identifies the class of basic neighborhood relations that are equivalent to itself. This class determines a neighborhood relation R^* by theorem 2.4. Let p be any point in S and let (p, N) be in R^*. Then $N \supseteq V$, where (p, V) is in R. Since (p, V) is in R, (p, V) is in R^+ and so (p, N) is in

R^+ by axiom N-II in the definition of a neighborhood relation (2.5). Hence, $R^* \subseteq R^+$. Conversely, let (p, M) be in R^+. By axiom N-IV and the definition of R, M must contain a set V such that (p, V) is in R; hence, (p, M) is in R^* by definition 1.3. Thus $R^+ = R^*$ and so R^+ is the unique neighborhood relation determined by R. ▮

The basic neighborhood relation, R, of the previous theorem is actually the largest (as a subset of $S \times P(S)$ and relative to inclusion) basic neighborhood relation in its equivalence class; moreover, its range is important. Both of these will be studied in the next section.

It must now be observed that two unique structures are at hand—one, a set and an equivalence class of basic neighborhood relations; the other, a set and a neighborhood relation. The following definition will be extended later, in section 3, to include more than the two pairs just mentioned and then, for convenience, abbreviated.

2.7 First Definition. A *topological space* or *space* is a set, $\{\{S, \{R_\nu\}\}, \{S, R^+\}\}$ where S is a set, $\{R_\nu\}$ is an equivalence class of basic neighborhood relations for S and R^+ is the neighborhood relation determined by $\{R_\nu\}$ on S. Since each pair in the set determines the other uniquely, the abbreviations "the topological space, $\{S, \{R_\nu\}\}$" and "the topological space $\{S, R^+\}$" will be used for convenience.

2.8 Theorem. *If* $\{S, R^+\}$ *is a space and* R_ν *is any basic neighborhood relation determined for* S *by* R^+, *then* $R_\nu \subseteq R^+$.

Proof: By theorem 2.6, R^+ is the neighborhood relation for S determined by R_ν. Hence by theorem 2.4, $R_\nu \subseteq R^+$. ▮

2.9 Example. Let S be the set of all ordered pairs of real numbers, $\{(x, y) \mid x$ is real and y is real$\}$. Let R_ν be the basic neighborhood relation, $\{((a, b), V^\epsilon_{(a,b)}) \mid V^\epsilon_{(a,b)} = \{(x, y) \mid \sqrt{(x-a)^2 + (y-b)^2} < \epsilon \text{ for } \epsilon > 0\}\}$ for S. The basic neighborhoods assigned to any point (a, b) by R_ν are the interiors of circles whose centers are at (a, b). The neighborhoods assigned to (a, b) by R_ν are the sets that contain the interior of a circle with center at (a, b). (See figure 4.)

On the basis of corollary 2.3 and the remark following it, continuity is defined now for functions whose domains and ranges are spaces.

2.10 Definition. A function f from a space $\{S, R_1^+\}$ onto a space $\{T, R_2^+\}$ is called *continuous* at the point x in S if and only if for every neighborhood M of $f(x)$ in T, $f^{-1}[M]$ is a neighborhood of x in S. f is called continuous on $\{S, R_1^+\}$ if and only if it is continuous at every point of S.

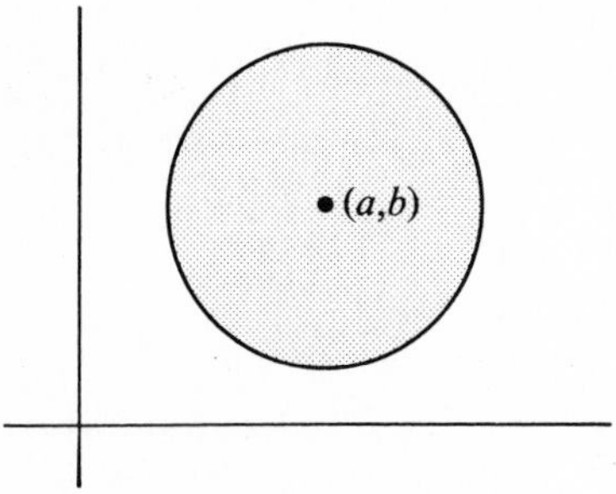

(a) Basic neighborhood of (a,b) from R_ν

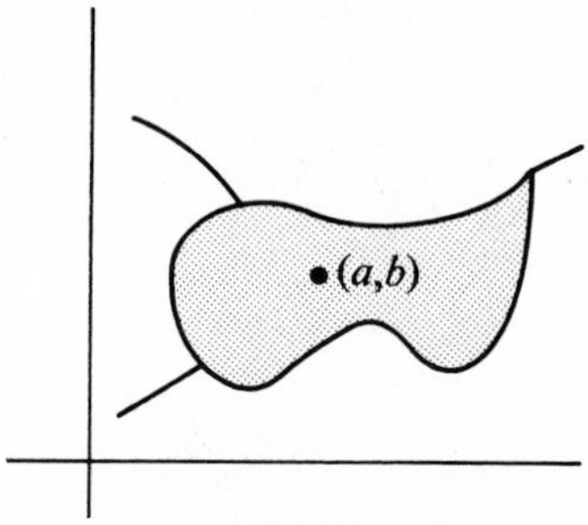

(b) Neighborhood of (a,b) but not a basic neighborhood of (a,b) from R_ν

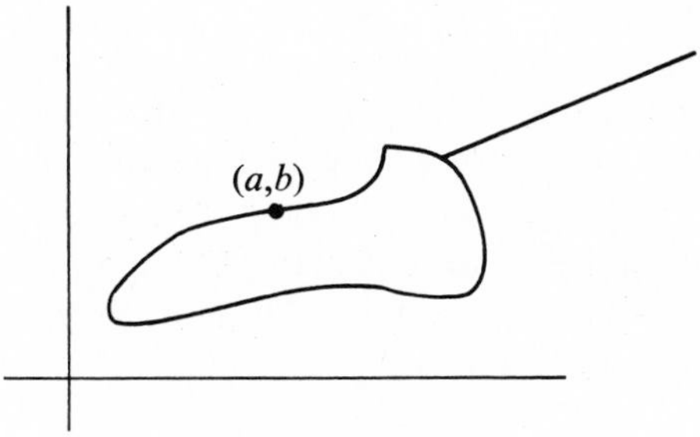

(c) Neither a basic neighborhood nor a neighborhood of (a,b) from R_ν

FIGURE 4

2.11 Theorem (Alternate Definition). *Let f be a function from a space* $\{S, R_1^+\}$ *onto a space* $\{T, R_2^+\}$. *Let* R_1 *and* R_2 *be basic neighborhood relations for* $\{S, R_1^+\}$ *and* $\{T, R_2^+\}$, *respectively. Then f is continuous at the point a in S if and only if* $(f(a), V)$ *in* R_2 *implies that there exists* (a, U) *in* R_1 *such that* $f[U] \subseteq V$.

Proof: Exercise.

This last theorem contains the direct generalization of the definition of continuity used in calculus; namely, for each basic neighborhood, V^ϵ, of $f(a)$ in the range, there exists a basic neighborhood, U^δ, of a in the domain, such that $f[U] \subseteq V$.

Certain other basic concepts that are important for a study of continuity and the topological structure are implicitly defined by axioms N-I, N-II, N-III and N-IV.

LIMIT POINTS (DERIVED SET)

2.12 Definition. Let $\{S, R^+\}$ be a topological space and let A be any subset of S. p, in S, is called a *limit point* of A if and only if every neighborhood N of p contains at least one point of $A \sim \{p\}$. The set of limit points of the set A is denoted by A' and is called the *derived set* of A.

2.13 Lemma. *If $\{S, R^+\}$ is a space, if R_ν is any basic neighborhood relation in the class determined by R^+ and if A is a subset of S, then p is a limit point of A if and only if every basic neighborhood of p assigned by R_ν contains a point of $A \sim \{p\}$.*

Proof: Exercise.

Thus, neighborhoods or basic neighborhoods determine limit points.

2.14 Example. Let $A = \{x \mid x = 1/n$ where n is a natural number$\}$. Let S be the real numbers and let R be the basic neighborhood relation $\{(p, V_\epsilon^p) \mid V_\epsilon^p = \{x \mid |p - x| < \epsilon, \epsilon > 0 \text{ and } \epsilon \text{ real}\}\}$. Then 0 is a limit point of A. For let $V_\epsilon^0 = \{x \mid -\epsilon < x < \epsilon\}$ be any basic neighborhood of 0. By archimedean order on the real numbers, there exists a natural number n such that $n \cdot 1 > 1/\epsilon$. Hence, every neighborhood of 0 contains a point of $A \sim \{0\}$.

EXERCISE 3. Let S be the set of real numbers. Let $R = \{(p, V_\epsilon^p) \mid V_\epsilon = \{x \mid |p - x| < \epsilon, \epsilon \text{ real and } \epsilon > 0\}\}$ define the space $\{S, R^+\}$. Find all limit points of the set $X = \{x \mid 0 \leq x \leq 1\}$.

2.15 Definition. The space $\{S, R^+\}$ defined in the previous exercise is called *Euclidean 1-space* and is denoted by E^1.

EXERCISE 4. Let S be the set of real numbers. Let $R = \{(p, V_p) \mid V_p = \{x \mid x \geq p\}\}$; R is a basic neighborhood relation for S. In the space $\{S, R^+\}$, find all limit points of the set $A = \{x \mid 0 \leq x \leq 1\}$.

2.16 Definition. Let S be the set of all ordered pairs of real numbers and let $R = \{((a, b), V_\epsilon^{(a,b)}) \mid V_\epsilon^{(a,b)} = \{(x, y) \mid |x - a| < \epsilon \text{ and } |y - b| < \epsilon \text{ for } \epsilon \text{ real and positive}\}\}$. R is a basic neighborhood relation for S. The space $\{S, R^+\}$ determined by R is called *Euclidean 2-space*, E^2. This is the usual topological structure associated with the plane of plane geometry.

EXERCISE 5. In the space E^2, find all the limit points of $\{(x, y) \mid x > 0\}$. Prove your answer.

EXERCISE 6. Let S be the set of all ordered pairs of real numbers; let $R = \{((a, b), V_\epsilon^{(a,b)}) \mid V_\epsilon^{(a,b)} = \{(x, y) \mid x = a \text{ and } |y - b| < \epsilon \text{ for } \epsilon \text{ real and positive}\}\}$.

In the space $\{S, R^+\}$ determined by R, find all limit points of

(a) $\{(x, y) \mid x > 0\}$. (b) $\{(x, y) \mid x^2 + y^2 < 1\}$.

Prove your answers.

EXERCISE 7. Find a non-empty subset of each of the spaces in the previous four exercises

(a) that contains all its limit points. (b) that has no limit points.

(c) that has each of its points as a limit point.

Three topological concepts have now been established: basic neighborhood, neighborhood and limit point (derived set). The construction of the deductive system begins.

The following properties for the set of derived sets in a space $\{S, R^+\}$ are implied by the defining property.

2.17 Theorem. $\emptyset' = \emptyset$.

Proof: Since $x \in \emptyset$ is false for every x in S, $\emptyset' = \emptyset$. ▮

2.18 Theorem. *If A and B are subsets in the space $\{S, R^+\}$, $(A \cup B)' = A' \cup B'$.*

Proof: Let p be an element of A'. Since every neighborhood of p contains a point of $A \sim \{p\}$, every neighborhood of p contains a point of $(A \cup B) \sim \{p\}$. Thus p is an element of $(A \cup B)'$. The proof is the same if p is in B'. Hence, $A' \cup B' \subseteq (A \cup B)'$. Conversely, let p be an element of $(A \cup B)'$. Assume there exist neighborhoods N_1 and N_2 of p such that N_1 contains no point of $A \sim \{p\}$ and N_2 contains no point of $B \sim \{p\}$. Then the neighborhood $N_1 \cap N_2$ of p contains no point of $A \sim \{p\} \cup B \sim \{p\}$. $(A \sim \{p\}) \cup (B \sim \{p\}) = (A \cup B) \sim p$. Hence p is not in $(A \cup B)'$. This is a contradiction. Thus, every neighborhood of p contains a point of $A \sim \{p\}$ or every neighborhood of p contains a point of $B \sim \{p\}$. This means that p is in $A' \cup B'$, and hence that $(A \cup B)' \subseteq A' \cup B'$. ▮

2.19 Corollary. *If $\{A_1, A_2, \ldots, A_n\}$ denotes a finite set of subsets in a space $\{S, R^+\}$, then $(A_1 \cup A_2 \cup \cdots \cup A_n)' = A_1' \cup A_2' \cup \cdots \cup A_n'$.*

Proof: The corollary follows from the previous theorem, 2.18, by induction. ▮

2.20 Corollary. *If A and B are subsets in the space $\{S, R^+\}$ and if $A \subseteq B$, then $A' \subseteq B'$.*

Proof: The corollary follows directly from the definition of limit point or from the previous theorem, 2.18. If $A \subseteq B$, then $A \cup B = B$. Hence if $(A \cup B)' = A' \cup B'$, $B' = A' \cup B'$. Therefore, $B' \supseteq A'$. ▮

2.21 Theorem. *If A is a subset in the space $\{S, R^+\}$ and if p is a point in A', then p is in $(A \sim \{p\})'$.*

Proof: If p is in A', then every neighborhood of p contains a point in $A \sim \{p\}$. Since $(A \sim \{p\}) \sim \{p\} = A \sim \{p\}$, every neighborhood of p contains a point of $(A \sim \{p\}) \sim \{p\}$. Hence p is in $(A \sim \{p\})'$. ∎

EXERCISE 8. Prove or disprove: If $\{S, R^+\}$ is any space and A is any subset of S, $A'' \subseteq A'$ where $A'' = (A')'$. [*Hint:* See exercise 6 in section 1.]

2.22 Theorem. *If $\{S, R^+\}$ is any space and A is any subset of S, then $A'' \subseteq A \cup A'$.*

Proof: Exercise.

The immediately preceding theorems and corollaries thus establish that, in any space $\{S, R^+\}$, each subset, A, has defined for it a subset A' satisfying the following rules: (1) $\emptyset' = \emptyset$, (2) $(A \cup B)' = A' \cup B'$, (3) $p \in A'$ implies that $p \in (A \sim \{p\})'$ and (4) $A'' \subseteq A \cup A'$.

2.23 Definition. Let S be a set. A function Ψ from $P(S)$ into $P(S)$ is called a *derivation* or a *derived set operation* if and only if: (1) $\Psi(\emptyset) = \emptyset$, (2) $\Psi(A \cup B) = \Psi(A) \cup \Psi(B)$, (3) $p \in \Psi(A)$ implies $p \in \Psi(A \sim \{p\})$ and (4) $\Psi(\Psi(A)) \subseteq A \cup \Psi(A)$.

Thus theorems 2.17, 2.18, 2.21 and 2.22 establish that any neighborhood relation for a set S determines a derivation for S, namely, the function Ψ from $P(S)$ into $P(S)$ defined by $\Psi(A) = A'$.

EXERCISE 9. Let $\Gamma(A) = A$ for $A \subseteq S$. Prove or disprove: Γ is a derivation on S.

EXERCISE 10. Let $\Gamma(A) = \emptyset$ for $A \subseteq S$. Prove or disprove: Γ is a derivation for S.

EXERCISE 11. Let $\Gamma(\emptyset) = \emptyset$ and let $\Gamma(A) = S$ for $A \neq \emptyset$ and $A \subseteq S$. Prove or disprove: Γ is a derivation for S.

3. CLOSURE. CLOSED SETS. OPEN SETS.

Once limit points are defined, three other concepts are immediately established: closure, closed set and open set.

CLOSURE

3.1 Definition. Let $\{S, R^+\}$ be a space and let $A \subseteq S$. The *closure* of A, denoted by $\overline{A}$, is defined to be the set $A \cup A'$.

EXERCISE 1. Prove that in any space $\{S, R^+\}$, $p \in \overline{A}$ if and only if every neighborhood of p contains a point of A.

EXERCISE 2. In the space E^1 (definition 2.15) let A denote the positive reals. Find $\overline{A}$.

EXERCISE 3. Let S denote the real numbers and let $R = \{(p, V) \mid p$ is real and $V = \{x \mid x \geq p$ and x is real$\}\}$. R is a basic neighborhood relation on S and so determines a space $\{S, R^+\}$. Let A denote the subset of natural numbers. Find $\overline{A}$.

EXERCISE 4. In the space of exercise 3 let $A = \{1\}$. Find $\overline{A}$.

The next four theorems establish certain properties for closures which are implied by the definition in terms of A'.

3.2 Theorem. *In any space* $\{S, R^+\}$, $\overline{\emptyset} = \emptyset$.

Proof: The proof follows directly from definition 3.1 and theorem 2.17. ▮

3.3 Theorem. *Let* $\{S, R^+\}$ *denote a space. Let* $A \subseteq S$. *Then* $A \subseteq \overline{A}$.

Proof: The theorem follows from definition 3.1. ▮

3.4 Theorem. *Let* $\{S, R^+\}$ *be a space; let* $A \subseteq S$ *and let* $B \subseteq S$. *Then* $\overline{A \cup B} = \overline{A} \cup \overline{B}$.

Proof: $\overline{A \cup B} = (A \cup B) \cup (A \cup B)'$. By theorem 2.18, $(A \cup B)' = A' \cup B'$. Therefore, $\overline{A \cup B} = A \cup B \cup A' \cup B' = (A \cup A') \cup (B \cup B') = \overline{A} \cup \overline{B}$. ▮

3.5 Corollary. *Let* $\{S, R^+\}$ *be a space; let* $A_i \subseteq S$ *for* $i = 1, 2, \ldots, k$ *and* k *a natural number. Then* $\overline{A_1 \cup A_2 \cup \cdots \cup A_k} = \overline{A}_1 \cup \overline{A}_2 \cup \cdots \cup \overline{A}_k$.

Proof: Exercise.

3.6 Corollary. *Let* $\{S, R^+\}$ *be a space and let* $A \subseteq B \subseteq S$. *Then* $\overline{A} \subseteq \overline{B}$.

Proof: If $A \subseteq B$, then $A \cup B = B$. Since $\overline{A \cup B} = \overline{A} \cup \overline{B}$, $\overline{B} = \overline{A} \cup \overline{B}$. Therefore, $\overline{A} \subseteq \overline{B}$. ▮

3.7 Theorem. *Let* $\{S, R^+\}$ *be a space; let* $A \subseteq S$. *Then* $\overline{\overline{A}} = \overline{A}$.

Proof: $\overline{\overline{A}} = \overline{A} \cup (\overline{A})' = \overline{A} \cup (A \cup A')' = \overline{A} \cup A' \cup A'' = A \cup A' \cup A' \cup A''$. Since $A'' \subseteq A \cup A'$ by theorem 2.22, $(A \cup A') \cup (A' \cup A'') = A \cup A' = \overline{A}$. Therefore $\overline{\overline{A}} = \overline{A}$. ▮

EXERCISE 5. Prove or disprove: In any space $\{S, R^+\}$ where A and B are subsets of S (a) $\overline{A} \cap \overline{B} \subseteq \overline{A \cap B}$, (b) $\overline{A} \cap \overline{B} \supseteq \overline{A \cap B}$.

The immediately preceding theorems and corollaries thus establish that in any space $\{S, R^+\}$, each subset A of S has defined for it a subset $\overline{A}$ satisfying the following rules: (1) $\overline{\emptyset} = \emptyset$, (2) $A \subseteq \overline{A}$, (3) $\overline{A \cup B} = \overline{A} \cup \overline{B}$, and (4) $\overline{\overline{A}} = \overline{A}$.

3.8 Definition. Let S be a set. A function Φ from $P(S)$ into $P(S)$ is called a *closure operation* for S if and only if (1) $\Phi(\emptyset) = \emptyset$, (2) $\Phi(A) \supseteq A$, (3) $\Phi(A \cup B) = \Phi(A) \cup \Phi(B)$, (4) $\Phi(\Phi(A)) = \Phi(A)$.

Thus theorems 3.2, 3.3, 3.4 and 3.7 establish that each neighborhood relation for a set S determines a closure operation for S.

EXERCISE 6. Let $H(A) = \emptyset$ for $A \subseteq S$. Prove or disprove: H is a closure operation for S.

EXERCISE 7. Let $H(\emptyset) = \emptyset$ and let $H(A) = S$ for $A \subseteq S$ and $A \neq \emptyset$. Prove or disprove: H is a closure operation for S.

EXERCISE 8. Let S be the set of real numbers. Let $H(\emptyset) = \emptyset$; let $H(A)$ for $A \neq \emptyset$ be $\{x \mid (\exists a)\ (a \in A \text{ and } x \leq a)\}$. Prove or disprove: H is a closure operation for S.

Closed Sets

3.9 Definition. Let $\{S, R^+\}$ be a space; let $A \subseteq S$. A is called *closed in* $\{S, R^+\}$ if and only if $A = \overline{A}$.

3.10 Example. The set of non-negative real numbers is closed in E^1 (definition 2.15).

3.11 Example. The set of positive real numbers is not closed in E^1.

3.12 Example. The set $\{(x, y) \mid x^2 + y^2 \leq 1\}$ is closed in E^2 (definition 2.16).

3.13 Example. The set $\{(x, y) \mid x > 0 \text{ and } y > 0\}$ is not closed in E^2.

EXERCISE 9. Show that in the space determined on the set of all real numbers by the basic neighborhood relation consisting of $\{(p, V) \mid V = \{x \mid x \geq p\}\}$, the set of non-negative real numbers is not closed.

EXERCISE 10. In the space of exercise 9 show that $\{p\}$, where p is any real number, is not closed.

EXERCISE 11. In the space of exercise 9, identify the set of all closed sets.

EXERCISE 12. Show that in E^2, $\{(x, y) \mid x \neq 5\}$ is not closed.

EXERCISE 13. Show that in E^2, $\{(x, y) \mid y = \sin 1/x,\ x \neq 0\}$ is not closed.

The next three theorems establish certain properties for the set of all closed sets which are implied by the definition.

3.14 Theorem. *Let $\{S, R^+\}$ be a space. Then S and $\emptyset$ are both closed in $\{S, R^+\}$.*

Proof: By theorem 3.2, $\overline{\emptyset} = \emptyset$, and by theorem 3.3, $\overline{S} \supseteq S$. ▌

3.15 Theorem. *Let $\{S, R^+\}$ be a space and let $\mathfrak{A}$ be any finite set of subsets which are closed in $\{S, R^+\}$. Then $\bigcup\mathfrak{A}$ is closed in $\{S, R^+\}$.*

Proof: If $\mathfrak{A}$ is empty, $\bigcup\mathfrak{A} = \emptyset$ and by theorem 3.14, $\bigcup\mathfrak{A}$ is closed. If $\mathfrak{A}$ is not empty, $\mathfrak{A} = \{A_1, A_2, \ldots, A_k\}$ for k a natural number. $\bigcup\mathfrak{A} = A_1 \cup A_2 \cup \cdots \cup A_k$. $\overline{\bigcup\mathfrak{A}} = \overline{A_1 \cup A_2 \cup \cdots \cup A_k} = \overline{A_1} \cup \overline{A_2} \cup \cdots \cup \overline{A_k}$ by theorem 3.5. Hence, since by hypothesis, $\overline{A_i} = A_i$ for $i = 1, 2, \ldots, k$, $\overline{\bigcup\mathfrak{A}} = \bigcup\mathfrak{A}$. Thus $\bigcup\mathfrak{A}$ is closed by definition 3.9. ▌

EXERCISE 14. In E^1 (definition 2.15), find a set of closed sets whose union is not closed in E^1.

3.16 Theorem. *Let $\{S, R^+\}$ be a space. Let $\mathfrak{F} = \{F_\nu \mid \nu \in \mathfrak{M}\}$ be a set of closed sets in $\{S, R^+\}$. Then $\bigcap\mathfrak{F}$ is closed in $\{S, R^+\}$.*

Proof: By definition of $\bigcap$, $\bigcap\mathfrak{F} \subseteq F_\nu$ for every F_ν in $\mathfrak{F}$. By corollary 3.6, $\overline{\bigcap\mathfrak{F}} \subseteq \overline{F_\nu} = F_\nu$. Hence $\overline{\bigcap\mathfrak{F}} \subseteq F_\nu$ for every F_ν in $\mathfrak{F}$. Thus $\overline{\bigcap\mathfrak{F}} \subseteq \bigcap\mathfrak{F}$. By theorem 3.3, $\overline{\bigcap\mathfrak{F}} = \bigcap\mathfrak{F}$. ▌

The immediately preceding theorems thus establish that in any space $\{S, R^+\}$, a set $\mathfrak{C}$ of subsets of S is determined satisfying the following rules: (1) S and $\emptyset$ are in $\mathfrak{C}$, (2) the intersection of any set of subsets in $\mathfrak{C}$ is in $\mathfrak{C}$ and (3) the union of any finite set of subsets in $\mathfrak{C}$ is in $\mathfrak{C}$.

REMARK: By definition of $\bigcup$, the union of the empty set of subsets of a set S is $\emptyset$ (i.e. $\bigcup\mathfrak{A} = \emptyset$ where $\emptyset = \mathfrak{A} \subseteq P(S)$) and by definition of $\bigcap$, the intersection of the empty set of subsets of S is S (i.e. $\bigcap\mathfrak{A} = S$ for $\emptyset = \mathfrak{A} \subseteq P(S)$).

3.17 Definition. Let S be a set. A subset $\mathfrak{C}$ of $P(S)$ is called a *cotopology* for S if and only if: (1) the union of any finite set of sets in $\mathfrak{C}$ is in $\mathfrak{C}$ and (2) the intersection of any set of sets in $\mathfrak{C}$ is in $\mathfrak{C}$.

Thus any neighborhood relation for a set S determines a cotopology for S. [It must be remarked that the word "cotopology" for the family of closed sets is new and is not standard.]

EXERCISE 15. Let S be the set of all real numbers. Let $K = \{F_a^b \mid a \text{ and } b \text{ are real numbers and } F_a^b = \{x \mid a \leq x \leq b\}\}$. Prove or disprove: K is a cotopology for S.

EXERCISE 16. Let S be any set; let $K = \{S, \emptyset\}$. Prove or disprove: K is a cotopology for S.

EXERCISE 17. Let S be any set; let $K = P(S)$. Prove or disprove: K is a cotopology for S.

EXERCISE 18. Let S be any set; let $K = \{S, A, \emptyset\}$, where $A \subseteq S$ and $\emptyset \neq A \neq S$. Prove or disprove $\{S, A, \emptyset\}$ is a cotopology for S.

EXERCISE 19. Let S denote the set of real numbers. Let K be the set of all subsets F of S such that $F \supseteq \{x \mid (\exists a)\ (a \in F \text{ and } x \leq a)\}$. Prove or disprove: K is a cotopology for S.

The next two theorems establish two useful alternate definitions—one for closed set and one for closure.

3.18 Theorem (Alternate Definition). *Let $\{S, R^+\}$ be a space and let $A \subseteq S$. Then A is closed in $\{S, R^+\}$ if and only if $A \supseteq A'$.*

Proof: Exercise.

3.19 Theorem (Alternate Definition). *Let $\{S, R^+\}$ be a space and let $A \subseteq S$. Then $\overline{A}$ is the intersection of all the closed sets which contain A.*

Proof: Let $\mathfrak{F} = \{\mathfrak{F}_\nu\}$ be the set of all closed sets of $\{S, R^+\}$ which contain A. $A \subseteq F_\nu$ for every F_ν in $\mathfrak{F}$. Hence, by corollary 3.6, $\overline{A} \subseteq \overline{F_\nu}$ for every F_ν in $\mathfrak{F}$. Since $\overline{F_\nu} = F_\nu$ by hypothesis, $\overline{A} \subseteq F_\nu$ for every F_ν in $\mathfrak{F}$. Hence, $\overline{A} \subseteq \bigcap \mathfrak{F}$. Now, since $\overline{\overline{A}} = \overline{A}$, by theorem 3.7, $\overline{A}$ is closed. Further, since $\overline{A} \supseteq A$, $\overline{A}$ is in $\mathfrak{F}$. Thus $\overline{A} \supseteq \bigcap \mathfrak{F}$. ▮

OPEN SETS

3.20 Definition. A subset G in a space $\{S, R^+\}$ is called *open in* $\{S, R^+\}$ if and only if $\sim G$, the complement of G in S, is closed in $\{S, R^+\}$.

3.21 Example. $\{x \mid 0 < x < 1\}$ is open in E^1 (definition 2.15).

3.22 Example. $\{(x, y) \mid x > 0 \text{ and } y > 0\}$ is open in E^2 (definition 2.16).

EXERCISE 20. Show that $\{x \mid 0 \leq x < 1\}$ is neither open nor closed in E^1.

EXERCISE 21. Show that $\{(x, y) \mid 0 < x < 1\}$ is open in E^2.

EXERCISE 22. Show that $\{(x, y) \mid x \geq 0 \text{ and } y > 0\}$ is neither open nor closed in E^2.

EXERCISE 23. Let S be the set of all ordered pairs of real numbers. Define on S the basic neighborhood relation $R = \{((a, b), U_\epsilon^{(a,b)}) \mid U_\epsilon^{(a,b)} = \{(x, y) \mid x = a \text{ and } b - \epsilon < y < b + \epsilon \text{ for } \epsilon > 0\}\}$. Show that, in the resulting space, $A = \{(x, y) \mid x = 5\}$ is both open and closed.

The next three theorems establish certain properties of the set of all open sets which are implied by the definition.

3.23 Theorem. *Let $\{S, R^+\}$ be a space. Then S and $\emptyset$ are both open in $\{S, R^+\}$.*

Proof: By theorem 3.14, S and $\emptyset$ are both closed. Since $\sim S = \emptyset$ and $\sim\emptyset = S$, S and $\emptyset$ are both open by definition 3.20. ▮

3.24 Theorem. *Let $\{S, R^+\}$ be a space. Let $\mathcal{A}$ be a finite set of open sets in $\{S, R^+\}$. Then $\bigcap\mathcal{A}$ is open in $\{S, R^+\}$.*

Proof: If $\mathcal{A} = \emptyset$, $\bigcap\mathcal{A} = S$ and by theorem 3.23, $\bigcap\mathcal{A}$ is open. If $\mathcal{A} \neq \emptyset$, $\sim\bigcap\mathcal{A} = \sim(A_1 \cap A_2 \cap \cdots \cap A_k) = \sim A_1 \cup \sim A_2 \cup \cdots \cup \sim A_k$, for k a natural number. By hypothesis and by definition 3.20, $\sim A_1, \ldots, \sim A_k$ are closed and by theorem 3.15, $\sim A_1 \cup \sim A_2 \cup \cdots \cup \sim A_k$ is closed. Therefore, $\sim\bigcap\mathcal{A}$ is closed and so $\bigcap\mathcal{A}$ is open. ▮

EXERCISE 24. In E^1 (definition 2.15), find a set of open sets whose intersection is not open.

3.25 Theorem. *The union of any set of open sets in a space $\{S, R^+\}$ is open in $\{S, R^+\}$.*

Proof: Let $\mathcal{G} = \{G_\nu\}$ denote a set of open sets in $\{S, R^+\}$. $\sim\bigcup_\nu G_\nu = \bigcap_\nu \sim G_\nu$. By hypothesis and by definition 3.20, each $\sim G_\nu$ is closed. Therefore, by theorem 3.16, $\bigcap_\nu \sim G_\nu$ is closed. Hence, $\bigcup_\nu G_\nu$ is open in $\{S, R^+\}$. ▮

The immediately preceding theorems thus establish that in any space $\{S, R^+\}$, a set $\mathfrak{J}$ of subsets of S is determined satisfying the following rules: (1) S and $\emptyset$ are in $\mathfrak{J}$, (2) the union of any set of sets in $\mathfrak{J}$ is in $\mathfrak{J}$ and (3) the intersection of any finite set of sets in $\mathfrak{J}$ is in $\mathfrak{J}$.

3.26 Definition. Let S be a set. A subset $\mathfrak{J}$ of $P(S)$ is called a *topology* for S if and only if (1) the intersection of any finite set of sets in $\mathfrak{J}$ is in $\mathfrak{J}$ and (2) the union of any set of sets in $\mathfrak{J}$ is in $\mathfrak{J}$.

EXERCISE 25. Let S be the set of real numbers; let $\mathcal{S}$ be the set of all subsets U_a^b of S such that $U_a^b = \{x \mid a < x < b\}$. Prove or disprove: $\mathcal{S}$ is a topology for S.

EXERCISE 26. Let S be a set; let $\mathcal{S} = \{S, \emptyset\}$. Prove or disprove: $\mathcal{S}$ is a topology for S.

EXERCISE 27. Let S be a set; let $\mathcal{S} = P(S)$. Prove or disprove: $\mathcal{S}$ is a topology for S.

EXERCISE 28. Let S be a set; let $\mathcal{S} = \{S, A, \emptyset\}$ where $A \subseteq S$ and $\emptyset \neq A \neq S$. Prove or disprove: $\mathcal{S}$ is a topology for S.

EXERCISE 29. Let S be the set of real numbers. Let $\mathcal{S}$ denote the set of all subsets G of S such that $G = S$, $G = \emptyset$ or $G = \{x \mid x > a\}$. Prove or disprove: $\mathcal{S}$ is a topology for S.

EXERCISE 30. Let S be any set. Show that the set consisting of $\emptyset$ and all subsets of S with finite complement is a topology for S.

EXERCISE 31. Let S be any set. Show that the set consisting of $\emptyset$ and all subsets of S with countable complements is a topology for S.

EXERCISE 32. Let S be any set of cardinality $\aleph_\alpha$. Show that the set consisting of $\emptyset$ and all subsets of S whose complements have cardinality less than $\aleph_\alpha$ is a topology for S. [*Hint:* $n \cdot \aleph_\alpha = \aleph_\alpha$, for n a natural number.]

The last three theorems establish that any neighborhood relation R^+ on a set S determines a topology $\mathfrak{J}$ for S; $\mathfrak{J}$ is the set of all open sets in the space $\{S, R^+\}$. It will be shown below that any topology on a set S is determined by a neighborhood relation, R^+, for S and is the set of all open sets in the space $\{S, R^+\}$. First, however, two very useful alternate definitions of open set will be established and then the largest basic neighborhood relation for any space relative to inclusion will be determined.

Interior and Boundary of Sets

In addition to closure, closed set and open set, there are two additional fundamental topological concepts: "interior" and "boundary."

3.27 Definition. A point p in a space, $\{S, R^+\}$, is said to be an *interior point* of $A \subseteq S$ if and only if there exists a neighborhood N of p such that $N \subseteq A$. A point p is called a *boundary point* of A if and only if $p \in \overline{A} \cap \overline{\sim A}$. p is called an *isolated point* of A if and only if p is in A and p has a neighborhood which contains no other point of A or, equivalently, $p \in A - A'$. The *interior* and *boundary* of A are defined to be, respectively, the set of all interior points of A and the set of all boundary points of A.

EXERCISE 33. In E^1 (definition 2.15), let A be the set of natural numbers. (a) What is the interior of A? (b) What is the boundary of A?

EXERCISE 34. In the space E^1, find an open set which is not the interior of its closure.

EXERCISE 35. Prove that the boundary of any subset A in a space $\{S, R^+\}$ is closed.

EXERCISE 36. Prove that any subset in a space $\{S, R^+\}$ consists exactly of its interior and boundary points.

3.28 Theorem (Alternate Definition). *A set G in a space $\{S, R^+\}$ is open if and only if G consists entirely of interior points.*

Proof: A. Let G be open in $\{S, R^+\}$. By definition 3.20, $\sim G$ is closed in $\{S, R^+\}$. By definition 3.9, $\sim G = \overline{\sim G}$. Therefore, $\sim G \supseteq (\sim G)'$ by definition 3.1. Thus no point of G is a limit point of $\sim G$. So if $p \in G$, then there exists at least one neighborhood N of p such that N contains no point of $\sim G$, i.e., $N \subseteq G$.

B. Let every point of G be an interior point of G. It follows that no point of G is a limit point of $\sim G$. Hence $\sim G \supseteq (\sim G)'$ and so $\sim G$ is closed by definitions 3.9 and 3.1. By definition 3.20, G, then, is open. ▮

3.29 Theorem (Alternate Definition). *A set G in a space $\{S, R^+\}$ is open if and only if G is a neighborhood of each of its points.*

Proof: Exercise.

The Largest Basic Neighborhood Relation

3.30 Theorem. *If $\{S, R^+\}$ is a space and if R is a basic neighborhood relation for $\{S, R^+\}$, then any basic neighborhood assigned by R is an open set in $\{S, R^+\}$.*

Proof: The theorem follows from axiom BN-III (definition 1.1) and theorem 3.28. ▮

The last theorem establishes that the range of any basic neighborhood relation for a space $\{S, R^+\}$ is a subset of the topology $\mathfrak{I}$ for $\{S, R^+\}$.

3.31 Theorem. *Let $\{S, R^+\}$ be a space and let $\mathfrak{I}$ denote the topology for $\{S, R^+\}$, i.e., the set of all open sets in $\{S, R^+\}$. Let $R_L = \{(p, G) \mid p \in G$ and $G \in \mathfrak{I}\}$. Then R_L is the largest basic neighborhood relation relative to inclusion for the space $\{S, R^+\}$.*

Proof: A. First it must be shown that R_L is a basic neighborhood relation for the set S. Since S is in $\mathfrak{I}$, for any point p in S, (p, S) is in R_L and hence S is the domain of R_L. If (p, G) is in R_L, $p \in G$ by definition of R_L. Thus axiom BN-I (definition 1.1) is satisfied. If (p, G) and (p, H) are in R_L, then $(p, G \cap H)$ is in R_L, since $G \cap H$ is in $\mathfrak{I}$ by theorem 3.24. Hence axiom BN-II is satisfied. If (p, G) is in R_L and if $q \in G$, then (q, G) is in R_L by definition of R_L. Thus axiom BN-III is satisfied.

B. Next it must be shown that R_L contains every basic neighborhood relation for $\{S, R^+\}$. Let R be any basic neighborhood relation for $\{S, R^+\}$ and let (p, V) be in R. By theorem 3.30, V is open in $\{S, R^+\}$, i.e., $V \in \mathfrak{I}$. Therefore $(p, V) \in R_L$ and, so, $R \subseteq R_L$.

C. It follows from theorems 2.6 and 3.29 that R_L is a basic neighborhood relation for the space $\{S, R^+\}$. ▮

3.32 Corollary (Alternate Definition). *A point p in a space $\{S, R^+\}$ is a limit point of a subset A of S if and only if every open set containing p contains a point of $A \sim \{p\}$.*

Proof: The corollary follows from theorem 3.31 and lemma 2.13. ▮

3.33 Corollary. *Let $\{S, R^+\}$ be a space; let $N \subseteq S$ and let $p \in N$. Then N is a neighborhood of p in $\{S, R^+\}$ if and only if there exists an open set G such that $G \subseteq N$ and $p \in G$.*

Proof: A. Let N be a neighborhood of p. By theorem 3.30, basic neighborhoods are always open. Hence by definition 1.3, N contains an open set G and $p \in G$.

B. Let $p \in N$, let G be an open set such that $p \in G$ and $G \subseteq N$. By theorem 3.29, G is a neighborhood of p and by axiom N-II (definition 2.5), N is a neighborhood of p. ▮

Extended and Conventional Definitions of a Topological Space

Figure 5 contains a sketch of the deductive development of the topological space starting with a neighborhood relation or an equivalence class of basic neighborhood relations.

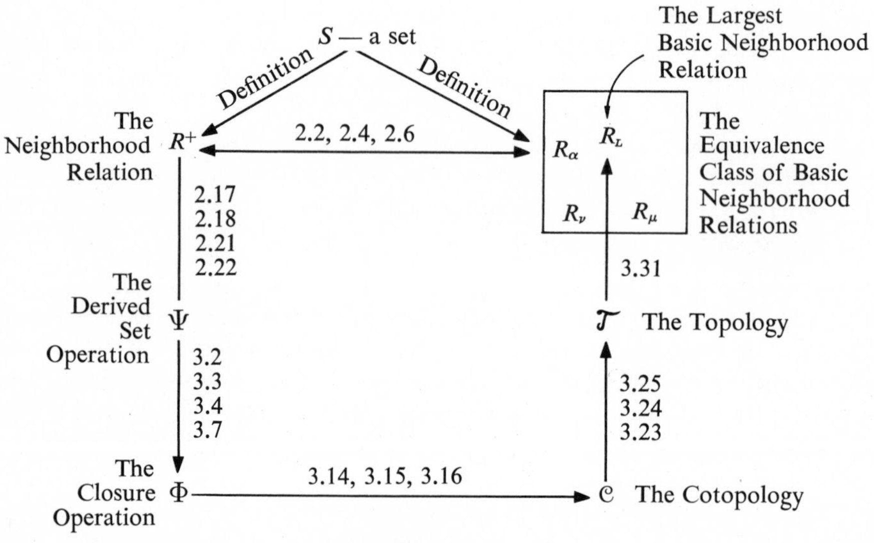

FIGURE 5

The next theorem establishes that the deductive development of the topological space can be started at $\mathfrak{T}$—the topology.

3.34 Theorem. *Let S be a set and $\mathfrak{T}$ a topology for S. Then $\mathfrak{T}$ is the set of all open sets for exactly one space $\{S, R^+\}$ on S.*

Proof: The proof is straightforward and is left as an exercise.

3.35 Lemma. *A topological space is determined uniquely by any pair $\{S, \mathfrak{T}\}$ consisting of a set S and a topology $\mathfrak{T}$ for S.*

Proof: The previous theorem implies the lemma. ▮

EXERCISE 37. Let S be a set and $\mathfrak{C}$ a cotopology (3.17) for S. Show that $\mathfrak{C}$ is the set of all closed sets for exactly one space $\{S, \mathfrak{I}\}$ on S. [*Hint:* Let $\mathfrak{I} = \{G \mid {\sim}G \in \mathfrak{C}\}$.]

3.36 Lemma. *A topological space is determined uniquely by any pair* $\{S, \mathfrak{C}\}$ *consisting of a set* S *and a cotopology for* S.

Proof: The previous exercise implies the lemma. ▮

EXERCISE 38. Let S be a set and Φ a closure operation (3.8) for S. Show that Φ is the closure operation for exactly one space $\{S, \mathfrak{C}\}$ on S. [*Hint:* Let $\mathfrak{C} = \{A \mid \Phi(A) = A\}$.]

3.37 Lemma. *A topological space is determined uniquely by any pair* $\{S, \Phi\}$ *consisting of a set* S *and a closure operation* Φ *on* S.

Proof: The previous exercise implies the lemma. ▮

EXERCISE 39. Let S be a set and Ψ a derivation (2.23) for S. Show that Ψ is the derivation for exactly one space $\{S, \Phi\}$ on S. [*Hint:* Let $\Phi(A) = A \cup \Psi(A)$.]

3.38 Lemma. *A topological space is determined uniquely by any pair* $\{S, \Psi\}$ *consisting of a set* S *and a derivation* Ψ *for* S.

Proof: The previous exercise implies the lemma. ▮

EXERCISE 40. Let $\{S, \mathfrak{I}\}$ be a space. Let A and B denote subsets of S and let $\mathrm{Int}(A)$ and $\mathrm{Int}(B)$ denote the interiors of A and B respectively. Show: (1) $\mathrm{Int}(S) = S$; (2) $\mathrm{Int}(A) \subseteq A$; (3) $\mathrm{Int}(\mathrm{Int}(A)) = \mathrm{Int}\, A$ and (4) $\mathrm{Int}(A \cap B) = \mathrm{Int}\, A \cap \mathrm{Int}\, B$.

3.39 Definition. Let S be any set. An *interior operator*, I, for S is a function from $P(S)$ into $P(S)$ such that: (1) $I(S) = S$; (2) $I(A) \subseteq A$; (3) $I(I(A)) = I(A)$ and (4) $I(A \cap B) = I(A) \cap I(B)$.

By exercise 40, every topology on a set determines an interior operator; namely, the function which assigns to every subset A its interior. The next exercise establishes that every interior operator comes from a topology.

EXERCISE 41. Let S be a set and I an interior operator for S. Show that I is the interior operator for exactly one space $\{S, \mathfrak{I}\}$ on S. [*Hint:* Let $\mathfrak{I} = \{A \mid I(A) = A\}$.]

3.40 Lemma. *A topological space is determined uniquely by any pair* $\{S, I\}$, *where* S *is a set and* I *is an interior operator for* S.

Proof: The previous exercise implies the lemma. ▮

EXERCISE 42. Let S be a set and let Φ be a closure operator for S. In the space $\{S, \Phi\}$, the boundary of any subset A of S has been defined to be $\Phi(A) \cap \Phi(\sim A)$. Let A and B be subsets of S and let $\mathrm{Bd}(A)$ and $\mathrm{Bd}(B)$ denote the boundaries of A and B respectively. Show: (1) $\mathrm{Bd}(S) = \emptyset$; (2) $\mathrm{Bd}(A) = \mathrm{Bd}(\sim A)$; (3) $\mathrm{Bd}(A \cup B) \subseteq \mathrm{Bd}(A) \cup \mathrm{Bd}(B)$ and (4) $(A \subseteq B \rightarrow (\mathrm{Bd}(A) \subseteq B \cup \mathrm{Bd}(B))$.

3.41 Definition. Let S be a set and let β be a function from $P(S)$ into $P(S)$. β is called a *boundary operator* for S if and only if: (1) $\beta(S) = \emptyset$; (2) $\beta(A) = \beta(\sim A)$; (3) $\beta(A \cup B) \subseteq \beta(A) \cup \beta(B)$ and (4) $A \subseteq B \rightarrow \beta(A) \subseteq B \cup \beta(B)$.

EXERCISE 43. Let S be a set and β a boundary operator for S. Show that β is the boundary operator for exactly one space $\{S, \Phi\}$ on S. [*Hint:* Let $\Phi(A) = A \cup \beta(A)$.]

3.42 Lemma. *A topological space is determined uniquely by any pair* $\{S, \beta\}$, *where S is a set and β is a boundary operator for S.*

Proof: The previous exercise implies the lemma. ▮

In Section 7, the concept of convergence is introduced and it will then be established that a topological space can be determined uniquely in still another way by designating the limits of sequences, nets and filters.

It is now clear from the theorems listed on figure 5 and from lemmas 3.35, 3.36, 3.37, 3.38, 3.40 and 3.42 that definition 2.7 is, in a sense, artificially restrictive, i.e., a topological space is no more a set and a neighborhood relation or a set and an equivalence class of basic neighborhood relations, than it is a set and a topology or a set and a cotopology or a set and a closure operation, etc. In fact, if one checks some of the books and papers listed in the bibliography, one can find a topological space defined in one as a set and a topology, in another as a set and a cotopology, in another as a set and a closure operation, and in a fourth one as a set and a derivation. The next definition will be an extension of definition 2.7 that will include all of the above pairs and then, this definition will in turn be amended to a briefer, more practical form—the now universally accepted, abbreviated definition (3.44) of a topological space.

3.43 Second (Extended) Definition. A *topological space* is a set $\{\{S, \{R_\nu\}\}, \{S, R^+\}, \{S, \Psi\}, \{S, \Phi\}, \{S, \mathfrak{C}\}, \{S, \mathfrak{J}\}, \{S, I\}, \{S, \beta\}\}$, where S is a set, $\{R_\nu\}$ is an equivalence class of basic neighborhood relations, R^+ is the neighborhood relation for S determined by $\{R_\nu\}$, Ψ is the derivation determined by R^+, Φ is the closure operation determined by Ψ, $\mathfrak{C}$ is the cotopology determined by Φ, $\mathfrak{J}$ is the topology determined by $\mathfrak{C}$, I is the interior operator determined by R^+, and β is the boundary operator determined by Φ.

The above definition is too clumsy and must be abbreviated. Since any one of the pairs in the set, which is the topological space, determines uniquely, and in turn is determined uniquely by the others, any one of them can, and actually has been used in various places in the literature, to identify the set and hence the space. It is now the universal custom, however, to choose the pair $\{S, \mathfrak{J}\}$—the set and the topology—to stand for the others and hence "be" the space.

3.44 Definition (Final). A *topological space* is a pair $\{S, \mathfrak{J}\}$ consisting of a set S and a topology $\mathfrak{J}$ for S. When no confusion seems likely to occur, the symbol $\{S, \mathfrak{J}\}$ is sometimes abbreviated to just S, and the term "topological space" is abbreviated to just "space."

Bases and Subbases

3.45 Definition. Let $\{S, \mathfrak{J}\}$ be a topological space. A *base*, $\mathfrak{B}$, for the topology, $\mathfrak{J}$, is a subset of $\mathfrak{J}$ with the property that any set in $\mathfrak{J}$ is the union of sets in $\mathfrak{B}$.

The following two theorems establish that the range of any basic neighborhood relation is a base for the topology it determines and conversely. Hence, the use of the word "basic" in the term "basic neighborhood" for Hausdorff's original neighborhoods seems justified.

3.46 Theorem. *If R is a basic neighborhood relation for a space $\{S, \mathfrak{J}\}$, then the range of R is a base for $\mathfrak{J}$.*

Proof: Let R be a basic neighborhood relation for the space $\{S, \mathfrak{J}\}$. Let $\mathfrak{B}$ denote the range of R. By theorem 3.30, $\mathfrak{B} \subseteq \mathfrak{J}$. Let $G \in \mathfrak{J}$. If $G = \emptyset$, then $\bigcup_{\emptyset} \mathfrak{B} = G$. If $G \neq \emptyset$, let $x \in G$. By theorem 3.28, and definitions 3.27 and 1.3, there exists a basic neighborhood V_x of x assigned by R such that $V_x \subseteq G$. Thus $G = \bigcup_{x \in G} V_x$, and, so, G is the union of sets in the range of R. ∎

The next theorem establishes that, conversely, any base for a topology $\mathfrak{J}$, minus $\emptyset$ is the range of a basic neighborhood relation.

3.47 Theorem. *If $\mathfrak{B}$ is a base for a topology $\mathfrak{J}$ on a set S, then $\mathfrak{B} \sim \{\emptyset\}$ is the range for a basic neighborhood relation on S.*

Proof: Let $R = \{(p, V) \mid p \in V \text{ and } V \in \mathfrak{B}\}$. By definitions of topology and base, S is the union of sets in $\mathfrak{J}$. Hence, if $x \in S$, there exists a set B_x in $\mathfrak{B}$ such that $x \in B_x$. Hence (x, B_x) is in R and the domain of R is S. Next, let B be any non-empty set in $\mathfrak{B}$. There exists x such that $x \in B$ and hence (x, B) is in R. Thus the range of R is $\mathfrak{B} \sim \{\emptyset\}$. Now let (x, V) be in R. By definition of R, $x \in V$ and so axiom BN-I (definition 1.1) is satisfied. Next, let (x, V) and (x, W) be in R. By definition 3.26, $V \cap W$ is in $\mathfrak{J}$; hence by definition 3.45, $V \cap W$ is the union of sets in $\mathfrak{B}$. Since $x \in V \cap W$, there exists B_x such that $x \in B_x$, $B_x \subseteq V \cap W$ and $B_x \in \mathfrak{B}$. Hence (x, B_x) is in R. Thus axiom BN-II is satisfied. Lastly, let (x, V) be in R and let y be in V. By definition of R, (y, V) is in R, and, hence, axiom BN-III is satisfied. ∎

3.48 Example. Let $I_a^b = \{x \mid x \text{ is real and } a < x < b\}$. Let $\mathcal{B} = \{I_a^b \mid a \text{ and } b \text{ are real}\}$. The set $\mathcal{B}$ is a base for the usual topology on E^1 (definition 2.15).

3.49 Example. Let

$$D_{(a,b)}^r = \{(x, y) \mid x \text{ and } y \text{ are real and } \sqrt{(x - a)^2 + (y - b)^2} < r\}.$$

Let $\mathcal{B} = \{D_{(a,b)}^r \mid a \text{ and } b \text{ are real and } r \text{ is positive real}\}$. $\mathcal{B}$ is a base for the usual topology on E^2 (definition 2.16).

A natural question that arises following the definition of a base (3.45), is: "is any set of subsets of a set S a base for a topology on S?" The next theorem answers this question.

3.50 Theorem. *Let S be a set. A necessary and sufficient condition that a subset $\mathcal{B}$ of $P(S)$ be a base for a topology on S is that any intersection of a finite number of sets in $\mathcal{B}$ be the union of sets in $\mathcal{B}$.*

Proof: A. Let any intersection of a finite number of sets in $\mathcal{B}$ be the union of sets in $\mathcal{B}$. Let $\mathfrak{I}$ be the set of all subsets of S which are unions of sets in $\mathcal{B}$. By definition of a base, (3.45), the sufficiency will be proved if $\mathfrak{I}$ is a topology for S. $S = \bigcap_\emptyset \mathcal{B}$; so, S is the union of sets in $\mathcal{B}$. S is then in $\mathfrak{I}$. $\emptyset = \bigcup_\emptyset \mathcal{B}$; therefore, $\emptyset$ is in $\mathfrak{I}$. Next let G_1 and G_2 be sets in $\mathfrak{I}$. By definition of $\mathfrak{I}$, $G_1 = \bigcup_\nu H_\nu$ and $G_2 = \bigcup_\alpha M_\alpha$, where each H_ν and each M_α is in $\mathcal{B}$. Hence, $G_1 \cap G_2 = (\bigcup_\nu H_\nu) \cap (\bigcup_\alpha M_\alpha)$. By the extended distributive laws for $\bigcup$ and $\bigcap$,

$$(\bigcup_\nu H_\nu) \cap (\bigcup_\alpha M_\alpha) = \bigcup_\nu [\bigcup_\alpha (H_\nu \cap M_\alpha)].$$

Now, by hypothesis, each intersection $H_\nu \cap M_\alpha$ is the union of sets in $\mathcal{B}$. Hence, by the extended associative law for $\bigcup$, $G_1 \cap G_2$ is the union of sets in $\mathcal{B}$. It follows immediately by finite induction that the intersection of any finite number of sets in $\mathfrak{I}$ is the union of sets in $\mathcal{B}$ and hence is in $\mathfrak{I}$. Further, if $\mathcal{G} = \bigcup_\nu G_\nu$ where each G_ν is in $\mathfrak{I}$, then each G_ν is a union of sets in $\mathcal{B}$. Hence $\bigcup_\nu G_\nu$ is the union of sets in $\mathcal{B}$. Thus $\mathfrak{I}$ is a topology and $\mathcal{B}$ is a base for $\mathfrak{I}$.

B. Let $\mathcal{B}$ be a base for a topology $\mathfrak{I}$ on a set S. $S \in \mathfrak{I}$; therefore, by definition 3.45, S is the union of sets in $\mathcal{B}$. Hence $\bigcap_\emptyset \mathcal{B}$ is the union of sets in $\mathcal{B}$ since $\bigcap_\emptyset \mathcal{B} = S$. Let G_1 and G_2 be in $\mathcal{B}$. G_1 and G_2 are then in $\mathfrak{I}$ and, hence, $G_1 \cap G_2$ is in $\mathfrak{I}$, by definition 3.26. By hypothesis, $G_1 \cap G_2$ is the union of sets in $\mathcal{B}$. Thus, by finite induction, it follows that the intersection of any finite set of sets in $\mathcal{B}$ is the union of sets in $\mathcal{B}$. ▮

3.51 Example. A subset $\mathfrak{A}$ of a topology, $\mathfrak{I}$, for a set S which has the property that every set in $\mathfrak{I}$ contains a set in $\mathfrak{A}$ need not be a base for $\mathfrak{I}$. Consider, e.g., $\mathfrak{A} = \{U_a^b \mid U_a^b = \{x \mid a < x < b \text{ for } a \text{ and } b \text{ real and both positive or both negative}\}\}$. If $\mathfrak{I}$ is the usual topology on the set of real numbers, every set in $\mathfrak{I}$ contains a set in $\mathfrak{A}$. $\mathfrak{A}$, however, is not a base for $\mathfrak{I}$.

Another useful concept for the study of topological spaces is the concept of "subbase."

3.52 Definition. Let $\{S, \mathfrak{I}\}$ be a space. A subset $\mathcal{V}$ of $\mathfrak{I}$ is called a *subbase* for $\mathfrak{I}$ if and only if the set of all intersections of finitely many sets in $\mathcal{V}$ is a base for $\mathfrak{I}$.

EXERCISE 44. Prove that any collection of subsets of a set X is a subbase for a topology on X.

EXERCISE 45. Let $A = \{(x, y) \mid x > -1\}$ and $B = \{(x, y) \mid x < 1\}$ constitute a subbase for a topology, $\mathfrak{I}$, on the set, S, of all ordered pairs of real numbers. In $\{S, \mathfrak{I}\}$, find $\overline{C}$, where $C = \{(x, y) \mid x = 0\}$.

EXERCISE 46. Show that the set of all interiors of squares of side 1 is a subbase for the topology on E^2 (definition 2.16).

EXERCISE 47. For a real and ϵ positive and real, let $V_a^\epsilon = \{(x, y) \mid x$ and y are real and $|x - a| < \epsilon\}$, and let $H_a^\epsilon = \{(x, y) \mid x$ and y are real and $|y - a| < \epsilon\}$. Show that $\mathcal{V} = \{M \mid M = V_a^\epsilon$ or $M = H_a^\epsilon$ for some real a and some positive real $\epsilon\}$ is a subbase for the topology on E^2 (definition 2.16).

A base and subbase for the cotopology $\mathcal{C}$ of a space $\{S, \mathfrak{I}\}$ are also defined.

3.53 Definition. Let $\{S, \mathfrak{I}\}$ be a space and let $\mathcal{C}$ denote the cotopology on the space (definition 3.17). A subset $\mathcal{B}^*$ of $\mathcal{C}$ is called a *base* for the cotopology, $\mathcal{C}$, if and only if every set in $\mathcal{C}$ is the intersection of sets in $\mathcal{B}^*$.

3.54 Definition. A subset $\mathcal{V}^*$ of a cotopology $\mathcal{C}$ on a set S is called a *subbase* for $\mathcal{C}$ if and only if the set of all unions of finitely many sets in $\mathcal{V}^*$ is a base for $\mathcal{C}$.

EXERCISE 48. Prove that if $\mathcal{B}$ is a base for a topology $\mathfrak{I}$ on a set $\mathcal{S}$, then the set $\mathcal{B}^*$ of all complements of sets in $\mathcal{B}$ is a base for the cotopology $\mathcal{C}$ determined by $\mathfrak{I}$ on S.

EXERCISE 49. Prove that if $\mathcal{V}$ is a subbase for a topology, $\mathfrak{I}$, on a set S, then the set $\mathcal{V}^*$ of all complements of sets in $\mathcal{V}$ is a subbase for the cotopology $\mathcal{C}$ determined on S by $\mathfrak{I}$.

EXERCISE 50. Prove that any set of subsets of a set S is a subbase for a cotopology on S.

EXERCISE 51. Let S denote the set of real numbers. Let $U_p^+ = \{x \mid x \geq p\}$ and let $U_p^- = \{x \mid x \leq p\}$. Let $\mathcal{V} = \{A \mid A = U_p^+$ or $A = U_p^-$ for some real number $p\}$ be the subbase for a cotopology, $\mathcal{C}$, on S. Find the closure of the set of positive reals in the space determined by $\mathcal{C}$ on S.

EXERCISE 52. Let N be the set of all natural numbers, $\{1, 2, \ldots\}$. Let $D_m = \{k \mid k$ divides m, for k and m in $N\}$. Let $R = \{(m, B) \mid B = D_m$ for m in $N\}$. (a) Prove R is a basic neighborhood relation for N (definition 1.1). (b) Prove that in the space determined by R on N, the set of all odd numbers is open. (c) Prove or disprove: in the space determined by R on S, the set of all even numbers is open.

EXERCISE 53. Let S be the set of real numbers. Let $U_p = \{x \mid x \geq p$, for x and p in $S\}$. Let $\mathfrak{B} = \{B \mid B = U_p$ for some real number $p\}$. Then $\mathfrak{B}$ is a base for a topology $\mathfrak{I}$ on S. In the space $\{S, \mathfrak{I}\}$, show that the union of any number of closed sets is closed and that the intersection of any number of open sets is open.

EXERCISE 54. Show that, in general, if S is a space, the union of any number of closed sets in S is not necessarily closed and that the intersection of any number of open sets in S is not necessarily open.

All of the basic topological concepts, except convergence, have now been introduced—basic neighborhood relation, neighborhood relation, derived set operation, closure operation, closed sets, open sets, interior operator and boundary operator. Any one of these, defined for a set S, determines uniquely a topological space on S. In the next section, it will be shown that continuity can be defined directly in terms of any one of these concepts. Convergence will be introduced in Section 7.

AN ABBREVIATED SUMMARY FOR SECTIONS 1, 2 AND 3

A *topological space* is a pair $\{S, \mathfrak{I}\}$ consisting of a set, S, and a topology, $\mathfrak{I}$. $\{S, \mathfrak{I}\}$ is sometimes abbreviated to just S. A *topology* $\mathfrak{I}$ is a subset of $P(S)$, the set of all subsets of S, which satisfies the following conditions: if $\mathfrak{A} \subseteq \mathfrak{I}$ then $\bigcup\mathfrak{A} \in \mathfrak{I}$ and if $\mathfrak{A} \subseteq \mathfrak{I}$ and $\mathfrak{A}$ is finite, then $\bigcap\mathfrak{A} \in \mathfrak{I}$. The sets in $\mathfrak{I}$ are called *open*. $\mathfrak{B}$ is a *base* for a topology, $\mathfrak{I}$, if and only if (1) $\mathfrak{B} \subseteq \mathfrak{I}$ and (2) $G \in \mathfrak{I}$ implies that $G = \bigcup\mathfrak{B}^*$ where $\mathfrak{B}^* \subseteq \mathfrak{B}$. $\mathfrak{V}$ is a *subbase* for $\mathfrak{I}$ if and only if $\mathfrak{V} \subseteq \mathfrak{I}$ and $\{\bigcap\mathfrak{A} \mid \mathfrak{A}$ is finite and $\mathfrak{A} \subseteq \mathfrak{V}\}$ is a base for $\mathfrak{I}$. Let $N \subseteq S$ and let $p \in S$. N is a *neighborhood* of p in $\{S, \mathfrak{I}\}$ if and only if $(\exists G)(G \in \mathfrak{I}, p \in G$ and $G \subseteq N)$. $\{(p, N) \mid p \in S$ and N is a neighborhood of p in $\{S, \mathfrak{I}\}\}$, denoted by R^+, is called *the neighborhood relation* for $\{S, \mathfrak{I}\}$. It follows that $R^+ \subseteq S \times P(S)$ and the domain of R^+ is S. A subset, R, of $S \times P(S)$ is called a *basic neighborhood relation* for $\{S, \mathfrak{I}\}$ if and only if (1) the domain of R is S, (2) (p, V) in R implies that $p \in V$ and (3) the range of R is a base for $\mathfrak{I}$. If (p, V) is in R, then V is called *a basic neighborhood of p relative to R*. The basic neighborhoods were originally called neighborhoods by Hausdorff. It then follows from the definitions that if R is any basic neighborhood relation for $\{S, \mathfrak{I}\}$ and if R^+ is the neighborhood relation for $\{S, \mathfrak{I}\}$, then $R \subseteq R^+$. Let $A \subseteq S$ and let $p \in S$. p is a *limit point* of A in $\{S, \mathfrak{I}\}$ if and only if $(\forall N)$ (N is a neighborhood of p in $\{S, \mathfrak{I}\}$ implies that $N \cap (A - \{p\}) \neq \emptyset$. The set of limit points of A, denoted by A', is called *the derived set* of A. $A \cup A'$, denoted by $\overline{A}$, is called *the closure* of A in $\{S, \mathfrak{I}\}$. A is called *closed* in $\{S, \mathfrak{I}\}$ if and only if $A = \overline{A}$. p is called *an interior point* of A if and only if $(\exists N)$ ($p \in N$, $N \subseteq A$ and N is a neighborhood of p in $\{S, \mathfrak{I}\}$). p is called a *boundary point* of A if and only if $p \in \overline{A} \cap \overline{(S - A)}$. It follows that a set, A, is open in $\{S, \mathfrak{I}\}$ if and only if its complement, $S - A$, is closed in $\{S, \mathfrak{I}\}$ and that a set, A, is closed in $\{S, \mathfrak{I}\}$ if and only if its complement, $S - A$, is open in $\{S, \mathfrak{I}\}$. Also, a subset G of S is open in $\{S, \mathfrak{I}\}$ if and only if G consists entirely of interior points. A function, f, from a topological space $\{S, \mathfrak{I}\}$ onto a topological space $\{T, \mathfrak{S}\}$ is called *continuous at the point p in* $\mathfrak{S}$ if and only if $f^{-1}[N]$ is a neighborhood of p in $\{S, \mathfrak{I}\}$ whenever N is a neighborhood of $f(p)$ in $\{T, \mathfrak{S}\}$ and f is called *continuous* if and only if f is continuous at each point of S.

4. CONTINUOUS FUNCTIONS.

Alternate Definitions of Continuity

In definition 2.10 and theorem 2.11 continuity was defined directly in terms of neighborhoods and basic neighborhoods respectively. The following theorems establish alternate definitions of continuity in terms of the other basic topological concepts.

4.1 Theorem. *Let S and T be topological spaces and let f be a function from S onto T. Then f is continuous at every point of S if and only if G open in T implies $f^{-1}[G]$ is open in S.*

Proof: A. Let f be continuous at every point of S; let G be any open set in T and let a be any point in $f^{-1}[G]$. $f(a)$ is, then, in G. By theorem 3.29, G is a neighborhood of $f(a)$ in T. By definition 2.10, $f^{-1}[G]$ is a neighborhood of a in S. Thus, again by theorem 3.29, $f^{-1}[G]$ is open in S.

B. Let f be a function from S onto T such that G open in T implies that $f^{-1}[G]$ is open in S. Let a be any point in S. Let N be any neighborhood of $f(a)$ in T. By corollary 3.33, N contains an open set G and $f(a) \in G$. By hypothesis, $f^{-1}[G]$ is open. Since $a \in f^{-1}[G]$, $f^{-1}[G]$ is a neighborhood of a, by theorem 3.29. Since $f^{-1}[N] \supseteq f^{-1}[G]$, $f^{-1}[N]$ is a neighborhood of a. By definition 2.10, f is then continuous at a. ▮

4.2 Theorem. *A function f from a topological space S onto a topological space T is continuous on S if and only if F closed in T implies $f^{-1}[F]$ is closed in S.*

Proof: A. Given that f is continuous at every point of S, let F be any closed set in T. Then $\sim F$ is open in T, by definition of open set (3.20). $f^{-1}[\sim F]$ is open in S by theorem 4.1. Hence, $\sim f^{-1}[\sim F]$ is closed in S, by definition 3.20. Now $\sim f^{-1}[\sim F] = f^{-1}[F]$; hence, $f^{-1}[F]$ is closed in S.

B. Given that F is closed in T implies that $f^{-1}[F]$ is closed in S, let G be any open set in T. $\sim G$ is closed in T; hence, $f^{-1}[\sim G]$ is closed in S. $\sim f^{-1}[\sim G]$ is then open in S. Since $\sim f^{-1}[\sim G] = f^{-1}[G]$, $f^{-1}[G]$ is open in S and by theorem 4.1 f is continuous. ▮

4.3 Theorem. *A function f from a topological space S onto a topological space T is continuous at every point of S if and only if the image, $f[\overline{A}]$, of the closure of any set A in S is contained in the closure, $\overline{f[A]}$, of the image, i.e., $f[\overline{A}] \subseteq \overline{f[A]}$.*

Proof: A. Let f be continuous on S and let A be any subset of S. $f[A] \subseteq \overline{f[A]}$. Therefore $A \subseteq f^{-1}[\overline{f[A]}]$. By theorem 4.2, $f^{-1}[\overline{f[A]}]$ is closed. By corollary 3.6 and definition 3.9, $\overline{A} \subseteq f^{-1}[\overline{f[A]}]$. Hence, $f[\overline{A}] \subseteq \overline{f[A]}$.

B. Let f be a function from S onto T such that for any set A in S, $f[\overline{A}] \subseteq \overline{f[A]}$. Let F be closed in T and let p be a limit point of $f^{-1}[F]$. p is in $\overline{f^{-1}[F]}$; hence, $f(p)$ is in $f[\overline{f^{-1}[F]}]$. By hypothesis, $f[\overline{f^{-1}[F]}] \subseteq \overline{f[f^{-1}[F]]} = F$. Hence $f(p)$ is in F and p is in $f^{-1}[F]$. $f^{-1}[F]$ is then closed and f is continuous by theorem 4.2. ▮

The next three theorems establish alternate definitions for continuity in terms of derived set, interior and boundary. However, these definitions are much less used than the previous three definitions.

4.4 Theorem. *A function f from a space S onto a space T is continuous at every point of S if and only if $f[A'] \subseteq f[A] \cup f[A]' = \overline{f[A]}$ for every subset A of S.*

Proof: A. Let f be continuous on S. By theorem 4.3, for $A \subseteq S$, $f[\overline{A}] \subseteq \overline{f[A]}$. Since $A' \subseteq \overline{A}$, $f[A'] \subseteq f[\overline{A}]$. Hence, $f[A'] \subseteq \overline{f[A]} = f[A] \cup f[A]'$.

B. Let f have the property that for $A \subseteq S$, $f[A'] \subseteq f[A] \cup f[A]' = \overline{f[A]}$. Since $\overline{A} = A \cup A'$, $f[\overline{A}] = f[A] \cup f[A']$. Now $f[A] \subseteq \overline{f[A]}$ and by hypothesis, $[A'] \subseteq \overline{f[A]}$. Hence $f[\overline{A}] \subseteq \overline{f[A]}$ and so f is continuous by theorem 4.3. ▮

EXERCISE 1. Give an example of a continuous function from a space S onto a space T such that: (a) $f[A'] \neq f[A]'$ for some $A \subseteq S$; (b) $f[\overline{A}] \neq \overline{f[A]}$ for some $A \subseteq S$; (c) G is open in S but $f[G]$ is not open in T for some $G \subseteq S$ and (d) F is closed in S but $f[F]$ is not closed in T for some $F \subseteq S$.

4.5 Theorem. *Let f be a function from a space S onto a space T. f is continuous on S if and only if $f^{-1}[I(A)] \subseteq I(f^{-1}[A])$ for all $A \subseteq S$.*

Proof: A. Let f be continuous from S onto T. Let $A \subseteq T$. Let $p \in I(A)$. By definition of $I(A)$ (3.27), there exists a neighborhood N of p such that $N \subseteq A$. By corollary 3.33, there exists an open set G such that $p \in G$ and $G \subseteq N$. By theorem 3.29, G is a neighborhood of each of its points; hence, $G \subseteq I(A)$. Thus, $I(A)$ is a neighborhood of p, by corollary 3.33. Since p was any point in $I(A)$, $I(A)$ is open by theorem 3.29. By hypothesis, f is continuous; hence, by theorem 4.1, $f^{-1}[I(A)]$ is open. By definition 3.27, $I(A) \subseteq A$; hence, $f^{-1}[I(A)] \subseteq f^{-1}[A]$. Since $f^{-1}[I(A)]$ is open, each point of $f^{-1}[I(A)]$ is interior to $f^{-1}[A]$, by theorem 3.29 and definition 3.27. Hence, $f^{-1}[I(A)] \subseteq I(f^{-1}[A])$.

B. Let f have the property that for $A \subseteq S$, $f^{-1}[I(A)] \subseteq I(f^{-1}[A])$. Let G be open in T. By theorem 3.28, $I(G) = G$. By hypothesis, $f^{-1}[I(G)] \subseteq I(f^{-1}[G])$. Hence, $f^{-1}[G] \subseteq I(f^{-1}[G])$. By definition 3.27, $I(f^{-1}[G]) \subseteq f^{-1}[G]$. Hence $f^{-1}[G] = I(f^{-1}[G])$ and $f^{-1}[G]$ is open by theorem 3.28. Thus, by theorem 4.1, f is continuous. ▮

EXERCISE 2. Give an example of a function, f, which is continuous from a space S onto a space T such that $f[I(A)] \not\subseteq I(f[A])$ for some $A \subsetneq S$.

4.6 Theorem. *Let f be a function from a space S onto a space T. Then f is continuous if and only if $f[\beta(A)] \subseteq f[A] \cup \beta(f[A])$ for all $A \subseteq S$.*

Proof: A. Let f be continuous. By definition 3.27, $\beta(A) \subseteq \overline{A}$. By theorem 4.3, $f[\overline{A}] \subseteq \overline{f[A]}$. However, $\overline{f[A]} = f[A] \cup \beta(f[A])$. Hence $f[\beta(A)] \subseteq f[A] \cup \beta(f[A])$.

B. Let f have the property that $f[\beta(A)] \subseteq f[A] \cup \beta(f[A])$. Let $A \subseteq S$. $\overline{A} = A \cup \beta(A)$, by definition 3.27. Now, $f[\overline{A}] = f[A] \cup f[\beta(A)]$. Hence, $f[\overline{A}] \subseteq f[A] \cup \beta(f[A])$, by hypothesis. Since $f[A] \cup \beta(f[A]) = \overline{f[A]}$, f is continuous by theorem 4.3. ∎

EXERCISE 3. Give an example of a function, f, which is continuous from a space S onto a space T and is such that $f[\beta(A)] \not\subseteq \beta(f[A])$ for some $A \subseteq S$.

COMPOSITE FUNCTIONS

One of the most important methods for generating functions is the method of putting functions f and g together to get the composite function $g \circ f$. A natural question to ask is, "If f and g are continuous, is $g \circ f$ continuous?"

4.7 Definition. Let f be a function from a space S onto a space T and let g be a function from a space T onto a space X. The *composite function* of f and g, denoted by $g \circ f$, is the function h from S onto X defined by $h(p) = g(f(p))$.

4.8 Theorem. *If f is a continuous function from a space S onto a space T and if g is a continuous function from T onto a space, X, then the composite function, $g \circ f$, from S onto X is continuous.*

Proof: Exercise.

BASES, SUBBASES AND CONTINUITY

4.9 Theorem. *Let f be a function from a space S onto a space T. Let $\mathcal{B}$ be a base for the open sets in T. Then f is continuous if and only if $B \in \mathcal{B}$ implies that $f^{-1}[B]$ is open in S.*

Proof: A. Let f be continuous. $B \in \mathcal{B}$ implies that $f^{-1}[B]$ is open in S by theorem 4.1 and definition 3.45.

B. Let $B \in \mathcal{B}$ imply that $f^{-1}[B]$ is open in S. Let G be any open set in T. $G = \bigcup_\nu B_\nu$ where each B_ν is in $\mathcal{B}$, by definition of a base. Hence, $f^{-1}[G] = f^{-1}[\bigcup_\nu B_\nu] = \bigcup_\nu f^{-1}[B_\nu]$. $f^{-1}[B_\nu]$, for each ν, is open in S by hypothesis. Hence, $f^{-1}[G]$ is open and by theorem 4.1, f is continuous. ∎

4.10 Theorem. *Let f be a function from a space S onto a space T. Let $\mathcal{V}$ be a subbase for the set of all open sets in T. Then f is continuous if and only if $V \in \mathcal{V}$ implies $f^{-1}[V]$ is open in S.*

Proof: A. Let f be continuous. By theorem 4.1 and definition 3.52, $f^{-1}[V]$ is open in S.

B. Let $V \in \mathcal{V}$ imply that $f^{-1}[V]$ is open in S and let G be any open set in T. $G = \bigcup_\nu B_\nu$, where $B_\nu = V_1^\nu \cap V_2^\nu \cap \cdots \cap V_{k_\nu}^\nu$, for V_i^ν in $\mathcal{V}$. Thus, $f^{-1}[G] = f^{-1}[\bigcup_\nu B_\nu] = \bigcup_\nu f^{-1}[B_\nu] = \bigcup_\nu [f^{-1}[V_1^\nu] \cap \cdots \cap f^{-1}[V_{k_\nu}^\nu]]$. Since the intersection of a finite number of open sets is open and since the union of any set of open sets is open, $f^{-1}[G]$ is open. By theorem 4.1, then, f is continuous. ∎

Continuity, for a function f from a space S onto a space T, can thus be defined in eight different ways as follows:

1. V is a basic neighborhood of $f(p)$ in T implies there exists a basic neighborhood U of p in S such that $f[U] \subseteq V$;
2. N is a neighborhood of $f(p)$ in T implies that $f^{-1}[N]$ is a neighborhood of p in S;
3. G is open in T implies that $f^{-1}[G]$ is open in S;
4. F is closed in T implies that $f^{-1}[F]$ is closed in S;
5. $A \subseteq S$ implies $f[\overline{A}] \subseteq \overline{f[A]}$;
6. $A \subseteq S$ implies $f[A'] \subseteq f[A] \cup f[A]'$;
7. $B \subseteq T$ implies $f^{-1}[I(B)] \subseteq I(f^{-1}[B])$, where $I(B)$ denotes the interior of B;
8. $A \subseteq S$ implies $f[\beta(A)] \subseteq f[A] \cup \beta(f[A])$, where $\beta(A)$ denotes the boundary of A.

The first five definitions are more often used than the last three.

EXERCISE 4. Let S denote the set of real numbers. Let $R = \{(x, V) \mid V = \{x\}$ for $x \in S\}$. Then R is a basic neighborhood relation for S. Let $\{S, \mathfrak{J}\}$ be the space determined on S by R. Prove that every function with domain $\{S, \mathfrak{J}\}$ is continuous.

EXERCISE 5. Prove that a strictly increasing (decreasing) function f, whose domain and range are both the space, E^1, of real numbers, is 1:1 and continuous on E^1.

EXERCISE 6. Let S be the set of real numbers and let the sets $U(p) = \{x \mid p \leq x\}$ constitute a base for a topology on S. Show that any non-decreasing function from S onto S is continuous on S and that these are the only continuous functions from S onto S.

EXERCISE 7. Find a continuous function f from E^1 onto E^1 and a set G open in the domain of f such that $f[G]$ is not open in the range of f.

EXERCISE 8. A function f from a space $\{S, \mathfrak{J}\}$ onto a space $\{T, \mathfrak{J}^*\}$ is called *quasi-continuous* at a point a in its domain if and only if for each open set G containing $f(a)$ in the range and each open set U containing a in the domain, there is a non-empty open set $V \subseteq U \cap f^{-1}[G]$. Find a function from E^1 onto E^1 which is quasi-continuous at some point but not continuous at the same point.

EXERCISE 9. Prove that a function from one space onto another which is continuous at a point a in its domain is quasi-continuous at a.

EXERCISE 10. Find a function from E^1 onto E^1 which is not quasi-continuous at some point of its domain.

5. COUNTABLE BASES AND LOCAL BASES.

5.1 Definition. In a space, $\{S, \mathfrak{I}\}$, a *local base*, $\mathcal{B}_x$, at a point x in S is any set of open sets such that x is in every set of $\mathcal{B}_x$ and every neighborhood of x contains a set of $\mathcal{B}_x$.

5.2 Example. In the space E^2, a local base at the point $(1, 0)$ is the collection of all interiors of circles whose centers are at $(1, 0)$.

5.3 Lemma. *If $\{S, \mathfrak{I}\}$ is a space and if x is a point of S, then the collection of basic neighborhoods assigned to x by any basic neighborhood relation, R_ν, for $\{S, \mathfrak{I}\}$ constitutes a local base at x.*

Proof: Exercise.

FIRST AND SECOND COUNTABILITY

The countability (denumerability) of bases and local bases is an important property of spaces.

5.4 Definition. A space $\{S, \mathfrak{I}\}$ is said to satisfy *the first axiom of countability* or to be *first countable* if and only if each point x of S has a countable local base.

5.5 Theorem. *If a space $\{S, \mathfrak{I}\}$ is first countable, then each point p has a countable local base $\mathcal{B} = \{B_1, B_2, \ldots, B_n, \ldots\}$ such that $B_j \subseteq B_i$ for $j \geq i$.*

Proof: Let $\{U_1, U_2, \ldots, U_n, \ldots\}$ be a countable local base for the point p in the first countable space $\{S, \mathfrak{I}\}$. Let $B_1 = U_1$, $B_2 = U_1 \cap U_2, \ldots, B_n = U_1 \cap \ldots \cap U_n, \ldots$. Each set B_j is open by theorem 3.24. Further, $p \in B_j$ for each j. Now let W be any neighborhood for p. Since $\{U_1, U_2, \ldots, U_n, \ldots\}$ is a local base at p, for some natural number n, $U_n \subseteq W$. Hence, $B_n \subseteq W$ and $\{B_1, B_2, \ldots, B_n, \ldots\}$ is a local base at p. ∎

5.6 Definition. A space $\{S, \mathfrak{I}\}$ is said to satisfy *the second axiom of countability* or to be *second countable* if and only if there exists a countable base for the topology $\mathfrak{I}$ on S.

5.7 Example. Let S be any uncountable set with the set of all subsets for its topology, $\mathfrak{J}$. Every subset containing only one point is open; and so each point has a local base consisting of one open set. S is thus first countable. Since any base $\mathcal{B}$ for $\mathfrak{J}$ must contain every one point subset of S, no base $\mathcal{B}$ can be countable and S is then not second countable.

5.8 Example. Let S be the space consisting of the set of all real numbers plus one element, α, which is not a real number, and let the topology consist of all open sets of E^1 plus the sets G_ν, where $\alpha \in G_\nu$ and $\sim G_\nu$ is finite. Thus, the open sets containing α have finite complements. Assume there exists a countable local base $\mathcal{B}_\alpha = \{V_1, V_2, \ldots, V_n, \ldots\}$ at α. If y is any real number in S, then $\sim\{y\}$ is open by definition of the topology on S. Hence, there exists a V_j in $\mathcal{B}_\alpha$ which does not contain y. Therefore, $\bigcap_{i=1}^{\infty} V_i = \{\alpha\}$ and $\sim\{\alpha\} = \sim \bigcap_{i=1}^{\infty} V_i = \bigcup_{i=1}^{\infty} (\sim V_i)$. Since $(\sim V_i)$ is finite for each i, $\bigcup_{i=1}^{\infty} (\sim V_i)$ is countable and is equal to $\sim\{\alpha\}$. This is a contradiction, since $\sim\{\alpha\}$ is the set of all real numbers. Hence S is not first countable.

5.9 Lemma. *A space which is second countable is first countable.*

Proof: Exercise.

EXERCISE 1. Prove that if a space S has a countable subbase, then it is second countable.

5.10 Theorem. *The space E^1 of real numbers is second countable and hence first countable.*

Proof: The open sets in E^1 are unions of intervals of real numbers of the form $\{x \mid a < x < b;\ a, b, \text{ real numbers}\}$. The set R of rational numbers is countable. Let r and δ be rational numbers and let J_r^δ denote $\{x \mid r - \delta < x < r + \delta\}$. For a fixed $r = r^*$, the collection $\{J_{r^*}^\delta \mid \delta \text{ is rational}\}$ is countable; hence, the set $\{J_r^\delta \mid \delta \text{ rational}, r \text{ rational}\}$ is a countable collection of countable sets and hence is countable. It is to be proved that this countable collection of intervals forms a base for the topology on E^1.

Let G be any open set in E^1 and y_0 any point of G. By theorem 3.28, G contains an interval $\{x \mid y_0 - \epsilon < x < y_0 + \epsilon, \text{ for } \epsilon > 0\}$. First, by the archimedean property of the order defined on the real numbers, there exists a natural number n such that $n \cdot 1 > 4/\epsilon$. Next assume $0 \leq y_0$; there exists a natural number m such that $m \cdot 1/n > y_0$. Since the natural numbers are well-ordered in their natural ordering, there exists a first natural number m^* such that

$$m^* \cdot 1/n > y_0; \qquad \text{then} \qquad \frac{m^* - 1}{n} \leq y_0.$$

Then,

$$\frac{m^* - 2}{n} < \frac{m^* - 1}{n} \leq y_0 < \frac{m^*}{n}.$$

Since

$$\frac{m^*}{n} - \left(\frac{m^* - 2}{n}\right) = \frac{2}{n} < \frac{\epsilon}{2},$$

then

$$y_0 - \epsilon < \frac{m^* - 2}{n} < y_0 < \frac{m^*}{n} < y_0 + \epsilon.$$

Hence the interval

$$\left(\frac{m^* - 2}{n}, \frac{m^*}{n}\right)$$

with rational midpoint $(m^* - 1)/n$ lies inside the interval $(y_0 - \epsilon, y_0 + \epsilon)$ and contains y_0. If $y_0 < 0$, let $x_0 = -y_0$. Then as above, $((m^* - 2)/n, m^*/n)$ contains x_0 and $(-m^*/n, (-m^* + 2)/n)$ contains $-x_0 = y_0$. Thus, G is the union of intervals J_r^δ with rational midpoint and rational radius. Hence, E^1 has a countable base. Since E^1 is second countable, it is also first countable. ▌

SEPARABILITY

5.11 Definition. A subset M of a space S is called *dense* in S if and only if $\overline{M} = S$.

5.12 Definition. A space S is called *separable* if and only if it contains a countable dense subset.

EXERCISE 2. Prove that the continuous image of a separable space is separable.

5.13 Corollary. *The space E^1 is separable and the set of rational numbers is dense in the set of real numbers.*

Proof: The proof of the previous theorem (using the same notation) showed that if y_0 is any real number and $(y_0 - \epsilon, y_0 + \epsilon)$ is any basic open set containing y_0 in E^1, then there exists a rational number, $(m^* - 1)/n$, in this interval. Hence, every real number is a rational number or a limit point of the set R of rationals and so $E^1 = \overline{R}$. ▌

5.14 Theorem. *Any space S with a countable base is separable.*

Proof: Let $\mathcal{B}$ be a countable base for S. Let $\mathcal{B} = \{B_i \mid i = 1, 2, 3, \ldots\}$. Choose one point b_i in each non-empty B_i (choice axiom); let $D = \{b_1, b_2, b_3, \ldots\}$. Let $x \in S$ and let U be any open set in S containing x; then there exists $B_j \subseteq U$ and $b_j \in U$. Therefore, every open set containing x contains an element of D; hence D is dense in S. Therefore, S is separable. ▌

The converse of the above theorem is false, i.e., a separable space does not have to be second countable.

5.15 Theorem. *A separable space is not necessarily second countable.*

Either one of the following two examples proves the theorem.

1. Let S be the set of all real numbers and let the sets $U_p = \{x \mid x \geq p\}$ form a base for a topology $\mathfrak{J}$ on S. The countable set of natural numbers 1, 2, 3, . . . is dense in this topology. Let $\mathfrak{B}$ be any base for $\mathfrak{J}$ and x^* any real number; consider the open set $U_{x^*} = \{x \mid x \geq x^*\}$. The only open set in $\mathfrak{J}$ which contains x^* and is contained in U_{x^*} is U_{x^*}; therefore $U_{x^*} \in \mathfrak{B}$. Since x^* was any real number, $\mathfrak{B}$ must contain all open sets, U_{x^*}, and so $\mathfrak{B}$ cannot be countable.

2. Consider the uncountable set S of real numbers and define an unusual topology, $\mathfrak{J}$, for this set. $\mathfrak{J}$ consists of the null set plus all sets which are complements of finite sets. Consider the set Z of natural numbers. Let x be any real number and U any open set containing x; U contains all but a finite number of natural numbers and so x is a limit point of Z. Thus Z is dense in S using the topology, $\mathfrak{J}$. However, assume there exists a countable base $\mathfrak{B}$ for $\mathfrak{J}$. Consider again any real number x and let $V_1, V_2, \ldots$ be the sets of $\mathfrak{B}$ which contain x. Let $y \in S$ and $y \neq x$; $\sim\{y\}$ is open, by definition of $\mathfrak{J}$, and $x \in \sim\{y\}$. $\sim\{y\}$ contains a set V_j of $\mathfrak{B}$, by the definition of a base, and $y \notin V_j$. Therefore, $\bigcap_{i=1}^{\infty} V_i = \{x\}$ and $\sim(\bigcap_{i=1}^{\infty} V_i) = \sim\{x\}$ is not countable. However, $\sim(\bigcap_{i=1}^{\infty} V_i) = \bigcup_{i=1}^{\infty} (\sim V_i)$. Since the V_i are non-empty and open, each $\sim V_i$ is finite by definition of $\mathfrak{J}$. Hence, $\bigcup_{i=1}^{\infty} (\sim V_i)$ is countable; hence, $\sim\{x\}$ is countable, and so S is countable. This is a contradiction. Thus there exists a countable dense subset for S with the topology $\mathfrak{J}$ but no countable base for $\mathfrak{J}$. ▮

EXERCISE 3. Generalize the above proof for any uncountable set S with the topology consisting of the null set and all complements of finite sets.

EXERCISE 4. Do the spaces of the previous theorem, (5.15), satisfy the first axiom of countability?

EXERCISE 5. Let S be any uncountable set with a topology consisting of the null set and all complements of countable sets. Is S separable? Does S have a countable base?

EXERCISE 6. If $\mathcal{V}$ is a subbase for a topology, $\mathfrak{J}$, on a set S, if A is a subset of S and if further $A \cap V \neq \emptyset$ for every V in $\mathcal{V}$, is A dense in S? [*Hint:* Consider the interiors of squares of side 1 in E^2.]

6. HOMEOMORPHISMS. TOPOLOGICAL INVARIANTS.

Although continuity can be defined only in topological terms, it appears from the theorems in section 4 that continuity is only half of a new property in the following sense. Theorem 4.1 (and 4.2) says that the inverse image of an open (closed) set is open (closed) when the function is continuous; they do not state that the image of an open (closed) set is open (closed). Theorem 4.3, states that the image of the closure of a set assigned by a continuous function is contained in the closure of the image; it does not state that the image of the closure is the closure of the image. Theorem 4.4 states that the image of the derived set of a set assigned by a continuous function is contained in the closure of the image; it does not state that the image of a derived set is the derived set of the image. The following examples are included, now, to show that the indicated omissions in the aforementioned theorems are mathematically necessary.

6.1 Example. Let f be the function from the space E^1 of real numbers onto the space T which contains just one element, α, and has just two open subsets in its topology, T and $\emptyset$. f is continuous since $f^{-1}[\emptyset] = \emptyset$ and $f^{-1}[T] = E^1$ so that the inverse image of any open set in T is an open set in E^1. Let P denote the positive real numbers; $f[P] = \alpha$; $\overline{P}$ is the set of non-negative real numbers; 0 is a limit point of P; $f(0) = \alpha$ and $f(0)$ is not a limit point of $f[P]$. Thus the image of a limit point of a set A assigned by a continuous function f is not always a limit point of $f[A]$.

6.2 Example. The following example shows that the image, assigned by a continuous function, of a closed set is not always closed; the image of an open set is not always open and the image of the closure of a set is not always the closure of the image. Let S denote the space E^1 and let T denote the space of real numbers with the null set and all complements of finite sets as the open sets. Let f be the function $x \rightarrow x = f(x)$ from S onto T. f is continuous since any open set in T is open in E^1. However, $A = \{x \mid 0 \leq x \leq 1\}$ is closed in $S = E^1$; its image, A, is not closed in T. Also, $B = \{x \mid 0 < x\}$ is open in $S = E^1$; its image, B, is not open in T. Further, 0 is not a limit point of the set $\{1, 2, 3, \ldots, n, \ldots\}$ in $S = E^1$; its image, 0, in T is a limit point of the set $\{1, 2, 3, \ldots, n, \ldots\}$ in T.

Theorems 4.1–4.6 and definition 2.10 establish that if f^{-1}, as well as f, is a continuous function, then closed sets, open sets, limit points, closures, boundaries, interiors and neighborhoods will be preserved by f. Hence such functions determine the basic topological equivalence for spaces.

6.3 Definition. A *topological function* or a *homeomorphism* f is a function from one topological space onto another such that:

1. f is 1:1 and continuous, and
2. f^{-1} is continuous.

Since $(f^{-1})^{-1} = f$, it is immediate that if f is a homeomorphism, f^{-1} is also.

NOTE: 1:1 functions are called *injections* and are said to be *injective*.

6.4 Definition. Two spaces S and T are called *homeomorphic* or *topologically equivalent* if and only if there exists a homeomorphism from S onto T.

The basic problem in topology is to establish procedures to determine when two spaces are topologically equivalent. Thus the study of properties of spaces which are preserved by homeomorphisms will be important. For if two spaces do not have the same properties, they cannot be homeomorphic.

6.5 Theorem. *Let S be a topological space and let h be a homeomorphism defined on S such that $h[S] = T$. If S satisfies the 1st axiom of countability, T is first countable; if S is second countable, T is second countable.*

Proof: A. Let y be any point in T, $y = h(x)$ for some x in S. Let $\{B_i \mid i = 1, 2, 3, \ldots\}$ be a countable local base at x in S. $h[B_i]$ is an open set in T for each i. Let G be any open set containing $h(x)$. $h^{-1}[G]$ is open, and contains x; therefore, there exists B_k from the collection $\{B_i \mid i = 1, 2, 3, \ldots\}$ such that $x \in B_k$ and $B_k \subseteq h^{-1}[G]$. Therefore, $h(x) \in h[B_k]$ and $h[B_k] \subseteq G$. Therefore, $\{h[B_i] \mid i = 1, 2, \ldots\}$ is countable and forms a local base at y in T.

B. The proof for a countable base for T is similar and is left as an exercise. ▌

If S is a space which is first or second countable and if f is s continuous function on S, then $f[S]$ need not be first or second countable, as the next example shows.

6.6 Example. In the proof of theorem 5.15, part 2, it was shown that the space S consisting of the set of all real numbers plus the topology consisting of the null set and all complements of finite sets is not second countable. This space is also not first countable. Let f be the identity function from E^1 onto S, i.e., $f(x) = x$. E^1 is first and second countable by theorem 5.10. f is continuous, since in E^1 the complement of any finite set is open and so $f^{-1}[G]$ is open in E^1, for G open in S.

EXERCISE 1. In the preceding example, is the function f from E^1 onto S, a homeomorphism?

6.7 Theorem. *If T is a separable space and if h is a homeomorphism from S onto T then S is separable.*

Proof: Exercise.

6.8 Definition. A *topological property* or *topological invariant* of a space S is a property P such that if T is homeomorphic to S, then T has P if and only if S has P. Thus, first countability, second countability and separability are topological properties.

Somewhat analogous to continuous functions are open and closed functions, which have some importance in analysis and topology. For example a complex-valued function of a complex variable, analytic in some region D in the plane, is open and since it is continuous, open sets are preserved in both directions. Hence, in this sense an analytic function is a generalization of a topological function.

6.9 Definition. A function f from a space S onto a space T is called *open* if and only if the image in T of every open set in S is open in T.

6.10 Definition. A function f from a space S onto a space T is called *closed* if and only if the image in T of every closed set in S is closed in T.

6.11 Example. The function $f(x) = x^2(x + 1)$ from the space E^1 onto the space E^1 is not open since the open set $\{x \mid -1/2 < x < 1/2\}$ is mapped onto the non-open set $\{y \mid 0 \leq y < 3/8\}$.

6.12 Example. The function $f(x) = x$ from E^1 onto the space consisting of the set of real numbers with the topology consisting of the null set and all complements of finite sets is not closed.

EXERCISE 2. If f is 1:1 and continuous, show that f is open $\Leftrightarrow f$ is closed $\Leftrightarrow f^{-1}$ is continuous.

EXERCISE 3. Give an example of a function that is continuous but neither open nor closed.

7. CONVERGENCE IN A TOPOLOGICAL SPACE.

There is a theorem in advanced calculus which says that if f is a function from the space of real numbers onto the space of real numbers and x_0 is a point in its domain, then f is continuous at the point x_0 if and only if $\lim_{n\to\infty} (x_n) = x_0$ implies that $\lim_{n\to\infty} \big(f(x_n)\big) = f(x_0)$. Thus continuity for such a function can be defined in terms of convergence of sequences of real numbers. In the light of section 1, a natural question to ask is "Can the general topological structure be defined in terms of convergence?" This question is investigated in this section. First, the problem of giving meaning to the concept of convergence in a general topological space must be considered.

SEQUENCES

7.1 Definition. A *sequence*, (a_n), or $(a_1, a_2, a_3, \ldots)$ of elements in any set S is a function, σ, from the set of all natural numbers into the set S. The symbol, a_n, denotes the image in S of the natural number, n, assigned by σ.

The following definition is the standard definition from calculus of the concepts of convergence and limit of a sequence of real numbers.

7.2 Definition. A sequence, $(a_1, a_2, \ldots, a_n, \ldots)$, of real numbers *converges* to the real number a^* if and only if for each real $\epsilon > 0$, there exists a natural number, N, such that $n \geq N$ implies that $|a_n - a^*| < \epsilon$. a^* is called the *sequential limit* or the *limit of the sequence*, (a_n).

It is to be observed that the ϵ serves only to identify a basic open set containing a^* in the space E^1 of real numbers. Thus the concepts of convergence and limit of a sequence can be defined in any topological space.

7.3 Definition. Let S be any topological space and let (a_n) be a sequence in S. The sequence, (a_n), is said to *converge* to the point, a^*, of S if and only if for each neighborhood, U, of a^*, there exists a natural number, N, such that if $n \geq N$ then a_n is in U. a^* is called a *sequential limit* or a *limit* of the sequence.

7.4 Example. Let S be the set of real numbers with the *trivial topology*, i.e., S and $\emptyset$ are the only open sets. The sequence, $(1, 2, 3, \ldots)$, of natural numbers converges to every real number in S, since there is only one open set, namely S, containing any real number and this open set contains the whole range of the sequence. Thus, a sequence can have more than one limit.

The following examples emphasize the difference between a limit of a sequence and a limit point of the range of a sequence.

7.5 Example. Let E^1 be the space of real numbers with the usual topology. Consider the sequence $(1, 1/2, 1, 1/3, 1, 1/4, \ldots)$ of real numbers. This sequence does not converge in E^1; however, the range of the sequence has one topological limit point, 0.

7.6 Example. The sequence $(1, 1, 1, \ldots)$ in E^1 converges to the real number 1; however, 1 is not a limit point of the range of the sequence.

7.7 Theorem. *Let $(a_1, a_2, \ldots, a_n, \ldots)$, in the space S, converge to p. Then p is in the closure of $\{a_n, a_{n+1}, \ldots, a_{n+j}, \ldots\}$ for every $n = 1, 2, \ldots$ and $j = 1, 2, \ldots$.*

Proof: If $p = a_{n+j}$ for some $j = 1, 2, \ldots$, then p is in the range of $(a_n, a_{n+1}, \ldots, a_{n+j}, \ldots)$. If $p \neq a_{n+j}$ for all $j = 1, 2, \ldots$, then, by definition of convergence, p is a limit point of the range of $(a_n, a_{n+1}, \ldots, a_{n+j}, \ldots)$. ∎

7.8 Theorem. *In a topological space, S, which satisfies the first axiom of countability, every limit point p of a subset A of S is a limit of a sequence in* $A - \{p\}$.

Proof: Let p be a limit point of a subset A of S. There exists a countable local base $\{V_1, V_2, \ldots, V_n, \ldots\}$ at p in S such that $V_1 \supseteq V_2 \supseteq V_3 \supseteq \cdots \supseteq V_n \supseteq \cdots$, by theorem 5.5. Now, there exists in V_1, by definition of limit point, a point or points of A different from p. A choice function for $P(S)$ or the axiom of choice assigns one of these to V_1; denote this point by x_1. Similarly there is assigned x_2 to V_2. There is, then, a set $\{x_1, x_2, \ldots, x_n, \ldots\}$ in $A - \{p\}$ such that $x_n \in V_n$. If the base has only k elements, $V_1, V_2, \ldots, V_k$, let $x_{k+j} = x_k$ for $j = 1, 2, \ldots$. Thus a sequence $(x_1, x_2, \ldots, x_n, \ldots)$ in $A - \{p\}$ is defined. Let G be any open set containing p. There exists a natural number k such that $V_k \subseteq G$ and so $x_k \in G$. Also if $m > k$, $V_m \subseteq V_k$; hence, $V_m \subseteq G$ and so $x_m \in G$. Thus $m \geq k$ implies $x_m \in G$ and so the sequence $(x_1, x_2, \ldots, x_n, \ldots)$ of $A - \{p\}$ converges to p. ∎

7.9 Corollary. *In the space E^1 of real numbers, every topological limit point p of a set A is a sequential limit of a sequence in* $A - \{p\}$.

Proof: By theorem 5.10, E^1 is first countable. ∎

Theorem 7.8 establishes that a first countable topological structure S can be defined by identifying those sequences which converge and the limits to which they converge; then, for any subset A of S, the set of limit points or derived set A' of A consists of all points p which are sequential limits of sequences in $A - \{p\}$.

7.10 Theorem. *Let S be any space and let A be any subset of S. If p is a sequential limit of a sequence in* $A - \{p\}$, *then p is a limit point of A.*

Proof: Let G be any open set in S which contains p. Let $(x_1, x_2, \ldots, x_n, \ldots)$ be a sequence in $A - \{p\}$ which converges to p. There exists a natural number k such that $n \geq k$ implies $x_n \in G$. Thus, G contains at least one point of $A - \{p\}$. ∎

7.11 Theorem. *Let S be any space and f a continuous function from S onto the space T. If the sequence, (a_n), in S converges to a^*, then $(f(a_n))$, in T, converges to $f(a^*)$.*

Proof: Let V be any open set in T which contains $f(a^*)$. $f^{-1}[V]$ is open, by continuity of f, and contains a^*. Thus, there exists a natural number N such that $n \geq N$ implies $a_n \in f^{-1}[V]$ and so $f(a_n) \in V$. This implies that the sequence $(f(a_n))$ converges to $f(a^*)$. ∎

7.12 Theorem. *Let S be a first countable space and f a function from S onto the space T with the property that if the sequence (a_n) in S converges to a^*, the sequence $\big(f(a_n)\big)$ in T converges to $f(a^*)$. Then f is continuous on S.*

Proof: Let A be any subset of S and p any limit point of A. By theorem 7.8, since S is first countable, there exists a sequence $(a_1, a_2, \ldots)$ in $A - \{p\}$ which converges to p. By hypothesis, $\big(f(a_1), f(a_2), \ldots\big)$ converges to $f(p)$. Let G be any open set containing $f(p)$. By definition of convergence, there is an element $f(a_k)$ in G and since $f(a_k) \in f(A)$, then $f(p)$ is in $\overline{f(A)}$. Hence, $f(\overline{A}) \subseteq \overline{f(A)}$ and, by theorem 4.3, f is continuous. ▮

7.13 Corollary. *A function f with E^1 as domain and range is continuous on E^1 if and only if (a_n) converges to a^* implies that $\big(f(a_n)\big)$ converges to $f(a^*)$.*

Proof: E^1 is first countable by theorem 5.10. Hence the corollary follows from the two previous theorems. ▮

Thus, in a first countable space the concepts of limit point and continuity can be characterized completely in terms of the concepts of sequential limit and convergence. Although the spaces of calculus and analysis are first countable, not all spaces are first countable and not every limit point is a sequential limit point in the way described in theorem 7.8.

7.14 Example. Let S be the set of real numbers with the topology consisting of the null set and all complements of countable sets. The real number, 0, is a limit point of the set P of positive reals. However, if $(x_1, x_2, \ldots)$ is any sequence of positive real numbers, $S \sim \bigcup_n \{x_n\}$ is open, contains 0 and contains no point of $\bigcup_n \{x_n\}$. Thus, 0 is not a sequential limit of any sequence in $P = P \sim \{0\}$.

EXERCISE 1. Let f be a continuous function from a space S onto a space T. Let $(a_1, a_2, \ldots, a_n, \ldots)$ be a sequence in S and let $\big(f(a_1), f(a_2), \ldots, f(a_n), \ldots\big)$ converge to $f(p)$. Prove or find a counterexample to the statement that $(a_1, a_2, \ldots, a_n, \ldots)$ converges to p.

EXERCISE 2. Let f be a continuous function from a space X onto a first countable space Y. Let a be in A', where $A \subseteq X$. Prove that there exists a sequence $(a_1, a_2, \ldots, a_n, \ldots)$ in $A \sim \{a\}$ such that $\big(f(a_1), f(a_2), \ldots, f(a_n), \ldots\big)$ converges to $f(a)$.

Generalized Sequences or Nets

The concepts of sequence and convergence can be generalized in two equivalent ways for a general space. One generalization introduces the concepts of filter and filter convergence; the other introduces generalized sequence, Moore-Smith sequence or net and generalized sequential limit, Moore-Smith limit or limit of a net. We first consider the net or generalized sequence.

7.15 Definition. A *directly ordered set* or a *directed set* is a pair $\{D, \mathcal{R}\}$ where $\mathcal{R} \subseteq D \times D$ for D a set and where (1) $\mathcal{R}$ is transitive, (2) $\mathcal{R}$ is reflexive on D and (3) $\mathcal{R}$ satisfies the condition that if p and q are in D then there exists r in D such that (r, p) and (r, q) are in $\mathcal{R}$. "(r, p) is in $\mathcal{R}$" is denoted by "$r \geq p$" i.e. $\mathcal{R}$ is denoted by $\geq$. $\mathcal{R}$ is called a *direct ordering.*

The directly ordered set in the definition of a net or generalized sequence plays a role analogous to that of the set of natural numbers in the definition of a sequence.

7.16 Definition. A *net* or *generalized sequence* in a set S is a function from a directly ordered set $\{D, \geq\}$ into S.

Every sequence is a net, since the set of natural numbers is directly ordered by $\geq$.

7.17 Example. Let $[a, b]$ denote the closed interval of real numbers $\{x \mid a \leq x \leq b;\ a, b, \text{real}\}$. The set, D, of all finite subsets of $[a, b]$ which include a and b is a directed set, ordered by inclusion, $\supseteq$. The identity function on such a directed set determines a net in $P([a, b])$ used in the definition of the Riemann Integral, $\int_a^b f(x)\,dx$.

7.18 Example. Let D be the set of all open sets containing any point x in a space S. Let $U \geq V$ for U, V in D if and only if $U \subseteq V$. D is directly ordered by $\subseteq$ and the identity function on D determines a net in $P(S)$.

7.19 Example. Let D be the set of all neighborhoods of any point x in a space S. For U, V in D, define $U \geq V$ if and only if $U \subseteq V$. D is directly ordered by $\subseteq$ and the identity function determines a net in $P(S)$.

7.20 Definition. In a space S, a net $\mathfrak{N} = (a_\nu)$ for ν in a directed set, D, is said to *converge* to a point x of S if and only if for each neighborhood N of x, there exists an element ρ of D such that if δ is in D and $\delta \geq \rho$, then a_δ is in N. x is then called a *limit* of the net.

7.21 Example. Let D denote the set of all finite sets of real numbers directed by $\supseteq$, i.e., $A \geq B$ if and only if $A \supseteq B$. Define the net $f\colon D \to E^1$ as follows. $f(\{p, q, \ldots, k\}) = \text{minimum } \{p, q, \ldots, k\}$; e.g., $f(\{1, 2, 3, 4\}) = 1$. It is to be shown that f does not converge to any real number. Assume that the net f converges to the real number a^* and let $(a^* - \epsilon, a^* + \epsilon)$ denote a basic open set containing a^* in E^1. Let β be any set in D; let $\beta = \{p, q, \ldots, k\}$, say. Let $f(\beta) = b^*$ and let c^* be less than b^* and $a^* - \epsilon$. Then, $\gamma = \{c^*, p, q, \ldots, k\}$ contains β and $f(\gamma) = c^*$ and $c^* < a^* - \epsilon$. Thus, $f(\gamma)$ is not in $(a^* - \epsilon, a^* + \epsilon)$ and $\gamma \geq \beta$. Since β was any element in D, f does not converge.

7.22 Theorem. *If (a_δ) is a net in the space S and if (a_δ) converges to p in S, then p is in the closure of the range of S.*

Proof: Exercise.

7.23 Theorem. *A point x in a space S is a limit point of a subset A of S if and only if there exists a net in $A - \{x\}$ which converges to x.*

Proof: A. Let x be a limit point of a subset A of S. Consider the set $\mathfrak{N}$ consisting of all neighborhoods of x in S. $\{\mathfrak{N}, \subseteq\}$ is a directed set. If N is in $\mathfrak{N}$, $N \cap (A \sim \{x\}) \neq \emptyset$. Hence, a choice function on $\{N \cap (A \sim \{x\}) \mid N \in \mathfrak{N}\}$ yields a net (a_u) in S such that $a_u \in U$ and a_u is in $A - \{x\}$ for every U in $\mathfrak{N}$. Let W be any neighborhood of x. There is a point a_w of the net (a_u) in W and if V is in $\mathfrak{N}$ and $V \subseteq W$, then a_v is in W. Therefore the net (a_u) in $A \sim \{x\}$ converges to x.

B. Let (a_u) be any net in $A \sim \{x\}$ which converges to x. By definition of convergence for a net (7.20), every neighborhood of x contains a point a_u of (a_u) and a_u is in $A \sim \{x\}$. Hence x is a limit point of A. ▮

7.24 Corollary. *If a net (a_δ) in a subset A of a space S converges to a^*, then a^* is in $\overline{A}$.*

Proof: Every neighborhood of a^* contains a point of A. ▮

7.25 Theorem. *If S and T are topological spaces then a function f from S onto T is continuous if and only if (a_ν) converging to a^* in S implies that $(f(a_\nu))$ converges to $f(a^*)$ in T, where (a_ν) is a net in S.*

Proof: A. If f is continuous and if N is any neighborhood of $f(a^*)$, then $f^{-1}[N]$ is a neighborhood of a^*. However, since the net (a_ν) converges to a^*, there exists $\nu \in D$, the domain of (a_ν) such that if $\mu \geq \nu$, then a_μ is in $f^{-1}[N]$. Hence, $f(a_\mu)$ is in N and $(f(a_\nu))$ converges to $f(a^*)$.

B. Let f be any function from the space S onto the space T with the property that if (a_ν) is a net in S which converges to a^*, then $(f(a_\nu))$ converges to $f(a^*)$ in T. In addition, let A be any subset of S and x any limit point of A in S. By theorem 7.23, there exists a net (b_μ) in $A - \{x\}$ which converges to x. Hence $(f(b_\mu))$ converges to $f(x)$ and $f(x)$ is in $\overline{f(A)}$. Therefore, $f(\overline{A}) \subseteq \overline{f(A)}$ and hence f is continuous by theorem 4.3. ▮

7.26 Example. Let $D = \{x \mid |x - x_0| < \epsilon \text{ for } \epsilon > 0\}$ with the order relation $y \geq x$ if and only if $|y - x_0| \leq |x - x_0|$. $\{D, \geq\}$ is a directed set and the identity function i_D on D determines a net in E^1. i_D as a net in E^1 converges to x_0. Hence, $f \circ i_D$, where f is a continuous function from E^1 into E^1, is a net in E^1 which converges to $f(x_0)$.

Since limit points and continuity can be completely characterized in terms of convergence of nets, a topological space can be defined by identifying those nets which converge and the elements to which they converge.

FILTERS

The other generalizations of sequences and convergence are the concepts of filters and filter convergence.

7.27 Definition. A *filter*, $\mathfrak{F}$, on a set S is a non-empty set of subsets of S, that satisfies the following three conditions:

1. $\emptyset$ does not belong to $\mathfrak{F}$.
2. Any intersection of a finite number of sets in $\mathfrak{F}$ belongs to $\mathfrak{F}$.
3. Any subset of S which contains a set in $\mathfrak{F}$ belongs to $\mathfrak{F}$.

The motivating structure for the above definition is the collection $\mathfrak{N}_x$ of all neighborhoods of a point x in a space S. In a first countable space, a decreasing and countable family of sets of $\mathfrak{N}_x$ is given and a choice function for this countable subset yields a converging sequence of points (theorem 7.8). However, in a general space, the set of all neighborhoods of a point is all that is available and the theory of filters uses this structure. If one checks definition 2.5, one finds that a neighborhood relation R^+ on a set S assigns to each point x of S a filter $\mathfrak{N}(x)$ on S which satisfies the conditions: (1) $A \in \mathfrak{N}(x)$ implies that $x \in A$ and (2) $N \in \mathfrak{N}(x)$ implies $(\exists V)\ \big(V \in \mathfrak{N}(x),\ V \subseteq N$ and $y \in V$ implies $V \in \mathfrak{N}(y)\big)$. Thus a neighborhood relation R^+ on a set S determines a function $\mathfrak{N}$ from S into $\mathfrak{F}(S)$, the set of filters on S.

EXERCISE 3. Prove that, in any space S, the set of all neighborhoods of a point x in S is a filter.

EXERCISE 4. Prove that the set of all sets of natural numbers whose complements are finite is a filter.

EXERCISE 5. Prove that the set of all sets of real numbers whose complements are countable is a filter on E^1.

EXERCISE 6. Prove that the set of all sets of real numbers whose complements are bounded is a filter on E^1.

EXERCISE 7. Determine which of the filters in the previous four exercises have a non-empty intersection.

7.28 Lemma. *A point p in a space S is a limit point of a subset A of S if and only if $\{N_\nu \cap (A \sim \{p\}) \mid N_\nu$ is a neighborhood of $p\}$ is a filter on $A \sim \{p\}$.*

Proof: A. Let p be a limit point of A in S. Every set in the filter of neighborhoods of p intersects $A - \{p\} = A^*$ on a non-empty set. Hence, $\mathfrak{N}^* = \{N_\nu \cap A^* \mid N_\nu$ is a neighborhood of $p\}$ does not contain the null set. Next, for any two sets $(N_\nu \cap A^*)$ and $(N_\mu \cap A^*)$ their intersection $(N_\nu \cap A^*) \cap (N_\mu \cap A^*) = (N_\nu \cap N_\mu) \cap A^* = N_\rho \cap A^*$ belongs to $\mathfrak{N}^*$. Lastly, if M is a subset of A and if $M \supseteq (N_\nu \cap A^*)$, then $M \cup N_\nu$ is a neighborhood of x in S and so $[(M \cup N_\nu) \cap A^*]$ belongs to $\mathfrak{N}^*$. However, $(M \cup N_\nu) \cap A^* = M$; hence, $\mathfrak{N}^*$ is a filter on $A^* = A - \{p\}$.

B. Let $\mathfrak{N}_p$ be the filter of neighborhoods of a point p in a space S and let the collection $\mathfrak{N}_p^* = \{N_\nu \cap A^* \mid N_\nu \text{ is in } \mathfrak{N}_p \text{ and } A^* = A - \{p\}\}$ be a filter on A^*. Since $\mathfrak{N}_p^*$ is a filter, the empty set does not belong to $\mathfrak{N}_p^*$; therefore, every neighborhood, N_ν, of p contains points of $A^* = A - \{p\}$ and so p is a limit point of A. ▮

7.29 Lemma. *If $\mathfrak{F}$ is a filter on a set S and f is a function from S onto T, then $\{B \mid B = f[A] \text{ and } A \in \mathfrak{F}\}$ is a filter on T.*

Proof: Exercise.

7.30 Theorem. *If f is a function from the space S onto the space T, then f is continuous at the point p in S if and only if $f^\#[\mathfrak{N}_p] \supseteq \mathfrak{N}_{f(p)}$, where $\mathfrak{N}_p$ and $\mathfrak{N}_{f(p)}$ denote, respectively, the filters of neighborhoods of p and of $f(p)$ and $f^\#[\mathfrak{N}_p]$ denotes the set of images of sets in $\mathfrak{N}_p$ assigned by f.*

Proof: A. Let f be continuous at p. Let N be any element of $\mathfrak{N}_{f(p)}$, i.e. N is a neighborhood of $f(p)$. $f^{-1}[N]$ is a neighborhood of p and $f[f^{-1}[N]] = N$. Thus N is in $f^\#[\mathfrak{N}_p]$; hence, $\mathfrak{N}_{f(p)} \subseteq f^\#[\mathfrak{N}_p]$.

B. Let $f^\#[\mathfrak{N}_p] \supseteq \mathfrak{N}_{f(p)}$ for some p in S. Let V be any neighborhood of $f(p)$. V is in $\mathfrak{N}_{f(p)}$ and hence V is in $f^\#[\mathfrak{N}_p]$. Hence there exists U in $\mathfrak{N}_p$ such that $f[U] = V$. Hence, f is continuous at p. ▮

7.31 Definition. A filter, $\mathfrak{F}$, on a space, S, is said to *converge* to the point, p, in S if and only if $\mathfrak{F}$ contains $\mathfrak{N}_p$, the filter of neighborhoods of p in S. p is then called a *limit* of the filter $\mathfrak{F}$ in S.

EXERCISE 8. Prove or disprove: p is a limit point of a subset A of a space S if and only if p is a limit of a filter $\mathfrak{F}$ on A.

7.32 Theorem. *Let f be a function from a space S onto a space T. Then f is continuous at p in S if and only if $f^\#[\mathfrak{N}_p]$ converges to $f(p)$.*

Proof: By theorem 7.30 and definition 7.31. ▮

7.33 Definition. Let $\mathfrak{F}$ be a filter on a set, S. A subset $\mathfrak{B}$ of $\mathfrak{F}$ is called a base for $\mathfrak{F}$ if and only if every set in $\mathfrak{F}$ contains a set in $\mathfrak{B}$.

EXERCISE 9. Let S be a set and let $\mathfrak{B}$ be a non-empty set of non-empty subsets of S with the property that the intersection of any finite number of sets in $\mathfrak{B}$ contains a set in $\mathfrak{B}$. Prove that $\mathfrak{B}$ is a base of a filter on S.

EXERCISE 10. Show that a local base at a point, p, in a space, S, is a base for the filter of neighborhoods of p in S. Thus, the set of all basic neighborhoods of p assigned by a basic neighborhood relation is a base for the filter of all neighborhoods of p.

7.34 Lemma. *If f is a function from a set S into a set T and if $\mathfrak{F}$ is a filter on S, then $f^{\#}[\mathfrak{F}]$ is a base of a filter on T.*

Proof: Exercise.

7.35 Definition. Let $\mathfrak{F}$ be a filter on a set S. A subset Σ of $\mathfrak{F}$ is called a subbase for $\mathfrak{F}$ or is said to generate $\mathfrak{F}$ if and only if every set in $\mathfrak{F}$ contains the intersection of a finite number of sets in Σ.

EXERCISE 11. Show that the collection $\{V_{-1}^{\epsilon} \mid V_{-1}^{\epsilon} = \{x \mid -1 < x < \epsilon, \epsilon > 0\}\} \cup \{V_{-\epsilon}^{1} \mid V_{-\epsilon}^{1} = \{x \mid -\epsilon < x < 1, \epsilon > 0\}\}$ constitutes a subbase for the filter $\mathfrak{N}_0$ of all neighborhoods of 0 in E^1. Show that the collection is not a base for $\mathfrak{N}_0$.

EXERCISE 12. Let $\mathfrak{F}$ be a filter on a set X. Let Ψ be a choice function with domain $\mathfrak{F}$. Define $F_1 \geq F_2$ if and only if $F_1 \subseteq F_2$. Prove that $\{\mathfrak{F}, \geq\}$ is a directed set and that Ψ is a net in X. Ψ is said to be a net determined by the filter, $\mathfrak{F}$.

EXERCISE 13. Let η be a net in the set X. For each α in the domain of η, define $T_\alpha = \{\eta(\nu) \mid \nu$ is in the domain η and $\nu \geq \alpha\}$. Prove $\{T_\alpha \mid \alpha$ is in the domain of $\eta\}$ is a base for a filter $\mathfrak{F}$ on X. $\mathfrak{F}$ is said to be determined by the net η.

EXERCISE 14. If $\mathfrak{F}$ is a filter on a space $\{X, \mathfrak{I}\}$ and if $\mathfrak{F}$ converges to p, show that any net Ψ determined by $\mathfrak{F}$ (see exercise 12, above) also converges to p.

EXERCISE 15. Let η be a net in a space $\{X, \mathfrak{I}\}$ which converges to a point p of X. Let $\mathfrak{F}$ be the filter determined by η as in exercise 13, above. Show that $\mathfrak{F}$ also converges to p.

EXERCISE 16. Let $\mathfrak{F}$ be a filter on a set X and let $\mathcal{S}$ be a subbase for $\mathfrak{F}$. Show that the collection $\mathcal{B}$ of all sets which are intersections of a finite number of sets in $\mathcal{S}$ constitutes a base for $\mathfrak{F}$.

EXERCISE 17. Show that any base for a filter $\mathfrak{F}$ on a set X is also a subbase for $\mathfrak{F}$.

7.36 Lemma. *If X is a set and $\mathcal{S}$ is a collection of non-empty subsets of X such that $\mathcal{S}$ is not empty and each finite collection of sets in $\mathcal{S}$ has a non-null intersection, then there exists a filter $\mathfrak{F}$ on X which contains $\mathcal{S}$ and for which $\mathcal{S}$ is a subbase. $\mathfrak{F}$ is the smallest filter on X that contains $\mathcal{S}$. $\mathcal{S}$ is said to generate $\mathfrak{F}$.*

Proof: Let $\mathfrak{F}$ be the collection of all subsets of X which contain the intersection of any finite number of sets of $\mathcal{S}$. If M is in $\mathcal{S}$, M belongs to $\mathfrak{F}$. Hence $\mathcal{S} \subseteq \mathfrak{F}$. X is in $\mathfrak{F}$. If $M_1, M_2, \ldots, M_k$, for k a natural number, is a finite collection of sets in $\mathfrak{F}$, then $M_i \supseteq A_1^i \cap A_2^i \cap \cdots \cap A_{t_i}^i$ for $1 \leq i \leq k$, t_i a natural number and A_j^i in $\mathcal{S}$ for $1 \leq j \leq t_i$. Hence, $M_1 \cap M_2 \cap \cdots \cap M_k$ contains $A_1^1 \cap \cdots \cap A_{t_1}^1 \cap \cdots \cap A_1^2 \cap A_2^2 \cap \cdots \cap A_{t_2}^2 \cap \cdots \cap A_1^k \cap \cdots \cap A_{t_k}^k$, which is the intersection of a finite number of sets in $\mathcal{S}$. Thus, $M_1 \cap \cdots \cap M_k$ belongs to $\mathcal{F}$. $\emptyset$ does not belong to $\mathcal{F}$. Let M belong to $\mathcal{F}$ and let $A \supseteq M$. Since M contains the intersection of a finite number of sets of $\mathcal{S}$, A does also and so A belongs to $\mathcal{F}$. $\mathcal{F}$ is then a filter. Let $\mathcal{F}^*$ be any filter on X that contains $\mathcal{S}$. Let Y be a subset of X that contains $\bigcap_{i=1}^{n} A_i$, for A_i in $\mathcal{S}$. Since $\mathcal{F}^*$ is a filter, Y belongs to $\mathcal{F}^*$. Hence $\mathcal{F}^* \supseteq \mathcal{F}$. ▮

EXERCISE 18. Let X be a space and let x be a nonisolated point of X. Show that $\{N \mid N = V - \{x\}$ and V is a neighborhood of $x\}$, generates a filter on X which contains the filter $\mathfrak{N}_x$ of all neighborhoods of x in X.

EXERCISE 19. Show that if x is an isolated point of X, then $\{D \mid D = N - \{x\}$, where N is a neighborhood of $x\}$ does not generate a filter on X.

7.37 Theorem. *If S and T are topological spaces and if f is a function from S onto T, then f is continuous at a point x if and only if for each filter $\mathcal{F}$ on S converging to x, $f^{\#}[\mathcal{F}]$ is a filter on T converging to $f(x)$.*

Proof: A. Let f be continuous at x and let $\mathcal{F}$ be any filter on S which converges to x. $\mathcal{F}$, then, by definition 7.31, contains $\mathfrak{N}_x$, the filter of neighborhoods of x. By theorem 7.30, $f^{\#}[\mathfrak{N}_x] \supseteq \mathfrak{N}_{f(x)}$. Hence, $f^{\#}[\mathcal{F}]$ contains $\mathfrak{N}_{f(x)}$. Thus $f^{\#}[\mathcal{F}]$ converges to $f(x)$.

B. Let f be any function from the space S onto the space T with the property that if $\mathcal{F}$ is a filter on S which converges to x in S, then $f^{\#}[\mathcal{F}]$ is a filter on T which converges to $f(x)$. Let $\mathfrak{N}_x$ be the filter of neighborhoods of x in S. By definition of convergence (7.31), $\mathfrak{N}_x$ converges to x. $f^{\#}[\mathfrak{N}_x]$ then converges to $f(x)$ in T. Hence, $f^{\#}[\mathfrak{N}_x] \supseteq \mathfrak{N}_{f(x)}$. Thus by theorem 7.32, f is continuous at x. ▮

Limit of a Function

Continuity can be characterized in still another manner with the aid of filters. In certain calculus books the concept of "limit of a function" is used to define continuity. An analysis and a generalization of this concept follow.

7.38 Definition. Let f be a function from a set X onto a space Y. A *limit of f relative to the filter*, $\mathcal{F}$, on X is an element y of Y with the property that the filter $f^{\#}[\mathcal{F}]$ which is the set of images in Y of the sets in $\mathcal{F}$ converges to y. This set of limits of f relative to $\mathcal{F}$ is denoted $\lim_{\mathcal{F}} f$. A filter can have several limits.

EXERCISE 20. Let S be the set of real numbers. Define, for each real number p, one basic neighborhood, $V_p = \{x \mid x \geq p\}$. Show that in this space the filter, $\mathcal{F}$, defined by the base, $\{U_1\}$, where $U_1 = \{x \mid x > 1\}$ converges to an uncountable infinity of points.

7.39 Example. Let f denote the function, $x \to 1/x$ for $x \neq 0$ and $0 \to 0$, from the space E^1 of real numbers with the usual open intervals for basic neighborhoods onto the same space E^1. Let $\mathfrak{F}$ be the filter defined by $\{U_1, U_2, \ldots\}$, where $U_i = \{x \mid x > i, \text{ for } i \text{ a natural number}\}$, as a base. $\lim_{\mathfrak{F}} f = 0$. This is usually denoted in calculus as $\lim_{x\to\infty} 1/x = 0$.

7.40 Theorem. *If f is a function from a space X onto a space Y, then f is continuous at a point x in X if and only if $f(x)$ is in $\lim_{\mathfrak{N}_x} f$, where $\mathfrak{N}_x$ is the filter of neighborhoods of x in X.*

Proof: A. Let f be continuous at x in X. By theorem 7.37, $f^{\#}[\mathfrak{N}_x]$ converges to $f(x)$. Hence $f(x)$ is in $\lim_{\mathfrak{N}_x} f$, by definition of $\lim_{\mathfrak{N}_x} f$.

B. Let $f(x)$ be in $\lim_{\mathfrak{N}_x} f$, where $\mathfrak{N}_x$ is again the filter of neighborhoods of x in X. Then, again by definition of $\lim_{\mathfrak{N}_x} f$, $f^{\#}[\mathfrak{N}_x] \supseteq \mathfrak{N}_{f(x)}$. Hence by theorem 7.30, f is continuous at x. ▮

7.41 Definition. If N is a neighborhood of x and $N - \{x\}$ is not empty, $N - \{x\}$ is called a deleted neighborhood of x.

7.42 Theorem. *If x is a nonisolated point of a space X and f is a function from X onto a space Y, then f is continuous at x if and only if $f(x)$ is in $\lim_{\mathfrak{D}} f$, where $\mathfrak{D}$ is the filter generated by the collection of deleted neighborhoods of x in X.*

Proof. A. Let f be continuous at x. Let N be any neighborhood of x in X. $N \supseteq N \sim \{x\}$. Hence N is in $\mathfrak{D}$. $\mathfrak{D}$, then, converges to x by definition of convergence (7.31). By theorem 7.37, it follows that $f^{\#}[\mathfrak{D}]$ converges to $f(x)$ and by definition of $\lim_{\mathfrak{D}} f$ (7.38), $f(x)$ is in $\lim_{\mathfrak{D}} f$.

B. let $f(x)$ be in $\lim_{\mathfrak{D}} f$. Let N be any neighborhood of $f(x)$ in Y. N is in $f^{\#}[\mathfrak{D}]$ by hypothesis and so there exists M in $\mathfrak{D}$ such that $f[M] = N$. $\{x\} \cup M$ contains x, and M contains a deleted neighborhood of x by definition of $\mathfrak{D}$. Thus $M \cup \{x\}$ is a neighborhood of x and $f[M \cup \{x\}] = N$. Therefore, f is continuous at x. ▮

Definition 7.41 and theorem 7.42 give the generalization of the definition of continuity found in the calculus books as $\lim_{x\to a} f(x) = f(a)$, where a is a non-isolated point of the domain. The $\lim_{x\to a} f$ is exactly $\lim_{\mathfrak{D}} f$ described above and in E^1, the space of reals, $\lim_{\mathfrak{D}} f$ is unique. This will be proved in chapter 3. However, continuity can be characterized in terms of this filter only at non-isolated points of the domain. For, at an isolated point, x, the collection of deleted neighborhoods of x in X contains the empty set, $\{x\} - \{x\}$, and so generates no filter.

Thus, limit point and continuity can be completely characterized in terms of filters.

The question as to how many limits a net or a filter can have is important. This will be investigated in chapter 3, and it will be found that a topology must satisfy an additional axiom, called the Hausdorff separation axiom, before it can be established that, in the space defined by the topology, nets and filters which converge, have unique limits.

Convergence brings to a close our introduction to the general topological structure. In chapter 2, the various ways of defining new spaces from a given space or given spaces are investigated.

SUMMARY FOR CHAPTER 1

The structure called a topological space consists of a set S and

1. a subset, $\mathfrak{T}$, of $P(S)$—a topology;
2. a subset, $\mathfrak{C}$, of $P(S)$—a cotopology;
3. a function, Φ: $P(S) \to P(S)$—a closure operation;
4. a function, Ψ: $P(S) \to P(S)$—a derivation;
5. a function, I: $P(S) \to P(S)$—an interior operator;
6. a function, β: $P(S) \to P(S)$—a boundary operator;
7. a subset, R^+, of $S \times P(S)$—a neighborhood relation;
8. an equivalence class, $\{R_\nu\}$, of subsets of $S \times P(S)$ called basic neighborhood relations;
9. a function, $\mathscr{C}$, from the nets or filters of S into $P(S)$, where $\mathscr{C}(n)$ or $\mathscr{C}(\mathfrak{F})$ is the set of limits of $\mathfrak{F}$ (filter) or of n (net).

Any one of the above defined for S determines the other eight uniquely.

The definition of continuity rests squarely on topological concepts. Continuity for a function can be defined directly in terms of open set, closed set, closure, derived set, neighborhood, basic neighborhood, or limits of nets and filters.

A function, called a topological function or a homeomorphism between spaces, is a function that preserves all properties that can be defined in terms of the basic topological concepts. Such a function is 1:1 and continuous and its inverse is continuous.

A topological invariant is a property of topological spaces that is preserved by a homeomorphism. The property of having a countable collection of open subsets from which all open sets can be obtained by taking unions is a topological invariant called second countability. The localization of this property is called first countability; this is also a topological invariant. Separability is a topological invariant. In a first countable space, a limit point, p, of a subset M is always a sequential limit of a sequence in $M - \{p\}$. In non-first countable spaces, the net or generalized sequence plays the role which the sequence plays in first countable spaces. A filter on a set S is a subset of $P(S)$ with certain properties. A generalized convergence can be defined for filters on spaces; in terms of this convergence, continuity for functions can be defined directly.

CHAPTER 2

Generation of Spaces

8. DIFFERENT TOPOLOGIES ON THE SAME SET.

8.1 Definition. A topology $\mathfrak{T}_1$ on a set S is said to be *finer than* or *larger than* a topology $\mathfrak{T}_2$ on S if and only if $\mathfrak{T}_1 \supsetneq \mathfrak{T}_2$. The *trivial, smallest* or *least fine* topology for S is the topology consisting of S and $\emptyset$ alone. The *discrete, finest* or *largest* topology for S is the topology $\mathfrak{T} = P(S)$, i.e., the topology containing all the subsets of S. In a discrete space single points constitute open subsets. A topology $\mathfrak{T}^*$ is said to be strictly *between* $\mathfrak{T}_1$ and $\mathfrak{T}_2$ if and only if $\mathfrak{T}_1 \subsetneq \mathfrak{T}^* \subsetneq \mathfrak{T}_2$ or $\mathfrak{T}_2 \subsetneq \mathfrak{T}^* \subsetneq \mathfrak{T}_1$.

EXERCISE 1. Prove that for any set S, (1) the collection $\{S, \emptyset\}$ is a topology for S, and (2) $P(S)$ is a topology for S.

EXERCISE 2. Prove that if a space S has the discrete topology, then any function of S onto a space T is continuous on S.

EXERCISE 3. Prove that if a space S has the trivial topology and a space T with more than one point has a non-trivial topology, then there exist no continuous function of S onto T.

EXERCISE 4. Find all the topologies for a set of three elements.

8.2 Theorem. *The set of all topologies for a set S is partially ordered by the relation $\subseteq$.*

Proof: Exercise.

8.3 Theorem. *Let $\mathfrak{T}_1$ and $\mathfrak{T}_2$ be two topologies on the same set. Then $\mathfrak{T}_1 \cap \mathfrak{T}_2$ is a topology for S which is contained in both $\mathfrak{T}_1$ and $\mathfrak{T}_2$.*

Proof: Exercise.

The union of two topologies on the same set S is not always a topology for S.

8.4 Example. Let S be the set of all real numbers. Let $U_p = \{x \mid x \geq p\}$. Let $\{U_p \mid p \text{ is real}\}$ be a base for a topology $\mathfrak{I}_1$ for S. Let $V_p = \{x \mid x \leq p\}$. Let $\{V_p \mid p \text{ is real}\}$ be a base for a topology $\mathfrak{I}_2$ for S. The collection, $\mathfrak{I}_1 \cup \mathfrak{I}_2$, of all sets in either $\mathfrak{I}_1$ or $\mathfrak{I}_2$ is not a topology for S since $U_p \cap V_p = \{p\}$ does not belong to $\mathfrak{I}_1 \cup \mathfrak{I}_2$. Since any topology must contain the intersection of any finite number of its elements, $\mathfrak{I}_1 \cup \mathfrak{I}_2$ is not a topology on S.

8.5 Example. $\mathfrak{I}_1 \cup \mathfrak{I}_2$ can be a topology. Let $S = \{a, b, c\}$ where a, b and c denote any three elements; let $\mathfrak{I}_1 = \{S, \emptyset, \{a\} \cup \{b\}\}$; let $\mathfrak{I}_2 = \{S, \emptyset, \{b\}\}$. Then $\mathfrak{I}_1 \cup \mathfrak{I}_2 = \{S, \emptyset, \{b\}, \{a\} \cup \{b\}\}$, and this is a topology for S.

In example 8.4, $\mathfrak{I}_1 \cup \mathfrak{I}_2$ was not a topology; however, this collection can be enlarged to a topology by adjoining to $\mathfrak{I}_1 \cup \mathfrak{I}_2$ all unions of intersections of any finite number of the sets in $\mathfrak{I}_1 \cup \mathfrak{I}_2$. When this is done, the collection $\mathfrak{I}_1 \cup \mathfrak{I}_2$ is said to generate the resulting topology, $(\mathfrak{I}_1 \cup \mathfrak{I}_2)^*$. By definition, (3.52), $\mathfrak{I}_1 \cup \mathfrak{I}_2$ is a subbase for $(\mathfrak{I}_1 \cup \mathfrak{I}_2)^*$. In example 8.4, the resulting topology is the discrete topology.

8.6 Definition. Any collection of subsets of a given set S is said to *generate the topology* for which it is a subbase.

8.7 Lemma. *If $\mathfrak{I}_1$ and $\mathfrak{I}_2$ are two topologies for a set S, then (1) $\mathfrak{I}_1 \cap \mathfrak{I}_2$ is the largest topology on S which is contained in both $\mathfrak{I}_1$ and $\mathfrak{I}_2$ and (2) $(\mathfrak{I}_1 \cup \mathfrak{I}_2)^*$ is the smallest topology on S which contains both $\mathfrak{I}_1$ and $\mathfrak{I}_2$.*

Proof: Exercise.

By definition, any topology on a set S is a subset of $P(S)$, and by theorem 8.2, the collection of all the topologies for a set S is partially ordered by the inclusion relation, $\supseteq$, which is reflexive, transitive, and antisymmetric. In addition, by lemma 8.7, given any two topologies $\mathfrak{I}_1$ and $\mathfrak{I}_2$ for S, there is a smallest topology which contains $\mathfrak{I}_1$ and $\mathfrak{I}_2$ and there is a largest topology which is contained in both $\mathfrak{I}_1$ and $\mathfrak{I}_2$. Hence, the set of all topologies for a set S has the structure of a "lattice."

8.8 Definition. A *lattice* is a pair $\{L, \rho\}$, where L is a set, and ρ is a partial ordering on L which satisfies the following condition: for a and b in L, there exist elements $a \vee b$ and $a \wedge b$ in L, called respectively the least upper bound and the greatest lower bound of $\{a, b\}$, which satisfy (1) $a\rho(a \vee b)$ and $b\rho(a \vee b)$; and if $b\rho d$ and $a\rho d$, then $(a \vee b)\rho d$; and (2) $(a \wedge b)\rho a$ and $(a \wedge b)\rho b$; and if $c\rho a$ and $c\rho b$, then $c\rho(a \vee b)$. The least upper bound and the greatest lower bound are defined for a non-empty subset A of L exactly as they are defined for the set $\{a, b\}$—even though they do not necessarily exist for every non-empty subset A.

REMARK: The terms "greatest lower bound," "lower bound," "least upper bound" and "upper bound" can be misleading. For example, if $L = \{1, 2, 3, 4, 5\}$ and ρ is the usual $\leq$ for positive integers, then $3 \vee 4 = 4$ and $3 \wedge 4 = 3$. However, with the same set L but ρ defined as the usual $\geq$ for positive integers,

$$3 \vee 4 = 3 \text{ and } 3 \wedge 4 = 4.$$

The terms "upper" and "lower" are intuitively correct for ρ defined as $\leq$ on the real numbers.

8.9 Lemma. *The set, L, of all topologies for a given set S, partially ordered by inclusion,* $\subseteq$, *with* $\mathfrak{I}_1 \wedge \mathfrak{I}_2 = \mathfrak{I}_1 \cap \mathfrak{I}_2$ *and* $\mathfrak{I}_1 \vee \mathfrak{I}_2 = (\mathfrak{I}_1 \cup \mathfrak{I}_2)^*$ *yields a lattice,* $\{L, \subseteq\}$.

Proof: By lemma 8.7 and definition 8.8. ▮

One property of lattices which will be used later in defining topologies from sets of functions is "completeness."

8.10 Definition. A lattice, $\{L, \rho\}$, is *complete* if and only if each non-empty subset A of L has a least upper bound and a greatest lower bound in L.

8.11 Lemma. *The lattice,* $\{L, \subseteq\}$, *of all topologies on a set S is a complete lattice.*

Proof: Let A be a non-empty subset of L. Then A is a set of topologies for S and $\bigcup A$ is the set of all subsets of S which lie in at least one topology in A. Thus $\bigcup A$ is a set of subsets of S, and by exercise 44, following definition 3.52 of a subbase, and definition 8.6, it generates a topology for S. It is immediate that this topology is the smallest topology containing $\bigcup A$, and so is a least upper bound in $\{L, \subseteq\}$ for A. Similarly, $\bigcap A$, as the set of all subsets of S which lie in all the topologies in A, is a topology for S. It is, again, immediate that $\bigcap A$ is the largest topology contained in every topology in A, and so is a greatest lower bound for A in $\{L, \subseteq\}$. ▮

8.12 Example. The set of all subsets of a set S, i.e., $P(S)$, forms a lattice with inclusion, $\supseteq$, as the partial ordering. For $A \subseteq S$ and $B \subseteq S$, what are $A \vee B$ and $A \wedge B$?

EXERCISE 5. Show that in a given space S, the set of all open sets of S which contain a given point p of S forms a lattice with inclusion, $\supseteq$, as the partial ordering. For U and V in L, what are $U \vee V$ and $U \wedge V$?

EXERCISE 6. Show that the collection of all cotopologies for a given set S, with inclusion, $\subseteq$, forms a lattice.

EXERCISE 7. If S is a set and $\mathfrak{I}_1$ and $\mathfrak{I}_2$ are two topologies for S, and if co-$\mathfrak{I}_1$ and co-$\mathfrak{I}_2$ are the corresponding cotopologies for S, what does $\mathfrak{I}_1 \supseteq \mathfrak{I}_2$ imply for co-$\mathfrak{I}_1$ and co-$\mathfrak{I}_2$?

9. SUBSPACES. THE RELATIVE TOPOLOGY.

One of the most important methods for generating new spaces from a given space S is the method of assigning to any subset of S, a topology, called the relative topology. The relative topology is, in a sense, borrowed from the topology on S.

9.1 Lemma. *If S is a space with topology $\mathfrak{J}$ and X is a subset of S, then the collection $\{U \mid (\exists G)\,(U = G \cap X$ and $G \in \mathfrak{J})\}$ is a topology for X.*

Proof: Exercise.

EXERCISE 1. Let $\mathfrak{F}$ be a filter on a set S; let $X \subseteq S$. Prove or disprove: $\{F \mid (\exists F^*)\,(F = F^* \cap X$ and $F^* \in \mathfrak{F})\}$ is a filter on X.

9.2 Definition. Let $\{S, \mathfrak{J}\}$ be a space and let X be any subset of S. The *relative topology*, r-$\mathfrak{J}$, for X consists of $\{U \mid (\exists G)\,(U = G \cap X$ and $G \in \mathfrak{J})\}$. X is then called a *subspace* of S; if $X \neq S$, then X is called a *proper subspace of S*.

9.3 Example. A space can be homeomorphic to a proper subspace of itself. Consider the space E^1 of real numbers with the usual topology. The function $f{:}x \to x/(1 + |x|) = y$ maps the space E^1 onto the subspace $X = \{y \mid -1 < y < 1\}$ in a 1:1 continuous manner; the inverse function $f^{-1}{:}y \to y/(1 - |y|) = x$ is continuous. Hence E^1 is homeomorphic to X.

EXERCISE 2. Let X be the subspace of the space E^1 of real numbers determined by the integers. Prove that every function from X onto any space S is continuous on S.

9.4 Definition. A point p in a space S is called an *isolated point of the space S* if and only if the subset $\{p\}$ consisting of the point p alone is open in S.

EXERCISE 3. Prove that any function is continuous at an isolated point p of the domain.

9.5 Theorem. *If X is a subspace of a space S and if F is a subset of X, then F is closed in X if and only if there exists F^* closed in S such that $F = F^* \cap X$.*

Proof: A. Let F be closed in X. Let $X \sim F$ denote the complement of F in X, and let $S \sim F$ denote the complement of F in S. $X \sim F$ is, then, open in X; hence, there exists a G, open in S, such that $G \cap X = X \sim F$. Now $F = X \sim [G \cap X]$, and $X \sim [G \cap X] = (S \sim G) \cap X$. Hence $F = (S \sim G) \cap X$ where $S \sim G$ is closed in S.

B. Let F^* be closed in S. $S \sim F^*$ is, then, open in S. Hence, $(S \sim F^*) \cap X$ is open in X by definition of the relative topology. Therefore, $X \sim [(S \sim F^*) \cap X]$ is closed in X. Now $X \sim [(S \sim F^*) \cap X] = F^* \cap X$; hence, $F^* \cap X$ is closed in X. ▮

Thus, closed sets in a subspace X of S can be generated either by taking complements of open sets in the subspace, or by taking intersections of the closed sets in S with X.

9.6 Theorem. *Let X be any subspace of a space S and let A be any subset of X. Then p in X is a limit point of A in X if and only if p is a limit point of A in S.*

Proof: A. Let p in X be a limit point of A in X and let G be any open set in S containing p. $G \cap X$ is open in X and contains p; therefore, $G \cap X$ contains at least one point of A different from p. Hence G contains a point of A different from p and so p is a limit point, in S, of A.

B. If p, in X, is a limit point, in S, of A contained in X and if G is any open set of X which contains p, then there exists G^*, open in S, such that $G^* \cap X = G$. Now G^* contains at least one point of A different from p by hypothesis. Since $A \subseteq X$, then $G^* \cap X = G$ must contain at least one point of A different from p. Hence p is a limit point, in X, of A. ▮

Thus the derived sets in a subspace X of a space S can be obtained either in the usual manner or by taking the intersections with X of the derived sets in S from the topology in S.

9.7 Theorem. *If X is any subspace of a space S and if A is any subset of X, then $\overline{A}_x = \overline{A}_s \cap X$, where $\overline{A}_x$ and $\overline{A}_s$ denote the closures of A in X and in S, respectively.*

Proof: Let A'_x and A'_s denote the derived sets of A in X and in S, respectively; then $\overline{A}_x = A \cup A'_x$, by definition of closures. By theorem 9.6, $A \cup A'_x = A \cup (A'_s \cap X)$. A, A'_s and X are all subsets of S; by the distributive laws for $\cup$ and $\cap$, $A \cup (A'_s \cap X) = (A \cup A'_s) \cap (A \cup X) = \overline{A}_s \cap (A \cup X)$. Since $A \subseteq X$, $A \cup X = X$. Hence, $\overline{A}_x = \overline{A}_s \cap X$. ▮

Thus the closures of subsets of X determined by the relative topology on X can be obtained from intersecting with X the closures of these subsets in S.

There are then four equivalent ways to set up the relative topology on a subset X of a space S. The open sets, closed sets, derived sets or closures in S can be intersected with X to determine the relative topology for X. Analogous theorems for bases, subbases, basic neighborhood relations and neighborhood relations for the relative topology now follow.

9.8 Theorem. *If S is any space, $\mathcal{B}$ any base for the topology on S and X any subspace of S, then $\mathcal{B}^* = \{U \mid (\exists B)(U = B \cap X$ and B is in $\mathcal{B})\}$ is a base for the relative topology on X.*

Proof: Let G be any open set in X. There exists H open in S such that $G = H \cap X$. H is the union of sets in $\mathcal{B}$, by definition of a base. Let $H = \bigcup_\nu B_\nu$, where B_ν is in $\mathcal{B}$. $G = (\bigcup_\nu B_\nu) \cap X = \bigcup_\nu (B_\nu \cap X)$. Hence any open set G in X is the union of sets from $\{U \mid (\exists B)(U = B \cap X$ and B in $\mathcal{B})\}$. Consequently, this collection is a base for the relative topology. ▮

9.9 Corollary. *If S is any space with subbase $\mathcal{V} = \{V_\alpha \mid \alpha \in \mathfrak{A}\}$ and if X is any subspace of S, then the collection $\mathcal{V}^* = \{V_\alpha \cap X \mid V_\alpha \in \mathcal{V}\}$ is a subbase for the relative topology on X.*

Proof: Exercise.

9.10 Theorem. *If R is a basic neighborhood relation for a space S and if X is a subspace of S, then $R_r = \{(p, V) \mid p \in X$ and $(\exists V^*)(V = V^* \cap X$ and (p, V^*) is in $R)\}$ is a basic neighborhood relation for the relative topology on X.*

Proof: Since R is a basic neighborhood relation for S, the domain of R_r is X, and (p, V) is in R_r implies p is in V. Let (p, V) and (p, W) be in R_r. By definition of R_r, there exist (p, V^*) and (p, W^*) in R such that $V = V^* \cap X$ and $W = W^* \cap X$. $V^* \cap W^*$ contains a G^* such that (p, G^*) is in R, by definition of a basic neighborhood relation. Hence, $(p, G^* \cap X)$ is in R_r. Since $G^* \subseteq V^* \cap W^*$, $G^* \cap X \subseteq [(V^* \cap W^*) \cap X] = [(V^* \cap X) \cap (W^* \cap X)] = V \cap W$. Hence, $G^* \cap X \subseteq V \cap W$, and so axiom BN-II is satisfied. Let (p, V) be in R_r and let q be in V. There exists V^* such that (p, V^*) is in R and $V = V^* \cap X$. q is in V^*; hence there exists $W^* \subseteq V^*$ such that (q, W^*) is in R. $(q, W^* \cap X)$ is then in R_r. Since $W^* \subseteq V^*$, $(W^* \cap X) \subseteq V^* \cap X = V$. Hence axiom BN-III is satisfied. Lastly, it must be established that R_r is a basic neighborhood relation for the relative topology on X. Let G be any open set in the relative topology and let p be in G. There exists G^* open in S such that $G^* \cap X = G$. Further, there exists $V^* \subseteq G^*$ such that (p, V^*) is in R. Hence, $(p, V^* \cap X)$ is in R_r and $V^* \cap X \subseteq G$. Next, let (p, W) be any pair in R_r. There exists W^* such that (p, W^*) is in R and $W = W^* \cap X$. W^* is open; hence, W is open in X, by definition of the relative topology. Thus R_r is equivalent to the largest basic neighborhood relation for X determined by the relative topology. Hence, R_r is a basic neighborhood relation for the relative topology on X. ▮

9.11 Theorem. *If S is a space, if X is a subspace of S and if R^+ is the neighborhood relation for S, then the relation $r\text{-}R^+ = \{(x, N) \mid x$ is in X and $(\exists N^*)(N = N^* \cap X$ and (x, N^*) is in $R^+)\}$ is the neighborhood relation for the relative topology on X.*

Proof: First, let x be in X and let N^* be any neighborhood of x in S. Consider $N^* \cap X$. Since N^* is a neighborhood of x in S, N^* contains G^* open in S which contains x. Hence, $G^* \cap X$ is open in the subspace X and contains x. Further, $G^* \cap X \subseteq N^* \cap X$ and $N^* \cap X$ is a neighborhood of x in the subspace. Conversely, let M be any neighborhood of x in the subspace. There exists a set G open in the subspace such that $G \subseteq M$ and x is in G. By definition of the relative topology, there exists a set G^* open in S such that $G = G^* \cap X$. Hence, $M \cup G^*$ is a neighborhood of x in S. Since $(M \cup G^*) \cap X = M$, (x, M) is in $r\text{-}R^+$. ▮

9.12 Example. Consider the space E^2 (definition 2.16). Let $X = \{(x, y) \mid x = 0 \text{ and } -1 < y < +1\}$ with the relative topology. Then $A = \{(x, y) \mid x = 0 \text{ and } 0 < y < 1\}$ is open in X, but is not open in E^2. Also, $B = \{(0, y) \mid 0 \leq y < 1\}$ is closed in the subspace X, but is not closed in E^2.

9.13 Example. Again consider the space E^2, and the subspace $A = \{(x, y) \mid x^2 + y^2 \leq 1\}$ of E^2. A is then the unit disc plus its circumference. A basic neighborhood for a point (a, b) on the circumference has the form $\{(x, y) \mid x^2 + y^2 \leq 1\} \cap \{(x, y) \mid \sqrt{(x - a)^2 + (y - b)^2} < \epsilon, \epsilon > 0\}$.

Heretofore, only functions from one topological space *onto* another were considered. Such functions are called *surjections.* Now the concept of a function from one topological space *into* another will be discussed.

9.14 Definition. A function f from a space $\{S, \mathfrak{I}\}$ *into* a space $\{T, \mathfrak{I}^*\}$ is a function from $\{S, \mathfrak{I}\}$ onto a subspace $\{Y, r\text{-}\mathfrak{I}^*\}$ of $\{T, \mathfrak{I}^*\}$.

9.15 Definition. Let X be a set and f a function from X into X. A *fixed point* for the function f is a point x^* in X such that $f(x^*) = x^*$.

9.16 Definition. A topological space X is said to have the *fixed point property* if and only if each continuous function f of X into X has at least one fixed point.

9.17 Theorem. *The fixed point property is a topological invariant.*

Proof: Let h be a homeomorphism from a space X onto a space Y; let X have the fixed point property; let f be a continuous function of Y into Y. $h^{-1} \circ f \circ h$ is a continuous function from X into X. Hence, there exists a point x^* in X such that $h^{-1}(f(h(x^*))) = x^*$. Hence $h(h^{-1}(f(h(x^*)))) = h(x^*)$. Let $h(x^*) = y^*$. Then $f(y^*) = y^*$ and so f has a fixed point. ▮

The fixed point property is very useful in topology and in the applications of topology to analysis. In Chapter 5, it will be proved that any closed interval of real numbers has the fixed point property.

EXERCISE 4. Show that E^1 and E^2 do not have the fixed point property.

EXERCISE 5. Does the circumference of the unit circle, as a subspace of E^2, have the fixed point property?

9.18 Definition. A function f from a space S into a space T is called *continuous on a subspace A* of S if and only if $f^* = f \cap (A \times T)$ is continuous on A. f^* is denoted by $f \mid A$ and is called the restriction of f to A.

9.19 Definition. A subspace A of a space S is called a *retract* of S if and only if there exists a continuous function r from S onto A such that $r \mid A$ is the identity on A. r is called a *retraction*.

9.20 Theorem. *If S is a space with the fixed point property and if A is a retract of S, then A has the fixed point property.*

Proof: Exercise.

Since the continuous image of a space with the fixed point property does not necessarily have the fixed point property, the last theorem shows that the concept of a retract has some significance for the study of the fixed point property.

9.21 Lemma. *Let f be a function from a space S onto a space T. If f is continuous on S and if A is a subspace of S, then $f \mid A$ is continuous on A.*

Proof: Exercise.

EXERCISE 6. Let $f: E^1 \to E^1$ be defined as follows: $f(x) = 0$ if x is rational, and $f(x) = 1$ if x is irrational. Let Q denote the subspace of rationals. Prove that $f \mid Q$ is continuous on Q.

EXERCISE 7. Prove that if F is a closed subset of a space S, then a subset M of F is closed in the subspace F if and only if M is closed in S.

EXERCISE 8. Prove that if G is an open subset of a space S, then a subset A of G is open in the subspace G if and only if A is open in S.

UNIONS OF CONTINUOUS FUNCTIONS

9.22 Theorem. *If S is any space such that $S = \bigcup_\nu G_\nu$, where ν is in some indexing set and each G_ν is open in S, if $\{f_\nu\}$ is a set of functions such that each f_ν maps the subspace G_ν continuously into the space T and if $f_\mu(x) = f_\nu(x)$ for x in $G_\nu \cap G_\mu$, then the function h from S into T defined by $h(x) = f_\nu(x)$, for $x \in G_\nu$, is continuous on S. Moreover, $h = \bigcup_\nu f_\nu$.*

Proof: Let G^* be any open set in $h[S]$, the subspace of T that is the image of S. $h^{-1}[G^*] = \bigcup_\nu (h^{-1}[G^*] \cap G_\nu) = \bigcup_\nu f_\nu^{-1}[G^*]$ by definition of h where

$f_\nu^{-1}[G^*] = \{x \mid (\exists y)(y \in G^* \text{ and } (x, y) \in f_\nu)\}$. Since each $f_\nu^{-1}[G^*]$ is open in the subspace G_ν, by definition of continuity, and since G_ν is open in S, each $f_\nu^{-1}[G^*]$ is open in S (see preceding exercises). Hence, $h^{-1}[G^*]$ is the union of open sets of S and so is open in S. Thus, h is continuous on S. By definition, $h = \bigcup_\nu f_\nu$. ▮

9.23 Theorem. *If S is any space such that $S = F_1 \cup \cdots \cup F_i \cup \cdots \cup F_k$, where k is a natural number and each F_i is closed in S, if $\{f_1, \ldots, f_i, \ldots, f_k\}$ is a set of functions such that f_i, $i = 1, 2, \ldots, k$, is continuous from F_i into a space T, and if $f_i(x) = f_j(x)$ for x in $F_i \cap F_j$, then the function h from S into T defined by $h(x) = f_i(x)$ for x in F_i is continuous on S. Moreover, $h = \bigcup_{i=1}^k f_i$.*

Proof: Let F^* be any closed set in $h[S]$, the subspace of T that is the image of S. $h^{-1}[F^*] = f_1^{-1}[F^*] \cup \cdots \cup f_i^{-1}[F^*] \cup \cdots \cup f_k^{-1}[F^*]$, by definition of h. Since f_i is continuous on F_i, $f_i^{-1}[F^*]$ is closed in F_i. Since each F_i is closed in S, each $f_i^{-1}[F^*]$ is closed in S (see preceding exercises). Hence $h^{-1}[F^*]$ is the union of a finite number of sets closed in S, and so is closed in S. Thus, h is continuous on S. By definition, $h = \bigcup_{i=1}^k f_i$. ▮

EXERCISE 9. Give an example to show that the union of an infinite number of functions defined on an infinite number of closed subspaces and satisfying the conditions of theorem 9.23, except for finiteness, is not necessarily a continuous function in the manner concluded in theorem 9.23.

9.24 Example. Let f be a function defined on the closed subspace $A = \{x \mid x \leq 1\}$ of the space E^1 by $f(x) = x$; let g be a function defined on the open subspace $B = \{x \mid x > 1\}$ of the space E^1 by $g(x) = x + 1$. $E^1 = A \cup B$ and $A \cap B = \emptyset$. f and g are continuous on A and B, respectively. However, h defined by $h(x) = f(x)$ for x in A and $h(x) = g(x)$ for x in B is not continuous on E^1, its domain. For let F be the closed set $\{y \mid y > 2\}$ in the subspace $h[E^1]$. $h^{-1}[F] = B$ is not closed in E^1.

Property Transference

When topological spaces are generated from a given space or from given spaces in any manner, a significant question that arises is "Which topological properties of the original space or spaces are necessarily possessed by the new topological structure or structures?" We now consider whether a subspace of a first or second countable space is necessarily first or second countable, respectively.

9.25 Theorem. *If S is a space that satisfies the first or the second axiom of countability, and if X is any subspace of S, then X is first or second countable, respectively.*

Proof: If S satisfies the second axiom of countability, then by theorem 9.8, X has a countable base. If S satisfies the first axiom of countability and x is any point in the subspace X, then there exists a countable local base $\mathcal{B} = \{B_1, B_2, \ldots, B_i, \ldots\}$ at x in S. Let H be any open set of X that contains x. There exists G, open in S, such that $H = G \cap X$, by definition of the relative topology on X; hence, G is an open set in S containing x. This implies that there exists an open set, B_j, of the local base at x in S such that $B_j \subseteq G$, by definition of a local base. Hence, $B_j \cap X$ is open in X, contains x and is contained in $H = G \cap X$. Thus the countable collection, $\{B_1 \cap X, B_2 \cap X, \ldots, B_i \cap X, \ldots\}$ forms a local base at x for the relative topology on X. ▮

9.26 Example. A subspace of a separable space is not necessarily separable. Consider the space consisting of the real numbers S with a topology $\mathfrak{J}$ consisting of $\{\emptyset, S$ and all complements of bounded, countable sets$\}$. These sets constitute a topology for S. The set of natural numbers is dense in $\{S, \mathfrak{J}\}$. Now consider the subspace M: $\{x \mid 0 \leq x \leq 1\}$. Let D be countable in M. Since D is bounded and countable, $S \sim D$ is open in S and D is closed in M. Since M is not countable, $M \sim D$ is not empty. Thus $\overline{D} \neq M$, and no countable set is dense in M.

9.27 Theorem. *If $\{S, \mathfrak{J}\}$ is a topological space and if $M \subseteq X \subseteq S$, then the relative topology for M from $\{X, r\text{-}\mathfrak{J}\}$ is the same as the relative topology for M from $\{S, \mathfrak{J}\}$.*

Proof: Exercise.

9.28 Definition. A topological space $\{X, \mathcal{S}\}$ is said to be *imbedded topologically* in a topological space $\{Y, \mathfrak{J}\}$ if and only if $\{X, \mathcal{S}\}$ is homeomorphic to a subspace of $\{Y, \mathfrak{J}\}$. $\{Y, \mathfrak{J}\}$ is then said to contain the space $\{X, \mathcal{S}\}$, since it contains as a subspace a model of the topological structure represented by $\{X, \mathcal{S}\}$.

10. TOPOLOGIES DEFINED BY FUNCTIONS.

In beginning calculus continuity appears to be an intrinsic property of functions, i.e., a function is either continuous or not continuous from its definition. The theorems in section 4 lead to another conclusion. First, if S is any space and T is a space with the trivial topology, then any function from S into T is continuous, by definition of a continuous function. Next, if S is any space with the discrete topology and T is any space, then any function from S into T is again continuous, by definition of continuity. These facts emphasize that continuity depends on the topologies involved as well as on the function itself. Hence, any function from one space onto another can be converted into a continuous function by increasing the topology on the domain or decreasing the topology on the range. In fact, a function f from a set into a space can be used to construct a topology on the domain, and a function g from a space into a set can be used to construct a topology on the range. A study of these two methods of setting up topologies follows.

The Weak Topology

10.1 Lemma. *If S is any set, T is any space and f is a function from S onto T, then the collection $\mathfrak{I} = \{A \mid (\exists G)(A = f^{-1}[G]$ and G is open in $T)\}$ is a topology for S.*

Proof: Since $f^{-1}[T] = S$ and $f^{-1}[\emptyset] = \emptyset$, S and $\emptyset$ are both in $\mathfrak{I}$. Let $A = f^{-1}[G]$ and $B = f^{-1}[H]$ be in $\mathfrak{I}$, where G and H are both open in T. Then $f^{-1}[G \cap H]$ belongs to $\mathfrak{I}$; hence, since $f^{-1}[G] \cap f^{-1}[H] = f^{-1}[G \cap H]$, then $A \cap B = f^{-1}[G] \cap f^{-1}[H]$ belongs to $\mathfrak{I}$. By induction, the intersection of any finite number of sets in $\mathfrak{I}$ belongs to $\mathfrak{I}$. Lastly, consider $\{f^{-1}[G_\nu] \mid \nu \in \mathfrak{A}$ and $G_\nu \in \mathfrak{I}\}$. $\bigcup_\nu (f^{-1}[G_\nu]) = f^{-1}[\bigcup_\nu G_\nu]$. Since $\bigcup_\nu G_\nu$ is open in T, $f^{-1}[\bigcup_\nu G_\nu]$ is in $\mathfrak{I}$. Hence $\bigcup_\nu (f^{-1}[G_\nu])$ is in $\mathfrak{I}$, and so the union of any number of sets in $\mathfrak{I}$ is in $\mathfrak{I}$. By definition, $\mathfrak{I}$ is a topology for S. ▮

10.2 Definition. If S is any set, T is any space and f is a function from S onto T, then the topology on S consisting of $\{A \mid (\exists G)(A = f^{-1}[G]$ and G is open in $T)\}$ is called the *weak* topology on S induced by f and the topology $\mathfrak{I}$ on T, or simply the weak topology when the meaning is clear.

10.3 Theorem. *If S is any set, T is any space and f is a function from S onto T, then the weak topology $\mathfrak{S}$ on S is the smallest topology for S with which f is continuous.*

Proof: By the definition of weak topology, f is continuous on S with the topology $\mathfrak{S}$. Let $\mathfrak{I}$ be any topology for S with which f is continuous. By definition of continuity, G open in T implies that $f^{-1}[G]$ is open in the space S, or that $f^{-1}[G]$ is in $\mathfrak{I}$. Hence, $\mathfrak{S} \subseteq \mathfrak{I}$. ▮

The problem of the continuity of f is completely solved when the smallest topology for S with which f is continuous is known. With any larger topology for S, f will certainly be continuous and with any smaller topology f will not be continuous.

EXERCISE 1. If the set S is the domain of a function f and if the space T is the range of f, show that f is continuous on S whenever S has any topology between the discrete topology and the weak topology.

EXERCISE 2. Let p be the function defined by $p((x, y)) = x$ from the set R^2 of all ordered pairs of real numbers onto the space E^1. The topology, $\mathfrak{S}$, induced by

p on R^2 has for a base the collection of vertical strips $\{V_a^b \mid V_a^b = \{(x, y) \mid a < x < b$ for a, b real$\}\}$. Is the weak topology larger than, smaller than, or equal to the usual topology for R^2? [The usual topology for R^2 is the topology for E^2 (definition 2.16).]

EXERCISE 3. Let D be the subspace of E^1 consisting of all non-negative real numbers, and let $f{:}x \to x^2$ map the set R of all real numbers onto the space D. What is the weak topology induced on R by f? Is this topology larger than, smaller than or equal to the usual topology on R? [The usual topology for R is the topology for E^1 (definition 2.15).]

EXERCISE 4. Let D denote the set of real numbers minus the numbers $(2k + 1)\pi$, for k an integer; let $f{:}x \to \tan x/2$ map D onto E^1. What is the weak topology on D induced by f? With this topology, what is the closure of the subset of positive reals in D?

EXERCISE 5. Let f be the function $(x, y) \to x^2 + y^2$ from the set S of all ordered pairs of real numbers onto the space of non-negative real numbers with the usual relative topology. What is the weak topology, $\mathcal{S}$, for S which is induced by f? Find a set which is in the usual topology for S, but is not in $\mathcal{S}$.

EXERCISE 6. Let S be a set, let T be a space with topology $\mathfrak{J}$ and f a function from S onto T. If $\mathcal{B}$ is a base for the topology $\mathfrak{J}$, show that the collection $\{A \mid (\exists B)$ $(A = f^{-1}[B]$ and B is in $\mathcal{B})\}$ is a base for the weak topology on S.

EXERCISE 7. Let S be a set, T a space with topology $\mathfrak{J}$ and f a function from S onto T. If $\mathcal{V}$ is a subbase for the topology $\mathfrak{J}$, show that the collection $\{W \mid W = f^{-1}[V]$ and V is in $\mathcal{V}\}$ is a subbase for the weak topology on S.

EXERCISE 8. Prove that the set of closed sets determined by the weak topology on a set X induced by a function f from X onto a space Y is $\{F \mid (\exists A)\ (F = f^{-1}[A]$ and A is closed in $X)\}$.

The Strong Topology

Analogous to the weak topology for the domain of a function, is the strong topology for the range of a function. First, however, it is to be observed that if $\mathfrak{J}$ is a topology on the domain S of a function $f{:}\, S \xrightarrow{\text{onto}} T$, then the collection $\{A \mid (\exists G)\ (A = f[G]$ and G is in $\mathfrak{J})\}$ is not necessarily a topology for T; i.e., there is no analogue to lemma 10.1. The next example shows this.

10.4 Example. Let S be the subspace of E^2 consisting of $\{(x, y) \mid 0 \le x \le 1$ and $y = 1\} \cup \{(x, y) \mid 1 \le x \le 2$ and $y = 2\}$. Let $p{:}\,(x, y) \to x$ map S onto $M = \{x \mid 0 \le x \le 2\}$. The subsets $\{(x, y) \mid .99 < x \le 1$ and $y = 1\}$ and $\{(x, y) \mid 1 \le x < 1.01$ and $y = 2\}$ of S are open in S; their images in M are, respectively, $U = \{x \mid .99 < x \le 1\}$ and $V = \{x \mid 1 \le x < 1.01\}$. However, $U \cap V$ consists of the real number 1 alone, and 1 is not the image of an open set in S. Thus the set of images of open sets in S does not contain all intersections of finitely many subsets in it, and hence the collection is not a topology for T.

Another way of emphasizing the difficulty is to recall that although $f^{-1}[A \cap B] = f^{-1}[A] \cap f^{-1}[B]$ for any function f, $f[A \cap B]$ is not in general equal to $f[A] \cap f[B]$. However, there is a way in which a significant topology can be defined for the range.

10.5 Lemma. *If S is a space, T a set and f a function from S onto T, then $\mathfrak{T}^* = \{A \mid f^{-1}[A]$ is open in $S\}$ is a topology for the range T.*

Proof: Since $f^{-1}[T] = S$ and $f^{-1}[\emptyset] = \emptyset$, both T and $\emptyset$ belong to $\mathfrak{T}^*$. If A and B belong to $\mathfrak{T}^*$, then $f^{-1}[A]$ and $f^{-1}[B]$ are open in S; hence, $f^{-1}[A] \cap f^{-1}[B]$ is open in S. This implies that $f^{-1}[A \cap B]$ is open in S since $f^{-1}[A \cap B] = f^{-1}[A] \cap f^{-1}[B]$. Therefore, $A \cap B$ belongs to $\mathfrak{T}^*$ and by finite induction, the intersection of any finite number of sets in $\mathfrak{T}^*$ belongs to $\mathfrak{T}^*$. Lastly, let $\{G_\nu\}$ denote a set of sets in $\mathfrak{T}^*$. $f^{-1}[\bigcup_\nu G_\nu] = \bigcup_\nu f^{-1}[G_\nu]$. Since G_ν is in $\mathfrak{T}^*$, $f^{-1}[G_\nu]$ is open in S for every ν and consequently $\bigcup_\nu f^{-1}[G_\nu]$ is open in S. $f^{-1}[\bigcup_\nu G_\nu]$ is then open in S since it is equal to the set $\bigcup_\nu f^{-1}[G_\nu]$. Thus $\bigcup_\nu G_\nu$ is in $\mathfrak{T}^*$ and the set is a topology for T. ▮

10.6 Definition. If S is any space with topology, $\mathcal{S}$, if T is any set and if f is a function from S onto T, then the *strong topology*, $\mathfrak{T}^*$, for T is, exactly, $\{A \mid f^{-1}(A)$ is open in $S\}$.

10.7 Theorem. *If S is a space, T a set and f a function from S onto T, then the strong topology $\mathfrak{T}^*$ for T is the largest topology for T with which f is continuous.*

Proof: Exercise.

EXERCISE 9. Show that if f is a function from a space S onto a set T and if $\mathfrak{T}^{**}$ is any topology for T "between" the trivial topology and the strong topology, then f is also continuous with $\mathfrak{T}^{**}$.

EXERCISE 10. Let S be a space with topology $\mathcal{S}$, T a set, f a function from S onto T and $\mathfrak{T}^*$ the strong topology for T. Is the weak topology $\mathcal{S}^*$ for S that is induced by f and $\mathfrak{T}^*$ larger than, smaller than, or equal to $\mathcal{S}$?

EXERCISE 11. Let f be a function from a set S onto a space T with topology $\mathfrak{T}$. Let $\mathcal{S}$ be the weak topology for S induced by f from $\mathfrak{T}$. Let $\mathfrak{T}^*$ be the strong topology for T that is defined by f from $\mathcal{S}$. Is $\mathfrak{T}^*$ larger than, smaller than, or equal to $\mathfrak{T}$?

EXERCISE 12. If f is a function from a space X onto a space Y, an inverse set, relative to f, is a subset A of the domain such that $A = f^{-1}[f[A]]$. Prove that the topology on Y contains the strong topology induced by f if and only if the image of every open inverse set is open.

EXERCISE 13. Prove that if f is continuous and open from X onto Y, then Y has the strong topology.

It is to be observed that the strong topology is the largest topology for the range with which the given function f is continuous (the topology on the domain being fixed); the smallest topology, in this case, is known and is the trivial topology.

Topologies Determined by Sets of Functions

Just as one function can determine a weak topology on a domain, so a set of functions can determine a weak topology on a common domain.

10.8 Example. Let S denote the set $\{(x, y) \mid x, y \text{ real}\}$. Let p_x and p_y denote functions from S onto the space of real numbers, E^1, defined as follows: $p_x((x, y)) = x$ and $p_y((x, y)) = y$. The weak topology, $\mathcal{S}$, for S induced by the function p_x has a base consisting of all vertical strips $V_a^\epsilon = \{(x, y) \mid a - \epsilon < x < a + \epsilon;\ a, \epsilon \text{ real and } \epsilon > 0\}$, i.e., the set of all inverse images of open intervals of real numbers. The set of all unions of such strips is the weak topology, $\mathcal{S}$, for S, induced by p_x. Similarly the function p_y induces a weak topology, $\mathcal{S}^*$, on S. $\mathcal{S}^*$ consists of the set of all unions of horizontal strips $H_b^\delta = \{(x, y) \mid b - \delta < y < b + \delta;\ \delta, b \text{ real}, \delta > 0\}$. In order for both p_x and p_y to be continuous, a new topology $\bar{\mathcal{S}}$ is needed which contains $\mathcal{S} \cup \mathcal{S}^*$. $\mathcal{S} \cup \mathcal{S}^*$ is not a topology, since the intersection of a vertical and a horizontal strip does not belong to $\mathcal{S} \cup \mathcal{S}^*$. Thus the smallest topology for S with which both p_x and p_y are continuous is the topology generated by the collection $\mathcal{S} \cup \mathcal{S}^*$ as subbase.

EXERCISE 14. What is $\bar{\mathcal{S}}$ in the previous example?

10.9 Definition. If S is a set, if $\{T_\nu\}$ is a set of spaces, for ν in some indexing set, and if $\{f_\nu\}$ is a set of functions such that $f_\nu : S \xrightarrow{\text{onto}} T_\nu$, then the *weak topology* $\mathfrak{I}^*$ *on* S *determined by the functions* f_ν is the topology generated by $\{A \mid \text{for some } \nu,\ A = f_\nu^{-1}[G] \text{ and } G \text{ is open in } T_\nu\}$.

10.10 Theorem. *If S is a set, if $\{T_\nu\}$ is a set of spaces, for ν in some indexing set, and if $\{f_\nu\}$ is a set of functions such that $f_\nu : S \xrightarrow{\text{onto}} T_\nu$, then the weak topology determined on S by the functions in $\{f_\nu\}$ is the smallest topology with which all functions in the set $\{f_\nu\}$ are continuous on $\mathcal{S}$.*

Proof: Exercise.

Analogously, a collection of functions can determine a strong topology on a common range.

10.11 Definition. Let $\{S_\nu\}$ be a set of spaces, for ν in some indexing set, let T be a set and let $\{f_\nu\}$ be a set of functions $f_\nu : S_\nu \xrightarrow{\text{onto}} T$. The *strong topology for* T is the topology $\mathfrak{I}^* = \bigcap_\nu \mathfrak{I}_\nu$, where $\mathfrak{I}_\nu$ is the strong topology for T determined by f_ν.

10.12 Theorem. *If $\{S_\nu\}$ is a set of spaces, for ν in some indexing set, if T is a set and if $\{f_\nu\}$ is a set of functions $f_\nu : S_\nu \xrightarrow{\text{onto}} T$, then the strong topology is the largest topology for T with which f_ν is continuous on S_ν for every ν.*

Proof: Exercise.

EXERCISE 15. (a) Show that $R = \{(p, U(p, \epsilon)) \mid U(p, \epsilon) = \{x \mid x < p + \epsilon; p, \epsilon$ are real and $\epsilon > 0\}\}$ is a basic neighborhood relation for the set of real numbers.

(b) A function f from the reals into the reals is called *upper semi-continuous* at x_0 if and only if for each $\epsilon > 0$, there exists $\delta > 0$, such that $f(x) - f(x_0) < \epsilon$ if $|x - x_0| < \delta$. Using the usual topology for the domain of all real numbers, find the strong topology for the range of all real numbers determined by all upper semi-continuous functions, i.e., find the largest topology for the range with which all upper semi-continuous functions are continuous.

The concepts of weak and strong topologies will be used in the next two sections in the important definitions of product space topologies and quotient space topologies.

11. PRODUCT OF A FINITE NUMBER OF SPACES.

For any sets X and Y there is defined a set $X \times Y$ called the cartesian product or product set of X and Y. $X \times Y$ consists of all ordered pairs (x, y), where $x \in X$ and $y \in Y$.

If $\{X, \mathfrak{I}_x\}$ and $\{Y, \mathfrak{I}_y\}$ are topological spaces, a topology for $X \times Y$ can be defined in terms of the topologies on X and Y; the resulting space is called the cartesian product space of X and Y and is said to have the cartesian product topology defined on it. The basic example of a cartesian product space is the product of the space of real numbers with itself, $E^1 \times E^1$; this gives the usual (x, y)-plane, E^2. As a first try one might attempt to define the open sets of $X \times Y$ to be the set of all products of an open set of X with an open set of Y. However, by examining the open sets of E^2, one sees that not all open sets in the plane are directly the product of an open set of E^1 with an open set of E^1. Consider for example, $M = \{(x, y) \mid 0 < x < 1 \text{ and } 0 < y < x\}$. If $M = U \times V$, then (.2, .1) and (.9, .8) are both in $U \times V$. This means that .2 is in U and .8 is in V. It follows then that (.2, .8) is in $U \times V$. This is a contradiction since (.2, .8) is not in M. M is, however, the union of product sets which are products of open sets of E^1.

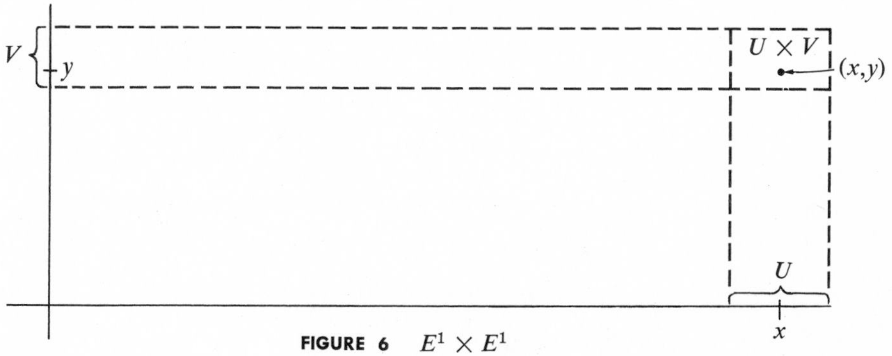

FIGURE 6 $E^1 \times E^1$

THE PRODUCT SPACE $X \times Y$

11.1 Theorem. *If* $\{X, \mathfrak{I}_x\}$ *and* $\{Y, \mathfrak{I}_y\}$ *are topological spaces, then* $\mathcal{B} = \{U \times V \mid U \text{ is in } \mathfrak{I}_x \text{ and } V \text{ is in } \mathfrak{I}_y\}$ *is a base for a topology for* $X \times Y$.

Proof: By theorem 3.50, it need only be shown that any intersection of a finite number of sets in $\mathcal{B}$ is the union of sets in $\mathcal{B}$. $\bigcap_\emptyset \mathcal{B} = S$. Let G_1 and G_2 denote sets in the collection $\mathcal{B}$. Let $G_1 = U_1 \times V_1$ and $G_2 = U_2 \times V_2$, where U_1, U_2 and V_1, V_2 are in $\mathfrak{I}_x$ and $\mathfrak{I}_y$, respectively. $G_1 \cap G_2 = (U_1 \times V_1) \cap (U_2 \times V_2) = (U_1 \cap U_2) \times (V_1 \cap V_2)$, by definition of cartesian product set. By finite induction, it follows that the intersection of any finite number of sets in $\mathcal{B}$ is a set in $\mathcal{B}$. Hence, $\mathcal{B}$ constitutes a base for a topology on $X \times Y$. ∎

11.2 Definition. Let $\{X, \mathfrak{I}_x\}$ and $\{Y, \mathfrak{I}_y\}$ be topological spaces. The *cartesian product* or *product topology* is the topology determined on the product set $X \times Y$ by $\mathcal{B} = \{U \times V \mid U \text{ is in } \mathfrak{I}_x \text{ and } V \text{ is in } \mathfrak{I}_y\}$ as a base.

11.3 Corollary. *If* $\mathcal{B}_x$ *is a base for a topology on* X *and* $\mathcal{B}_y$ *is a base for a topology on* Y, *then* $\{M \mid M = B_x \times B_y$, *for some* B_x *in* $\mathcal{B}_x$ *and some* B_y *in* $\mathcal{B}_y\}$ *is a base for the product topology.*

Proof: Exercise.

11.4 Theorem. *Euclidean 2-space* E^2 *is the product space* $E^1 \times E^1$.

Proof: Exercise.

11.5 Example. Let Z denote the set of integers with the discrete topology. $Z \times E^1$ is shown partially in Figure 7.

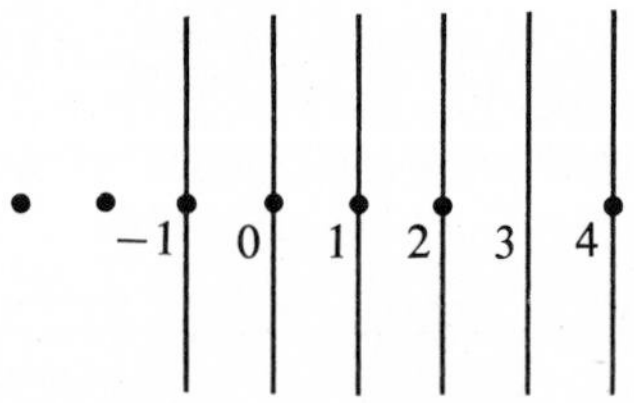

FIGURE 7 Part of $Z \times E^1$

11.6 Example. Let $M = \{(x, y) \mid x^2 + y^2 = 1\}$ and assign to M the relative topology from E^2. $E^1 \times M$ is shown partially in Figure 8.

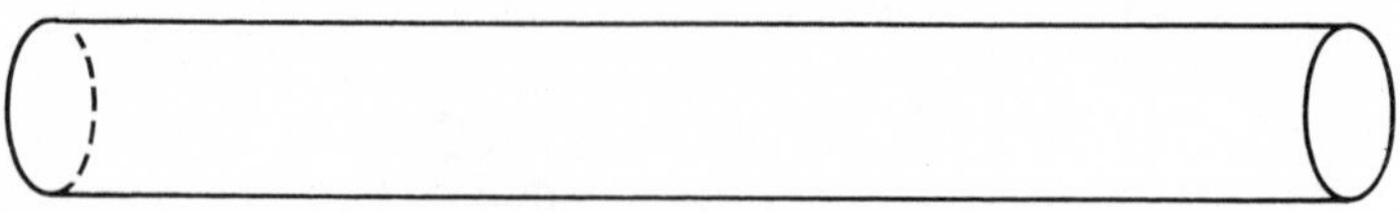

FIGURE 8 Part of $E^1 \times M$

11.7 Example. Let I denote the unit interval, $\{x \mid 0 \leq x \leq 1\}$, and let $M = \{(x, y) \mid x^2 + y^2 = 1\}$. Assign to I and M the relative topologies from E^1 and E^2 respectively. $M \times I$ is sketched in Figure 9.

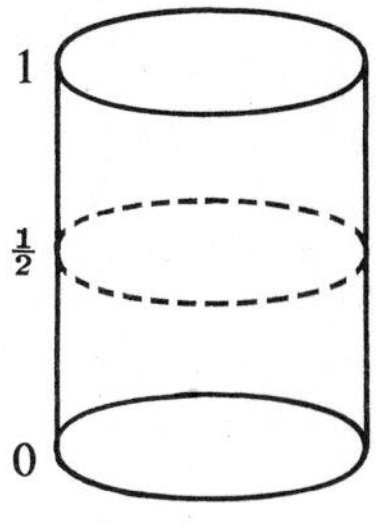

FIGURE 9 $M \times I$

The cartesian product space is the analogue in topology of the direct sum or direct product of groups in algebra, i.e., two sets G_1 and G_2 with group structure defined on them determine a group, $G_1 \oplus G_2$ or $G_1 \times G_2$, in which the operation is defined in terms of the operations in G_1 and G_2.

Projection Functions

Two important functions, p_x and p_y, called *projection functions* are defined in a natural manner on a non-empty product space $X \times Y$ as follows: $p_x((x, y)) = x$ and $p_y((x, y)) = y$.

11.8 Theorem. *The projection functions p_x and p_y from the non-empty product space $X \times Y$ onto X and Y, respectively, are continuous and open.*

Proof: Let G be any open set in X. $p_x^{-1}[G] = G \times Y$, by definition of p_x. Since G is open in X and Y is open in Y, $G \times Y$ is open in $X \times Y$. Hence p_x is continuous. Similarly, p_y is continuous. Next $p_x[\emptyset] = \emptyset$; so, let $U \times V$ be any non-empty basic open set in $X \times Y$. $p_x(U \times V) = U$ and $p_y(U \times V) = V$. Next, let G^* be any open set in $X \times Y$. $G^* = \bigcup_\nu B_\nu$, where each B_ν is a basic open set in $X \times Y$. $p_x[G^*] = p_x[\bigcup_\nu B_\nu]$. However, $p_x[\bigcup_\nu B_\nu] = \bigcup_\nu p_x[B_\nu]$. Since each $p_x[B_\nu]$ is open in X, $p_x[G^*]$ is open in X. Similarly for p_y. ∎

EXERCISE 1. Let $f:(x, y) \rightarrow x$ be the projection function of $E^2 = E^1 \times E^1$ onto E^1. Show that f is not closed.

EXERCISE 2. Let f be the projection function $f((x, y)) = x$ from E^2 onto E^1. Show that f restricted to the subspace $\{(x, y) \mid 0 \leq x \leq 1 \text{ and } y = 1\} \cup \{(x, y) \mid 1 \leq x \leq 2 \text{ and } y = 2\}$ is not open.

11.9 Theorem. *The Cartesian product topology on a non-empty set $X \times Y$ is the weak topology for $X \times Y$ determined by the projection functions p_x and p_y from the topologies on X and Y.*

Proof: The weak topology has for a subbase $\{G_\nu \mid G_\nu = p_x^{-1}[U_\nu]$ or $G_\nu = p_y^{-1}[V_\nu]$, for some U_ν open in X or V_ν open in $Y\}$. The intersection $(U_1 \times Y) \cap (X \times V_1) \cap (U_2 \times Y) \cap \cdots \cap (X \times V_k)$ of a finite number of such sets has the form $(U_1 \cap U_2 \cap \cdots \cap U_i) \times (V_1 \cap \cdots \cap V_k) = U^* \times V^*$, where U^* is open in X and V^* is open in Y. Hence the weak topology has the same base as the product topology, and so the two topologies are the same. ▮

Thus, the cartesian product topology for a non-empty product $X \times Y$ of two spaces can be characterized in two ways: first, as the topology with a base consisting of the set of all products of open sets of X and Y; and second, as the weak topology determined by the projection functions.

11.10 Alternate Definition. Let X and Y be non-empty topological spaces. The *cartesian product* or *product topology* for the set $X \times Y$ is the weak topology determined by the projection functions p_x and p_y.

THE PRODUCT SPACE $X_1 \times X_2 \times \cdots \times X_k$

The cartesian product topology for a product of a finite number of spaces is defined in a manner completely analogous to the manner of defining the product topology for a product of two spaces.

11.11 Definition. The *cartesian product set*, $\prod_{i=1}^k X_i$, of a set $\{X_1, X_2, \ldots, X_k\}$ of k sets, for k a natural number, is defined to be the set of all functions f from the set of the first k natural numbers into $\{X_1 \cup X_2 \cup \cdots \cup X_k\}$ such that $f(i)$ is in X_i, i.e., $\prod_{i=1}^k X_i$ consists of all k-sequences or ordered k-tuples, $(x_1, x_2, \ldots, x_k)$ such that x_i is in X_i.

11.12 Definition. The *cartesian product* or *product topology* for a non-empty product $\prod_{i=1}^k X_i$ of a finite set of non-empty spaces $\{X_1, \ldots, X_k\}$ is defined to be the weak topology determined by the projection functions $\{p_1, p_2, \ldots, p_k\}$, where $p_i((x_1, x_2, \ldots, x_k)) = x_i$.

11.13 Example. Euclidean 3-space of solid geometry is, topologically, the product space $E^1 \times E^1 \times E^1$.

11.14 Definition. *Euclidean n-space* E^n is defined, topologically, to be the product space $\prod_{i=1}^n X_i$, where $X_i = E^1$, for $i = 1, 2, \ldots, n$.

11.15 Theorem. *Let* $\{X_1, X_2, \ldots, X_k\}$ *denote a finite set of spaces. The cartesian product topology for* $\prod_{i=1}^k X_i$ *has for a base the sets* $\prod_{i=1}^k U_i$, *where* U_i *is open in* X_i.

Proof: Exercise.

11.16 Theorem. *The projection functions, p_i, defined for a non-empty product space $\prod_{i=1}^{k} X_i$ are open.*

Proof: Exercise.

EXERCISE 3. Prove that each space X_i is topologically imbedded in any non-empty product $X_1 \times \cdots \times X_k$.

EXERCISE 4. Let $F^* = \prod_{i=1}^{k} F_i$ denote a non-empty subset of $X^* = \prod_{i=1}^{k} X_i$. Then F^* is closed in X^* if and only if each F_i is closed in X_i.

A sequence of complex numbers converges if and only if the sequence of real parts converges and the sequence of imaginary parts converges. This establishes a connection between convergence in the factor spaces, both E^1, and convergence in the product space, E^2. The following theorem generalizes this fact for any product of a finite number of spaces.

11.17 Theorem. *Let (a_n^*) denote any sequence in the non-empty product space $X^* = \prod_{i=1}^{k} X_i$. (a_n^*) converges to an element A^* in X^* if and only if for each i the projection sequence $\big(p_i(a_n^*)\big)$ in X_i converges to $p_i(A^*)$.*

Proof: A. If (a_n^*) converges to A^* in X^*, then by theorem 7.11, since p_i is continuous on X^* for each i, $\big(p_i(a_n^*)\big)$ converges to $p_i(A^*)$ in X_i.

B. If (a_n^*) is any sequence in X^* such that $p_i(a_n^*)$ converges to β_i in X_i for each i, then let $\beta^* = (\beta_1, \ldots, \beta_i, \ldots, \beta_n)$; $p_i(\beta^*) = \beta_i$. Let G^* denote any base element in the product topology that contains β^*; $G^* = \prod_{i=1}^{k} U_i$ with U_i open in X_i. The sequence $\big(p_i(a_n^*)\big)$ converges to β_i in X_i; hence, for each i there exists a natural number N_i such that if $m \geq N_i$, then $p_i(a_m^*)$ is in U_i. Now if $m \geq N_1 + N_2 + \cdots + N_k$, then $p_i(a_m^*)$ is in U_i for $i = 1, 2, \ldots, k$. Therefore, $p_1^{-1}[U_1] \cap p_2^{-1}[U_2] \cap \cdots \cap p_k^{-1}[U_k]$ contains a_m^*. However, $p_1^{-1}[U_1] \cap \cdots \cap p_1^{-1}[U_k] = G^*$. Thus, if $m \geq N_1 + \cdots + N_k$, a_m^* is in G^*. Hence, (a_n^*) converges to β^*. ▮

11.18 Corollary. *The sequence $(z_n) = (x_n + iy_n)$ of complex numbers converges to the complex number $z^* = A + iB$ if and only if the sequence (x_n), of so-called real parts, converges to A in E^1 and the sequence (y_n), of so-called imaginary parts, converges to B in E^1.*

Proof: The complex number system, $\mathbb{C}$, is both an algebraic and a topological structure. Convergence, however, depends solely on the topology on $\mathbb{C}$. The topological part of $\mathbb{C}$ is topologically equivalent to $E' \times E'$. Thus the complex number $A + iB$ for topological considerations, such as convergence, can be represented as the ordered pair (A, B) in $E' \times E'$, and the sequence $(x_n + iy_n)$ as the sequence (x_n, y_n) of ordered pairs in $E^1 \times E^1$. Hence, $(x_n + iy_n)$ converges to $A + iB$ in $\mathbb{C}$ if and only if the sequence (x_n, y_n) converges to (A, B) in $E^1 \times E^1$. Thus the corollary follows from the previous theorem. ▮

11.19 Theorem. *A function f from a space X into a non-empty product space $\prod_{i=1}^k Y_i$ is continuous on X if and only if the composite functions $p_i \circ f$ are continuous on X for all i.*

Proof: A. If f is continuous, $p_i \circ f$ is a composite of two continuous functions and hence is continuous.

B. Let $p_i \circ f$ be continuous for $i = 1, 2, \ldots, k$. $f[X]$ is a subspace of $\prod_{i=1}^k Y_i$ with the relative topology. By corollary 9.9, the sets $\{p_i^{-1}[G] \cap f[X]\}$, where G is open in Y_i, form a subbase for this relative topology. By the continuity of $p_i \circ f$, $(p_i \circ f)^{-1}[G]$ is open in X. However, $(p_i \circ f)^{-1}[G] = f^{-1}(p_i^{-1}[G] \cap f[X])$. Therefore, $f^{-1}[A]$ is open in X, where A is any subbase element for the relative topology. By theorem 4.10, f is continuous. ▮

The previous theorem is a generalization of the fact that a pair of continuous functions $x = x(t)$, $y = y(t)$ defines a curve in the plane, E^2, i.e., defines a continuous function, f, from $X = \{t \mid 0 \leq t \leq 1, t \text{ real}\}$ into E^2. In this particular case, $f(t) = (x(t), y(t))$; $p_1(f(t)) = x(t)$ and $p_2(f(t)) = y(t)$.

Property Transference

11.20 Theorem. *A non-empty product space, $\prod_{i=1}^k X_i$, is first countable if and only if X_i is first countable for $i = 1, 2, \ldots, k$.*

Proof: A. Let X_i, $i = 1, 2, \ldots, k$, be first countable. Let x^* be any point in $\prod_{i=1}^k X_i$. $x^* = (x_1, x_2, \ldots, x_k)$. Each x_i, for $i = 1, 2, \ldots, k$, has a countable local base, $\{B_j^i\} = \{B_1^i, B_2^i, \ldots\}$. Now $p_i^{-1}[B_j^i]$ is open in $\prod_{j=1}^k X_i$, since p_i is continuous. These ests $p_i^{-1}[B_j^i]$, for a fixed i, form a countable set of open sets in $\prod_{i=1}^k X_i$. Hence $\bigcup_{i=1}^k [\bigcup_{j=1}^\infty \{p_i^{-1}[B_j^i]\}]$ is the union of a finite set of countable sets, and so is countable. Let $\{U_1^*, U_2^*, \ldots, U_m^*, \ldots\}$ denote the countable set of all intersections of any finite number of sets in this countable collection. It remains to show that $\{U_1^*, U_2^*, \ldots, U_m^*, \ldots\}$ is a local base at x^* in $\prod_{i=1}^k X_i$. Let G^* be any open set of $\prod_{i=1}^k X_i$ that contains x^*. G^* contains a base element $\prod_{i=1}^k W_i$, for W_i open in X_i and x_i in W_i. Now W_i in X_i contains a base element $B_{j_i}^i$ that contains x_i, by definition of $\{B_1^i, B_2^i, \ldots, B_j^i, \ldots\}$ above. Hence $p_i^{-1}[B_{j_i}^i]$ contains x^* for every i and is contained in $p_i^{-1}[W_i]$. This means that $p_1^{-1}[B_{j_1}^1] \cap p_2^{-1}[B_{j_2}^k] \cap \cdots \cap p_k^{-1}[B_{j_k}^k]$ is contained in $p_1^{-1}[W_1] \cap \cdots \cap p_k^{-1}[W_k] = \prod_{i=1}^k W_i \subseteq G^*$. Hence, $\{U_1^*, U_2^*, \ldots, U_m^*, \ldots\}$ is a countable local base at x^* and $\prod_{i=1}^k X_i$ is first countable.

B. Let $\prod_{i=1}^k X_i$ be first countable. Let x_i be any element in X_i, $i = 1, 2, \ldots$, or k. There exists x^* in $\prod_{i=1}^k X_i$ whose i-th coordinate is x_i. Let G^i be any open set of X_i that contains x_i. x^* is in $p_i^{-1}[G^i]$ which is open in $\prod_{i=1}^k X_i$. Since $\prod_{i=1}^k X_i$ is first countable, let $\{B_1^*, B_2^*, \ldots, B_j^*, \ldots\}$ denote a countable local base at x^*. B_j^*, say, is contained in $p_i^{-1}[G^i]$, by definition of local base. Hence, $p_i[p_i^{-1}[G^i]] \supseteq p_i[B_j^*]$ or $p_i[B_j^*] \subseteq G^i$. Thus, the sets $p_i[B_1^*]$, $p_i[B_2^*]$, ...,

$p_i[B_j^*], \ldots,$ since p_i is open, form a countable local base at x_i in X_i and so X_i is first countable. ∎

A theorem analogous to theorem 11.20 for second countability now follows.

11.21 Theorem. *A non-empty product space $\prod_{i=1}^k X_i$ has a countable base if and only if each factor space X_i has a countable base.*

Proof: A. Let X_i, for $i = 1, 2, \ldots, k$, have a countable base: $\{B_1^i, B_2^i, \ldots, B_j^i, \ldots\}$. The collection $\{p_i^{-1}[B_1^i], p_i^{-1}[B_2^i], \ldots, p_i^{-1}[B_j^i], \ldots\}$ is countable and each set $p_i^{-1}[B_j^i]$ is open in $\prod_{i=1}^k X_i$. Further, the collection $\{p_1^{-1}[B_1^1], \ldots, p_1^{-1}[B_j^1], \ldots ; p_2^{-1}[B_1^2], p_2^{-1}[B_2^2], \ldots, p_2^{-1}[B_j^2], \ldots ; \ldots ; p_k^{-1}[B_1^k], p_k^{-1}[B_2^k], \ldots, p_k^{-1}[B_j^k], \ldots\}$ is countable. Let $\{U_1^*, U_2^*, \ldots, U_m^*, \ldots\}$ denote the collection of all intersections of finitely many sets in this collection. It remains to be shown that $\{U_1^*, U_2^*, \ldots, U_m^*, \ldots\}$ is a base for the product topology. Let G^* be any non-empty open set in $\prod_{i=1}^k X_i$ and let y^* be any point in G^*. G^* contains a set $\prod_{i=1}^k V_i$ which contains y^*, where V_i is open in X_i. V_i contains a set $B_{j_i}^i$ from the countable base $\{B_1^i, B_2^i, \ldots, B_j^i, \ldots\}$ for X_i such that $p_i(y^*)$ is in $B_{j_i}^i$, by definition of base. Hence y^* is in $p_i^{-1}[B_{j_i}^i]$ for each i and so y^* is in $p_1^{-1}[B_{j_1}^i] \cap \cdots \cap p_k^{-1}[B_{j_k}^k]$. Further since $B_{j_i}^i \subseteq V_i$, $p_i^{-1}[B_{j_i}^i] \subseteq p_i^{-1}[V_i]$. Therefore, $p_1^{-1}[B_{j_1}^1] \cap \cdots \cap p_k^{-1}[B_{j_k}^k] \subseteq \prod_{i=1}^k V_i \subseteq G^*$. Hence, $\{U_1^*, U_2^*, \ldots, U_m^*, \ldots\}$, as defined above, constitutes a countable base for $\prod_{i=1}^k X_i$.

B. Let $\prod_{i=1}^k X_i$ be second countable. Let $\mathcal{B}^* = \{B_1^*, B_2^*, \ldots, B_n^*, \ldots\}$ denote a countable base for $\prod_{i=1}^k X_i$. Consider $\{p_i[B_1^*], p_i[B_2^*], \ldots, p_i[B_n^*] \ldots\}$. Since p_i is an open function, these are open sets of X_i. Let G_i be any non-empty open set in X_i and let y_i be a point of G_i. Let $y^* = (x_1, x_2, \ldots, y_i, \ldots, x_k)$ denote a point of $\prod_{i=1}^k X_i$ whose i-th coordinate is y_i. $p_i^{-1}[G_i]$ is open in $\prod_{i=1}^k X_i$ and contains y^*. Hence, there is a set B_j^* in the countable base for $\prod_{i=1}^k X_i$ such that $B_j^* \subseteq p_i^{-1}[G_i]$ and y^* is in B_j^*. This means that $p_i[B_j^*] \subseteq G_i$ and y_i is in $p_i[B_j^*]$. Thus X_i has a countable base. ∎

11.22 Corollary. *Euclidean n-space, E^n, for $n = 1, 2, \ldots,$ is second countable and hence first countable.*

Proof: $E^n = \prod_{i=1}^n X_i$, where $X_i = E^1$ for $i = 1, 2, \ldots, n$. By theorem 5.10, E^1 is second countable. ∎

11.23 Corollary. *The complex number system, $\mathbb{C}$, is second countable and hence first countable.*

Proof: The topological part of $\mathbb{C}$ is $E^1 \times E^1$ or E^2. ∎

11.24 Corollary. *Any subspace of Euclidean n-space, E^n, is second countable and hence first countable.*

Proof: By theorem 9.25, any subspace of a second or first countable space is second or first countable, respectively. ∎

11.25 Theorem. *The product $X_1 \times X_2$ of separable spaces is separable.*

Proof: Let X_1 and X_2 be separable spaces. Let D_1 and D_2 be countable dense sets in X_1 and X_2 respectively. If $X_1 \times X_2 = \emptyset$, then $X_1 \times X_2$ is separable. So, let (a, b) be any point in the product space $X_1 \times X_2$ and let $U \times V$ be any basic open set containing (a, b) in $X_1 \times X_2$. There exists d_1 in $U \cap D_1$ and d_2 in $V \cap D_2$. Hence (d_1, d_2) is in $U \times V$. Thus the countable set $D_1 \times D_2$ is dense in $X_1 \times X_2$, and so $X_1 \times X_2$ is separable. ▌

11.26 Corollary. *The product of any finite number of separable spaces is separable.*

Proof: By theorem 11.25, the product $X_1 \times X_2$ of separable spaces is separable. Assume the product of any k separable spaces, for k some natural number, is separable. Let $X_1 \times X_2 \times \cdots \times X_k \times X_{k+1}$ be any product of $(k + 1)$ separable spaces. By assumption the space $X_1 \times \cdots \times X_k = S$ is a separable space. By theorem 11.25, the space $S \times X_{k+1}$ is separable. By definition of product set and space, $S \times X_{k+1}$ is homeomorphic to $X_1 \times X_2 \times \cdots \times X_k \times X_{k+1}$. ▌

Exercise 2 of section 5 establishes that the continuous image of a separable space is separable. Hence a non-empty product space $X_1 \times X_2 \times \cdots \times X_k$ is separable if and only if each space X_i, $i = 1, \ldots, k$ is separable.

12. GENERAL PRODUCT SPACES. CANTOR TERNARY SPACE. FUNCTION SPACES.

THE GENERAL PRODUCT SPACE

The next question which arises naturally is whether a product space can be defined from any set of spaces.

12.1 Definition. Let $\mathfrak{A}$ denote any non-empty indexing set, and for each ν in $\mathfrak{A}$ let a set X_ν be defined. The *cartesian product* or *product set* $\prod_{\nu \in \mathfrak{A}} X_\nu$ is defined to be $\{\Phi \mid \Phi: \mathfrak{A} \to \bigcup_\nu X_\nu \text{ and } \Phi(\nu) \text{ is in } X_\nu\}$. $\Phi(\nu)$ is called the ν-th coordinate of Φ. The sets X_ν are called factors of the product set. It is to be observed that if $\mathfrak{A}$ is the set of all natural numbers, then $\prod_{\nu \in \mathfrak{A}} X_\nu$ is the set of all sequences $(x_1, x_2, \ldots, x_i, \ldots)$ such that x_i is in X_i. In order to insure that $\prod_{\nu \in \mathfrak{A}} X_\nu$ is not empty when $\mathfrak{A}$ and each X_ν are not empty, the axiom of choice must be used. If each X_ν is non-empty, then the axiom of choice states that there is a function Ч whose domain is $\{X_\nu \mid \nu \in \mathfrak{A}\}$, whose range is contained in $\bigcup_\nu X_\nu$ and such that Ч(X_ν) is an element in X_ν. Thus Φ, defined by $\Phi(\nu) =$ Ч(X_ν), is an element in $\prod_{\nu \in \mathfrak{A}} X_\nu$ and hence $\prod_{\nu \in \mathfrak{A}} X_\nu$ is not empty.

12.2 Definition. Let $\prod_{\nu \in \mathfrak{A}} X_\nu$ be any non-empty product set. The functions in $\{p_\nu \mid p_\nu : \prod_{\nu \in \mathfrak{A}} X_\nu \to X_\nu \text{ and } p_\nu(\Phi) = \Phi(\nu)\}$ are called *projection functions.*

The next step is to define a topology for the product set. The natural procedure is to define the topology in a manner analogous to that used in the finite case, i.e., define the topology by its base, the sets $\prod_{\nu \in \mathfrak{A}} U_\nu$, where U_ν is open in X_ν or define the topology as the weak topology determined by the projection functions, $\{p_\nu\}$. It is soon to be observed, however, that in the case of the non-empty product of an infinite number of spaces, the two topologies are not the same.

12.3 Theorem. *If $\mathfrak{A}$ is any non-empty indexing set and if for each ν in $\mathfrak{A}$ there corresponds a space X_ν, then $\mathcal{B} = \{\prod_{\nu \in \mathfrak{A}} U_\nu \mid U_\nu$ is open in $X_\nu\}$ is a base for a topology on $\prod_{\nu \in \mathfrak{A}} X_\nu$.*

Proof: By theorem 3.50, since $\prod_{\nu \in \mathfrak{A}} X_\nu$ has this form, it is sufficient to show that the intersection of any finite number of sets of the form $\prod_{\nu \in \mathfrak{A}} U_\nu$, for U_ν open in X_ν, has this same form. Let $B_1 = \prod_{\nu \in \mathfrak{A}} U_\nu$ and $B_2 = \prod_{\nu \in \mathfrak{A}} V_\nu$ be any two sets in $\mathcal{B}$. $B_1 \cap B_2 = (\prod_{\nu \in \mathfrak{A}} U_\nu) \cap (\prod_{\nu \in \mathfrak{A}} V_\nu)$. By definition of $\bigcap$ and $\prod$, $(\prod_{\nu \in \mathfrak{A}} U_\nu) \cap (\prod_{\nu \in \mathfrak{A}} V_\nu) = \prod_{\nu \in \mathfrak{A}} (U_\nu \cap V_\nu)$. However, $U_\nu \cap V_\nu$ for any ν is open in X_ν. Hence $B_1 \cap B_2 = \prod_{\nu \in \mathfrak{A}} W_\nu$, for W_ν open in X_ν. It follows immediately by induction that the intersection of any finite number of sets in $\mathcal{B}$ is a set in $\mathcal{B}$. Hence, the set of all unions of sets in $\mathcal{B}$ is a topology. ▮

12.4 Definition. The *box topology* for a product $\prod_{\nu \in \mathfrak{A}} X_\nu$ of any set of spaces X_ν is the topology defined by the sets $\prod_{\nu \in \mathfrak{A}} U_\nu$ as base, where U_ν is any open set in X_ν.

12.5 Definition. The *Tychonoff* or *product topology* for a non-empty product $\prod_{\nu \in \mathfrak{A}} X_\nu$ of any set of non-empty spaces X_ν is the weak topology determined by the set $\{p_\nu\}$ of projection functions.

12.6 Theorem. *The Tychonoff or product topology, $\mathfrak{J}_P$ is contained in the box topology, $\mathfrak{J}_B$ and they constitute different topologies for a non-empty product set $\prod_{\nu \in \mathfrak{A}} X_\nu$ for which an infinite number of the factor spaces, X_ν, have a non-trivial topology.*

Proof: By definition, the product topology has for a subbase $\{G \mid G = p_\nu^{-1}[U_\nu]$, for some ν in the indexing set $\mathfrak{A}$ and for U_ν open in $X_\nu\}$. The elements of such a subbase have the form $\prod_{\nu \in \mathfrak{A}} G_\nu$, where $G_\nu = X_\nu$, except for at most one element ν in $\mathfrak{A}$. Any intersection of a finite number of such sets has the form $\prod_{\nu \in \mathfrak{A}} A_\nu$, where $A_\nu = X_\nu$ except for at most a finite number of elements in $\mathfrak{A}$. Thus, a base for the product topology $\mathfrak{J}_p$ is $\{A^* \mid A^* = \prod_{\nu \in \mathfrak{A}} A_\nu$, where A_ν is open in X_ν and $A_\nu = X_\nu$ for $\nu \neq \alpha_1, \nu \neq \alpha_2, \ldots, \nu \neq \alpha_k$ in $\mathfrak{A}$, where k is a natural number$\}$. Since X_ν is open in X_ν, it follows that any such set is in the box topology; hence, $\mathfrak{J}_B \supseteq \mathfrak{J}_P$. However, if $B^* = \prod_{\nu \in \mathfrak{A}} B_\nu$ is a base element in the box topology $\mathfrak{J}_B$, where $B_\nu \neq X_\nu$ for an infinite number of elements ν, and if $A^* = \prod_{\nu \in \mathfrak{A}} A_\nu$ is any non-empty base element for the Tychonoff topology, where $A_\nu = X_\nu$ for $\nu \neq \alpha_1, \nu \neq \alpha_2, \ldots, \nu \neq \alpha_k$, say; then there exists an element β in $\mathfrak{A}$ such that $A_\beta = X_\beta$ and $B_\beta \neq X_\beta$; therefore, A_β is not contained in B_β; hence, $\prod_{\nu \in \mathfrak{A}} A_\nu$ is not contained in $\prod_{\nu \in \mathfrak{A}} B_\nu$. Thus, no non-empty base element from the Tychonoff topology, $\mathfrak{J}_P$, is contained in B^*. Hence B^* does not belong to the Tychonoff topology, by definition 3.45. Thus, $\mathfrak{J}_B \supsetneq \mathfrak{J}_P$. ▌

12.7 Corollary. *If $\prod_{\nu \in \mathfrak{A}} X_\nu$ denotes the non-empty product set of spaces X_ν, then the projection functions, p_ν, are continuous in both the box topology, $\mathfrak{J}_B$, and the product topology, $\mathfrak{J}_P$.*

Proof: Definition 12.5, theorem 12.6 and theorem 10.10 imply the corollary. ▌

EXERCISE 1. Let $\mathfrak{A}$ denote an infinite set, and for each ν in $\mathfrak{A}$ let there correspond a non-empty space X_ν. In addition, let X_ν have the trivial topology, except for at most a finite number of elements of $\mathfrak{A}$. Prove that for $\prod_{\nu \in \mathfrak{A}} X_\nu$, the box topology, $\mathfrak{J}_B$, and the product topology, $\mathfrak{J}_p$, are equal.

It has now been shown that there exist two distinct "natural" topologies for the cartesian product set of an infinite number of spaces with non-trivial topologies. It turns out that the product topology determined by the projection mappings is the more useful for the theory of general spaces. Hence, the term product space will always mean a product set plus the weak topology determined by the projection mappings.

The rest of this section consists, for the most part, of the analogues for the general product space of the theorems in section 11.

12.8 Theorem. *The projection functions, $\{p_\nu\}$, of a non-empty product space $\prod_{\nu \in \mathfrak{A}} X_\nu$ onto the factor spaces are open.*

Proof: Let G^* be any non-empty basic open set in $X^* = \prod_{\nu \in \mathfrak{A}} X_\nu$. Let $G^* = \prod_\nu U_\nu$. $p_\nu[G^*] = U_\nu$ and U_ν is open in X_ν. Now, let V^* be any open set in $\prod_{\nu \in \mathfrak{A}} X_\nu$. $V^* = \bigcup_\mu B_\mu^*$, where each B_μ^* is a basic open set. Hence, $p_\nu[V^*] = p_\nu[\bigcup_\mu B_\mu] = \bigcup_\mu p_\nu[B_\mu]$. Since each $p_\nu[B_\mu]$ is open, $p_\nu[V^*]$ is open. ▌

EXERCISE 2. Prove or find a counterexample to the statement that the projection functions from a non-empty box space, i.e. a product set with the box topology, onto the factor spaces are open.

EXERCISE 3. Prove that each space X_ν is imbedded topologically in any non-empty $\prod_\nu X_\nu$.

Consider now convergence in the general product space.

12.9 Theorem. *Let* (a_δ^*), *for* δ *in some directed set* $\{D, \geq\}$ *be a net or generalized sequence in a non-empty product space* $X^* = \prod_{\nu \in \mathfrak{A}} X_\nu$. *Then* (a_δ^*) *converges to an element* γ^* *of* X^* *if and only if the projection net* $(p_\nu(a_\delta^*))$ *in each* X_ν *converges to* $p_\nu(\gamma^*)$.

Proof: A. If the net (a_δ^*) converges to γ^* in X^*, then by theorem 7.25, since p_ν is continuous on X^* for each ν, the net $(p_\nu(a_\delta^*))$ converges to $p_\nu(\gamma^*)$ in X_ν.

B. If (a_δ^*) is any net in X^* such that $(p_\nu(a_\delta^*))$ converges to β_ν in X_ν for each ν in $\mathfrak{A}$, then let β^* denote the point of X^* whose ν-th coordinate is β_ν, and let G^* be any base element in $X^* = \prod_{\nu \in \mathfrak{A}} X_\nu$ that contains β^*. By definition of the product topology, $G^* = \prod_{\nu \in \mathfrak{A}} U_\nu$, where $U_\nu = X_\nu$ for $\nu \neq \alpha_1$, $\nu \neq \alpha_2$, $\ldots$, $\nu \neq \alpha_k$ and k is some natural number. Since the net $(p_\nu(a_\delta^*))$ converges to β_ν for each ν in $\mathfrak{A}$, then for each α_i, $i = 1, 2, \ldots, k$, there exists δ_i in D such that $\delta \geq \delta_i$ implies that $p_{\alpha_i}(a_\delta^*)$ is in $p_{\alpha_i}[G^*] = U_{\alpha_i}$. There exists in the directed set $\{D, \geq\}$ δ^* such that $\delta^* \geq \delta_i$, for all $i = 1, 2, \ldots, k$. Hence if $\delta \geq \delta^*$, then $p_{\alpha_i}(a_\delta^*)$ is in $p_{\alpha_i}[G^*] = U_{\alpha_i}$ for $i = 1, 2, \ldots, k$, and so $p_{\alpha_1}^{-1}[U_{\alpha_1}] \cap p_{\alpha_2}^{-1}[U_{\alpha_2}] \cap \cdots \cap p_{\alpha_k}^{-1}[U_{\alpha_k}]$ contains a_δ^*. However, $p_{\alpha_1}^{-1}[U_{\alpha_1}] \cap \cdots \cap p_{\alpha_k}^{-1}[U_{\alpha_k}] = G^*$. Thus, for each base element G^* of the product topology containing β^*, there exists a δ^* in D such that $\delta \geq \delta^*$ implies that a_δ^* is in G^*. Hence the net (a_δ^*) converges to β^*. ∎

Just as convergence of nets in a product space is related to convergence of nets in the factor spaces, so convergence of filters in a product space is related to convergence of filters in the factor spaces, as the next theorem shows.

12.10 Theorem. *A filter* $\mathfrak{F}$ *in a non-empty product space* $X^* = \prod_{\nu \in \mathfrak{A}} X_\nu$ *converges to a point* $x^* = \prod_{\nu \in \mathfrak{A}} \{x_\nu\}$ *of* X^* *if and only if the filter* $p_\nu^\#[\mathfrak{F}]$, *for each* ν, *converges to* $x_\nu = p_\nu(x^*)$ *in* X_ν.

Proof: A. Let $\mathfrak{F}$ converge to x^* in X^*. Since p_ν is continuous for each ν, by theorem 7.37, the filter $p_\nu^\#[\mathfrak{F}]$ converges to $p_\nu(x^*)$.

B. Conversely, if $\mathfrak{F}$ is a filter in $X^* = \prod_{\nu \in \mathfrak{A}} X_\nu$ such that the filter $p_\nu^\#[\mathfrak{F}]$ converges to a point x_ν in X_ν for each ν, then let x^* denote the point of X^*, whose ν-th coordinate is x_ν. Let N be any neighborhood of x^* in X^*. N contains a base element $G^* = \prod_{\nu \in \mathfrak{A}} U_\nu$, where U_ν is open in X_ν and $U_\nu = X_\nu$ for $\nu \neq \alpha_1$, $\nu \neq \alpha_2$, $\ldots$, $\nu \neq \alpha_k$, k a natural number, and x^* is in G^*. $p_{\alpha_i}[G^*] = U_{\alpha_i}$, which is a neighborhood of x_{α_i}, $i = 1, 2, \ldots, k$. Since $p_{\alpha_i}^\#[\mathfrak{F}]$ converges to x_{α_i} by hypothesis, $p_{\alpha_i}^\#[\mathfrak{F}]$ must contain U_{α_i} (definition 7.31), for $i = 1, 2, \ldots, k$; hence, $p_{\alpha_i}^{-1}[U_{\alpha_i}]$ contains an element of $\mathfrak{F}$. Since $\mathfrak{F}$ is a filter,

$p_{\alpha_i}^{-1}[U_{\alpha_i}]$, for $i = 1, 2, \ldots, k$, belongs to $\mathfrak{F}$. Therefore, $p_{\alpha_1}^{-1}[U_{\alpha_1}] \cap p_{\alpha_2}^{-1}[U_{\alpha_2}] \cap \cdots \cap p_{\alpha_k}^{-1}[U_{\alpha_k}]$ belongs to $\mathfrak{F}$. However, $p_{\alpha_1}^{-1}[U_{\alpha_1}] \cap p_{\alpha_2}^{-1}[U_{\alpha_2}] \cap \cdots \cap p_{\alpha_k}^{-1}[U_{\alpha_k}] = G^*$; hence, G^* belongs to $\mathfrak{F}$. Since $N \supseteq G^*$, N belongs to $\mathfrak{F}$. Since N was any neighborhood of x^* in X^*, $\mathfrak{F}$ converges to x^*. ▮

12.11 Theorem. *Let X^* be the non-empty product space $\prod_{\nu \in \mathfrak{A}} X_\nu$. A non-empty product subset $F^* = \prod_{\nu \in \mathfrak{A}} F_\nu$ is closed in X^* if and only if each F_ν is closed in X_ν.*

Proof: A. Let $\{F_\nu\}$ be a collection of sets such that each F_ν is closed in X_ν. Since p_ν is continuous for each ν in $\mathfrak{A}$, $p_\nu^{-1}[F_\nu]$ is closed in X^* for each ν in $\mathfrak{A}$. Since $F^* = \bigcap_\nu p_\nu^{-1}[F_\nu]$, F^* is closed in X^*.

B. Let F^* be non-empty and closed in X^* and let $F^* = \prod_{\nu \in \mathfrak{A}} M_\nu$. Let α be any element of $\mathfrak{A}$ and let q_α be a limit point, in X_α, of M_α. Consider x^*, where $p_\alpha(x^*) = q_\alpha$ and $p_\nu(x^*)$ is any element in M_ν, for $\nu \neq \alpha$. Let G^* be any base element for the product topology containing x^*. $p_\alpha[G^*]$ is open, by theorem 12.8, and contains x_α; thus it must also contain a point m_α of M_α, by definition of limit point. Therefore, G^* contains t^*, where $p_\nu(t^*) = p_\nu(x^*)$ for $\nu \neq \alpha$ and $p_\alpha(t^*) = m_\alpha$. Hence, G^* contains a point of $\prod_{\nu \in \mathfrak{A}} M_\nu$. Since G^* was any base element containing x^*, x^* is a limit point of $\prod_{\nu \in \mathfrak{A}} M_\nu$. Since $\prod_{\nu \in \mathfrak{A}} M_\nu = F^*$ and F^* is closed in X^*, x^* is in F^*. Since $x_\alpha = p_\alpha(x^*)$, x_α is in $p_\alpha[F^*] = M_\alpha$. Since x_α was any limit point of M_α, M_α is closed. ▮

It is to be observed that not every closed set in a product space is the product of closed sets, e.g., the set $\{(x, y) \mid 0 \leq x \leq 1 \text{ and } y = x\}$ in the plane, E^2, is closed, but is not the product of two closed sets.

12.12 Corollary. *If $\prod_\nu X_\nu$ is a product space and if $M_\nu \subseteq X_\nu$ for each ν, then $\overline{\prod_\nu M_\nu} = \prod_\nu \overline{M}_\nu$.*

Proof: By theorem 12.11, $\prod_\nu \overline{M}_\nu$ is closed. Further, $\prod_\nu \overline{M}_\nu \supseteq \prod_\nu M_\nu$. Hence, by theorem 3.19, $\prod_\nu \overline{M}_\nu \supseteq \overline{\prod_\nu M_\nu}$. If, for some ν, $M_\nu = \emptyset$, then $\overline{\prod_\nu M_\nu} = \prod_\nu \overline{M}_\nu = \emptyset$. Assume then that for all ν, $M_\nu \neq \emptyset$ and let y^* be any point in $\prod_\nu \overline{M}_\nu$. Let G^* be any basic open set containing y^*. $G^* = \prod_\nu W_\nu$, where W_ν is open in X_ν. $p_\nu[G^*]$ is open in X_ν; $p_\nu(y^*)$ is in $W_\nu = p_\nu[G^*]$ and $p_\nu(y^*)$ is in $\overline{M}_\nu$, by definition of y^*. Hence for each ν, W_ν must contain a point of M_ν. Hence, $\prod_\nu W_\nu$ contains a point of $\prod_\nu M_\nu$. Therefore, y^* is in $\overline{\prod_\nu M_\nu}$. Thus $\prod_\nu \overline{M}_\nu \subseteq \overline{\prod_\nu M_\nu}$, and so $\prod_\nu \overline{M}_\nu = \overline{\prod_\nu M_\nu}$. ▮

12.13 Theorem. *A function f from a space X into a non-empty product space $Y^* = \prod_\nu Y_\nu$ is continuous if and only if the functions $\Psi_\nu : x \to p_\nu[f(x)]$ are continuous for all ν.*

Proof: A. If f is continuous, Ψ_ν is a composite of two continuous functions and so is continuous.

B. Let $p_\nu \circ f$ be continuous for every ν. $f[X]$ with the relative topology constitutes a subspace of Y^*. By corollary 9.9, $\{p_\nu^{-1}[G] \cap f[X] \mid G \text{ is open in } Y_\nu\}$ forms a subbase for this relative topology. By continuity of Ψ_ν, $(p_\nu \circ f)^{-1}[G]$ is open in X. However, $(p_\nu \circ f)^{-1}[G] = f^{-1}[p_\nu^{-1}[G] \cap f[X]]$. Therefore, $f^{-1}[A]$ is open in X, where A is any subbase element for the relative topology. By theorem 4.10, f is continuous. ▮

The Cantor Ternary Space

Generating spaces by forming product spaces is a useful procedure for obtaining new spaces in topology. An example of an important topological space defined in this manner follows.

12.14 Definition. The *Cantor ternary space, CTS,* is defined to be $\prod_{i=1}^{\infty} Y_i$, where $Y_i = \{x \mid x = 0 \text{ or } x = 1\}$ with the discrete topology. The symbol $\prod_{i=1}^{\infty}$ is used when the indexing set, $\mathfrak{A}$, is the set of natural numbers. Thus, the Cantor ternary space is a product space whose elements are sequences $(a, a_2, \ldots, a_n, \ldots)$ such that $a_n = 0$ or $a_n = 1$ for every n.

The Cantor ternary space is the product space of discrete spaces; however, the Cantor ternary space itself is not discrete.

12.15 Theorem. *No point of the Cantor ternary space is open.*

Proof: By definition of the product topology, any base element U^* is $\prod_{i=1}^{\infty} U_i$, where U_i is open in Y_i and $U_i = Y_i$ for $i > k$, k a natural number. Hence, if $(x_1, x_2, \ldots, x_i, \ldots)$ denotes any point in CTS, no set containing this one point contains a base element since $\{x_{k+1}\}$ does not contain Y_{k+1}. Hence, $\prod_{i=1}^{\infty} \{x_i\}$ does not contain U^*, and so no one-point set is open. ▮

EXERCISE 4. Show that the product space of any finite number of discrete spaces is discrete.

The Cantor ternary space will now be studied in detail for two reasons. First, it is an important topological structure in its own right; and second, the procedure used, i.e., the establishing of two equivalent definitions and the deducing of information from both, is of general topological importance. The Cantor ternary space will serve as a means of illustrating this procedure. The space will be mapped homeomorphically onto a subspace of the real numbers; then, our knowledge of the space of real numbers as well as our knowledge of product spaces can be used to investigate CTS.

The Cantor ternary space will be imbedded in the subspace $[0, 1]$ of E^1.

It is established in the development of the space E^1 of real numbers that every real number can be represented by a symbol $K.\, a_1 a_2 \ldots a_n \ldots$, where K is an integer and $a_i = 0, 1, 2, \ldots, 9$, for $i = 1, 2, \ldots$. Such a representation is called a decimal representation, and in turn represents the Cauchy sequence of rationals, K, $K + a_1/10$, $K + a_1/10 + a_2/10^2, \ldots, K + a_1/10 + \cdots + a_n/10^n, \ldots$ if K is positive; and K, $K - a_1/10$, $K - a_1/10 - a_2/10^2, \ldots$, $K - a_1/10 - \cdots - a_n/10^n, \ldots$ if K is negative. It can be shown that the Cauchy sequences denoted by $K.a_1a_2 \ldots a_n999 \ldots$ and $K.a_1a_2, \ldots (a_n + 1)000 \ldots$ for $a_n \neq 9$ are equivalent, i.e., they represent the same real number. Otherwise, the decimal representation for a real number is unique. If instead of the base 10, i.e., powers of 10, the base 3, (i.e., powers of 3), is used, the decimal expansions become "tresimal" expansions $K.b_1b_2 \ldots b_n \ldots$ where $b_i = 0$, 1 or 2. Also, $K.b_1b_2 \ldots b_n222 \ldots$ for $b_n \neq 2$ represents the same real number as $K.b_1b_2 \ldots (b_n + 1)000 \ldots$. The real numbers between $0.00 \ldots 0 \ldots$ and $1.00 \ldots 0 \ldots$ are accordingly represented, base 3, by symbols $0.b_1b_2 \ldots b_n \ldots$, where $b_i = 0$, 1 or 2. The distance between two such real numbers $0.a_1a_2 \ldots a_n \ldots$ and $0.b_1b_2 \ldots b_n \ldots$ is defined to be the positive real number represented by $limit_{n\to\infty} |0.a_1a_2 \ldots a_n - 0.b_1b_2 \ldots b_n|$. Since the difference of two Cauchy sequences of rationals is a Cauchy sequence of rationals, the distance between any two real numbers is defined. It is to be recalled that the basic neighborhoods $\{x \mid |x - x_0| < \epsilon, \epsilon > 0\}$ for the space E^1 of calculus are defined in terms of this distance. This method of defining the topology for a space by using a "distance" will be studied in great detail in Chapter 4 on metric spaces.

12.16 Definition. The *no middle third* set, NMT, of real numbers is defined to be the set of all real numbers between $0.000 \ldots$ and $1.000 \ldots$ which have a "tresimal" (base 3) expansion which does not contain the digit 1. Thus, $NMT \subseteq [0, 1]$.

Since $1.000 \ldots$ can be represented, base 3, by $0.222 \ldots$, it belongs to NMT. $\frac{1}{3} = 0.1000 \ldots = 0.0222 \ldots$ and $\frac{2}{3} = 0.200 \ldots$ belong to NMT. However, any real number between $\frac{1}{3}$ and $\frac{2}{3}$ is represented by an expansion $0.1\,a_2a_3 \ldots a_n \ldots$ in which, for some natural number i, $a_i \neq 2$; otherwise $0.1\,a_2a_3 \ldots a_n \ldots = 0.2000 \ldots = \frac{2}{3}$. This representation is then unique, and so the digit 1 in the first place cannot be removed. Hence, no number between $\frac{1}{3}$ and $\frac{2}{3}$ belongs to NMT. Similarly $\frac{1}{9} = 0.0100 \ldots = 0.002222 \ldots$ and $\frac{2}{9} = 0.0200 \ldots$ both belong to NMT. However, any real number which lies between $\frac{1}{9} = 0.0100 \ldots$ and $\frac{2}{9} = 0.0200 \ldots$ has a "tresimal," base 3, representation $0.01\,a_3a_4 \ldots a_n \ldots$, where for some i beyond 2, $a_i \neq 2$; hence, no such number belongs to NMT. Similarly, no real number between $\frac{7}{9} = 0.2100 \ldots = 0.20222 \ldots$ and $\frac{8}{9} = 0.22000 \ldots$ belongs to NMT. We recall that the real number α is less than the real number β, $\alpha < \beta$, if and only if $\beta - \alpha$ is positive. This means that if $\alpha < \beta$, where $\alpha = 0.a_1a_2 \ldots a_n \ldots$ and $\beta = 0.b_1b_2 \ldots b_n \ldots$, then $a_i < b_i$, where i is the smallest natural number such that $a_i \neq b_i$.

12.17 Theorem. *The subset NMT is closed in the subspace* $[0, 1]$ *of* E^1.

Proof: The expansions used throughout the proof are all in base 3. Let $G_{-1} = \{x \mid x < 0 \text{ or } x > 1\}$, $G_0 = \{x \mid 0.100\ldots0\ldots < x < 0.20\ldots0\ldots\}$, and $G_1 = \{x \mid 0.01\ldots0\ldots < x < 0.020\ldots0\ldots\} \cup \{x \mid 0.210\ldots0\ldots < x < 0.220\ldots0\ldots\}$. Let σ_n denote an ordered n-tuple $(a_1, a_2, \ldots, a_n)$ in the digits 0 and 2. Define $G_n = \bigcup_{\sigma_n} I_{\sigma_n}$, where $I_{\sigma_n} = \{x \mid 0.a_1a_2\ldots a_n10\ldots0\ldots < x < 0.a_1\ldots a_n20\ldots0\}$.

There are 2^n ordered n-tuples $(a_1, a_2, \ldots a_n)$ for $a_i = 0$ or 2, $1 \leq i \leq n$ and $n \geq 1$. Each G_n, for $n \geq 1$, is then the union of 2^n open intervals of real numbers and is open in $[0, 1]$, by definition of the relative topology.

Since G_0 and G_{-1} are also open in E^1, $\bigcup_{n=-1}^{\infty} G_n$ is open in E^1. By definition of $\bigcup_{n=-1}^{\infty} G_n$, any element in $\bigcup_{n=-1}^{\infty} G_n$ is in $\sim NMT$, the complement of NMT. Conversely, if r is in $\sim NMT$ and $r < 0$ or $r > 1$, then r is in $\bigcup_{n=-1}^{\infty} G_n$; if $0 < r < 1$, and r is in $\sim NMT$ then $r = 0.b_1b_2\ldots b_{i-1}1.b_{i+1}\ldots b_n\ldots$, where $b_t \neq 1$ for $1 \leq t \leq i-1$ and $b_n \neq 2$ for some $n > i$. Hence, $0.b_1b_2\ldots b_{i-1}10\ldots0\ldots < r < 0.b_1b_2\ldots b_{i-1}20\ldots0$ and r is in G_{i-1}. Thus, $\bigcup_{n=-1}^{\infty} G_n = \sim NMT$ and $\sim NMT$ is open in E^1. Therefore, NMT is closed in E^1. Since $NMT \subseteq [0, 1]$, NMT is closed in $[0, 1]$. ∎

12.18 Definition. A subset M of a space S is called *nowhere dense* in S if and only if any open set G of S contains a non-empty open set U of S such that $U \cap M = \emptyset$.

12.19 Example. Any finite set of real numbers is nowhere dense in E^1.

12.20 Example. The set of natural numbers is nowhere dense in E^1.

12.21 Lemma. *A set M in a space S is nowhere dense in S if and only if $\overline{M}$ contains no interior points and hence no non-empty open sets.*

Proof: Exercise.

12.22 Lemma. *A set M in a space S is nowhere dense in S if and only if $\sim\overline{M}$ is dense in S.*

Proof: Exercise.

12.23 Theorem. *The subset NMT is nowhere dense in* $[0, 1]$.

Proof: By definition of E^1, every non-empty open set in E^1 contains an open interval, $(\alpha, \alpha + \epsilon)$, where $\epsilon > 0$. By lemma 12.22, it will be sufficient to show that every such interval contains a point of $\sim NMT$. If $\alpha < 0$ or $\alpha \geq 1$, then $(\alpha, \alpha + \epsilon)$ contains a point in $\sim NMT$. Hence, let $0 \leq \alpha < \alpha + \epsilon \leq 1$ and let k be a natural number such that $2/3^k < \epsilon$. Such a k exists by the archimedean order on the real numbers. If $\alpha = 0.a_1a_2a_3\ldots a_n\ldots$, where $a_n = 0$, 1 or 2 for $n = 1, 2, \ldots$, then $a_k = 0$ or $a_k = 1$ or $a_k = 2$.

A. Let $a_k = 0$. If $\alpha = 0.a_1a_2 \ldots a_{k-1}0222\ldots$, then $\alpha < \alpha + 1/3^{k+1} < \alpha + \epsilon$ and $\alpha + 1/3^{k+1}$ is in $\sim NMT$. If $\alpha = 0.a_1a_2 \ldots a_{k-1}0_{k+1}\ldots$, where $a_{k+j} \neq 2$, for some natural number j, then $\alpha + 1/3^k$ is in $\sim NMT$ and $\alpha < \alpha + 1/3^k < \alpha + \epsilon$.

B. Let $a_k = 1$. If $\alpha = 0.a_1a_2 \ldots a_{k-1}1222\ldots$, then $\alpha = 0.a_1a_2 \ldots a_{k-1}2000\ldots$. Hence $\alpha + 1/3^{k+1}$ is in $\sim NMT$ and $\alpha < \alpha + 1/3^{k+1} < \alpha + \epsilon$. If $\alpha = 0.a_1a_2 \ldots a_{k-1}111\ldots$ then $\alpha + 1/3^k$ is in $\sim NMT$ and $\alpha < \alpha + 1/3^k < \alpha + \epsilon$. If for some natural number j, $a_{k+j} = 0$ then the procedure in part A establishes that $\alpha + 1/3^{k+j+1}$ or $\alpha + 1/3^{k+j}$ is in $\sim NMT$ and $\alpha < \alpha + 1/3^{k+j+1} < \alpha + 1/3^{k+j} < \alpha + \epsilon$.

C. Let $a_k = 2$. If $a_{k+1} = 0$ or if $a_{k+1} = 1$, then the procedures in parts A and B establish that there is a point of $\sim NMT$ in $(\alpha, \alpha + \epsilon)$. If $a_{k+1} = 2$, then $\alpha = 0.a_1a_2 \ldots a_{k-1}22a_{k+2}\ldots$, $\alpha + 1/3^k + 1/3^{k+1}$ is in $\sim NMT$ and $\alpha < \alpha + 1/3^k + 1/3^{k+1} < \alpha + 2/3^k < \alpha + \epsilon$. Thus, in all cases, $(\alpha, \alpha + \epsilon)$ contains a point of $\sim NMT$ and the theorem is proved. ∎

12.24 Corollary. *NMT contains no open subsets of E^1 except $\emptyset$.*

Proof: Any non-empty open set G of E^1 contains an open interval, and by theorem 12.23, no open interval of real numbers is contained in *NMT*. ∎

12.25 Theorem. *The subset NMT of E^1 is not countable.*

Proof: The Cantor diagonal procedure for proving that the set of real numbers is not countable works here. Assume that there exists a 1:1 correspondence f from the set Z of natural numbers onto *NMT*. Each number in *NMT* has a unique representation $0.a_1a_2 \ldots a_n \ldots$, where $a_n = 0$ or $a_n = 2$. Let $f(1) = 0.a_1^1a_2^1a_3^1 \ldots a_n^1 \ldots$, $f(2) = 0.a_1^2a_2^2a_3^2 \ldots a_n^2 \ldots$, $f(n) = 0.a_1^na_2^n \ldots a_n^n \ldots$. Let β denote the real number $0.b_1b_2 \ldots b_n \ldots$, where $b_i = 2$ when $a_i^i = 0$, and $b_i = 0$ when $a_i^i = 2$. β is in *NMT*. Let k be any natural number; $f(k) = 0.a_1^ka_2^k \ldots a_k^k \ldots a_k^k \ldots$. Since $b_k \neq a_k^k$ and representations are unique, then $f(k) \neq \beta$. Thus, β is not the image of any natural number assigned by f. Hence, no 1:1 mapping from Z onto *NMT* can exist, and so *NMT* is not countable. ∎

12.26 Theorem. *The Cantor ternary space (definition 12.14) can be imbedded in the subspace* [0, 1] *in such a way that its image is NMT with the relative topology.*

Proof: Let $(a_1, a_2, \ldots, a_n, \ldots)$, where $a_i = 0$ or 1, denote any element of the Cantor ternary space. Let f denote the following function: $f((a_1, a_2, \ldots, a_n, \ldots)) = 0.b_1b_2 \ldots b_n \ldots$, where $b_i = a_i$ if $a_i = 0$, and $b_i = 2$ if $a_i = 1$. Then, $0.b_1b_2 \ldots b_n \ldots$ is a unique element of *NMT*. By definition, f is 1:1 and onto. Next, it will be shown that f is continuous. Let $x_0 = (a_1, a_2, \ldots, a_n, \ldots)$, for $a_n = 0$ or 1, be any point of *CTS*, the Cantor ternary space. Let

$y_0 = f(x_0)$. $f(x_0) = 0.b_1b_2 \ldots b_n \ldots$, where $b_n = a_n$ if $a_n = 0$, and $b_n = 2$ if $a_n = 1$. Let $V = \{y \mid |y - y_0| < \epsilon; \epsilon < 0$ and y is in $NMT\}$ be any basic neighborhood of y_0 in NMT with the relative topology. Let k be a natural number such that $1/3^k < \epsilon$. Let $U = \{x \mid x$ is in $\{a_1\} \times \{a_2\} \times \cdots \times \{a_k\} \times \{0, 1\} \times \{0, 1\} \times \cdots\}$, where $\{0, 1\}$ denotes the space consisting of 0 and 1 with the discrete topology. $U \subseteq CTS$ and U is open in CTS by definition of the product topology. Further, $x_0 = (a_1, a_2, \ldots, a_n, \ldots)$ is in U. Let z be any other element in U. $z = (a_1, a_2, \ldots, a_k, c_{k+1}, \ldots, c_n, \ldots)$, where $c_n = 0$ or $c_n = 1$ for $n \geq k + 1$. $f(z) = 0.b_1b_2 \ldots b_k, d_{k+1} \ldots d_n \ldots$; hence, $|f(z) - f(x_0)| \leq 1/3^k < \epsilon$. $f(z)$ is then in V and $f[U] \subseteq V$. The continuity of f is thus established. Let $g = f^{-1}$. g has for its domain NMT with the relative topology and for its range CTS. Let $y_0 = 0.b_1b_2 \ldots b_n \ldots$ be any point in NMT and let $g(y_0) = (a_1, a_2, \ldots, a_n, \ldots)$ be its image in CTS. Let V be any base element containing $g(y_0)$. $V = \{a_1\} \times \{a_2\} \times \cdots \times \{a_k\} \times \{0, 1\} \times \{0, 1\} \times \ldots$, where k is a natural number. Let $U = \{y \mid |y - y_0| < 1/3^k$ and y is in $NMT\}$. Let $z = 0.c_1c_2 \ldots c_n \ldots$ be any point in U. $c_n = 0$ or $c_n = 2$ by definition of NMT. $(0.c_1c_2 \ldots c_{n-1}20000\ldots) - (0.c_1c_2 \ldots c_{n-1}0222\ldots) = 1/3^n$. Hence if $b_i \neq c_i$, then $|z - y_0| \geq 1/3^i$. Hence, $z = 0.b_1b_2 \ldots b_k, c_{k+1} \ldots c_n \ldots$ and $g(z) = (a_1, a_2, \ldots, a_k, d_{k+1}, \ldots, d_n, \ldots)$ and $g(z)$ is in V. Since z was any point in U, $g(U) \subseteq V$, g is continuous and the theorem is proved. ▌

It has thus been established that the Cantor ternary space and the no-middle-third subset with the relative topology are indistinguishable topologically, and so any topological property possessed by one is possessed by the other. Consequently, the term "Cantor ternary space" will be used to denote either structure.

12.27 Definition. A subset P of a space S is called *perfect* if and only if P is closed in S and every point of P is a limit point of P.

12.28 Theorem. *The Cantor ternary set is a perfect subset of* E^1.

Proof: By theorem 12.17, NMT is closed in E^1. By theorem 12.15, no single point, x^*, of CTS, constitutes an open subset of CTS; hence, any open set containing x^* contains points of $\sim\{x^*\}$. Thus, x^* is a limit point of CTS. ▌

Property Transference and Function Spaces

It was shown in theorem 12.15 that a product of discrete spaces need not be discrete. Two natural questions to ask are: first, "Is the product of first countable spaces always first countable," and second, "Is the product of second countable spaces always second countable." The following example answers these questions in the negative.

12.29 Example. Let $\{X_\nu\}$ denote a collection of spaces such that to each real number ν there corresponds a space X_ν and let each space X_ν consist of exactly two points with the discrete topology. The product space $X^* = \prod_{\nu \in \mathfrak{A}} X_\nu$, where $\mathfrak{A}$ is the set of real numbers, is then the set of all mappings of the set of real numbers into the discrete space with two elements. Each space X_ν is first and second countable. Let x^* be any point in X^*. Assume there exists a countable local base $\mathfrak{B}$ at x^* and let $(G^1, G^2, \ldots, G^n, \ldots)$ denote this local base. These sets are open in X^*; hence, by the definition of the product topology, each set G^n contains a set B^n from the defining base; $B^n = \prod_{\nu \in \mathfrak{A}} U_\nu$, where U_ν is open in X_ν and $U_\nu = X_\nu$ for $\nu \neq \alpha_1^n, \alpha_2^n, \ldots, \alpha_{k_n}^n$, where k and n are natural numbers. This means that $p_\nu[G^n] = X_\nu$ for $\nu \neq \alpha_1^n, \ldots, \nu \neq \alpha_{k_n}^n$. Let $A = \bigcup_n \{\alpha_1^n, \alpha_2^n, \ldots, \alpha_{k_n}^n\}$. A is the union of a countable number of finite sets and so is countable. There exists a real number t which is not in A, since the set of real numbers is not countable. Consider the set $V^* = \prod_{\nu \in \mathfrak{A}} V_\nu$, where $V_\nu = X_\nu$ for $\nu \neq t$ and $V_t = \{x_t\}$, where x_t denotes the t-th coordinate of x^*. V^* is open in X^* and V^* contains x^*. However, for any G^n, $p_t[G^n] = X_t$ and $p_t[V^*] = \{x_t\}$. Therefore, $p_t[G^n]$ is not contained in $p_t[V^*]$, and so G^n is not contained in V^* for any n. Hence, $\{G^1, G^2, \ldots, G^n, \ldots\}$ does not form a local base at x^*. Thus, there exists no countable local base at x^*. Since X^* is not first countable, it cannot be second countable. Hence, the product of first or second countable spaces is not necessarily first or second countable, respectively.

The Cantor ternary space is the product of an infinite, but countable, number of spaces and yet, since it is also a subspace of the space E^1 of real numbers, by theorems 5.10 and 9.25, it must be first and second countable. Significant questions to ask are then (1) "Do there exist additional conditions which, if satisfied by the factor spaces, insure second or first countability for the product space?" and (2) "Does countability for the number of factor spaces have anything to do with the conditions?" The answers are found in the following theorems.

12.30 Theorem. *A non-empty product space $\prod_{\nu \in \mathfrak{A}} X_\nu$, for $\mathfrak{A}$ any indexing set, is first countable if for every ν, X_ν is first countable and if X_ν has the trivial topology except for at most a countable number of elements in $\mathfrak{A}$.*

Proof: It is given that all but at most a countable number of the spaces in the collection $\{X_\nu\}$ have the trivial topology, with X_ν and $\emptyset$ as the only open sets. Let A be the countable subset of $\mathfrak{A}$ such that c in $\sim A$ implies that X_c has the trivial topology, and let x^* be any point in $\prod_{\nu \in \mathfrak{A}} X_\nu$. If c is in $\sim A$, then X_c contains just the open sets $\emptyset$ and X_c. Now, each coordinate, x_ν, of x^* has a countable local base in X_ν, by hypothesis. Denote this base by $\mathfrak{B}^\nu = \{B_1^\nu, B_2^\nu, \ldots\} = \{B_i^\nu\}$, $i = 1, 2, 3, \ldots$. Each such set B_i^ν identifies one open set

$p_\nu^{-1}[B_j^\nu]$, by definition of the product topology. For each ν, these open sets in $\prod_{\nu\in\mathfrak{A}} X_\nu$ form a countable collection; therefore, the set $\bigcup_{\nu\in A}\{p_\nu^{-1}[B_1^\nu], p_\nu^{-1}[B_2^\nu], \ldots, p_\nu^{-1}[B_i], \ldots\}$ as the union of a countable collection of countable sets, is countable. For ν in $\sim A$, $B_1^\nu = B_2^\nu = B_3^\nu = \cdots = B_i^\nu = \cdots = X_\nu$. Thus, for ν in $\sim A$, $p_\nu^{-1}[B_i^\nu] = \prod_{\nu\in\mathfrak{A}} X_\nu$ and the same set is obtained for every ν in $\sim A$ and every i. Thus $\bigcup_{\nu\in\mathfrak{A}}\{p_\nu^{-1}[B_1^\nu], p_\nu^{-1}[B_2^\nu], \ldots, p_\nu^{-1}[B_i^\nu], \ldots\}$ is a countable collection, say $\{V_1^*, V_2^*, V_3^*, \ldots\}$, of open sets of $\prod_{\nu\in\mathfrak{A}} X_\nu$. The set $\mathcal{B}^*$ of all intersections of the V_i^* taken finitely many at a time is again countable, since each intersection is identified by a k-tuple of indices and the set of all k-tuples of natural numbers is countable. It remains to be shown that $\mathcal{B}^*$ is a local base at x^*. Let G^* be any open set of the product space, $\prod_{\nu\in\mathfrak{A}} X_\nu$, such that $x^* \in G^*$; then G^* contains a base element $U^* = \prod_{\nu\in\mathfrak{A}} U_\nu$, where U_ν is open in X_ν and $U_\nu = X_\nu$ for $\nu \neq \alpha_1, \ldots, \nu \neq \alpha_k$. For $\nu = \alpha_i$, $1 \leq i \leq k$, U_ν contains the ν-th coordinate of x^*. Hence, by definition of the local base $\mathcal{B}^\nu = \{B_1^\nu, B_2^\nu, \ldots\}$, U_ν contains B_j^ν for some natural number j. Therefore, $U_{\alpha_1} \supseteq B_{j_1}^{\alpha_1}$; $U_{\alpha_2} \supseteq B_{j_2}^{\alpha_2}$; $\ldots$; $U_{\alpha_k} \supseteq B_{j_k}^{\alpha_k}$, where $j_1, j_2, \ldots, j_k$ are natural numbers. Since $U^* = \prod_{\nu\in\mathfrak{A}} U_\nu$, then $U^* \supseteq \bigcap_{t=1}^k p_{\alpha_t}^{-1}[B_{j_t}^{\alpha_t}]$. However, $\bigcap_{t=1}^k p_{\alpha_t}^{-1}[B_{j_t}^{\alpha_t}]$ is an element of $\mathcal{B}^*$; hence, the collection $\mathcal{B}^*$ is a local base at x^*, and so $\prod_{\nu\in\mathfrak{A}} X_\nu$ is first countable. ▌

12.31 Theorem. *If $\prod_{\nu\in\mathfrak{A}} X_\nu$ is a non-empty first countable space, then each X_ν is first countable and every X_ν has the trivial topology except for at most a countable number of elements of $\mathfrak{A}$.*

Proof: A. Let α be any element of $\mathfrak{A}$ and x_α any element in X_α. Let G^α be any open set containing x_α in X_α and let x^* be a point of $\prod_{\nu\in\mathfrak{A}} X_\nu$ whose α-th coordinate is x_α. x^* is in $p_\alpha^{-1}[G^\alpha]$, which is open in X^*; hence, $p_\alpha^{-1}[G_\alpha]$ contains an element, B_i^*, of the countable local base $\mathcal{B}^*$ at x^*. Therefore $p_\alpha[B_i^*] \subseteq p_\alpha[p_\alpha^{-1}[G^\alpha]] = G^\alpha$ and since p_α is an open mapping, the images $p_\alpha[B_i^*]$, $i = 1, 2, \ldots$, of the sets in the countable local base at x^* in $\prod_{\nu\in\mathfrak{A}} X_\nu$ form a countable local base at x_α in X_α. Thus, each X_ν is first countable.

B. Let A denote the subset $\{a \mid a \in \mathfrak{A}$ and X_a has a non-trivial topology$\}$. If A is empty, A is finite and hence countable. If A is not empty, choose (by the axiom of choice) for each ν in A, an open, non-empty proper subset, U_ν, of X_ν, and for ν in $\sim A$, let $U_\nu = X_\nu$. Let U^* denote the subset, $\prod_{\nu\in\mathfrak{A}} U_\nu$, of $\prod_{\nu\in\mathfrak{A}} X_\nu$. U^* is not empty. Let x^* be any point in U^*; then, denote $p_\nu(x^*)$ by x_ν; x_ν is in U_ν. x^* has a countable local base $\mathcal{B}^* = (B_1^*, B_2^*, \ldots, B_n^*, \ldots)$. Each B_i^* in $\mathcal{B}^*$ can be considered to be a product $\prod_{\nu\in\mathfrak{A}} V_\nu$, where V_ν is open in X_ν and $V_\nu = X_\nu$ for $\nu \neq \alpha_1^i, \ldots, \nu \neq \alpha_{k_i}^i$, and k_i a natural number. The latter follows from the definitions of a local base and the product topology on X^*. Denote this finite set $\{\alpha_1^i, \ldots, \alpha_{k_i}^i\}$ by C^i. C^i is a finite subset of $\mathfrak{A}$. Each set B_i^* in the local base, $\mathcal{B}^*$, at x^* identifies such a finite subset C^i of $\mathfrak{A}$. $\bigcup_{i=1}^\infty C^i$ is then the union of a countable collection of finite sets, and so is countable. Let $C = \bigcup_{i=1}^\infty C^i$. Let γ be in $\sim C$, the complement of C, in $\mathfrak{A}$. $p_\gamma[U^*] = U_\gamma$

and U_γ is open in X_γ by definition of U^*. $x_\gamma = p_\gamma(x^*)$ and x_γ is in U_γ. Hence $p_\gamma^{-1}[U_\gamma]$ contains x^* and by continuity of p_γ, $p_\gamma^{-1}[U_\gamma]$ is open. Therefore, there exists a set B_j^*, say, from the local base, $\mathcal{B}^*$, at x^* such that $B_j^* \subseteq p_\gamma^{-1}[U_\gamma]$. This implies that $p_\gamma[B_j^*] \subseteq p_\gamma[p_\gamma^{-1}[U_\gamma]] = U_\gamma$. However, $p_\gamma[B_j^*] = X_\gamma$, since γ is in $\sim C$; hence, $U_\gamma \supseteq X_\gamma$ and so $U_\gamma = X_\gamma$. Thus γ is in $\sim A$, since for ν in A, $U_\nu \neq X_\nu$. Since γ was any element in $\sim C$, $\sim C \subseteq \sim A$. Therefore $A \subseteq C$. Since C is countable and any subset of a countable set is countable, A is countable. ▮

12.32 Theorem. *A non-empty product space $\prod_{\nu \in \mathfrak{A}} X_\nu$ has a countable base if and only if each factor space has a countable base and all but a countable number of the factor spaces have the trivial topology.*

Proof: A. Let $A = \{\nu \mid \nu \text{ is in } \mathfrak{A} \text{ and } X_\nu \text{ has a non-trivial topology}\}$. Let A be countable and let X_ν, for every ν, be second countable. If A is empty, $\emptyset$ and $\prod_{\nu \in \mathfrak{A}} X_\nu$ are the only open sets in $\prod_{\nu \in \mathfrak{A}} X_\nu$, and hence $\prod_{\nu \in \mathfrak{A}} X_\nu$ has a countable base. If A is not empty, let $\alpha_1, \alpha_2, \ldots, \alpha_i, \ldots$, where i is a natural number, denote the elements of A. Let $\mathcal{S}^{\alpha_i} = \{B_1^{\alpha_i}, B_2^{\alpha_i}, \ldots\}$ be the countable base for X_{α_i}, α_i in A. Let $\mathcal{S} = \bigcup_{\alpha_i \in A} \mathcal{S}^{\alpha_i}$. $\mathcal{S}$ is the union of a countable collection of countable sets and hence is countable: $\mathcal{S} = \{B_1^{\alpha_1}, B_2^{\alpha_1}, \ldots; B_1^{\alpha_2}, B_2^{\alpha_2}, \ldots; B_1^{\alpha_i}, B_2^{\alpha_i}, \ldots, B_j^{\alpha_i}, \ldots; \ldots; \ldots\}$. Let $\mathcal{S}^* = \{p_{\alpha_1}^{-1}[B_1^{\alpha_1}], p_{\alpha_1}^{-1}[B_2^{\alpha_1}], \ldots; p_{\alpha_2}^{-1}[B_1^{\alpha_2}], p_{\alpha_2}^{-1}[B_2^{\alpha_2}], \ldots; \ldots; p_{\alpha_i}^{-1}[B_1^{\alpha_i}], p_{\alpha_i}^{-1}[B_2^{\alpha_i}], \ldots, p_{\alpha_i}^{-1}[B_j^{\alpha_i}], \ldots; \ldots\}$.

$\mathcal{S}^*$ is a countable collection of subsets of X^*. Let $\mathcal{B}^*$ denote the collection of all sets that are intersections of finitely many sets in $\mathcal{S}^*$. Since $\mathcal{S}^*$ is countable, each set in $\mathcal{B}^*$ can be made to correspond to a k-tuple of natural numbers in such a way as to establish that $\mathcal{B}^*$ is countable. It remains to be shown that $\mathcal{B}^*$ is a base for the product topology on $\prod_{\nu \in \mathfrak{A}} X_\nu$. Let G^* be any open set in $\prod_{\nu \in \mathfrak{A}} X_\nu$ and let y^* be any point in G^*. Again let y_ν denote the ν-th coordinate of y^*, i.e., $y_\nu = p_\nu(y^*)$ and y_ν is in X_ν. Now, G^* must contain an open set U^* which contains y^* and which belongs to the defining base for the product topology, i.e., y^* is in U^* and $U^* = \prod_{\nu \in \mathfrak{A}} U_\nu$, where U_ν is open in X_ν and $U_\nu = X_\nu$ for $\nu \neq \beta_1, \ldots, \nu \neq \beta_t$, for t a natural number and $\{\beta_1, \ldots, \beta_t\} \subseteq A$. Thus y_ν is in U_ν for every ν. By definition of a base, there exist $B_{j_1}^{\beta_1}, \ldots, B_{j_i}^{\beta_i}, \ldots, B_{j_t}^{\beta_t}$ such that y_{β_i} is in $B_{j_i}^{\beta_i}$ and $B_{j_i}^{\beta_i} \subseteq U_{\beta_i}$. Hence, $p_{\beta_i}^{-1}[B_{j_i}^{\beta_i}] \subseteq p_{\beta_i}^{-1}[U_{\beta_i}]$. Further, since y_{β_i} is in $B_{j_i}^{\beta_i}$, y^* is in $p_{\beta_i}^{-1}[B_{j_i}^{\beta_i}]$ for $i = 1, \ldots, t$. Therefore, y^* is in $p_{\beta_1}^{-1}[B_{j_1}^{\beta_1}] \cap p_{\beta_2}^{-1}[B_{j_2}^{\beta_2}] \cap \cdots \cap p_{\beta_t}^{-1}[B_{j_t}^{\beta_t}]$. Also, $p_{\beta_1}^{-1}[B_{j_1}^{\beta_1}] \cap \cdots \cap p_{\beta_t}^{-1}[B_{j_t}^{\beta_t}] \subseteq p_{\beta_1}^{-1}[U_{\beta_1}] \cap \cdots \cap p_{\beta_t}^{-1}[U_{\beta_t}] = U^* \subseteq G^*$. Now, $p_{\beta_1}^{-1}[B_{j_1}^{\beta_1}] \cap \cdots \cap p_{\beta_t}^{-1}[B_{j_t}^{\beta_t}]$ is a set in $\mathcal{B}^*$; it contains y^* and is contained in G^*. Hence G^* is the union of sets in $\mathcal{B}^*$, and so $\mathcal{B}^*$ constitutes a countable base for $\prod_{\nu \in \mathfrak{A}} X_\nu$.

B. Let $\prod_{\nu \in \mathfrak{A}} X_\nu$ have a countable base, $\mathcal{B}^* = \{B_1^*, B_2^*, \ldots, B_i^*, \ldots\}$. First it will be shown that each X_ν has a countable base. Let α be a given element in $\mathfrak{A}$; p_α is open by theorem 12.8. Hence, the collection $\{p_\alpha[B_1^*], p_\alpha[B_2^*], \ldots, p_\alpha[B_i^*], \ldots$ is a countable set of open sets in X_α. Let G^α be any open set in X_α. $G^* = p_\alpha^{-1}[G^\alpha]$ is open in $\prod_{\nu \in \mathfrak{A}} X_\nu$. Hence G^* is the union of sets in $\mathcal{B}^*$. Let $G^* = \bigcup_j B_j^*$. $p_\alpha[G^*] = p_\alpha[\bigcup_j B_j^*] = \bigcup_j p_\alpha[B_j^*]$. Since p_α is open, $p_\alpha[B_j^*]$

is open for each j. Hence the sets $p_\alpha[B_1^*], \ldots, p_\alpha[B_i^*], \ldots$ constitute a base for X_α. Now, it must be shown that all but a countable number of the spaces X_ν have the trivial topology. Let $A = \{\nu \mid \nu$ is in $\mathfrak{A}$ and X_ν has a non-trivial topology$\}$. Consider, again, the given countable base $\mathfrak{B}^* = \{B_1^*, B_2^*, \ldots\}$ for $\prod_\nu X_\nu$. Each B_j^* can be shown to be the union of a countable number of open product sets $\prod_\nu U_\nu$ and so a countable base $\{U_1^*, U_2^*, \ldots, U_n^*, \ldots\}$ of open product sets can be defined. Thus without loss of generality each B_j^* can be considered to be a product set $\prod_{\nu\in\mathfrak{A}} U_\nu^j$, where either $U_\nu^j = X_\nu$ for all ν in $\mathfrak{A}$, or $U_\nu^j = X_\nu$ except for $\nu = \nu_1^j, \nu_2^j, \ldots, \nu_{k_j}^j$, and k_j a natural number. Hence, $p_\nu[B_j^*] = X_\nu$ for all ν in the first case and for all ν except $\nu = \nu_1^j, \nu_2^j, \ldots, \nu_{k_j}^j$, in the second case. In the first case, let $C^j = \emptyset$ and in the second case let $C^j = \{\nu_1, \nu_2, \ldots, \nu_{k_j}^j\}$. In either case, C^j is a finite subset of $\mathfrak{A}$ and if ν is in $\sim C^j$, then $p_\nu[B_j^*] = X_\nu$. Let $C = \bigcup_j C^j$. C is a countable subset of $\mathfrak{A}$. Now let γ be any point in $\sim C$ and let G^γ be any non-empty open subset of X_γ. $p_\gamma^{-1}[G^\gamma]$ is open in X^* by continuity of p_γ. Hence, $p^1{}_\gamma^{-}[G^\gamma]$ contains some base set, say, B_n^* in the countable base, $\mathfrak{B}^*$. Since $p_\gamma^{-1}[G^\gamma] \supseteq B_n^*$, it follows that $p_\gamma\left[p_\gamma^{-1}[G^\gamma]\right] \supseteq p_\gamma[B_n^*]$. However, since γ is in $\sim C$, $p_\gamma[B_n^*] = X_\gamma$. Therefore, $G^\gamma = X_\gamma$ since $p_\gamma\left[p_\gamma^{-1}[G^\gamma]\right] = G^\gamma$. Hence, X_γ has the trivial topology. Thus, γ is in $\sim A$, by definition of A. Hence, $\sim C \subseteq \sim A$, and so $A \subseteq C$. Since C is countable, A is countable, and so the theorem is proved. ▌

12.33 Corollary. *Any non-empty product space of a countable number of spaces is second or first countable if and only if each factor space is second or first countable, respectively.*

Another question which arises naturally in the present discussion is whether the product of infinitely many separable spaces is separable. If the indexing set is countable, the separability of such a product space is easily established.

12.34 Theorem. *A non-empty product space of a countable number of separable spaces is separable.*

Proof: Let $X_1 \times X_2 \times \cdots \times X_k \times \cdots$ denote a non-empty product space of a countable number of separable spaces. Let D_k be a countable dense subset in X_k, $k = 1, 2, \ldots$. Let $(a_1, a_2, \ldots, a_k, \ldots)$ be a chosen point in $X_1 \times X_2 \times \cdots \times X_k \times \cdots$. Consider the sets:

$$\delta_1 = \{(d_1, a_2, \ldots, a_k, \ldots) \mid d_1 \in D_1\}$$
$$\delta_2 = \{(d_1, d_2, a_3, \ldots, a_k, \ldots) \mid d_1 \in D_1, d_2 \in D_2\}$$
$$\vdots$$
$$\delta_k = \{(d_1, d_2, d_3, \ldots, d_k, a_{k+1} \ldots) \mid d_i \in D_i, i = 1, 2, 3, \ldots, k\}$$

Each set δ_k is countable, $k = 1, 2, \ldots$; hence $\bigcup_k \delta_k = D^*$ is countable. Now let $(\alpha_1, \alpha_2, \ldots, \alpha_k \ldots)$ be any point in $X_1 \times X_2 \times \cdots \times X_k \times \cdots$ and let G be any open set containing $(\alpha_1, \alpha_2, \ldots, \alpha_k, \ldots)$. G contains a base element $B = U_1 \times U_2 \times \cdots \times U_k \times X_{k+1} \times X_{k+2} \times \cdots$, where U_i is open in X_i, $i = 1, 2, \ldots, k$ and B contains $(\alpha_1, \alpha_2, \ldots, \alpha_k, \ldots)$. There exists $d_1 \in U_1$ and $d_2 \in U_2 \ldots d_k \in U_k$ such that $d_i \in D_i$ for $i = 1, 2, \ldots, k$. Hence the point $(d_1, d_2, \ldots, d_k, a_{k+1}, a_{k+2}, \ldots)$ of D^* lies in G. Hence D^* is dense in $X_1 \times X_2 \times \cdots \times X_k \times \cdots$, and so $X_1 \times X_2 \times \cdots \times X_k \times \cdots$ is separable. ▮

When the cardinal number of the indexing set $\mathfrak{A}$ is greater than $\aleph_0$, the situation is more complicated. E. Marczewski was the first to solve this problem. The next several lemmas and theorems establish that if the cardinal of $\mathfrak{A}$ is $\leq c$, the cardinal of the set of real numbers, then the corresponding product of separable spaces is separable. First, however, notation and terminology for a special case of the product space is introduced. If X and Y are finite sets containing m and n elements, respectively, then there are n choices for an image in Y for each element in X. Hence, there are n^m mappings of X into Y. In general, if $\overline{X}$ is the cardinal number of X and $\overline{Y}$ is the cardinal of Y then $\overline{Y}^{\overline{X}}$ denotes the cardinal number of the set of all functions of X into Y, and this set itself is denoted by Y^X. Thus Y^X is the cartesian product set $\prod_{\nu \in X} Y_\nu$, where $Y_\nu = Y$ for every ν in X. This set can then be assigned the product topology to yield a function space. By theorem 12.9, a net (f_δ^*) in the product space Y^X converges to a point f^* in Y^X if and only if each projection net $(f_\delta^*(x^*)) = (p_{x^*}(f_\delta^*))$, where p_{x^*} denotes a projection function, converges to $f(x^*)$ in Y. Hence, the term "the topology of pointwise convergence" is used for the product topology on Y^X.

12.35 Definition. The *topology of pointwise convergence* for a set of functions, Y^X, is the product topology for Y^X. The *topology of pointwise convergence* for a subset C of Y^X is the relative product topology for C.

For applications of function spaces to topology and analysis, the topology of pointwise convergence is not the most natural or significant. In chapters 4 and 6 two more topologies for sets of functions from one topological space X into a topological space Y will be introduced: the topology of uniform convergence, in chapter 4, and the compact open topology, in chapter 6.

12.36 Theorem. *If N denotes the space of natural numbers with the discrete topology and if T has cardinality $\leq c$, then N^T is separable.*

Proof: First, a countable set of functions in N^T will be defined. Since T has cardinality $\leq c$, there exists a 1:1 correspondence $\Psi: T \longrightarrow R$, where R denotes the set of real numbers. Let $\{a_1, a_2, \ldots, a_n\}$ denote any finite increasing set of real numbers. There exist rational numbers $r_1, r_2, \ldots, r_{n-1}$ such that $a_1 \leq r_1 < a_2 \leq r_2 < \cdots \leq r_{n-1} < a_n$. Consider the subsets $A_1 = \{x \mid x \leq r_1\}$, $A_2 = \{x \mid r_1 < x \leq r_2\}, \ldots, A_n = \{x \mid r_{n-1} < x\}$.

The sets $A_1, A_2, \ldots, A_n$ constitute a finite partition of the reals into disjoint sets, such that $a_i \in A_i$ and $a_i \notin A_j$ for $i \neq j$. Thus for each finite set of real numbers there exists such a partition; further, since the set of all n-tuples of rationals is countable, the set of all such partitions is countable. Hence the set, $\mathcal{P}$, of all the corresponding partitions of T assigned by Ψ^{-1} is countable. Next, let $P = \{B_1, B_2, \ldots, B_n\}$ denote one of these partitions of T and consider $\{f \text{ in } N^T \mid f \text{ is constant on each } B_i \text{ in } P\}$. Each such f determines, and is determined, by an ordered n-tuple of natural numbers, and so there can be at most a countable number of such functions. Since there are at most a countable number of such partitions, the set D of all functions f which are constant on the sets of at least one partition in $\mathcal{P}$ is countable. It must now be shown that D is dense in N^T. Let g be any function in N^T and let G^* be any basic open set in N^T which contains g. $G^* = \prod_{t \in T} G_t$, where $G_t = N$ for $t \neq t_1, t \neq t_2, \ldots, t \neq t_k$. Let $P = \{B_1, B_2, \ldots, B_k\}$ be a partition of T such that t_i is in B_i and t_i is not in B_j for $i \neq j$. Consider the function f in D such that $f(B_i) = g(t_i)$. f is in G^* and D is dense in N^T. ▮

12.37 Lemma. *If D is a countably infinite space, then D is the* 1:1 *continuous image of N.*

Proof: Exercise.

12.38 Lemma. *If $\{D_t\}$ denotes a collection of spaces, each of which is countably infinite, then $D^* = \prod_{t \in T} D_t$ is the* 1:1 *continuous image of N^T.*

Proof: Since each D_t is countably infinite, by lemma 12.37 there exists a 1:1 continuous function f_t from N onto each D_t. Let γ be the function from N^T into D^* which assigns to each function h in N^T the element of D^* whose t-th coordinate is $f_t(h(t))$.

A. γ is onto. Let (x_t) denote any point in the product space $D^* = \prod_{t \in T} D_t$. Since each f_t is 1:1, $f_t^{-1}(x_t)$ is a unique natural number k_t. Let $g(t) = k_t$. Then $\gamma(g)$ is the element of D^* whose t-th coordinate is $f_t(g(t)) = f_t(k_t) = x_t$, and so $\gamma(g) = (x_t)$.

B. γ is 1:1. Let h and g be functions in N^T such that $h \neq g$. There exists, then, an element t in T such that $h(t) \neq g(t)$. The t-th coordinate of $\gamma(h)$ in D^* will be $f_t(h(t))$ and the t-th coordinate of $\gamma(g)$ in D^* will be $f_t(g(t))$. Since f_t is 1:1, $f_t(h(t)) \neq f_t(g(t))$. Hence, $\gamma(h) \neq \gamma(g)$.

C. γ is continuous. Let G^* be any basic open set containing $\gamma(h)$ in $D^* = \prod_{t \in T} D_t$. $G^* = \prod_{t \in T} G_t$ where $G_t = D_t$ for $t \neq t_1, t_2, \ldots, t_n$. Consider in N^T, the set $W = \prod_{t \in T} V_t$ where $V_t = N$ for $t \neq t_1, t_2 \ldots, t_n$ and $V_{t_i} = \{h(t_i)\}$ for $i = 1, 2, \ldots, n$. W is open in N^T and contains h. Let g be any element in W. $\gamma(g)$ is the element of D^* whose t-th coordinate is $f_t(g(t))$. Since g is in W, $g(t_i) = h(t_i)$ for $i = 1, 2, \ldots, n$. Thus $f_{t_i}(g(t_i)) = f_{t_i}(h(t_i))$ and $\gamma(g)$ is in G^*. γ is then continuous and the lemma is proved. ▮

12.39 Lemma. *If M is a dense subspace of X and if M is separable, then X is separable.*

Proof: Let D be a countable dense subset of M. Let x be any point in X and let G be any open set containing x. G contains a point in M, since M is dense in X. Hence $G \cap M$ is a non-empty open subset in M. $G \cap M$ must then contain a point of D. ▮

12.40 Theorem. *If $X^* = \prod_{t \in T} X_t$ is any non-empty product space and if D_t is dense in X_t, then $D^* = \prod_{t \in T} D_t$ is dense in X^*.*

Proof: Let (x_t) be any point in X^* and let $G^* = \prod_{t \in T} G_t$ be any basic open set which contains (x_t). $G_t = X_t$ for $t \neq a_1, a_2, \ldots, a_k$. Further, G_{a_i} must contain a point d_i from the dense set D_{a_i} in X_{a_i} for $i = 1, 2, \ldots, k$. Hence, the point (y_t) of X^*, where y_t is some point of D_t for $t \neq a_1, a_2, \ldots, a_k$ and $y_{a_i} = d_i$, is a point of D^* which lies in G^*. ▮

12.41 Theorem. *If $X^* = \prod_{t \in T} X_t$ is any non-empty product of separable spaces, X_t, where T has cardinality $\leq c$, then X^* is separable.*

Proof: Since X_t is separable, it contains a countable dense set D_t. By lemma 12.38, $D^* = \prod_{t \in T} D_t$ is the continuous image of N^T and hence is separable. By theorem 12.40, D^* is dense in X^*, and by lemma 12.39, X^* is separable. ▮

12.42 Theorem. *If $X^* = \prod_{t \in T} X_t$, where the cardinality of T is greater than c and each X_t has at least one pair of disjoint open sets, then X^* is not separable.*

Proof: Assume that X^* is separable. Let $\{d_1, d_2, \ldots, d_n, \ldots\}$ be a countable dense subset in X^*. In each X_t, choose two disjoint non-empty open sets G_t^1 and G_t^2. For each t in T define the following sequence $(a_1(t), a_2(t), \ldots, a_n(t), \ldots)$, where $a_n(t) = 0$ if $p_t(d_n)$, the t-th coordinate of d_n, is not in G_t, and $a_n(t) = 1$ if $p_t(d_n)$ is in G_t^1. Let t_1 and t_2 be distinct points in T. Since $\{d_1, d_2, \ldots, d_n, \ldots\}$ is dense in X^*, there exists d_k for some natural number, k, in $p_{t_1}^{-1}(G_{t_1}^1) \cap p_{t_2}^{-1}(G_{t_2}^2)$. Hence $p_{t_1}(d_k) = 1$, but $p_{t_2}(d_k) = 0$. Hence, $(a_1(t_1), a_2(t_1), \ldots, a_n(t_1), \ldots) \neq (a_1(t_2), a_2(t_2), \ldots, a_n(t_2), \ldots)$. Thus the correspondence is 1:1 and T can be mapped in a 1:1 manner into the set of all sequences whose ranges are contained in $\{0, 1\}$. This set has cardinality c; hence, T has cardinality $\leq c$. This is a contradiction. Hence X^* is not separable. ▮

12.43 Example. Let X denote the space consisting of the real numbers and the following topology: $\emptyset$ and all complements of finite subsets. The set of natural numbers is dense in X. Consider the product space X^T for any non-empty T. Let $f_n : t \to n$ for n a natural number and all t in T. The set $\{f_1, f_2, \ldots, f_n, \ldots\}$ is countable. Now, let γ be any element in X and G^* any basic open set containing γ. $G^* = \prod_{t \in T} G_t$, where $G_t = X$ for

$t \neq a_1, a_2, \ldots, a_k$. Then $G_{a_1} \cap G_{a_2} \cap \cdots \cap G_{a_k} \neq \emptyset$ since each G_{a_i} has a finite complement. Since $G_{a_1} \cap \cdots \cap G_{a_k}$ is open, it contains a natural number m. Consider $f_m : t \to m$ for all t in T. f_m is in G^* and $\{f_1, f_2, \ldots, f_n, \ldots\}$ is dense. The procedure in the preceding example can be generalized to yield a theorem.

12.44 Theorem. *If X^T is a product space such that X has no disjoint open sets and X is separable, then X^T is separable for any non-empty T.*

Proof: Let $D = \{d_1, d_2, \ldots, d_n, \ldots\}$ denote a countable dense set in X^T. Let f_n denote the constant function $f_n(t) = d_n$ for all t in T. Now let γ be any element of X^T and let G^* be any basic open set in X^T which contains γ. $G^* = \prod_{t \in T} G_t$, where $G_t = X$ for $t \neq a_1, a_2, \ldots, a_k$. $G_{a_1} \cap G_{a_2} \cap \cdots \cap G_{a_k}$, by hypothesis, is a non-empty open set in X. Hence, $G_{a_1} \cap G_{a_2} \cap \cdots \cap G_{a_k}$ contains a point d_j, say, of the countable dense set D in X. Consider the function f_j in X^T. $f_j(t) = d_j$ for every t in T. Hence $f_j(a_i)$ is in G_{a_i} for $i = 1, 2, \ldots, k$, and f_j is in G^*. Thus the countable set $\{f_1, f_2, \ldots, f_j, \ldots\}$ is dense in X^T. ▌

12.45 Example. Let S denote the set of real numbers with the topology consisting of $\emptyset$ and all complements of countable sets. There exist no non-empty disjoint open sets in S, but S is not separable.

One more theorem is obtained by repeating the procedure in the proof of lemma 12.38.

12.46 Theorem. *If $\{X_t\}$ is a non-empty collection of separable topological spaces all of which are* 1:1 *continuous images of a particular separable topological space Y, and if Y has no disjoint open sets, then for any non-empty set T, $\prod_{t \in T} X_t$ is separable.*

Proof: Y^T is separable by theorem 12.44. Further, X_t, for no t in T has disjoint open sets. For let f be 1:1 and continuous from Y onto X_t. If $G_1 \cap G_2 = \emptyset$ in X_t, then $f^{-1}(G_1) \cap f^{-1}(G_2) = \emptyset$ in X_t, and both are open. By the procedure in the proof of lemma 12.38, $\prod_{t \in T} X_t$ is the continuous image of Y^T and hence is separable. ▌

The Inverse Limit Space

Another type of topological space is the so-called inverse limit space; an inverse limit space is a subspace of a product space.

12.47 Definition. An *inverse limit system* consists of (1) an indexing set T with a direct ordering, $\geq$, (2) a net of spaces X_t with $\{T, \geq\}$ as domain, and (3) a collection of continuous functions $\{f_\alpha^\beta\}$ indexed by the subset $A = \{(\alpha, \beta) \mid \alpha \leq \beta\}$ of $T \times T$, and such that $f_\alpha^\beta : X_\beta \xrightarrow{\text{into}} X_\alpha$, $f_\alpha^\beta \circ f_\beta^\gamma = f_\alpha^\gamma$ for $\alpha \leq \beta \leq \gamma$. f_α^α is the identity function.

12.48 Definition. Let $[\{T, \geq\}, (X_t), \{f_\alpha^\beta\}]$ be an inverse limit system. An *inverse limit space*, $\overleftarrow{L}$, is a subspace of $\prod_{t \in T} X_t$ such that $\overleftarrow{L} = \{x^* \mid x^*$ is in $\prod_{t \in T} X_t$ and $p_\alpha(x^*) = f_\alpha^\beta(p_\beta(x^*))$ for every pair (α, β) in $T \times T$ for which $\alpha \leq \beta\}$. Since $p_\beta(x^*)$ and $p_\alpha(x^*)$ are the α-th and β-th coordinates, respectively, of x^*, a point is in $\overleftarrow{L}$ if and only if its coordinates are images of one another under the functions f_α^β in the above manner.

An inverse limit space is, in a sense, a generalization of a subspace of the plane which is the graph of a continuous function, g, defined on the y-axis as domain. Such a graph is the subspace of E^2 determined by the set of all ordered pairs $(g(y), y)$.

12.49 Example. Let $[\{T, \geq\}, \mathfrak{N}, \{f_\alpha^\beta\}]$ be an inverse limit system, where T is the set of natural numbers, $\mathfrak{N} = (E^1, E^1, \ldots, E^1, \ldots)$, and f_m^n is the identity function for every pair (n, m) where $n \geq m$. Then the corresponding inverse limit space, $\overleftarrow{L}$, is the set of all sequences of real numbers, i.e., elements of $\prod_{i=1}^\infty Y_i$, where $Y_i = E^1$, which represent constant functions from T into E^1. $\overleftarrow{L} = \{\sigma \mid \sigma = (x, x, x, \ldots)$ and x is a real number$\}$.

EXERCISE 5. Prove that the inverse limit space, $\overleftarrow{L}$, of example 12.49 is homeomorphic to E^1.

12.50 Example. Let $[\{\mathfrak{A}, \geq\}, \mathfrak{N}, \{f_\alpha^\beta\}]$ be an inverse limit system, where $\mathfrak{A}$ is the set of natural numbers, $\mathfrak{N} = (R^+, R^+, \ldots)$, R^+ is the subspace of E^1 consisting of the positive reals, and $f_\alpha^\beta(x) = x + (\beta - \alpha)$. If x is a positive real number, $x + k$ is a positive real number for k a natural number; hence, $f_\alpha^\beta : R^+ \to R^+$. Let x be any positive real number; x is not the first coordinate of any element in the corresponding inverse limit space, $\overleftarrow{L}$, since the corresponding element $(x, x - 1, \ldots, x - n, ?, \ldots)$ of $\overleftarrow{L}$ has no n- or $(n + 1)$-th coordinate where $n = [x]$, the largest integer less than or equal to x. Hence $\overleftarrow{L}$ is empty.

12.51 Example. (See figure 10.) Let $[\{T, \geq\}, (X_t), \{f_\alpha^\beta\}]$ be an inverse limit space, where T is the set of natural numbers, $X_n = \{(x, y) \mid x = n$ and $0 \leq y \leq 1$ for y a real number$\}$ and $f_n^{n+1} : X_{n+1} \to X_n$ is defined by

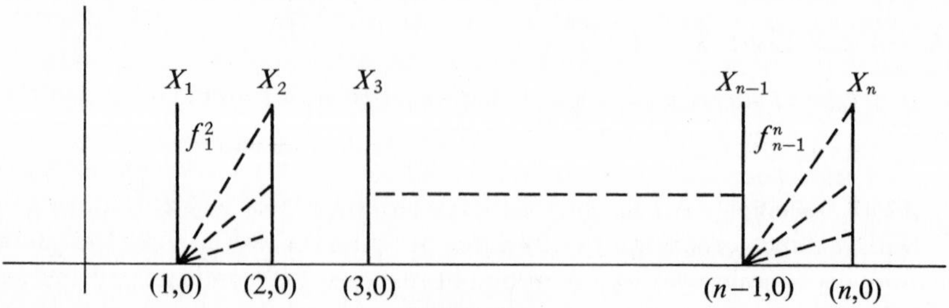

FIGURE 10

$f_n^{n+1}((n+1, y)) = (n, 0)$, and so f_n^m, for $m > n$, is defined by

$$f_n^m((m, y)) = (n, 0).$$

This space consists of one element, namely, the sequence

$$((1, 0), (2, 0), (3, 0), \ldots, (n, 0), \ldots).$$

If additional properties are added to the spaces X_α involved in the definition of the inverse limit space, $\overleftarrow{L}$, then further properties can be proved for $\overleftarrow{L}$. Certain of these properties will be established in succeeding chapters.

The inverse limit space is the topological analogue of the inverse limit group in algebra. Instead of an inverse limit system of topological spaces and continuous functions, there is a system of groups and homomorphisms. An inverse limit group, $\overleftarrow{G}$, is never empty since $\overleftarrow{G}$ always contains the element whose α-th coordinate is e, where e is the identity of G_α. Inverse limit groups and spaces are important concepts in algebraic topology and topological algebra.

13. QUOTIENT SPACES (DECOMPOSITION SPACES).

Another significant method for generating topological spaces is the method of identifying points of a given space. For example, the unit circle can be generated topologically by identifying or "pasting together" the end points of the closed interval $[0, 2\pi]$ of real numbers. This amounts to combining the real numbers 0 and 2π into one new element. Similarly, by taking any rectangle and identifying two opposite edges, i.e., "pasting them together," a cylinder is obtained; then, by "pasting together" the circular ends of the cylinder, a "doughnut" or torus is obtained. It is this "pasting procedure" made rigorous which leads to quotient spaces and the so-called identification topology.

13.1 Definition. Let X be any set and R be any equivalence relation on X. The set of equivalence classes in X established by R or the set of R-equivalence classes is denoted by X/R and is called the *quotient set* of X divided by R or also a *decomposition of* X.

13.2 Definition. Let X be a set and let X/R be the quotient set of X divided by the equivalence relation R. The *identification* or *quotient function*, q, from X onto X/R, is defined by the statement that $q(x) = D$, where x is in D and D is an equivalence class defined by R.

13.3 Definition. Let X be a space and let R be an equivalence relation defined on X. The *identification or quotient topology* on X/R is the strong topology determined by the identification function, q. A quotient set X/R with the identification topology becomes a *quotient space or a decomposition space,* which is also denoted by X/R.

It is to be recalled that the strong topology is the largest topology for X/R with which q, the identification function, is continuous. Thus, any quotient space, X/R, is the continuous image of the original space X, and so X/R will necessarily possess all properties which are preserved by a continuous function and which the original space X possesses.

The quotient space is the topological analogue of the quotient group in algebra. A subgroup $(H, \boxplus)$ of a group $(G, \boxplus)$ identifies an equivalence relation R on G; (x, y) is in R if and only if $x \boxplus y^{-1}$ is in H. The set $\{Hx \mid x \in G\}$ of equivalence classes is denoted by G/H. The identification function is called the natural mapping. If $(H, \boxplus)$ is an invariant subgroup of $(G, \boxplus)$, then G/H becomes a group $(G/H, *)$, where $Hx * Hz$ is defined as $H(x \boxplus z)$. The natural mapping is then a homomorphism. Thus all factor groups of a group G are homomorphic images of G. The following theorems are analogues of theorems in group theory.

13.4 Theorem. *A function g of a quotient space X/R into a space Y is continuous on X/R if and only if the composite function $g \circ q$, where q denotes the identification function, is continuous on the space X.*

Proof: A. By definition 13.3, q is continuous; hence, if g is continuous, then $g \circ q$ is a composite of two continuous functions and so is continuous.

B. Given that $g \circ q$ is continuous on X, let G be any open set in the range of g. Since $g \circ q$ is continuous on X, $(g \circ q)^{-1}[G]$ is open in X. $(g \circ q)^{-1}[G] = q^{-1}[g^{-1}[G]]$, by definition of a composite function. Since $q^{-1}[g^{-1}[G]]$ is open in X, $g^{-1}[G]$ is open in X/R, by definition of the quotient topology. Hence g is continuous on X/R. ▮

13.5 Theorem. *If f is a continuous function from a space X onto a space Y and if R is the equivalence relation on X such that (x, y) is in R if and only if $f(x) = f(y)$, then Y is a 1:1 continuous image of the quotient space X/R; further, if Y has the strong topology determined by f, then X/R and Y are homeomorphic.*

Proof: Define the correspondence $h: X/R \xrightarrow{\text{onto}} Y$ as follows: $h(D) = f(d)$, where d is in the equivalence class D. First it must be shown that h is a function, i.e., a single-valued correspondence. If x is in D and y is in D, then $f(x) = f(y)$, and so h is a single-valued correspondence. Next, if $h(D_1) = h(D_2)$, where D_1 and D_2 are two equivalence classes, then by definition of h, there exists d_1 in D_1 and d_2 in D_2 such that $f(d_1) = f(d_2)$, and so (d_1, d_2) is in R and $D_1 = D_2$. Thus, h is a 1:1 function of X/R onto Y. Next, it is shown that h is continuous. Since the composite mapping $h \circ q: X \to Y$ is equal to f, by definition of h and R, and since f is continuous by hypothesis, then h is continuous by theorem 13.4. Next, assume that Y has the strong topology and that V is open in X/R. $q^{-1}(V)$ is open in X, since q is continuous. $q^{-1}(V)$ is the union of equivalence classes. Hence, $q^{-1}(V)$ is an inverse set relative to f (see exercise 12 in section 10) and so $q^{-1}[V] = f^{-1}[U]$ for some subset, U, of Y. Since $f^{-1}[U]$ is open in X, if Y carries the strong topology, U is open in Y. However, $f[f^{-1}[U]] = h[q[q^{-1}[V]]]$, by definition of h. Hence, $U = h[V]$ and so h is open. ∎

EXERCISE 1. Let $X^* = \prod_{\alpha \in T} X_\alpha \neq \emptyset$. Prove that each X_α is homeomorphic to a quotient space of X^*, (a) if T is a finite indexing set; (b) if T is any indexing set.

13.6 Corollary. *If f is a continuous function from a space X onto a space Y, then f can be "factored" into $h \circ q$, where (1) q is the quotient function of X onto X/R, (2) (x, y) is in R if and only if $f(x) = f(y)$, and (3) h is a 1:1 continuous function from X/R onto Y.*

Proof: By theorem 13.5 and its proof. ∎

13.7 Theorem. *If X and Y are topological spaces and if X/R is a quotient space of X, then any continuous function $f: X \xrightarrow{\text{onto}} Y$ induces a continuous function g from X/R onto Y, provided (x, y) in R implies $f(x) = f(y)$, i.e. $R \subseteq \{(x, y) \mid f(x) = f(y)\}$.*

Proof: Define $g[(x]) = f(x)$, where $[x]$ denotes the equivalence class containing x. Let $[x] = [y]$; then (x, y) is in R and $f(x) = f(y)$. Hence, $g([y]) = g([x])$ and so g is single-valued. Further, $f = g \circ q$. Hence by theorem 13.4, g is continuous. ∎

There are other conditions that insure that the continuous image $f[X]$ of a topological space X is homeomorphic to a quotient or decomposition space, e.g., if X is compact and $f[X]$ is Hausdorff. (See chapter 6, theorem 29.11.)

The analogue of theorem 13.5 in algebra is one of the fundamental isomorphism theorems for groups. If Φ is a homomorphism from a group G onto a group G^*, then the quotient group corresponding to the quotient space X/R of theorem 13.5 is the group G/K, where K is the kernel of Φ. This follows from the fact that $\Phi(x) = \Phi(y)$ if and only if $x \cdot y^{-1}$ is in K. In algebra, however, the homomorphism corresponding to the continuous function h of theorem 13.5 always turns out to be an isomorphism. Thus every image of a group G under a homomorphism is isomorphic to a factor group of G.

Since it was established by example 6.6 that the continuous image of a second or first countable space need not be second or first countable, respectively, it would appear that a quotient space may not satisfy these countability conditions even though the original space does. The following example proves that a space X can be second countable, while a quotient space X/R need not be even first countable.

13.8 Example. Let $L_n = \{(x, y) \mid y = n, n \text{ is an integer and } x \text{ is real}\}$. Let X be the subspace $\bigcup_n L_n$ of E^2. Then X consists of all points in the (x, y) plane which lie on the horizontal lines $y = n$, for n an integer; basic neighborhoods for points are horizontal open intervals. As a subspace of E^2, X is first and second countable by corollary 11.24. Let R denote the following equivalence relation on X: (1) $((x, y), (x, y))$ is in R, and (2) $((0, v), (0, y))$ is in R, for any integers v and y. It is now shown that the quotient space X/R is not first countable and so is not second countable. Let O^* denote the R-equivalence class, $\{(x, y) \mid x = 0$ and y is an integer$\}$; all other R-equivalence classes contain one point only. Let $\{U_1, U_2, \ldots, U_j, \ldots\}$ be any countable local base at O^* in X/R. A set G in X/R is open if and only if $q^{-1}[G]$ is open in X, where q is the quotient function. Hence, $q^{-1}[U_j]$ is open in X, for every j, and contains all points of X on the y-axis. Hence, each U_j contains a union of sets, $J_k^j = \{(x, y) \mid y = k, 0 < |x| < \epsilon_k^{(j)}, \epsilon_k^{(j)} > 0$ and k is an integer$\}$. Next, define the set $U^* = \bigcup_m K_m$, where $K_m = \{(x, y) \mid y = m, m$ is an integer, $0 < |x| < \epsilon_m^{(m)}/2\} \cup \{O^*\}$. U^* is open and contains O^*. Let U_j be any set in the countable base for O^*. The point $(\frac{3}{4}\epsilon_j^{(j)}, j)$ lies in U_j, by definition of $\epsilon_j^{(j)}$; however, $(\frac{3}{4}\epsilon_j^{(j)}, j)$ does not lie in U^* and $U^* \not\supseteq U_j$, $j = 1, 2, \ldots$. Thus no such countable collection $\{U_1, U_2, \ldots, U_n, \ldots\}$ is a base at O^*. Since X/R is not first countable it is not second countable.

EXERCISE 2. Prove that any quotient space of a separable space is separable.

The following important spaces are quotient spaces.

13.9 Definition. Let I be the closed unit interval of real numbers, $\{x \mid 0 \leq x \leq 1\}$, with the relative topology. $I \times I$ is then a product space and a subspace of E^2. Let R denote the following equivalence relation on $I \times I$ (aRb means (a, b) is in R):

(1) $(x, 0)\, R\, (x, 1)$ and $(x, 1)\, R\, (x, 0)$, for $0 \leq x \leq 1$;

(2) $(0, y)\, R\, (1, y)$ and $(1, y)\, R\, (0, y)$, for $0 \leq y \leq 1$; and

(3) $(x, y)\, R\, (x, y)$.

The quotient space $(I \times I)/R$ is called the *Torus*.

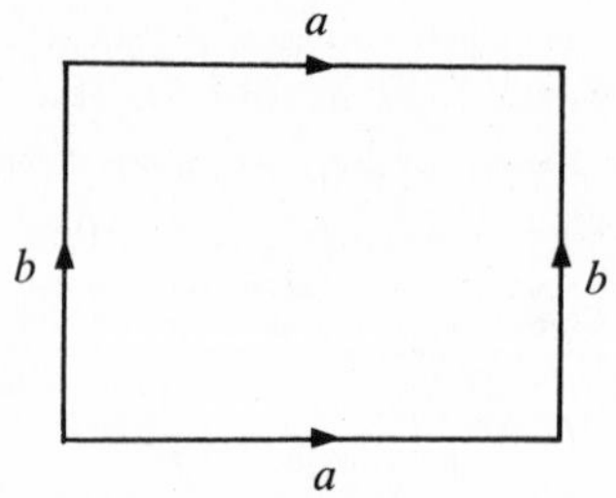

FIGURE 11 The Torus

13.10 Definition. Let R^* denote the following equivalence relation in $I \times I$:
(1) $(x, 0)\ R^*\ (1 - x, 1)$ and $(1 - x, 1)\ R^*\ (x, 0)$ for $0 \leq x \leq 1$; and
(2) $(x, y)\ R^*\ (x, y)$.
The quotient space $(I \times I)/R^*$ is called the *Moebius strip.*

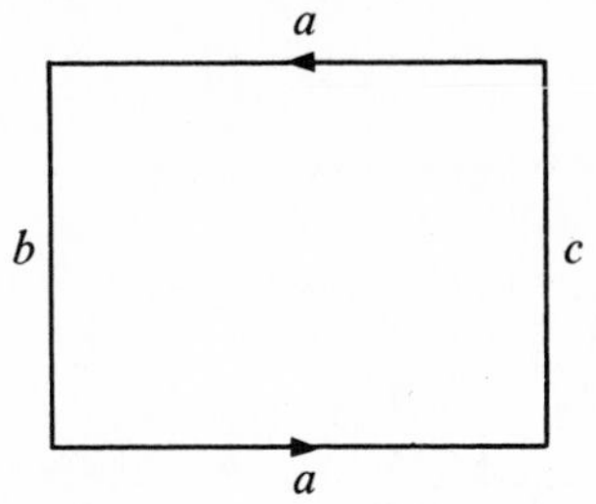

FIGURE 12 The Moebius Strip

13.11 Definition. Let R' denote the following equivalence relation in $I \times I$:
(1) $(x, 0)\ R'\ (x, 1)$ and $(x, 1)\ R'\ (x, 0)$ for $0 \leq x \leq 1$;
(2) $(0, y)\ R'\ (1, 1 - y)$ and $(1, 1 - y)\ R'\ (0, y)$ for $0 \leq y \leq 1$; and
(3) $(x, y)\ R'\ (x, y)$.
The quotient space $(I \times I)/R'$ is called the *Klein bottle.*

13.12 Definition. Let R'' denote the following equivalence relation on $I \times I$:
(1) $(1 - x, 0)\ R''\ (x, 1)$ and $(x, 1)\ R''\ (1 - x, 0)$ for $0 \leq x \leq 1$;
(2) $(0, y)\ R''\ (1, 1 - y)$ and $(1, 1 - y)\ R''\ (0, y)$ for $0 \leq y \leq 1$; and
(3) $(x, y)\ R''\ (x, y)$.
The quotient space $(I \times I)/R''$ is called the *Projective plane.*

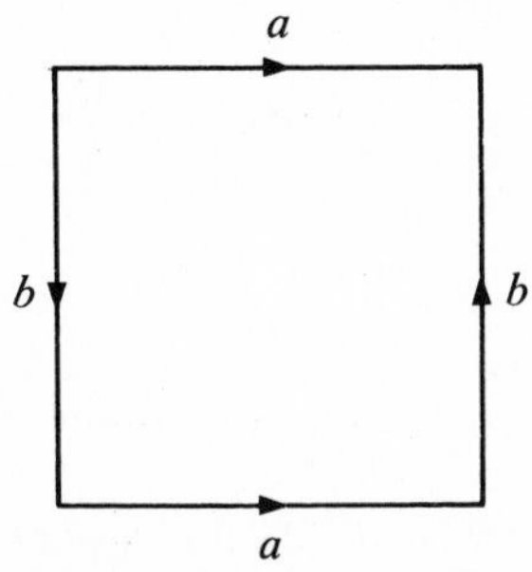

FIGURE 13 The Klein Bottle

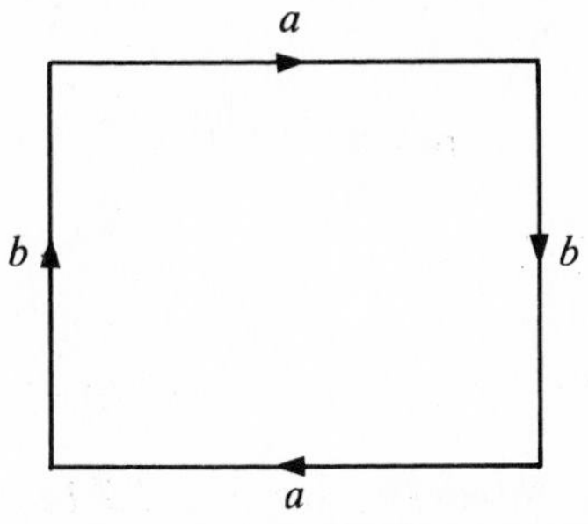

FIGURE 14 The Projective Plane

13.13 Definition. Let X denote any topological space. Again let I denote the closed unit interval, $[0, 1]$, with the usual relative topology. The product space $X \times I$ is called the *cylinder of* X and is denoted by ZX. The quotient space $(X \times I)/R$, where $R = \{((x_1, t_1), (x_2, t_2)) \mid x_1 = x_2 \text{ and } t_1 = t_2 \text{ or } t_1 = t_2 = 1\}$, is called the *cone of* X and is denoted by CX. The quotient space $(X \times I)/R^*$, where $R = \{((x_1, t_1), (x_2, t_2)) \mid x_1 = x_2 \text{ and } t_1 = t_2 \text{ or } t_1 = t_2 = 0 \text{ or } t_1 = t_2 = 1\}$, is called the *suspension of* X and is denoted by ΣX.

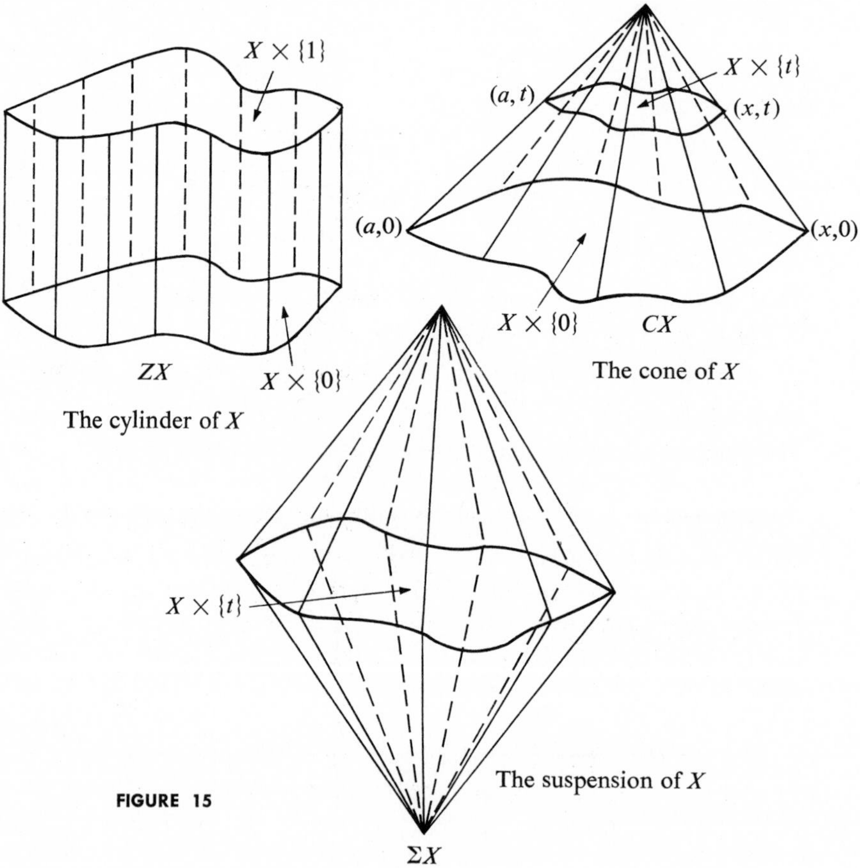

FIGURE 15

Another type of quotient space has become important in modern topology.

13.14 Lemma. *Let X and Y be disjoint sets; let $A \subseteq X$ and let f be a function from A into Y. Further, let $R_f = \{(a, b) \mid a = b \text{ or } f(a) = f(b) \text{ or } b = f(a) \text{ or } a = f(b)\}$. R_f is an equivalence relation on $X \cup Y$.*

Proof: Exercise.

13.15 Definition. Let $\{X, \mathfrak{J}_1\}$ and $\{Y, \mathfrak{J}_2\}$ be spaces such that $X \cap Y = \emptyset$. The space $\{X \cup Y, \mathfrak{J}_1 + \mathfrak{J}_2\}$ where $\mathfrak{J}_1 + \mathfrak{J}_2 = \{G \mid G \subseteq X \cup Y, G \cap X \in \mathfrak{J}_1$, and $G \cap Y \in \mathfrak{J}_2\}$ is called the *disjoint union space* of $\{X, \mathfrak{J}_1\}$ and $\{Y, \mathfrak{J}_2\}$.

13.16 Definition. Let S and T denote disjoint spaces. Let $A \subseteq S$ and let f be a function from A into T. The quotient space $(S \cup T)/R_f$, where $S \cup T$ is the disjoint union space of S and T and R_f is the equivalence relation of lemma 13.14, is called "S attached to T by f." (See figure 16.)

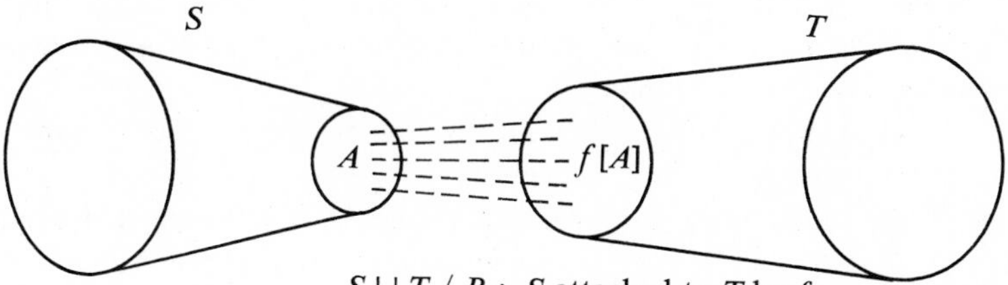

$S \cup T / R_f$: S attached to T by f

FIGURE 16

13.17 Theorem. *Let S and T be disjoint spaces. Let A be a closed subset of S and let f be continuous from A into T. Then in the quotient space $(S \cup T)/R_f$, $q[T]$ is closed, q/T is a homeomorphism, $q[S \sim A]$ is open and $q/S \sim A$ is a homeomorphism, where q is the quotient function.*

Proof: A. By definition of R_f, if $x \in S \sim A$, then $q(x) = \{x\}$. Hence q is 1:1 on $S \sim A$. Also, since $q^{-1}[q[S \sim A]] = S \sim A$ and since $S \sim A$ is open in $S \cup T$, $q[S \sim A]$ is open in $(S \cup T)/R_f$ by definition of the quotient topology. Now let G be an open subset of $S \sim A$. Since $q^{-1}[q[G]] = G$, $q[G]$ is open, by definition of the quotient topology. Since $q \mid S \sim A$ is continuous by lemma 9.21, $q \mid S \sim A$ is a homeomorphism onto an open subset of $(S \cup T)/R_f$.

B. Next, consider $q[T]$. By definition of R_f, $q \mid T$ is 1:1. Now, $q^{-1}[q[T]] = T \cup A$. Since $T \cup A$ is closed in $S \cup T$, it follows from the definition of the quotient topology that $q[T]$ is closed in $(S \cup T)/R_f$. $q \mid T$ is continuous, again by lemma 9.21. Now let F be closed in Y. By definition of R_f and q, $q^{-1}[q[F]] = F \cup f^{-1}[F]$. Since f is continuous, $f^{-1}[F]$ is closed in S. Hence, $F \cup f^{-1}[F]$ is closed in $S \cup T$. Thus, $q[F]$ is closed in $S \cup T$ by definition of the quotient topology. $q \mid T$ is then a homeomorphism. ▌

SUMMARY FOR CHAPTER 2

Associated with any set S is the set $\mathfrak{L}$ *of all topologies for S.* $\mathfrak{L}$ has the structure of a lattice with inclusion as the partial order relation. $\mathfrak{L}$ has a largest element, the *discrete topology*, $P(S)$, and a smallest element, the *trivial topology*, $\{S, \emptyset\}$.

For any subset M in a space $\{S, \mathfrak{T}\}$, a topology, r-$\mathfrak{T}$, called the *relative topology* for M exists. r-$\mathfrak{T}$ consists of all intersections with M of sets in $\mathfrak{T}$.

Functions from a set onto spaces can be used to define a topology on the common domain called the *weak topology*. This topology is the smallest topology for the domain with which the original functions are continuous. Similarly, functions from spaces onto a set can be used to define a topology on the common range called the *strong topology*. This is the largest topology for the range with which the original functions are continuous.

One of the most important instances of the weak topology is the product topology. The functions used are the projection functions. These functions are generalizations of the projection functions $p_x(x, y) = x$ and $p_y(x, y) = y$ of the plane E^2 onto the usual space E^1 of real numbers. Function spaces with the weak topology are product spaces.

Inverse limit spaces are subspaces of product spaces. The Cantor ternary space is a product space.

One of the most important basic instances of the strong topology is the topology on a quotient or decomposition space. A quotient space is a set of equivalence classes assigned the strong topology which is determined by the quotient function which assigns to every point in the original spaces its equivalence class. Further, if a space Y has the strong topology determined by a single function, f, then Y is homeomorphic to a quotient space X/R of the domain X of f. The relation that determines this quotient space is $\{(a, b) \mid f(a) = f(b)\}$. The Torus, the Moebius strip, the Klein bottle and the Projective plane are important examples of quotient spaces.

CHAPTER 3

Separation Axioms

In E^1, the space of real numbers with the usual topology, two different real numbers a and b, where $a < b$, have disjoint neighborhoods, e.g., $\{x \mid |x - a| < (b - a)/2\}$ and $\{x \mid |x - b| < (b - a)/2\}$. No such condition was found necessary for the definition of continuity. However, if a space is endowed with special properties by axiomatic definition, then still more properties of the space can be established by deduction. If, in particular, the special properties are also enjoyed by the spaces E^1 and E^2 of analysis, for example, then these properties identify a very important special class of spaces. Any property deduced for spaces in this class will be possessed by E^1 and E^2. The more complicated, and hence more interesting theories occur with special classes of spaces whose topologies satisfy more than the two requirements mentioned in definition 3.26 of a topology. This is a consequence of the nature of a proof.

The separation axioms identify such special classes of spaces and these classes all contain E^1 and E^2. Thus every theorem in chapter 3 will be true for E^1 and E^2, and most of the other spaces of function theory.

14. T_0-SPACES.

14.1 Definition. A space X is called a T_0-*space* if and only if it satisfies the T_0-*axiom:* For any two distinct points in X, there exists, in the topology on X, at least one open set which contains one of the points and not the other point.

EXERCISE 1. Prove that the following statement is logically equivalent to the T_0-axiom: for any two points of a space X there exists a neighborhood of one of these points which does not contain the other point.

14.2 Example. Let X be any set with at least two points and let X have the trivial topology. X is a topological space but it does not satisfy the T_0-axiom.

14.3 Example. Let S denote the set of real numbers and let R denote $\{(x^*, U) \mid x^* \text{ is a real number and } U = \{x \mid x \geq x^*\}\}$. R is a basic neighborhood relation which assigns to each point of S exactly one basic neighborhood. $\{S, R^+\}$ is a T_0-space, where again R^+ is the unique neighborhood relation for S determined by R.

14.4 Theorem. *A space X is a T_0-space if and only if $\overline{\{p\}} \neq \overline{\{q\}}$, where $p \in X$, $q \in X$ and $p \neq q$.*

Proof: A. Let X be a T_0-space; let x and y be two different points of X. Then there exists an open set in X which contains one of the points, say x, and not the other. Therefore, x is not a limit point of $\{y\}$. Since x is not in $\overline{\{y\}}$ and x is in $\overline{\{x\}}$, $\overline{\{x\}} \neq \overline{\{y\}}$.

B. Let $\overline{\{x\}} \neq \overline{\{y\}}$ for $x \neq y$. Further, assume that every open set which contains x contain y. Then, x is in $\overline{\{y\}}$, and by corollary 3.6 and theorem 3.7, $\overline{\{x\}} \subseteq \overline{\{y\}}$. Similarly, if every open set which contains y contains x, then y is in $\overline{\{x\}}$ and $\overline{\{y\}} \subseteq \overline{\{x\}}$. Hence, $\overline{\{y\}} = \overline{\{x\}}$ and this is a contradiction. Thus, there must exist an open set containing x which does not contain y or an open set containing y which does not contain x. X is then a T_0-space. ▌

14.5 Theorem. *Every space X can be converted into a T_0-space, which is a quotient space of X, by identifying points which have the same closures.*

Proof: Let $D = \{(x, y) \mid x \in X,\ y \in X \text{ and } \overline{\{x\}} = \overline{\{y\}}\}$. D is an equivalence relation on X. X/D with the quotient topology determines a quotient space of X. It must be proved that X/D is a T_0-space. Let α and β be two different points of X/D and let q be the quotient function from X onto X/D. $q^{-1}(\alpha)$ and $q^{-1}(\beta)$ are two distinct D-equivalence classes in X, by definition of q. Let a be in $q^{-1}(\alpha)$ and let b be in $q^{-1}(\beta)$. Then $\overline{\{a\}} \neq \overline{\{b\}}$, by definition of D. This implies that at least one of them is not contained in the other, say $\overline{\{b\}} \not\subseteq \overline{\{a\}}$. Now consider $\overline{\{a\}}$. If c is in $\overline{\{a\}}$, then $\overline{\{c\}} \subseteq \overline{\{a\}}$ by corollary 3.6 and theorem 3.7. If (z, c) is in D, then $\overline{\{z\}} = \overline{\{c\}}$ and so $\overline{\{z\}} \subseteq \overline{\{a\}}$. Hence, z is in $\overline{\{a\}}$ and $\overline{\{a\}}$ is the union of D-equivalence classes. $\sim\overline{\{a\}}$, the complement of $\overline{\{a\}}$ in X, must also be the union of D-equivalence classes, i.e. $\sim\overline{\{a\}}$ is an inverse set. Also $\sim\overline{\{a\}}$ is open in X. It follows by definition of the quotient topology that $W = q[\sim\overline{\{a\}}]$ an open set in X/D. Since $\overline{\{b\}} \not\subseteq \overline{\{a\}}$, b is not in $\overline{\{a\}}$; hence, b is in $\sim\overline{\{a\}}$ and $q(b) = \beta$ is in W. Since a is not in $\sim\overline{\{a\}} = q^{-1}(W)$, $q(a)$ is not in W. However, $q(a) = \alpha$; therefore, α is not in W and X/D is a T_0-space. ▌

EXERCISE 2. In a T_0-space distinct one-point subsets have distinct closures. Prove or disprove: In a T_0-space distinct subsets have distinct closures. (Distinct means unequal but not necessarily disjoint.)

EXERCISE 3. Do there exist spaces in which distinct subsets always have distinct closures? Classify such spaces.

EXERCISE 4. Let S denote the set of real numbers. Let $V_a = \{x \mid x > a\}$. Let $R = \{(p, V_a) \mid p \in S \text{ and } a < p\}$. R is a basic neighborhood relation for S, and hence determines a topology $\mathfrak{I}$ on S. Prove that $\{S, \mathfrak{I}\}$ is a T_0-space.

15. T_1-SPACES.

15.1 Definition. A space X is called a *T_1-space* if and only if it satisfies the *T_1-axiom:* if x and y are two distinct points of X, there exist open sets U and V such that U contains x but not y and V contains y but not x.

EXERCISE 1. Prove that the following statement is logically equivalent to the T_1-axiom: each of any two distinct points of a space X has a neighborhood that does not contain the other point.

15.2 Example. The spaces defined in example 14.3 and exercise 4 of section 14 are T_0 but not T_1.

15.3 Example. Let X be the set consisting of all real numbers and one other element, ω, which is not a real number. Let $R = \{(x, U) \mid x$ is a real number in U and U is an open interval of real numbers$\} \cup \{(x, U) \mid x = \omega$, and $\sim U$ in X is a finite subset of the set of real numbers$\}$. $\{X, R^+\}$ is a topological space and a T_1-space, where again R^+ is the unique neighborhood relation for X determined by R.

The following theorems yields a useful characterization of T_1-spaces.

15.4 Theorem. *A space X is a T_1-space if and only if each one-point subset of X constitutes a closed set.*

Proof: A. Let X be a T_1-space; let x be any point of X and let y be any other point of X. There exists an open set U containing y and not containing x; hence, y is not in $\overline{\{x\}}$. Since y was any point of X different from x, no point of X is a limit point of $\{x\}$, and so $\{x\}$ is closed.

B. For any x in the space X, let $\{x\}$ be closed. Let y and z be two distinct points of X. Since $\{y\}$ is closed, $\sim\{y\}$ is open in X and contains z but not y. Similarly $\sim\{z\}$ is open, contains y but does not contain z. Hence, X is a T_1-space. ▌

15.5 Corollary. *Let X be any space and D an equivalence relation defined on X. The quotient space X/D is a T_1-space if and only if the D-equivalence classes are closed subsets of X.*

Proof: Exercise.

15.6 Theorem. *A space X is a T_1-space if and only if every finite subset is closed.*

Proof: A. If X is a T_1-space, then any finite set is by theorem 15.4 the union of a finite number of closed sets, and hence by theorem 3.15 is closed.

B. If every finite subset of the space X is closed, then the sets containing a single point are closed. By theorem 15.4, the space is T_1. ▌

15.7 Corollary. *Any finite T_1-space, X, is discrete.*

Proof. Each one-point subset, $\{x\}$, of X is the complement of a finite and hence closed set. Hence, each one-point subset is an open set. ▌

15.8 Lemma. *The collection $\mathscr{C}$ consisting of a set X and all finite subsets of X is a cotopology for the set X.*

Proof: Since $\emptyset$ is finite, $\emptyset$ is in $\mathscr{C}$; X is in $\mathscr{C}$ by hypothesis. The union of a finite number of finite sets is finite. Further, $F_1 \cup F_2 \cup \cdots \cup F_k = X$, for k a natural number and $F_i = X$; for some i such that $1 \leq i \leq k$. The intersection of any number of finite sets is finite and $\bigcap_\nu F_\nu$, where each F_ν is in $\mathscr{C}$, is X or a finite subset. Hence, this collection is a cotopology, by definition 3.17. ▌

15.9 Definition. The *minimal T_1-cotopology* for a set X is the cotopology consisting of X and all finite subsets of X. By theorem 15.6, the minimal T_1-cotopology is contained in every T_1-cotopology for X and every cotopology which contains the minimal T_1-cotopology is T_1.

EXERCISE 2. Prove that the minimal T_1-cotopology for a set X determines the smallest topology with which X is a T_1-space.

15.10 Theorem. *X is a T_1-space if and only if the intersection of all open sets containing a subset M is M itself.*

Proof: A. Let X be a T_1-space and let x be any point in $\sim M$, the complement of M. $X \sim \{x\}$ is open, contains M, and does not contain x. Hence x is not in every open set containing M. Since x was any point of $\sim M$, the intersection of all open sets containing M is exactly M.

B. Let the intersection of all the open sets containing a subset M be M. Let a and b be two points of X. Since the intersection of all the open sets containing a is $\{a\}$, there must exist at least one open set which contains a and does not contain b. Similarly, there must exist at least one open set which contains b and not a. ▌

15.11 Corollary. *A space X is a T_1-space if and only if the intersection of all the neighborhoods of a given point x is $\{x\}$.*

Proof: This corollary follows directly from theorem 15.10. ▌

15.12 Example. Let X be any space with the trivial topology. The intersection of all open sets containing any non-empty subset is the whole set X.

15.13 Example. Let S be the space defined in example 14.3, where the basic neighborhood for a real number a is the set $U_a = \{x \mid x \geq a\}$. Let M be the subset of negative real numbers. The only open set containing M is the whole set S.

15.14 Theorem. *If x is a limit point of a set M in a T_1-space X, then every open set containing x contains an infinite number of distinct points of M.*

Proof: Let x be a limit point of M in X, and let G be an open set containing x. Let $\{m_1, m_2, \ldots, m_k\} = F$ for k a natural number, where $F = (G \cap M) \sim \{x\}$. F is the union of a finite number of closed sets and hence is closed. Therefore, $\sim F$ is open and contains x. $(\sim F) \cap G$ is then also open, contains x, and contains no point of M different from x. This contradicts the hypothesis that x is a limit point of M. Hence $(G \cap M) \sim \{x\}$ is not finite. ▌

15.15 Corollary. *In a T_1-space only infinite sets can have limit points.*

Proof: Since any subset of a finite set is finite, no finite set can contain an infinite subset. Thus, the corollary follows directly from theorem 15.14. ▌

16. HAUSDORFF SPACES (T_2-SPACES).

16.1 Definition. A space X is called a *Hausdorff* or *T_2-space* if and only if it satisfies the *Hausdorff* or *T_2-axiom:* if x and y are two distinct points of X, then there exist open sets U and V such that x is in U, y is in V, and $U \cap V = \emptyset$.

16.2 Theorem. *A space X is Hausdorff if and only if for any two distinct points x and y, there exist closed sets F_1 and F_2 such that:*

(1) $F_1 \cup F_2 = X$;

(2) x is in F_1, but y is not in F_1;

(3) y is in F_2, but x is not in F_2.

Proof: Exercise.

16.3 Theorem. *If X is a finite T_1-space, then X is Hausdorff.*

Proof: Exercise.

EXERCISE 1. Show that the following statement is logically equivalent to the Hausdorff or T_2-axiom: any two distinct points of the space X possess disjoint neighborhoods.

16.4 Example. Consider the space X defined in example 15.3, where X consists of the real numbers plus one element, ω. The basic neighborhoods for the real numbers are the usual open intervals and those for ω are sets U which contain ω and are the complements of finite sets. X is T_1, but is not Hausdorff (T_2). For let r be any real number and V any basic neighborhood of r. Every basic neighborhood U of ω intersects V. Hence, ω and r do not possess disjoint neighborhoods.

16.5 Example. Let X be the space consisting of the set of all real numbers with the usual basic neighborhoods except for the number 0. Let a basic neighborhood for 0 be any set $U_\epsilon = \{x \mid x \neq 1/n$, for n any natural number and $|x| < \epsilon$, for $\epsilon > 0\}$. X is a T_2-space since any two points have disjoint basic neighborhoods.

16.6 Theorem. *If X is a T_2-space, then X is a T_1-space; and if X is a T_1-space, then X is a T_0-space.*

Proof: Exercise.

EXERCISE 2. Let $(X, \mathfrak{I})$ be a space, where X is the set and $\mathfrak{I}$ is the topology; let $\mathfrak{I}^+$ be a topology for the set X which is larger than $\mathfrak{I}$. If $(X, \mathfrak{I})$ is a T_0-, T_1-, or T_2-space, prove that $(X, \mathfrak{I}^+)$ is a T_0-, T_1-, or T_2-space, respectively.

EXERCISE 3. Prove that E^1 and E^2 are Hausdorff, and hence T_0 and T_1.

16.7 Theorem. *If f and g are two continuous functions of a space X into a Hausdorff space, then $\{x \mid f(x) = g(x)\}$ is closed in X.*

Proof: Exercise.

16.8 Corollary. *If f and g are two continuous real-valued or complex-valued functions defined on any space X, then the set of points on which the two functions coincide is closed in X.*

Proof: Exercise.

The previous theorem implies that any retract A of a Hausdorff space X is closed in X.

In section 7 of chapter 1, convergence for nets (generalized sequences) and filters was defined as a topological concept. It will now be shown that the Hausdorff axiom has a striking effect on convergence for nets and filters.

UNIQUENESS OF LIMITS

16.9 Theorem. *If a space X is Hausdorff, then any net or any filter has at most one limit, and conversely, any space X in which any net or any filter has at most one limit is Hausdorff.*

Proof: A. Let (a_δ) denote any net or generalized sequence in X. Let α and β be two distinct limits for (a_δ) in X. X is Hausdorff; hence, there exist open sets U and V such that U contains α, V contains β, and $U \cap V = \emptyset$. By definition of limit of a net, there exists δ' in the domain of (a_δ) such that $\delta \geq \delta'$ implies a_δ is in U, and there exists δ'' in the domain of (a_δ) such that $\delta \geq \delta''$ implies a_δ is in V. By definition of a directed set, there exists δ^* in the domain of (a_δ) such that $\delta^* \geq \delta'$ and $\delta^* \geq \delta''$. Hence, a_{δ^*} is in U and a_{δ^*} is in V, and $U \cap V \neq \emptyset$. This is a contradiction. Hence two distinct limits for (a_δ) cannot exist.

B. Let $\mathfrak{F}$ be any filter in the Hausdorff space X. Let α and β be two distinct limits for $\mathfrak{F}$. By definition of convergence of a filter, $\mathfrak{F}$ contains all neighborhoods of α in X, and $\mathfrak{F}$ also contains all neighborhoods of β in X. Since X is Hausdorff there exist a neighborhood A of α and a neighborhood B of β such that $A \cap B = \emptyset$. Now A is in $\mathfrak{F}$ and B is in $\mathfrak{F}$; by definition of a filter, $A \cap B$ is in $\mathfrak{F}$. This is a contradiction since no filter contains the null set. Hence, $\mathfrak{F}$ cannot have two distinct limits.

C. Let X be a space such that any filter $\mathfrak{F}$ on X has at most one limit in X. Let α and β be any two distinct points of X. Let $\mathfrak{F}^\alpha$ and $\mathfrak{F}^\beta$ denote the filters of neighborhoods of α and β, respectively. Let U^α be a neighborhood of α. If there exists V^β, a neighborhood of β, such that $U^\alpha \cap V^\beta = \emptyset$, then the two points have disjoint neighborhoods. If there does not exist such a V^β, then the intersection of U^α with every neighborhood of β is a non-empty set. Hence, the collection $\mathfrak{F}^\beta \cup \{U^\alpha\}$ generates a filter $\mathfrak{F}'$ consisting of all intersections of a finite number of sets in $\mathfrak{F}^\alpha \cup \{U^\alpha\}$ and all subsets of X which contain any such intersection. The null set does not belong to $\mathfrak{F}'$; the intersection of any finite number of elements does belong, by definition; and any set containing a set in $\mathfrak{F}'$ belongs to $\mathfrak{F}'$, also by definition. Hence, $\mathfrak{F}'$ is a filter on X. Similarly, if no neighborhood of α is disjoint from any neighborhood of β, the collection $\mathfrak{F}^\alpha \cup \mathfrak{F}^\beta$ generates a filter $\mathfrak{F}^*$ on X consisting of all intersections of a finite number of sets in $\mathfrak{F}^\alpha \cup \mathfrak{F}^\beta$ and all subsets of X which contain such an intersection. Again by definition, $\mathfrak{F}^*$ is a filter. Since $\mathfrak{F}^*$ contains $\mathfrak{F}^\alpha$ and $\mathfrak{F}^*$ contains $\mathfrak{F}^\beta$, $\mathfrak{F}^*$ converges to both α and β. This contradicts the hypothesis that no filter on X can have distinct limits. Hence, no such filter $\mathfrak{F}^*$ can exist. But $\mathfrak{F}^*$ does exist, unless there exists at least one neighborhood U of α and one neighborhood V of β such that $U \cap V = \emptyset$. Hence, X must be Hausdorff.

D. Let X be a space such that any net in X converges to at most one limit and let α and β be two distinct points of X. If the intersection of every neighborhood U of α with every neighborhood V of β is a non-empty set, then the set $\mathfrak{D}$ consisting of all intersections of finitely many neighborhoods of α or of β, with $\subseteq$, is a directed set of non-empty sets. A choice function defines a net $\mathfrak{N}$ whose domain is $\mathfrak{D}$ and whose range is in X. Let G_1 be open and contain α; let G_2 be open and contain β. If $V \subseteq G_1 \cap G_2$, and $V \in \mathfrak{D}$ then $\mathfrak{N}(V) \in G_1$ and $\mathfrak{N}(V) \in G_2$. Hence $\mathfrak{N}$ converges to α and to β. This contradicts the hypothesis that a net can have at most one limit. Hence, no such net can exist. But $\mathfrak{N}$ does exist unless there exists a neighborhood U of α and a neighborhood V of β such that $U \cap V = \emptyset$. Hence, X must be Hausdorff. ▮

16.10 Corollary. *In a Hausdorff space, sequential limits are unique.*

Proof: Since a sequence is a net, then by theorem 16.9, each sequence can have at most one limit. ▮

A natural question to ask at this point seems to be whether the converse of corollary 16.10 holds, i.e., if any sequence in a space X has at most one limit, is X necessarily Hausdorff? The following example answers the question negatively.

16.11 Example. Let X consist of the real numbers plus one element, ω, which is not a real number, and let the basic neighborhoods be defined as follows: if x is a real number, then its basic neighborhoods are the usual open intervals; if x is ω, then its basic neighborhoods are sets whose complements consist of the ranges of a finite number of converging sequences of real numbers and the limits to which these sequences converge. These sets satisfy the axioms for basic neighborhoods. In X, sequential limits are unique, for if σ denotes the range of any sequence of real numbers which converges to the real number, l, then $\sim(\sigma \cup \{l\})$ in X is a basic neighborhood of ω and contains no element of σ. Hence no sequence which converges to a real number can converge to ω and no sequence can converge to two distinct real numbers. However, it will be shown that X is not Hausdorff. If r is any real number in X, let $U = \{x \mid |x - r| < \epsilon, \epsilon > 0\}$. Let V be any basic neighborhood of ω in X. $(\sim V) \cap U$ is at most a countably infinite set of real numbers. So, $[(\sim V) \cap U] \not\supseteq U$. Hence, $U \not\subseteq \sim V$ and $V \cap U \neq \emptyset$. Thus, every basic neighborhood of ω intersects every basic neighborhood of r, and so X is not Hausdorff even though sequential limits are unique.

EXERCISE 4. Let X be the set of real numbers with the topology consisting of $\emptyset$ and all complements of countable sets. Prove that in X no sequence has more than one limit and that X is not Hausdorff.

16.12 Theorem. *If X is a space in which no sequence has more than one limit, then X is a T_1-space.*

Proof: Let α and β be two distinct points of X. The constant sequences $(\alpha, \alpha, \alpha, \ldots)$ and $(\beta, \beta, \beta, \ldots)$ converge to α and β, respectively. Hence, $(\beta, \beta, \ldots)$ cannot converge to α and $(\alpha, \alpha, \ldots)$ cannot converge to β. Therefore, α must have a neighborhood which does not contain β and β must have a neighborhood which does not contain α. ▮

16.13 Theorem. *If X is a first countable space in which sequential limits are unique, then X is Hausdorff.*

Proof: Let α and β be two distinct points of X. X is a T_1-space by theorem 16.12. If X is finite, then X is Hausdorff by theorem 16.3. Thus, let X be infinite. If α has a finite local base $\{U_1, U_2, \ldots, U_k\}$, then $\bigcap_{i=1}^{k} U_i$ is open and equals $\{\alpha\}$, by corollary 15.11. Since X is T_1, β has a neighborhood which does not contain α. Thus, the points α and β possess disjoint neighborhoods. It will now be assumed that α and β both have countably infinite local bases and that the intersection of every neighborhood of α with every neighborhood of β is a non-empty set. Let $\{U_1, U_2, \ldots, U_j, \ldots\}$ and $\{V_1, V_2, \ldots, V_i, \ldots\}$ denote countably infinite local bases at α and β, respectively. Consider the sequence $(U_1, V_1, U_2, V_2, \ldots, U_i, V_i, \ldots)$. Let $W_1 = U_1 \cap V_1$; $W_2 = U_1 \cap V_1 \cap U_2 \cap V_2; \ldots; W_i = U_1 \cap V_1 \cap U_2 \cap V_2 \cap \cdots \cap U_i \cap V_i; \ldots$. $W_1 \supseteq W_2 \supseteq$

$W_3 \supseteq \cdots \supseteq W_i \supseteq \cdots$ and each W_i is non-empty. A choice function assigns to each set W_i an element x_i in W_i. Consider the sequence $(x_1, x_2, \ldots, x_i, \ldots)$ in X. Let G^α be any open set containing α. There is a set U_k in the local base at α such that $U_k \subseteq G^\alpha$. Since $W_k \subseteq U_k$, then $x_k, x_{k+1}, \ldots$ are all in G^α. Hence, the sequence $(x_1, x_2, \ldots, x_i, \ldots)$ converges to α. Similarly the sequence converges to β. This is a contradiction. No such sequence can exist in X; so $W_j = \emptyset$ for some j. Thus, there must exist neighborhoods U^α of α and V^β of β such that $U^\alpha \cap V^\beta = \emptyset$. X is then Hausdorff. ▮

Thus, unique sequential limits imply the T_1-axiom. Unique sequential limits plus first countability imply the T_2-axiom.

Alternate Definitions

16.14 Theorem. *A space X is Hausdorff if and only if for every point α in X, $\{\alpha\} = \bigcap_\nu F_\nu$, where $\{F_\nu\}$ denotes the set of all closed neighborhoods of α in X.*

Proof: A. Let X be a Hausdorff space; let α be any point of X and β any other point of X. There exist open neighborhoods U and V of α and β, respectively, such that $U \cap V = \emptyset$. Hence, $U \subseteq \sim V$. Since $\sim V = \overline{\sim V}$, $\bar{U} \subseteq \sim V$ by corollary 3.6. $\bar{U}$ is a closed neighborhood of α and $\bar{U}$ does not contain β, so $\beta \notin \bigcap_\nu F_\nu$. Since β was any other point of X, $\{\alpha\} = \bigcap_\nu F_\nu$.

B. Let $\bigcap_\nu F_\nu = \{\alpha\}$, where $\{F_\nu\}$ is the collection of all closed neighborhoods of α in X. Let β be any other point in X. There exists a closed neighborhood N of α which does not contain β, by hypothesis, since β is not in $\bigcap_\nu F_\nu$. $\sim N$ is open, contains β, and so is a neighborhood of β. $N \cap \sim N = \emptyset$ and so X is Hausdorff. ▮

EXERCISE 5. Prove that if S is the set of real numbers and if $\mathfrak{J}$ is the minimal T_1-topology, then no point is the intersection of its closed neighborhoods.

16.15 Definition. Let X be any set. The identity relation on X or the subset $D = \{(\alpha, \beta) \mid \alpha \text{ is in } X \text{ and } \beta = \alpha\}$ of $X \times X$ is called the *diagonal* of $X \times X$.

16.16 Theorem. *A space X is Hausdorff if and only if the diagonal D in the product space $X \times X$ is closed.*

Proof: A. Let X be a Hausdorff space; let (α, β) be any element in the product space $X \times X$ such that $\alpha \neq \beta$. There exist, in X, open neighborhoods U and V of α and β, respectively, such that $U \cap V = \emptyset$. $U \times V$ is open in $X \times X$, by definition of the product topology; (α, β) is in $U \times V$, by definition of product set; and $(U \times V) \cap D = \emptyset$. Thus, every point of $\sim D$ is interior and so $\sim D$ is open. Hence, D is closed in $X \times X$.

B. Let X be a space and let D be closed in the product space $X \times X$. Let α and β be two distinct points of X. (α, β) is in $\sim D$ in $X \times X$. $\sim D$ is open in $X \times X$, by hypothesis; hence, there exists a base element $U \times V \subseteq (\sim D)$ such that (α, β) is in $U \times V$. Since $U \times V \subseteq (\sim D)$, $U \cap V = \emptyset$ in X. Since (α, β) is in $U \times V$, α is in U and β is in V. Further, U and V are open in X. Hence, X is Hausdorff. ▮

Subspaces, Products and Quotient Spaces of Hausdorff Spaces

16.17 Theorem. *If X is a T_0-, T_1-, or T_2-space, then any subspace of X is a T_0-, T_1-, or T_2-space, respectively.*

Proof: By definition of the relative topology, the conclusion follows. ▮

EXERCISE 6. Let $\{X_1, X_2, \ldots, X_k\}$ be a non-empty, finite collection of non-empty spaces. Prove that the non-empty product space $\prod_{i=1}^{k} X_i$ is a T_0-, T_1-, or T_2-space, respectively, if and only if each X_i is.

16.18 Theorem. *Let $\{X_\nu\}$, for ν in some non-empty indexing set $\mathfrak{A}$, denote a collection of non-empty spaces. The non-empty product space $\prod_{\nu \in \mathfrak{A}} X_\nu$ is a T_0-, T_1- or T_2-space, respectively, if and only if each X_ν is.*

Proof: Let x^* and y^* be two distinct points of $\prod_{\nu \in \mathfrak{A}} X_\nu$. There is an α in $\mathfrak{A}$, such that $p_2(x^*) \neq p_2(y^*)$, where p_α denotes the projection mapping of $\prod_{\nu \in \mathfrak{A}} X_\nu$ onto X_α. Let $p_\alpha(x^*)$ be x_α in X_α and let $p_\alpha(y^*)$ be y_α in X_α.

A. If each X_ν is a T_0-space, then there exists an open set U_α in X_α such that x_α, say, is in U_α and y_α is not in U_α. Hence, the set $G^* = \prod_{\nu \in \mathfrak{A}} G_\nu$, where $G_\nu = X_\nu$ for $\nu \neq \alpha$ and $G_\alpha = U_\alpha$, is open in $\prod_{\nu \in \mathfrak{A}} X_\nu$, x^* is in G^* and y^* is not in G^*. Thus, $\prod_{\nu \in \mathfrak{A}} X_\nu$ is a T_0-space.

B. If X_α is a T_1-space, there exists an open set G^α in X_α which contains x_α and not y_α, and there exists an open set H^α in X_α which contains y_α and not x_α. Hence, $G^* = p_\alpha^{-1}[G^\alpha]$ and $H^* = p_\alpha^{-1}[H^\alpha]$, are both open in $\prod_{\nu \in \mathfrak{A}} X_\nu$. It follows that G^* contains x^* but not y^* and H^* contains y^* but not x^*. Hence, $\prod_{\nu \in \mathfrak{A}} X_\nu$ is a T_1-space.

C. If X is a T_2-space (Hausdorff), then $G^\alpha \cap H^\alpha = \emptyset$, where G^α and H^α are as defined in part B. Let z be in $G^* \cap H^*$, also as defined in part B. $p_\alpha(z)$ is in G^α and $p_\alpha(z)$ is in H^α. This contradicts the statement that $G^\alpha \cap H^\alpha = \emptyset$. Hence, G^* and H^* are disjoint and $\prod_{\nu \in \mathfrak{A}} X_\nu$ is a Hausdorff space.

D. Let $\prod_{\nu \in \mathfrak{A}} X_\nu$ be T_0, T_1 or T_2. For α in $\mathfrak{A}$, let a_α and b_α be two points in X_α. Choose points x^* and y^* of $\prod_{\nu \in \mathfrak{A}} X_\nu$ such that x^* and y^* differ only on the α-th coordinate and such that $p_\alpha(x^*) = a_\alpha$ and $p_\alpha(y^*) = b_\alpha$. If $\prod_{\nu \in \mathfrak{A}} X_\nu$ is T_1, then there exists a basic open set $\prod_{\nu \in \mathfrak{A}} G_\nu$ containing x^* and not y^* and there exists a basic open set $\prod_{\nu \in \mathfrak{A}} H_\nu$ containing y^* and not x^*. G_α is open in X_α and contains a_α and not b_α; H_α is open in X_α and contains b_α and not a_α. Hence, X_α is T_1. The other cases are similar. ▮

Any function, f, from a topological space X into a topological space Y determines a subspace Γ of the product space $X \times Y$. Γ consists of $\{(x, y) \mid y = f(x)\}$ and the relative topology. Γ is called the graph of f. The inverse limit space of section 12 was seen to be a generalization of the concept of graph. The following two theorems are concerned with graphs and inverse limit spaces.

16.19 Theorem. *If f is a continuous function from the space X into the Hausdorff space Y, then $f = \{(x, y) \mid y = f(x)\}$ is closed in the product space $X \times Y$.*

Proof: Let (a, b) be a point in $\sim f$. $b \neq f(a)$. Since Y is Hausdorff, there exist disjoint open sets U and V such that b is in U and $f(a)$ is in V. $W = f^{-1}(V)$ is open and contains a. Consider $W \times U$. (a, b) is in $W \times U$ and $W \times U$ is open in $X \times Y$. Let (c, d) be any point in $W \times U$. Since c is in W, $f(c)$ is in V. Since d is in U and $U \cap V = \emptyset$, $d \neq f(c)$. Hence (c, d) is not in f and $W \times U \subseteq \sim f$. $\sim f$ is then open and f is closed. ∎

EXERCISE 7. Let X denote the set of real numbers with the minimal T_1-topology. Prove that the product space $X \times X$ does not have the minimal T_1-topology.

EXERCISE 8. Let X denote the set of real numbers with the minimal T_1-topology. Prove that the graph of f is not closed in $X \times X$, where f is identity function $f(x) = x$.

Definition 12.47 states that an inverse limit space is a special subspace of a product space defined from a net of spaces. The next theorem states that if the spaces in the defining net are all Hausdorff, then the inverse limit space is necessarily closed in the product space. This theorem then is a generalization of theorem 16.19.

16.20 Theorem. *If $[X_\nu, D, f_\alpha^\beta]$ is an inverse limit system of Hausdorff spaces X_ν, ν in D, D a directed set, and $f_\alpha^\beta: X_\beta \to X_\alpha$ continuous, then the corresponding inverse limit space, $\overleftarrow{L}$, is a closed subset of $\prod_{\nu \in D} X_\nu$.*

Proof: Let x^* be any point in $\sim\overleftarrow{L}$, the complement of $\overleftarrow{L}$ in $\prod_{\nu \in D} X_\nu$. Then, there exist β and α in D such that $\beta \geq \alpha$ and $f_\alpha^\beta(x_\beta) \neq x_\alpha$, where x_β and x_α are, respectively, the β-th and α-th coordinates of x^*. Let $f_\alpha^\beta(x_\beta) = y_\alpha$. Since X_α is Hausdorff, there exist open sets U^α and V^α in X_α such that x_α is in U^α, y_α is in V^α, and $U^\alpha \cap V^\alpha = \emptyset$. Since f_α^β is continuous on X_β, $(f_\alpha^\beta)^{-1}[V^\alpha]$ is open in X_β. Let $(f_\alpha^\beta)^{-1}[V^\alpha]$ be denoted by V^β and let $G^* = \prod_{\nu \in D} G_\nu$, where $G_\nu = X_\nu$ for $\nu \neq \alpha$ and $\nu \neq \beta$, $G_\beta = V^\beta$, and $G_\alpha = U^\alpha$. x^* is in G^*. If z^* is in G^* and z_β is the β-th coordinate of z^*, then z_β is in V^β and $f_\alpha^\beta(z_\beta)$ is in V^α. Hence, $f_\alpha^\beta(z_\beta)$ is not in U^α, since $U^\alpha \cap V^\alpha = \emptyset$. Since by definition of G^*, z_α is in U^α, z^* is not in $\overleftarrow{L}$. Thus, no point of G^* is in $\overleftarrow{L}$ and $G^* \subseteq \sim\overleftarrow{L}$ in $\prod_{\nu \in D} X_\nu$. Since every point of $\sim\overleftarrow{L}$ is interior, then $\sim\overleftarrow{L}$ is open by theorem 3.28. Hence, $\overleftarrow{L}$ is closed in $\prod_{\nu \in D} X_\nu$. ∎

In general, as example 16.22 below shows, a quotient space of a Hausdorff space need not be Hausdorff. The next theorem, however, gives a useful sufficient condition for a quotient space to be Hausdorff.

16.21 Theorem. *If X is a space, R an equivalence relation which is a closed subset in $X \times X$, and if $R[A]$ is open in X for each open $A \subseteq X$, then X/R is Hausdorff.*

Proof: Let α and β be two distinct points of X/R. Let $q(a) = \alpha$ and $q(b) = \beta$, where q is the quotient function. (a, b) is not in R, by definition of q. Since R is closed, there is a basic open set $U \times V$ in $X \times X$ such that $(U \times V) \cap R = \emptyset$, (a, b) is in $U \times V$ and U and V are open in X. Since $(U \times V) \cap R = \emptyset$, $R[U] \cap R[V] = \emptyset$. By hypothesis, $R[U]$ and $R[V]$ are open. By definition of the quotient function and the quotient topology, $q[R[U]]$ and $q[R[V]]$ are open and disjoint. Since α is in $q[R[U]]$ and β is in $q[R[V]]$, X/R is Hausdorff. ▮

EXERCISE 9. Prove that if q is the quotient function from a space X onto a quotient space X/R, then q is open if and only if $R[A]$ is open in X for every open subset A of X.

16.22 Example. In the space E^2, let K denote the collection containing as elements the following subsets of E^2: (1) K contains all one-pair subsets $\{(x, y)\}$ where $x \neq 0$; (2) K contains the set $Q = \{(x, y) \mid x = 0$ and $y = 1/n$, for n a natural number$\}$; and (3) K contains the set M which is $\{(x, y) \mid x = 0$ and $y \neq 1/n$, for n a natural number$\}$. Let $((x, y), (u, v))$ be in D if and only if (x, y) and (u, v) belong to the same set in the collection K. D is an equivalence relation on E^2. Let q denote the quotient function from E^2 onto the quotient space E^2/D. Any open set U in E^2/D which contains the point $q[M]$ must be such that $q^{-1}[U]$ is open in E^2 and contains M. Since $(0, 0)$ is in M, $q^{-1}[U]$ must contain a circle of positive radius about $(0, 0)$, by definition of the topology on E^2. Such a circle must contain points of Q. Hence, U must contain $q[Q]$ in E^2/D. Again, any open set V which contains $q[Q]$ in E^2/D must be such that $q^{-1}[V]$ is open in E^2 and contains Q. Such a set must then contain a circle of positive radius about $(0, 1/2)$, in Q, and such a circle must contain points of M. Hence, V must contain $q[M]$. Thus, there is no open set in E^2/D which contains $q[Q]$ and does not contain $q[M]$, and there is no open set of E^2/D which contains $q[M]$ and does not contain $q[Q]$. Hence E^2/D is not a T_0-space and so cannot be a T_1- or a T_2-space. The conclusions are, then, (1) that a quotient space of a T_0-, T_1- or T_2-space need not be a T_0-, T_1-, or T_2-space, respectively, and (2) that the continuous image of a T_0-, T_1-, or T_2-space need not be a T_0-, T_1-, or T_2-space, respectively.

EXERCISE 10. Prove that any homeomorphic image of a T_0-, T_1-, or T_2-space is a T_0-, T_1-, or T_2-space, respectively.

UNIQUENESS OF EXTENSIONS OF CERTAIN FUNCTIONS

The following theorem contains an important implication of the Hausdorff (T_2-) axiom.

16.23 Definition. Let f be a function whose domain is a subset A of a set X and whose range is contained in the set Y. A function f^* whose domain is X is called an *extension* of f to X if and only if $f^*(a) = f(a)$ for a in A.

16.24 Theorem. *If f is a continuous function of a subspace D of a space X into a Hausdorff space Y and if the set D is dense in X, then there exists at most one continuous extension of f to X.*

Proof: Let f^* and g^* be two distinct continuous extensions of f to X. Let z be a point in $\sim D$, the complement of D in X, such that $f^*(z) \neq g^*(z)$. There exist neighborhoods W_1 and W_2 of $f^*(z)$ and $g^*(z)$, respectively, in Y such that $W_1 \cap W_2 = \emptyset$ since Y is Hausdorff. Since f^* and g^* are both continuous, there exist neighborhoods U_1 and U_2 of z in X such that $f^*[U_1] \subseteq W_1$ and $g^*[U_2] \subseteq W_2$. Since z is a limit point of D by definition of a dense set, $U_1 \cap U_2$ as a neighborhood of z, must contain a point d of D. $f^*(d) = f(d)$ and is in $f^*[U_1]$; hence, $f(d)$ is in W_1. Similarly, $g^*(d) = f(d)$ and is in $g^*[U_2]$; hence, $f(d)$ is in W_2. So $W_1 \cap W_2 \neq \emptyset$. This is a contradiction. Hence no such z can exist and $f^* = g^*$. ▮

The problem of extending functions while preserving certain properties occurs in many places in mathematics. It is to be observed that the previous theorem does not say that a continuous extension exists; it states only that if a continuous extension exists, it is the only one. The function denoted by $x \to 1/(x - \pi)$ is continuous from the dense set of rationals into the reals, but no continuous extension exists to the space of all reals.

Another way of stating the previous theorem is to say that any continuous function from a space X into a Hausdorff space Y is uniquely determined by its values on any dense subset of X. This is perhaps not as startling a conclusion as that of the theorem in complex function theory which says that a complex-valued function f which is analytic (has a derivative at every point) in an open subspace G of $\mathbb{C}$ is uniquely determined by its values on the countably infinite subset $\{a_1, a_2, \ldots, a_n, \ldots\}$ of G so long as $(a_1, a_2, \ldots, a_n, \ldots)$ converges to a point in G. This means that such a function, analytic throughout $\mathbb{C}$, is completely determined by its values on the set $\bigcup_n \{(0, 1/n)\}$, for n a natural number. However, the hypothesis of analyticity is a much stronger hypothesis than that of continuity.

EXERCISE 11. Prove that the only continuous function f on E^1 into E^1 such that $f(r) = 0$, for r any rational number, is the constant function $f(x) = 0$, for every real number x.

EXERCISE 12. Prove that the only continuous function f on E^1 into E^1 such that $f(r) = r^2$, for r a rational number, is the function $x \to x^2$.

THE CATEGORY OF HAUSDORFF SPACES

The word "category" is used with two different meanings in modern mathematics. One, introduced here, gives a generalization of the concepts of set and function and tends to unify all of modern mathematics. The other identifies a topological invariant. The latter meaning is introduced in section 22.

16.25 Definition. A *category* is a triple, $\{\mathfrak{A}, \mathfrak{M}, \circ\}$, where

(1) $\mathfrak{A}$ is a non-empty collection of elements called objects of the category;
(2) $\mathfrak{M}$ is a collection of elements called morphisms of the category;
(3) to each ordered pair (A, B) such that A and B are objects there corresponds a set $M(A, B)$ of morphisms in $\mathfrak{M}$;
(4) if α is in $M(A, B)$ and β is in $M(B, C)$ then there exists a morphism denoted by $\beta \circ \alpha$ in $M(A, C)$;
(5) if α is in $M(A, B)$, β is in $M(B, C)$ and γ is in $M(C, D)$ then $\gamma \circ (\beta \circ \alpha) = (\gamma \circ \beta) \circ \alpha$;
(6) for each object A in $\mathfrak{A}$, there exists a morphism 1_A in $M(A, A)$ such that if α is in $M(A, B)$ and β is in $M(C, A)$ then $\alpha \circ 1_A = \alpha$ and $1_A \circ \beta = \beta$;
(7) $M(A, B) \cap M(C, D) = \emptyset$ unless $A = C$ and $B = D$.

A category, in the above sense, is a generalization of the collection of all sets as objects and all ordered triples (f, A, B) as morphisms where f is a function with domain A and $f \subseteq A \times B$, with $(g, B, C) \circ (f, A, B) = (g \circ f, A, C)$. $g \circ f$ is the usual composition of g and f.

EXERCISE 13. Let $\mathcal{E}$ denote the collection of all sets and let $\mathfrak{M}$ denote $\{(f, A, B) \mid f$ is a function with domain A and $f \subseteq A \times B\}$. For A and B in $\mathcal{E}$, define $M(A, B)$ as $\{(f, A, B) \mid (f, A, B)$ is in $\mathfrak{M}\}$. Further, let $(g, B, C) \circ (f, A, B) = (g \circ f, A, C)$. Show that $\{\mathcal{E}, \mathfrak{M}, \circ\}$ satisfies the conditions for a category.

EXERCISE 14. Let $\mathfrak{N}$ denote the collection of all topological spaces and let $\mathfrak{M}$ be $\{(f, A, B) \mid f$ is a continuous function with domain A and $f \subseteq A \times B\}$. For each A and B in $\mathfrak{N}$, let $M(A, B) = \{(f, A, B) \mid (f, A, B)$ is in $\mathfrak{M}\}$. Lastly let $(g, B, C) \circ (f, A, B) = (g \circ f, A, C)$ where again $g \circ f$ is the composite of f and g. Show that $\{\mathfrak{N}, \mathfrak{M}, \circ\}$ satisfies the conditions for a category.

EXERCISE 15. Let $\mathcal{H}$ denote the collection of all Hausdorff spaces and let $\mathfrak{M}$ be $\{(f, A, B) \mid A$ and B are Hausdorff spaces, f is a continuous function with domain A and $f \subseteq A \times B\}$. For each A and B in $\mathcal{H}$, let $M(A, B) = \{(f, A, B) \mid (f, A, B)$ is in $\mathfrak{M}\}$. Lastly, let $(g, B, C) \circ (f, A, B) = (g \circ f, A, C)$ where again $\circ$ denotes composition. Show that $\{\mathcal{H}, \mathfrak{M}, \circ\}$ satisfies the conditions of a category.

16.26 Definition. Let $\{\mathfrak{A}, \mathfrak{M}, \circ\}$ be a category. A morphism m in $\mathfrak{M}$ is called a *monomorphism* in the category if and only if $m \circ \alpha = m \circ \beta$ implies $\alpha = \beta$ for all α, β in $\mathfrak{M}$ such that $m \circ \alpha$ and $m \circ \beta$ are defined and equal. A morphism e is called an *epimorphism* if and only if $f \circ e = g \circ e$ implies $f = g$ for all f, g in $\mathfrak{M}$ such that $f \circ e$ and $g \circ e$ are defined and equal.

16.27 Theorem. *In the category $\{\mathcal{E}, \mathcal{M}, \circ\}$ of sets, functions and composition, a morphism, (f, A, B), is a monomorphism if and only if f is 1:1, i.e. injective, and (f, A, B) is an epimorphism if and only if B is the range of f, i.e. f is surjective with respect to B.*

Proof: Exercise.

16.28 Theorem. *In the category $\{\mathcal{H}, \mathcal{M}, \circ\}$ of Hausdorff spaces, continuous functions and composition, a morphism (f, A, B) is a monomorphism if and only if f is 1:1, i.e. injective. Further, if B is the range of f then (f, A, B) is an epimorphism.*

Proof: Exercise.

16.29 Example. Let D be a dense subspace of a Hausdorff space X such that $D \neq X$. Let e be the continuous function from D into X defined by $e(d) = d$. Now let f and g be any continuous functions from X into the Hausdorff space Y sucht hat $f \circ e = g \circ e$. Now if d is in D, then $f \circ e(d) = g \circ e(d)$. However, $e(d) = d$. Therefore, $f(d) = g(d)$ for all d in D. It then follows by theorem 16.24 that $f = g$. Thus (e, D, X) is an epimorphism in $\{\mathcal{H}, \mathcal{M}, \circ\}$ but e is not onto X, i.e., X is not the range of e.

Monomorphisms are generalizations or abstractions of 1:1 functions and epimorphisms are generalizations or abstractions of "onto" functions as theorem 16.27 shows. However, because of theorem 16.24, epimorphisms in the category $\{\mathcal{H}, \mathcal{M}, \circ\}$ of Hausdorff spaces, continuous function and composition are not exactly the same as "onto" functions. Also, there are categories in which monomorphisms are not the same as 1:1 functions.

17. REGULAR SPACES.

Basic Definitions and Theorems

17.1 Definition. A space, X, is called a *T_3-space* if and only if it satisfies the T_3-axiom: if x is a point of X and if F is a closed subset of X not containing x, then the topology of X contains disjoint subsets U and V such that x is in U and F is contained in V.

17.2 Example. Let X be any space with the trivial topology and more than one point. X satisfies the T_3-axiom, but X is not a T_0-, T_1- or T_2-space.

17.3 Definition. A space, X, is called a *regular space* if and only if X is a T_1-space and a T_3-space.

17.4 Theorem. *Any regular space X is a Hausdorff space, and hence is T_0.*

Proof: Since X is a T_1-space by hypothesis, a subset of X containing a single point is closed. Hence, two distinct points possess disjoint neighborhoods, by axiom T_3, and so X is Hausdorff. ▮

17.5 Example. In example 16.5, the T_2-space X consists of the set of all real numbers with the usual basic neighborhoods except at the point 0. The basic neighborhoods for 0 are $\{U_\epsilon \mid U_\epsilon = \{x \mid |x| < \epsilon, \epsilon > 0$ and $x \neq 1/n$ for n any natural number$\}\}$. $F = \{x \mid x = 1/n$ and n is a natural number$\}$ is closed in X. 0 is not in F. Let G be any open set containing 0; G contains a basic neighborhood U of 0. Let $U = \{x \mid |x| < \epsilon, \epsilon > 0$ and $x \neq 1/n$ for n any natural number$\}$. There exists a natural number n^* such that $1/n^* < \epsilon$, by the archimedean property of the order on the real numbers. Let H be any open set containing F. H must contain a basic neighborhood, V, for the point $1/n^*$ which lies in H. $V \cap U$ is not the null set. Hence, X is not a regular space.

It is to be observed that the topology for the real numbers described above is larger than the usual topology, but is not regular. Thus there is no analogue for exercise 2 of section 16 for regular spaces.

17.6 Theorem. *A space, X, satisfies the T_3-axiom if and only if for any point x in X and any open set G containing x, there exists an open set U which contains x and whose closure is contained in G.*

Proof: A. Let X be a T_3-space; let x be any point in X and let G be any open set containing x. $\sim G$, the complement of G in X, is closed in X and does not contain x. Hence, by the T_3-axiom, there exist disjoint open sets U and V such that x is in U and $\sim G$ is contained in V. Then $U \subseteq \sim V$ and $\sim V \subseteq G$. Since $\sim V$ is closed, $\overline{U} \subseteq \sim V$. Hence, $\overline{U} \subseteq G$.

B. Let X have the property that for any x in X and any open set G containing x there exists an open set U containing x such that $\overline{U} \subseteq G$. Let F denote any closed set in X which does not contain the point y. Since y is not in F and F is closed, y is not a limit point of F. Hence, by definition of limit point, there must exist an open set G which contains y and contains no point of F. By hypothesis, there exists an open set U containing y such that $\overline{U} \subseteq G$. $U \cap (\sim\overline{U}) = \emptyset$. y is in U; $F \subseteq (\sim\overline{U})$. U and $(\sim\overline{U})$ are both open. Hence, X is a T_3-space. ▮

17.7 Corollary. *A space X is regular if and only if X is T_1 and for any point x in X and any open set G containing x, there exists an open set U containing x such that $\overline{U} \subseteq G$.*

Proof: The corollary follows from theorem 17.6. ▮

Corollary 17.7 offers a characterization of regular spaces alternate to the defining characterization. In example 17.5, there exists no closed neighborhood of 0 which is contained in any basic neighborhood of 0.

EXERCISE 1. Prove that E^1 and E^2 are regular spaces.

Existence of Extensions for Certain Functions

Theorem 16.23 states that for any continuous function on a dense subspace of a space X into a Hausdorff space, there exists at most one continuous extension to the whole space X. With the condition of regularity on the range space a stronger result can be obtained.

In section 7, the concept of limit of a function relative to a filter on the domain was defined. A special instance of such a limit will now be needed.

17.8 Definition. If f is a function from a set X into a space Y and if $\mathfrak{F}$ is a filter on X, then *limit*$_{\mathfrak{F}}$ f or *lim*$_{\mathfrak{F}}$ f denotes the set of all points y in Y such that the filter $\mathfrak{F}^*$ which has $f^{\#}[\mathfrak{F}]$ for a base converges to y. Note that $f^{\#}[\mathfrak{F}]$ is a filter on $f[X]$, but is not necessarily a complete filter on Y. It is always the base of a filter on Y.

17.9 Lemma. *If D is a dense subset of a space X and if x is any point of X, then $\mathfrak{F}^* = \{U \mid U = N \cap D$ where N is a neighborhood of x in $X\}$ constitutes a filter on D.*

Proof: Since D is dense in X, x is in D or x is a limit point of D. If x is in D, $\mathfrak{F}^*$ is the collection of all neighborhoods of x in the subspace D (relative topology) and hence is a filter on D. If x is not in D, then x is a limit point of D. By lemma 7.28, the collection $\mathfrak{F}^*$ is a filter on D. ▮

17.10 Lemma. *If f is a function from a space X into a space Y and if y is in $\lim_{\mathfrak{F}} f$ for some filter $\mathfrak{F}$ on X, then y is in $\overline{f[X]}$ in Y.*

Proof: Let N be any neighborhood of y in Y. Since y is in $\lim_{\mathfrak{F}} f$, there exists a set F in $\mathfrak{F}$ such that $f[F] \subseteq N$. Since $\mathfrak{F}$ does not contain the empty set, N contains points of $f[X]$. ▮

17.11 Theorem. *If f is a continuous function from a dense subset D of a space X into a regular space Y and if $\lim_{\mathfrak{N}_x^-} f$ exists for each x, where $\mathfrak{N}_x^-$ is the filter $\{U \mid U = N \cap D$, where N is a neighborhood of x in $X\}$, then f has a unique continuous extension to all of X.*

Proof: Since Y is regular, it is Hausdorff, and by theorem 16.24, any continuous extension will be unique. By theorem 16.9, any filter on Y has at most one limit. Thus, for each x in X, $\lim_{\mathfrak{N}_x^-} f$ is a unique element of Y. Define the function f^* from X into Y as follows: $f^*(x) = f(x)$ if x is in D and $f^*(x) = \lim_{\mathfrak{N}_x^-} f$ if x is in $\sim D$. f^* is, by definition, an extension of f to all of X. It remains to be shown that f^* is continuous on X. Let x be any point of X and $f^*(x)$ its image in Y assigned by f^*. By definition of f^*, $f^*(x) = \lim_{\mathfrak{N}_x^-} f$ or $f^*(x) = f(x)$. If x is in D, then since f is continuous, $\lim_{\mathfrak{N}_x^-} f$ must be equal to $f(x)$ by theorem 7.37 and definition 7.38. Now, let W be any neighborhood of $f^*(x)$ in Y. Since Y is regular, W contains a neighborhood V of $f^*(x)$ such that $\overline{V} \subseteq W$. Since $f^*(x) = \lim_{\mathfrak{N}_x^-} f$, there exists in X an open set U^* containing x such that $f[U^* \cap D] \subseteq V$, by definition of $\lim_{\mathfrak{N}_x^-} f$. Now let z be any other element in U^*. $f^*(z)$ is in $\overline{f[U^* \cap D]}$ since for any neighborhood N of $f^*(z)$, N and $f[U^* \cap D]$ both belong to the filter generated by $f[\mathfrak{N}_z^-]$ on Y and hence $N \cap f[U^* \cap D] \neq \emptyset$. Thus, $f^*[U^*] \subseteq \overline{f[U^* \cap D]} \subseteq \overline{V}$ and $\overline{V} \subseteq W$. Therefore, $f^*[U^*] \subseteq W$ and so f^* is continuous. ▌

17.12 Example. Let X be the space E^1 and let Y be the Hausdorff space of example 17.5. Y consists of the real numbers with the usual basic neighborhoods except at 0. The basic neighborhoods for 0 are the sets $U_\epsilon = \{x \mid |x| < \epsilon, \epsilon > 0 \text{ and } x \neq 1/n \text{ for } n \text{ any natural number}\}$. Let f be the identity function from the irrationals, D, in X onto the irrationals in Y. f is continuous on D; D is dense in X. $\lim_{\mathfrak{N}_x^-} f$ exists for every real number x in X (in fact, is actually x) where $\mathfrak{N}_x^-$ is the filter described in the previous theorem. Assume h is a continuous extension of f to all of X. By theorem 7.40, since Y is Hausdorff, $h(x) = \lim_{\mathfrak{N}_x} h$, where $\mathfrak{N}_x$ is the filter of neighborhoods of x in X. Next, it must be shown that $\lim_{\mathfrak{N}_a} h = a$. Assume $\lim_{\mathfrak{N}_a} h = b$ and that $|b - a| = \epsilon \neq 0$. Let $V = \{y \mid |y - b| < \epsilon/2\}$ or, in case $b = 0$, let $V = \{y \mid |y| < \epsilon/2 \text{ and } y \neq 1/n \text{ for any natural number } n\}$. Further, let $U = \{x \mid |x - a| < \delta < \epsilon/2 \text{ and } \delta > 0\}$. Let i be irrational and let i be in U. $|i - a| < \delta < \epsilon/2$. Hence, since $h(i) = i$, $|h(i) - b| > \epsilon/2$ and $h[U] \nsubseteq V$. This contradicts the continuity of h. Therefore, $h(a) = a$ and in particular $h(0) = 0$. Consider now the neighborhood $W = \{y \mid |y - 0| < 1/4 \text{ and } y \neq 1/n \text{ for any natural number } n\}$ of 0 in the range space, Y. Let $U = \{x \mid |x - 0| < \epsilon\}$ be any basic neighborhood of 0 in the domain, X. U contains a number $1/m$, for m a natural number such that $1/m < 1/4$. $h(1/m) = 1/m$ and $1/m$ is not in W. Hence, $h[U] \nsubseteq W$ and h is not continuous at 0. f, then, has no continuous extension to all of X and $\text{limit}_{\mathfrak{N}_x^-} f$ exists for every x in X. Y is, of course, not regular.

Subspaces, Products and Quotient Spaces of Regular Spaces

17.13 Theorem. *Any subspace, S, of a T_3-space, X, is a T_3-space.*

Proof: Let x be in S and let U be an open set of S which contains x. By definition of the relative topology, there exists an open set U^* in X such that $U = U^* \cap S$. Since X is a T_3-space, there exists an open set V^* in X such that V^* contains x and $\overline{V^*} \subseteq U^*$. By theorem 9.5, $\overline{V^*} \cap S$ is closed in S. Also, $\overline{V^*} \cap S \subseteq U^* \cap S = U$. Hence, $V^* \cap S$ is open in S, it contains x and its closure in S, which is a subset of $\overline{V^*} \cap S$, is contained in U. By theorem 17.6, S then is a T_3-space. ▌

17.14 Corollary. *Any subspace of a regular space is regular.*

Proof: The proof follows from theorems 17.13 and 16.17. ▌

EXERCISE 2. Let $\{X_1, X_2, \ldots, X_k\}$ denote a non-empty finite collection of non-empty spaces. Prove that the non-empty product space $\prod_{i=1}^k X_i$ is a T_3-space if and only if each X_i is a T_3-space.

EXERCISE 3. Let $\{X_1, X_2, \ldots, X_k\}$ denote a non-empty finite collection of non-empty spaces. Prove that the non-empty product space $\prod_{i=1}^k X_i$ is a regular space if and only if each X_i is regular.

17.15 Theorem. *Let $\{X_\nu\}$ denote a non-empty collection of spaces. The non-empty product space $\prod_{\nu\in\mathfrak{A}} X_\nu$ is a T_3-space if and only if each X_ν is a T_3-space.*

Proof: A. Let each X_ν be T_3. Let x^* be a point in the product space $\prod_{\nu\in\mathfrak{A}} X_\nu$ and let G^* be a basic open set containing x^*. Let $p_\nu(x^*) = x_\nu$, where p_ν is a projection mapping. $G^* = \prod_{\nu\in\mathfrak{A}} W_\nu$, where W_ν is open in X_ν, and if $\mathfrak{A}$ is infinite, $W_\nu = X_\nu$ for $\nu \neq \alpha_1, \ldots, \alpha_k$, for k a natural number. Since each X_ν is a T_3-space, for each ν there exists an open set V_ν in X_ν such that V_ν contains x_ν and $\overline{V_\nu} \subseteq W_\nu$. Let $V^* = \prod_{\nu\in\mathfrak{A}} \overline{V_\nu}$. V^* is closed, by theorem 16.11, and contains x^*. Further, since $\overline{V_\nu}$ is contained in W_ν, $\prod_{\nu\in\mathfrak{A}} \overline{V_\nu} \subseteq \prod_{\nu\in\mathfrak{A}} W_\nu = G^*$. Hence, $V^* \subseteq G^*$ and so $\prod_{\nu\in\mathfrak{A}} X_\nu$ is a T_3-space.

B. Conversely, let $X^* = \prod_{\nu\in\mathfrak{A}} X_\nu$ be a non-empty T_3-product space. Let α be in $\mathfrak{A}$. Let x_α be a point in X_α and let G_α be an open set in X_α which contains x_α. Since X^* is not empty, there is an element x^* in X^* such that $p_\alpha(x^*) = x_\alpha$. Let $G^* = p_\alpha^{-1}[G_\alpha]$. $x^* \in G^*$ and G^* is open in X^*. Since X^* is a T_3-space, there exists a basic open set $V^* = \prod_{\nu\in\mathfrak{A}} V_\nu$ such that $\overline{V^*} \subseteq G^*$ and x^* is in V^*. By corollary 12.12, $\overline{\prod_{\nu\in\mathfrak{A}} V_\nu} = \prod_{\nu\in\mathfrak{A}} \overline{V_\nu}$. Hence $p_\alpha[\overline{V^*}] = \overline{V_\alpha}$, $x_\alpha \in V_\alpha$ and $\overline{V_\alpha} \subseteq G_\alpha$. X_α is then a T_3-space. ▮

17.16 Corollary. *A non-empty product space $\prod_\nu X_\nu$ is a regular space if and only if each space X_ν is regular.*

Proof: The proof follows from theorems 17.15 and 16.18. ▮

The following example shows that the quotient space of a T_3-space need not be a T_3-space, and that the quotient space of a regular space need not be regular.

17.17 Example. Let X be the quotient space of E^2 whose points are the following equivalence classes: any point $(0, y)$, for y a real number, constitutes a whole equivalence class, C_0^y. For any real number a such that $a \neq 0$, $C_a = \{(x, y) \mid x = a\}$ is an equivalence class. The space X then consists of the point set $\{C_0^y \mid y \text{ is a real number}\} \cup \{C_a \mid a \text{ is a non-zero real number}\}$ with the quotient topology. Define the subset A of X to be $\{C_0^y \mid 1/2 \leq y \leq 1\}$. Thus, A consists of the points on the y-axis between 1/2 and 1 inclusive. Let α denote the point $C_0^{1/4}$; $C_0^{1/4} = \{(0, 1/4)\}$ on the y-axis. $C_0^{1/4}$ does not belong to A. A is closed in X since $q^{-1}[A] = \{(x, y) \mid x = 0 \text{ and } 1/2 \leq y \leq 1\}$, where q is the quotient function is closed in E^2. Let G be any open set in X which contains $\{(0, 1/4)\}$ and let G^* be any open set in X which contains $A = \{(0, y) \mid 1/2 \leq y \leq 1\}$. $q^{-1}[G]$ must be open in E^2 and must contain $(0, 1/4)$ of E^2. Hence, $q^{-1}[G]$ must contain a circle γ with center $(0, 1/4)$ and positive radius δ, by definition of the topology on E^2. Thus, G must contain all points C_a of X with $0 < |a| < \delta$. Similarly, $q^{-1}[G^*]$ must be open in E^2 and must contain the interval $\{(0, y) \mid 1/2 \leq y \leq 1\}$. Hence, $q^{-1}[G^*]$ must contain a circle with center at the point $(0, 1/2)$ and with positive radius ϵ. Thus, G^* must contain all points C_a of X such that $0 < |a| < \epsilon$. Let $\epsilon^* = \min(\delta, \epsilon)$. Then $G \cap G^* \supseteq \{C_a \mid 0 < |a| < \epsilon^*\}$, and so $G \cap G^*$ is not empty. Thus, each open set containing $(0, 1/4)$ intersects each open set containing $A = \{C_0^y \mid 1/2 \leq y \leq 1\}$ on a non-empty set. Hence X is not a T_3-space and X is not regular, although E^2 is both.

18. NORMAL SPACES. COMPLETELY REGULAR SPACES.

The separation axioms have so far placed conditions on the topology for a space which insure the existence of enough open sets to "separate" points in the manners described; and in the case of regularity, the topology must "separate" individual points from closed sets not containing them. The next separation axiom continues the conditioning one step further and insures that disjoint closed sets are "separated" by the topology in this same sense.

Normal Spaces

18.1 Definition. A topological space S is said to be a T_4-space if and only if it satisfies the T_4-axiom: If F_1 and F_2 are two disjoint closed sets in S, then there exist disjoint open sets U and V such that U contains F_1 and V contains F_2.

18.2 Example. If $X = \{a, b, c\}$ and $\mathfrak{I} = \{X, \{a\}, \emptyset\}$, then $\{X, \mathfrak{I}\}$ is T_4, but not T_3.

18.3 Definition. A space X is called normal if and only if it is a T_1- and a T_4-space.

18.4 Example. The following space S is regular and not normal. The space consists of the set of all ordered pairs of real numbers with the following basic neighborhood relation. The basic neighborhoods of any point $P:(x, y)$ are the squares with horizontal and vertical diagonals with P as the lowest vertex and with the interior and the sides adjacent to P included, but with no point on the other two sides included. S is a T_1-space. Also in S the basic neighborhoods are closed; hence, every open set containing P contains the closure of an open set containing P and so, by corollary 17.7, S is regular. Consider the subset $A = \{(x, y) \mid y = 0 \text{ and } x \text{ is rational}\}$

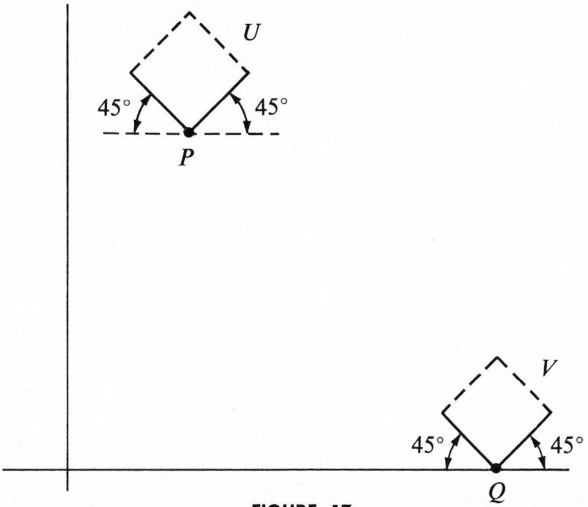

FIGURE 17

and the subset $B = \{(x, y) \mid y = 0 \text{ and } x \text{ is irrational}\}$. A and B are both closed in S. $A \cap B = \emptyset$. It will be shown that there exist no disjoint open sets G and H which contain A and B, respectively. Since A consists of the rational points on the x-axis, denote A by $\{(r_1, 0), (r_2, 0), \ldots, (r_k, 0), \ldots\}$; A is countable. Assume there exists an open set G and an open set H in S such that $G \cap H = \emptyset$, $A \subseteq G$ and $B \subseteq H$. There exists a basic neighborhood N_k of each $(r_k, 0)$ in A such that $N_k \subseteq G$. Let the length of the side of N_k be ϵ_k. Let $(a, 0)$ be any other point on the x-axis. If $|a - r_k| \geq \epsilon_k\sqrt{2}/n$, for n a natural number, then $(a, 0)$ has a basic neighborhood W in S of side-length ϵ_k/n such that W does not intersect N_k. Consider, then, for each r_k the open interval $I_k^n = (r_k - \epsilon_k\sqrt{2}/n, r_k + \epsilon_k\sqrt{2}/n)$ of real numbers. Let $\bigcup_k I_k^n = M_n$. M_n is an open set of real numbers in E^1, the space of real numbers and the usual topology. Consider $E^1 \sim M_n = C_n$. C_n is the set of all real numbers x such that $(x, 0)$ has a basic neighborhood in S of side length $\geq(\epsilon_k/n)$, for all $k = 1, 2, \ldots$, which does not intersect $\bigcup_k N_k$. By the assumption that H exists, is disjoint from G and contains $B = \{(x, y) \mid y = 0 \text{ and } x \text{ is irrational}\}$, it follows that $L \subseteq \bigcup_n C_n$, where L is the set of irrationals in E^1. Now, in E^1 each set C_n is closed, and so

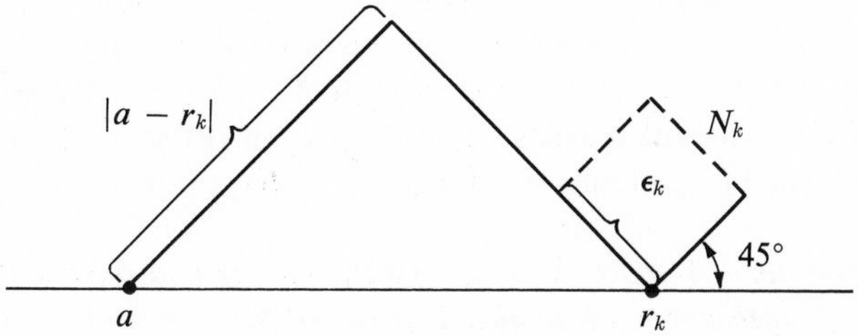

FIGURE 18

its complement, the set M_n, is open. Further M_n is dense in E^1, since for each n, M_n contains all the rational numbers. Hence, by lemma 12.22, the sets C_n are nowhere dense in E^1 and $L = \bigcup_n C_n$. Corollary 22.29, in chapter 4, establishes that the irrationals in E^1 cannot be obtained as the union of a countable number of nowhere dense sets. Thus, the existence of the disjoint open sets G and H in S leads to a contradiction in E^1, the space of reals with the usual topology. Thus, S is not a normal space.

18.5 Theorem. *E^1 is normal.*

Proof: E^1 is T_1, by exercise 3 of section 16. So let F_1 and F_2 be disjoint closed sets in E^1, and let a be in F_1. Since $F_1 \cap F_2 = \emptyset$, $F_1 \subseteq {\sim}F_2$. ${\sim}F_2$ is open; hence, there exists an open interval $(a - \delta_a, a + \delta_a)$, for δ_a real and positive, such that $(a - \delta_a, a + \delta_a) \subseteq {\sim}F_2$. Define for each a in F_1 the open interval $U_a = (a - \delta_a/2, a + \delta_a/2)$. Let $G_1 = \bigcup_{a \in F_1} U_a$. G_1 is open and $F_1 \subseteq G_1$. Similarly, define for each b in F_2 an open interval $(b - \epsilon_b, b + \epsilon_b)$, for ϵ_b real and positive, such that $(b - \epsilon_b, b + \epsilon_b) \subseteq {\sim}F_1$. Then let V_b be the interval $(b - \epsilon_b/2, b + \epsilon_b/2)$ and let $G_2 = \bigcup_{b \in F_2} V_b$. G_2 is open and $F_2 \subseteq G_2$. Now let $c \in G_1 \cap G_2$. By definition of $\bigcup$, there exists a in F_1 and b in F_2 such that $c \in U_a \cap V_b$. Let γ be the minimum of $\{\delta_a/2, \epsilon_b/2\}$. Then $|a - c| < \gamma$ and $|b - c| < \gamma$. Hence, $|a - c| + |b - c| < 2\gamma$ and so $|a - b| < 2\gamma$. Thus, $|a - b| < \delta_a$ and $|a - b| < \epsilon_b$. This contradicts the definition of δ_a and ϵ_b, and so $G_1 \cap G_2 = \emptyset$. E^1 is, then, normal. ▮

All Euclidean spaces are normal. This is established as a corollary in the next chapter.

18.6 Theorem. *A space X satisfies axiom T_4 if and only if for any closed set F and any open set G containing F, there exists an at least one open set U containing F such that $\overline{U} \subseteq G$.*

Proof: A. Let G be open in the T_4-space X, and let G contain a closed subset, F, of X. ${\sim}G$ is closed in X and $F \cap ({\sim}G) = \emptyset$. Since X is a T_4-space, there exist disjoint open sets U and V such that U contains F and V contains ${\sim}G$. ${\sim}V$ is closed and ${\sim}V \subseteq {\sim}({\sim}G) = G$. Also, since $U \cap V = \emptyset$, $U \subseteq {\sim}V$. Hence, $\overline{U} \subseteq \overline{{\sim}V} = {\sim}V$ and $\overline{U} \subseteq G$.

B. Let X be a space with the property that if G is an open set which contains a closed set F, then there exists an open set U such that $F \subseteq U$ and $\overline{U} \subseteq G$. Let F_1 and F_2 be two disjoint closed sets in X. ${\sim}F_1$ is open and contains F_2. Hence, by hypothesis, there exists an open set U such that $\overline{U} \subseteq {\sim}F_1$ and $F_2 \subseteq U$. Hence, ${\sim}\overline{U}$ is open, contains F_1 and $({\sim}\overline{U}) \cap U = \emptyset$. ▮

18.7 Corollary. *A space X is a normal space if and only if it is a T_1-space and every open set G containing any closed set F contains the closure of an open set U which also contains F, i.e., $F \subseteq U \subseteq \overline{U} \subseteq G$.*

Proof: The corollary follows directly from theorem 18.6. ▮

EXERCISE 1. Prove that any set with the discrete topology is a normal space.

18.8 Theorem. *Any normal space is a regular space.*

Proof: Let X be any normal space. X is a T_1-space and so any point constitutes a closed set. By theorems 18.6 and corollary 17.7, X is a regular space. ▮

18.9 Corollary. *Normality implies regularity; regularity implies the Hausdorff property; the Hausdorff property implies T_1; and T_1 implies T_0.*

Proof: From theorems 18.8 and 17.4 the corollary follows. ▮

Open Coverings and Second Countability

In example 18.4, it was shown that a space can be regular and not normal. With certain additional conditions, a regular space must also be normal; the next three theorems show this. These theorems will introduce the concept of an "open covering" of a topological space, a concept which is much used in topology. Open coverings will be studied in more detail in chapter 6 on compactness.

18.10 Definition. Let X be a set and S a subset of X. A collection $\mathcal{G}$ of subsets of X is called a *covering* or *cover* of S if and only if the union of the sets in $\mathcal{G}$ contains S.

18.11 Definition. Let $\mathcal{G}$ be a covering of a subset, S, of a set X. The collection $\mathcal{H}$ is called a *subcovering* or *subcover* of $\mathcal{G}$ if and only if $\mathcal{H}$ covers S and every set in $\mathcal{H}$ is a set in $\mathcal{G}$.

18.12 Definition. Let $\mathcal{G}$ be a covering of a subset, S, of a set X. A collection G^* is called a *refinement* of the covering $\mathcal{G}$ if and only if $\mathcal{G}^*$ is a covering of S and each set of $\mathcal{G}^*$ is contained in a set of $\mathcal{G}$.

EXERCISE 2. Show that every subcovering of a covering $\mathcal{G}$ of a subset, S, in a set X is a refinement of $\mathcal{G}$ and that not every refinement of $\mathcal{G}$ is a subcovering.

18.13 Definition. Let X be a space. A collection, $\mathcal{G}$, of subsets of X is called an *open covering* or an *open cover* of a subset A of X if and only if $\mathcal{G}$ is a covering of A and every set in $\mathcal{G}$ is open in X.

18.14 Theorem. *If X is a regular space and if every open covering of X contains a countable subcovering, then X is normal.*

Proof: Let F_1 and F_2 be any two disjoint closed sets in X. Since X is regular, for each point x in F_1, there exists an open set U_x containing x such that $\overline{U_x} \cap F_2 = \emptyset$. The collection $\mathcal{G} = \{U_x \mid x \in F_1\} \cup \{(\sim F_1)\}$ is an open covering of X; hence, by hypothesis, $\mathcal{G}$ contains a countable subcovering, $(\sim F_1, U_1, U_2, \ldots, U_i, \ldots)$. $F_1 \subseteq \bigcup_{i=1}^{\infty} U_i$; in addition, $\overline{U_i} \cap F_2 = \emptyset$ for $i = 1, 2, 3, \ldots$. Similarly a countable collection of open sets, $(V_1, V_2, \ldots, V_i, \ldots)$ such that $F_2 \subseteq \bigcup_{i=1}^{\infty} V_i$ and $\overline{V_i} \cap F_1 = \emptyset$, for $i = 1, 2, 3, \ldots$ can be obtained. Define $U_1^* = U_1 \sim \overline{V_1}$, $U_2^* = U_2 \sim (\overline{V_1} \cup \overline{V_2})$, $\ldots$, $U_k^* = U_k \sim (\overline{V_1} \cup \overline{V_2} \cup \cdots \cup \overline{V_k})$, $\ldots$. Since $(\overline{V_1} \cup \cdots \cup \overline{V_k})$ is closed, $\sim(\overline{V_1} \cup \cdots \cup \overline{V_k})$ is open and $\sim(\overline{V_1} \cup \cdots \cup \overline{V_k}) \cap U_k$ is open. Thus U_k^* is open for each k. Also, since $\overline{V_i} \cap F_1 = \emptyset$ for every i and since $F_1 \subseteq \bigcup_{i=1}^{\infty} U_i$, then $F_1 \subseteq \bigcup_{i=1}^{\infty} U_i^*$. Now let $G_1 = \bigcup_{i=1}^{\infty} U_i^*$; G_1 is an open set containing F_1. Similarly, the collection $(V_1^*, V_2^*, \ldots, V_i^*, \ldots)$ of open sets is defined, where $V_1^* = V_1 \sim \overline{U_1}, \ldots, V_i^* = V_i \sim (\overline{U_1} \cup \overline{U_2} \cup \cdots \cup \overline{U_i})$. Again, each V_i^* is open and $F_2 \subseteq \bigcup_{i=1}^{\infty} V_i^*$, which is open. Let $G_2 = \bigcup_{i=1}^{\infty} V_i^*$ and let z be in $G_1 \cap G_2$. Since z is in G_1, z is in U_j^*, say; since z is in G_2, z is in V_k^*, say. Let $j \leq k$. $V_k^* = V_k \sim (\overline{U_1} \cup \cdots \cup \overline{U_j} \cup \cdots \cup \overline{U_k})$. Since z is in U_j^*, z is in U_j and so z is in $\overline{U_j}$. This is a contradiction. Hence, $G_1 \cap G_2 = \emptyset$ and so X is normal. ▮

EXERCISE 3. Prove that if X is a space in which every open covering of X contains a countable open subcovering, then every open covering of X has a countable open refinement which also covers X. Conversely, prove that if X is a space in which every open covering of X has a countable open refinement which covers X, then every open covering contains a countable open subcovering.

The following theorem shows that second countable spaces possess an important covering property.

18.15 Theorem (Lindelöf). *If X is a second countable space, then every open covering of X contains a countable subcovering.*

Proof: Let $\mathcal{G}$ be any open covering of X and let $\mathcal{B}$ denote a countable base for X. Let $\{B_1', B_2', \ldots, B_j', \ldots\}$ denote the sets in $\mathcal{B}$ that are contained entirely in some set in $\mathcal{G}$. Now, each x in X is in some set G in $\mathcal{G}$ and since this set G is open, there is a set B_i such that x is in B_i and $B_i \subseteq G$, by definition of a base. Thus, this B_i is B_j', say, and so the collection $(B_1', B_2', \ldots, B_j', \ldots)$ covers X. Now let $\mathcal{G}_j$ denote the collection of sets in $\mathcal{G}$ that contain B_j'. Choose for each B_j' one set, G_j in $\mathcal{G}_j$ such that $G_j \supseteq B_j'$. This collection $\{G_1, G_2, \ldots, G_j, \ldots\}$ is countable, covers X and is a subcovering of $\mathcal{G}$. ▮

EXERCISE 4. Prove that the property "every open covering of a space X contains a countable subcovering" is a topological property.

18.16 Definition. A space $\{X, \mathfrak{T}\}$ is said to have the *Lindelöf property* or be *Lindelöf* if and only if every open covering of X contains a countable subcovering.

18.17 Example. Let X be the set of real numbers with the discrete topology. Let the open covering $\mathcal{G}$ be $\{G_x \mid G_x = \{x\}\}$. $\mathcal{G}$ is an open covering of X which contains no countable subcovering.

18.18 Example. Let X be E^1. The sets $V_n = \{x \mid x < n$ and n is a natural number$\}$ constitute an open covering of the space E^1.

18.19 Example. Each Euclidean space, E^n, has the property that every open covering contains a countable subcovering. This fact follows from theorems 18.15, 11.21 and 5.10.

18.20 Example. The converse of theorem 18.15 is false. Let X denote the set of reals. Define for each real number x_0 one basic neighborhood, $U_{x_0} = \{x \mid x \leq x_0\}$. The resulting space is not second countable. However, let $\mathcal{G}$ be any open covering of the space. 1 lies in some set G_1 of $\mathcal{G}$ and $G_1 \supseteq \{x \mid x \leq 1\}$; similarly, 2 lies in some set G_2 of $\mathcal{G}$ and $G_2 \supseteq \{x \mid x \leq 2\}$; . . . ; and k lies in some set G_k in $\mathcal{G}$ and $G_k \supseteq \{x \mid x \leq k\}$, for k a natural number. Thus the collection $\{G_1, G_2, \ldots, G_k, \ldots\}$ forms a countable subcover of $\mathcal{G}$ which covers X. Thus the space X is Lindelöf but not second countable.

18.21 Corollary. *If A is any subspace of a second countable space, then A has the Lindelöf property.*

Proof: The corollary follows from theorem 18.15 and theorem 9.25. ▮

EXERCISE 5. Let $\{X, \mathfrak{J}\}$ be a second countable space and let $\mathcal{B}$ be any base for the topology $\mathfrak{J}$. Show that $\mathcal{B}$ contains a countable subset $\{B_1, B_2, \ldots, B_n, \ldots\}$ which is a base for $\mathfrak{J}$.

18.22 Theorem. *If X is a second countable, regular space, then X is normal.*

Proof: Since X is second countable, then by theorem 18.15, every open covering of X contains a countable subcovering. By theorem 18.14, X is normal. ▮

Continuous Real-Valued Functions on Normal Spaces

A normal space, by definition, satisfies a certain "separation" condition for disjoint closed sets. The topology, or collection of all open sets of X, was used to describe this condition. The next theorem opens up a new approach to the separation problem and introduces a new tool for the study of spaces, namely, the set of continuous functions of a space into the space E^1 of real numbers. As the theorem points out, the separation property possessed by a normal space, X, is reflected in the set of continuous functions of X into E^1.

18.23 Theorem (Urysohn's Lemma). *If X is any T_4-space and if F_1 and F_2 are any two non-empty disjoint closed subsets of X, then there exists a continuous function f from X into the unit interval, $\{x \mid 0 \leq x \leq 1$ and x is real$\}$ in E^1, such that $f[F_1] = \{0\}$ and $f[F_2] = \{1\}$.*

Proof: A. The proof begins with a countable set of real numbers which is dense in the closed unit interval, [0, 1] with the relative topology from E^1. The set which is used is the set of dyadic rational numbers, D, in [0, 1]. $D = \{x \mid x = m/2^n$, where m and n are non-negative integers and $m \leq 2^n\}$. Let

$$M_1 = \left\{\frac{0}{2^1}\right\} \cup \left\{\frac{1}{2^1}\right\} \cup \left\{\frac{2}{2^1}\right\}.$$

$$M_2 = \left\{\frac{0}{2^2}\right\} \cup \left\{\frac{1}{2^2}\right\} \cup \left\{\frac{2}{2^2}\right\} \cup \left\{\frac{3}{2^2}\right\} \cup \left\{\frac{4}{2^2}\right\}.$$

$$\vdots$$

$$M_i = \left\{\frac{0}{2^i}\right\} \cup \left\{\frac{1}{2^i}\right\} \cup \cdots \cup \left\{\frac{2^i - 1}{2^i}\right\} \cup \left\{\frac{2^i}{2^i}\right\}.$$

$$\vdots$$

$$D = \bigcup_{i=1}^{\infty} M_i.$$

Further, if $i < j$ then $M_i \subseteq M_j$, for

$$\frac{l}{2^i} = \frac{2^{j-i} \cdot l}{2^{j-i} \cdot 2^i} = \frac{2^{j-i} \cdot l}{2^j}.$$

D is dense in [0, 1]; between any two real numbers in [0, 1] lies an element of D.

B. The next step is to define by induction, using the T_4-axiom and the choice axiom, an open set $G(d)$ in X for each d in D with the following inclusion relation: $d_1 < d_2$ implies $\overline{G(d_1)} \subseteq G(d_2)$. A function, δ, will be defined whose domain is D and whose range is contained in the topology, $\mathfrak{J}$, on X. Let $n = 1$:

$$M_1 = \left\{\frac{0}{2^1}\right\} \cup \left\{\frac{1}{2^1}\right\} \cup \left\{\frac{2}{2^1}\right\}.$$

Define $G(1)$ to be the set $X \sim F_2$. $G(1)$ is open and contains F_1. Since X is T_4, $G(1)$ contains open sets which contain F_1 and whose individual closures are contained in $G(1)$. The choice axiom distinguishes one of these sets that is then defined to be $G(0)$. Then, $F_1 \subseteq G(0) \subseteq \overline{G(0)} \subseteq G(1)$. Again by T_4, the choice axiom can distinguish an open set, $G(1/2)$, such that $F_1 \subseteq G(0) \subseteq \overline{G(0)} \subseteq G(1/2) \subseteq \overline{G(1/2)} \subseteq G(1)$. Thus a function δ_1 has been defined from M_1 into the topology, $\mathfrak{J}$, on X. $\delta_1(0/2) = G(0)$, $\delta_1(1/2) = G(1/2)$, $\delta_1(2/2) = G(1)$ and $G(0) \subseteq \overline{G(0)} \subseteq G(1/2) \subseteq G(1)$. Next, it is assumed that δ_k has been defined from M_k into $\mathfrak{J}$ such that

$$G\left(\frac{0}{2^k}\right) \subseteq \overline{G\left(\frac{0}{2^k}\right)} \subseteq G\left(\frac{1}{2^k}\right) \subseteq \cdots \subseteq \overline{G\left(\frac{i}{2^k}\right)} \subseteq G\left(\frac{i+1}{2^k}\right) \subseteq \cdots \subseteq G(1).$$

$M_{k+1} = \{0/2^{k+1}\} \cup \{1/2^{k+1}\} \cup \cdots \cup \{i/2^{k+1}\} \cup \cdots \cup \{2^{k+1}/2^{k+1}\}$. If m is even, $m/2^{k+1} = 2j/2^{k+1} = j/2^k$, for j a natural number. Define $G(2j/2^{k+1})$ to be $G(j/2^k)$ which has been defined by the induction assumption. Thus sets $G(0/2^{k+1})$, $G(2/2^{k+1})$, $\ldots$, $G(2j/2^{k+1})$, $\ldots$, $G(2^{k+1}/2^{k+1})$ have now been defined, where

$$G\left(\frac{0}{2^{k+1}}\right) \subseteq \overline{G\left(\frac{0}{2^{k+1}}\right)} \subseteq \cdots \subseteq \overline{G\left(\frac{2j}{2^{k+1}}\right)} \subseteq G\left(\frac{2j+2}{2^{k+1}}\right) \subseteq \cdots \subseteq G\left(\frac{2^{k+1}}{2^{k+1}}\right).$$

Next, let $(2j+1)/2^{k+1}$ denote any element in M_{k+1} with odd numerator. $\overline{G(2j/2^{k+1})}$ has been defined, is closed and is contained in $G((2j+2)/2^{k+1})$, which also has been defined and is open. Again the T_4-axiom and the choice axiom, as above for $G(0)$, determine an open set U^j such that

$$\overline{G\left(\frac{2j}{2^{k+1}}\right)} \subseteq U^j \subseteq \overline{U^j} \subseteq G\left(\frac{2j+2}{2^{k+1}}\right).$$

Define $G((2j+1)/2^{k+1})$ as U^j. Thus, for each element $m/2^{k+1}$ of M_{k+1}, an open set $G(m/2^{k+1})$ has been defined such that

$$G\left(\frac{0}{2^{k+1}}\right) \subseteq \overline{G\left(\frac{0}{2^{k+1}}\right)} \subseteq G\left(\frac{1}{2^{k+1}}\right) \subseteq \cdots$$
$$\subseteq \overline{G\left(\frac{m}{2^{k+1}}\right)} \subseteq G\left(\frac{m+1}{2^{k+1}}\right) \subseteq \cdots \subseteq G\left(\frac{2^{k+1}}{2^{k+1}}\right).$$

Thus the induction is complete. For every set M_k a function δ_k has been defined from M_k into the topology, $\mathfrak{J}$, of X and the required inclusion relations hold. Further, if a is in both M_i and M_j, then $a = n/2^i$ and $a = m/2^j$. Assume $i < j$; then

$$a = \frac{2n}{2^{i+1}} = \frac{2^2 n}{2^{i+2}} = \frac{2^{(j-i)} \cdot n}{2^j} \qquad \text{and} \qquad G_a = \delta_j(a) = G\left(\frac{2^{j-1} \cdot n}{2^j}\right) = \delta_i(a).$$

As a result of this condition, we can define a mapping δ from all of D into the topology $\mathfrak{J}$ as follows. $D = \bigcup_k M_k$; hence, if d is in D, then d is in M_k for some natural number k. Define $\delta(d)$ to be $\delta_k(d) = G_d$. $\delta(d)$ is uniquely defined in $\mathfrak{J}$. Now let $d_1 < d_2$ for d_1, d_2 in D. Let d_1 be in M_i and d_2 be in M_j; let $i \leq j$. Since $M_i \subseteq M_j$, d_1, d_2 are both in M_j; hence, $\delta(d_1) = \delta_j(d_1)$, $\delta(d_2) = \delta_j(d_2)$ and $\overline{G(d_1)} \subseteq G(d_2)$, by definition of δ_j.

C. The third step in the proof is to define, using δ, a new function, η, from the half-open interval $(0, 1]$, $\{y \mid 0 < y \leq 1\}$, into $\mathfrak{J}$. Let $\eta(t) = \bigcup_{d<t,\, d \text{ in } D} G(d)$. The real numbers in $(0, 1]$ are linearly ordered; therefore, each t in $(0, 1]$ divides the remaining elements of D into two parts—those less than t and those greater than t. Hence, $\{d \mid d < t \text{ for } t \text{ in } (0, 1]\}$ is uniquely defined. So, $\bigcup_{d<t,\, d \text{ in } D} G(d)$ is uniquely defined by definition of $\bigcup$. $\bigcup_{d<t,\, d \text{ in } D} G(d)$, as the union of open

sets, is open and hence is in $\mathfrak{I}$. Denote $\bigcup_{d<t,\ d \text{ in } D} G(d)$ by H_t. $\eta(t) = H_t$. It remains to be established that the above mentioned inclusion relations hold for these sets H_t. Let t_1 and t_2 be any two elements of (0, 1] and let $t_1 < t_2$. Since D is dense in (0, 1], there exist elements d_1 and d_2 of D such that $t_1 < d_1 < d_2 < t_2$. By definition of H_{t_1} and H_{t_2}, $H_{t_1} \subseteq G(d_1)$ and $G(d_2) \subseteq H_{t_2}$. Therefore, $\overline{H_{t_1}} \subseteq \overline{G(d_1)} \subseteq G(d_2) \subseteq H_{t_2}$ and so $\overline{H_{t_1}} \subseteq H_{t_2}$. Thus, the inclusion condition is satisfied by the sets H_t.

D. The next step is to define a function, f, from X into [0, 1] such that $f[F_1] = \{0\}$, $f[F_2] = \{1\}$ and $0 \leq f(x) \leq 1$ for all x in X. So let x be any element in X and consider the subset $A_x = \{t \mid x \text{ is in } H_t \text{ or } t \geq 1\}$. A_x, for all x, is a set of positive real numbers and so is bounded from below by 0. Every set of real numbers bounded from below has a unique greatest lower bound and so every x in X defines a unique real number in [0, 1]. Define $f(x)$ to be the unique greatest lower bound of A_x. By the definition of A_x, $f(x)$ is in [0, 1] for every x in X. Further, if x is in F_1, then x is in G_0 and so x is in H_t for every t in (0, 1]. Thus A_x, in this case, is the set of all positive real numbers and its greatest lower bound is 0. Hence, $f[F_1] = \{0\}$. If x is in F_2, then x is not in $X \sim F_2$ which is $G(1)$; so, x is not in any $G(d)$ since $G(d) \subseteq G(1)$ for every d in D. Hence x is not in any H_t; $A_x = \{t \mid t \geq 1\}$ and the greatest lower bound of A_x is 1. Thus $f[F_2] = \{1\}$.

E. The last step in the proof is to establish that f is continuous. The range of f is contained in [0, 1] and has the relative topology from E^1. Hence, the set of all sets $[0, s^*) = \{t \mid 0 \leq t < s^* \text{ and } s^* \leq 1\}$ and $(t^*, 1] = \{t \mid t^* < t \leq 1 \text{ and } t^* \geq 0\}$, forms a subbase for the relative topology on [0, 1], and so, by corollary 9.9, identifies a subbase for the range space. By theorem 4.10, if the inverse image of every set in this subbase is open, then f is continuous. If $f(x)$ is in $[0, s^*)$, then $f(x) < s^*$. If $f(x) < s^*$, then there exists t such that $0 < t < s^*$ and x is in H_t. $H_t \subseteq H_{s^*}$. Therefore x is in H_{s^*}. Thus, $f^{-1}[[0, s^*] \cap f[X]] \subseteq H_{s^*}$. Conversely, if x is in H_{s^*}, then x is in $\bigcup_{d<s^*,\ d\in D} G(d)$ and so x is in $G(d)$ for some d which is less than s^*. There exists t such that $d < t < s^*$. Hence, x is in $\bigcup_{d<t,\ d\in D} G(d)$, which is H_t. Hence $f(x)$ is less than s^*. This proves that $f^{-1}[[0, s^*) \cap f[X]] \supseteq H_{s^*}$. Thus $f^{-1}[[0, s^*) \cap f[X]] = H_{s^*}$ and is open in X, for $0 < s^* \leq 1$. Next, consider $f^{-1}[(t^*, 1] \cap f(X)]$ for $0 \leq t^* < 1$. The complement of $f^{-1}[(t^*, 1] \cap f(X)]$ in X is the set $f^{-1}[[0, t^*] \cap f(X)]$; i.e., for any x, $f(x) > t^*$ or $f(x) \leq t^*$. It will be shown that $f^{-1}[[0, t^*] \cap f(X)]$ is closed in X. If x is in $f^{-1}[[0, t^*] \cap f(X)]$, then $0 \leq f(x) \leq t^*$. This means that x is in H_t for every t greater than t^*, by definition of $f(x)$. Hence, x is in $\overline{H_t}$ for every $t > t^*$ and so x is in $\bigcap_{t>t^*} \overline{H_t}$. Thus, $f^{-1}[[0, t^*] \cap f(X)] \subseteq \bigcup_{t>t^*} \overline{H_t}$. Conversely, let x be in $\bigcap_{t>t^*} \overline{H_t}$. Let $t^* < t$. Then, there exists t_1 such that $t^* < t_1 < t$ and $\overline{H_{t_1}} \subseteq H_t$. Now, x is in $\overline{H_{t_1}}$ and so x is in H_t. Thus, $0 \leq f(x) \leq t^*$, by definition of $f(x)$. Hence, $f^{-1}[[0, t^*] \cap f[X]] = \bigcap_{t>t^*} \overline{H_t}$. Since the intersection of any number of closed sets is closed, $f^{-1}[[0, t^*] \cap f[X]]$ is closed and so its complement, $f^{-1}[(t^*, 1] \cap f[X]]$, is open in X. The continuity of f is thus established and the theorem is proved. ∎

18.24 Corollary. *If X is a T_4-space and if F_1 and F_2 are two non-empty disjoint closed subsets of X, then there exists a continuous function, f, from X into the interval* $[a, b]$, $\{x \mid a \leq x \leq b$; *a and b are real numbers*$\}$, *in E^1 such that* $f[F_1] = a$ *and* $f[F_2] = b$.

Proof: Let g be any continuous function given by theorem 18.23. Let $h(t) = a + t(b - a)$, where $0 \leq t \leq 1$; then $h \circ g : x \rightarrow h[g(x)]$ is a continuous function of X into $[a, b]$ such that $h \circ g[F_1] = a$ and $h \circ g[F_2] = b$. ▮

18.25 Definition. A collection, L, of functions from a space X into a space Y is said to *separate the disjoint subsets* A and B of X if and only if there exists at least one function f in L such that $f(\overline{A}) \cap f(\overline{B}) = \emptyset$. A set of functions, L, from a space X into a space Y is said *to separate points* of X if and only if for any two distinct points x_1 and x_2 of X, there exists at least one function, f, in L such that $f(x_1) \neq f(x_2)$.

18.26 Corollary. *The set of continuous functions from any T_4-space into E^1 separates disjoint closed sets.*

18.27 Corollary. *The set of continuous functions from any normal space into E^1 separates points.*

18.28 Theorem. *If X is a space such that for any two non-empty disjoint closed subsets F_1 and F_2 of X there exists at least one continuous function, f, from X into* $[0, 1]$ *such that* $f[F_1] = \{0\}$ *and* $f[F_2] = \{1\}$, *then X is T_4.*

Proof: Let F_1 and F_2 be any two non-empty disjoint closed subsets of X. Let f be a continuous function from X into $[0, 1]$ such that $f[F_1] = \{0\}$ and $f[F_2] = \{1\}$. Let $U = \{t \mid 0 \leq t < 1/4$ and t is in $f[X]\}$, and let $V = \{t \mid 3/4 < t \leq 1$ and t is in $f[X]\}$. U and V are open in the relative topology on $f[X]$. Hence, since f is continuous, $f^{-1}[U]$ and $f^{-1}[V]$ are open in X. Further, $f^{-1}[U] \cap f^{-1}[V] = \emptyset$, $F_1 \subseteq f^{-1}[U]$ and $F_2 \subseteq f^{-1}[V]$. Hence, X is T_4. ▮

Thus, theorems 18.23 and 18.28 together establish an alternate definition of T_4 in terms of the set of continuous functions from the space X into E^1; namely, a space X is T_4 if and only if for each pair of non-empty disjoint closed sets F_1 and F_2 there exists a continuous function f from X into $[0, 1]$ such that $f[F_1] = \{0\}$ and $f[F_2] = \{1\}$.

The following theorem gives a useful result concerning the extension of continuous functions from closed subsets of T_4-spaces to the whole space. The proof rests squarely on Urysohn's lemma.

18.29 Theorem (Tietze's Extension Theorem). *If X is a T_4-space, F is closed subset of X and g is a continuous and bounded function from F into the space E^1 (i.e., the range of g is bounded), then there exists a continuous, bounded extension, s, of g which is defined on the whole of X.*

Proof: A. A series $\Phi_0 + \Phi_1 + \Phi_2 + \cdots + \Phi_m + \cdots$ of continuous functions each with domain X is defined. Let g be a continuous function which maps the closed set F of X into the real number space E^1 and for which there exists a positive real number α such that, for all x in F, $|g(x)| \leq \alpha$. Thus, for x in F, $-\alpha \leq g(x) \leq \alpha$. Let $A_0 = \{x \mid x \in F \text{ and } -\alpha \leq g(x) \leq (-1/3)\alpha\}$ and let $B_0 = \{x \mid x \in F \text{ and } (1/3)\alpha \leq g(x) \leq \alpha\}$. Since $A_0 = g^{-1}[[-\alpha, (-1/3)\alpha] \cap g[X]]$, $B_0 = g^{-1}[[(1/3)\alpha, \alpha] \cap g[X]]$ and g is continuous. A_0 and B_0 are disjoint closed subsets of the subspace F. Since F is closed in X, A_0 and B_0 are both, by theorem 9.5, the intersection of closed sets of X with F. Hence, A_0 and B_0 are closed in X. If $A_0 \neq \emptyset \neq B_0$, then by Urysohn's lemma there exists a function Φ_0 from X into $[-\alpha/3, \alpha/3]$ such that $\Phi_0[A_0] = \{(-1/3)\alpha\}$ and $\Phi_0[B_0] = \{(1/3)\alpha\}$ and $(-1/3)\alpha \leq \Phi_0(x) \leq (1/3)\alpha$ for all x in X. Thus $|\Phi_0(x)| \leq (1/3)\alpha$ for all x in X. Since the function described in the conclusion of this theorem must be an extension of g to all of X, the difference $|g(x) - \Phi_0(x)|$ for x in F is of interest. $F = A_0 \cup B_0 \cup (\sim(A_0 \cup B_0) \cap F)$. If x is in A_0, then $-\alpha \leq g(x) \leq -(1/3)\alpha$, $\Phi_0(x) = -(1/3)\alpha$ and therefore, $|g(x) - \Phi_0(x)| \leq (2/3)\alpha$. If x is in B_0, $(1/3)\alpha \leq g(x) \leq \alpha$, $\Phi_0(x) = (1/3)\alpha$ and therefore, $|g(x) - \Phi_0(x)| \leq (2/3)\alpha$. If x is in $\sim(A_0 \cup B_0) \cap F$, then both $g(x)$ and $\Phi_0(x)$ lie between $(-1/3)\alpha$ and $(1/3)\alpha$ and $|g(x) - \Phi_0(x)| \leq (2/3)\alpha$. Hence for all x in F, $|g(x) - \Phi_0(x)| \leq (2/3)\alpha$. However, unless $g(x) - \Phi_0(x) = 0$ for every x in F, Φ_0 is not an extension of g to all of X. Denote the "error" $g(x) - \Phi_0(x)$ by $e_0(x)$. e_0 is defined and continuous from F into $[(-2/3)\alpha, (2/3)\alpha]$ and hence, $|e_0(x)| \leq (2/3)\alpha$. $g(x) = \Phi_0(x) + e_0(x)$. The above procedure will be repeated once before making the induction assumption. Let A_1 and B_1 be defined as follows: $A_1 = e_0^{-1}[[(-2/3)\alpha, (-1/3)\,(2/3)\alpha]]$ and $B_1 = e_0^{-1}[[(1/3)\,(2/3)\alpha, (2/3)\alpha]]$, where $e_0^{-1}[C]$ is an abbreviation for $e_0^{-1}[C \cap e_0[X]]$. A_1 and B_1 are disjoint closed subsets of X. If $A_1 \neq \emptyset \neq B_1$ by Urysohn's lemma, there exists a function $\Phi_1(x)$ defined on all of X such that $\Phi_1[A_1] = \{(-1/3)\,(2/3)\alpha\}$, $\Phi_1[B_1] = \{(1/3)\,(2/3)\alpha\}$ and $(-1/3)\,(2/3)\alpha \leq \Phi_1(x) \leq (1/3)\,(2/3)\alpha$, for all x in X. Thus, $|\Phi_1(x)| \leq (1/3)\,(2/3)\alpha$. For x in F, $|e_0(x) - \Phi_1(x)| \leq (2/3)\,(2/3)\alpha$. Let $e_0(x) \sim \Phi_1(x) = e_1(x)$; then e_1 is continuous from F into $[-(2/3)^2\alpha, (2/3)^2\alpha]$. For x in F, $e_0(x) = \Phi_1(x) + e_1(x)$ and $g(x) = \Phi_0(x) + \Phi_1(x) + e_1(x)$; further, $\Phi_0 + \Phi_1$ is continuous on all of X and $|g(x) - \Phi_0(x) - \Phi_1(x)| = |e_1(x)| \leq (2/3)^2\alpha$. The continuous function $\Phi_0 + \Phi_1$, although not necessarily an extension of g to all of X, deviates from g by not more than the deviation of Φ_0 at each point of F. Now, assume that for each integer i such that $0 \leq i \leq k - 1$, Φ_i has been defined such that (1) Φ_i is continuous on all of X and $|\Phi_i(x)| \leq (1/3)(2/3)^i\alpha$, and (2) $|g(x) - \Phi_0(x) - \Phi_1(x) - \cdots - \Phi_i(x) - \cdots - \Phi_{k-1}(x)| \leq (2/3)^k\alpha$ for all x in F. Let $g(x) - \Phi_0(x) - \Phi_1(x) - \cdots - \Phi_{k-1}(x) = e_{k-1}(x)$. e_{k-1} is defined and continuous on F and $|e_{k-1}(x)| \leq (2/3)^k\alpha$. Let $A_k = e_{k-1}^{-1}[[-(2/3)^k\alpha, -(1/3)\,(2/3)^k\alpha]]$ and $B_k = e_{k-1}^{-1}[[(1/3)\,(2/3)^k\alpha, (2/3)^k\alpha]]$, where again $e_{k-1}^{-1}[C]$ means $e_{k-1}^{-1}[C \cap e_{k-1}[X]]$. Again A_k and B_k are disjoint closed subsets of X. If $A_k \neq \emptyset \neq B_k$ by Urysohn's lemma, there exists a continuous function Φ_k defined on all of X such that $\Phi_k[A_k] = -(1/3)\,(2/3)^k\alpha$ and $\Phi_k[B_k] = (1/3)\,(2/3)^k\alpha$ and $-(1/3) \cdot (2/3)^k\alpha \leq \Phi_k(x) \leq (1/3)\,(2/3)^k\alpha$ for all x in X. Now $|\Phi_k(x)| \leq$

$(1/3)(2/3)^k\alpha$ and $|e_{k-1}(x) - \Phi_k(x)| \leq (2/3)(2/3)^k\alpha$. Hence, Φ_k has been defined from all of X into $[-(1/3)(2/3)^k\alpha, (1/3)(2/3)^k\alpha]$ and $|g(x) - \Phi_0(x) - \cdots - \Phi_k(x)| \leq (2/3)^{k+1}\alpha$, for all x in X. Thus, the induction is complete and there has been defined for every non-negative integer n a function Φ_n, continuous on all of X such that $|\Phi_n(x)| \leq (1/3)(2/3)^n\alpha$. Further, $|g(x) - \Phi_0(x) - \Phi_1(x) - \cdots - \Phi_n(x)| \leq (2/3)^{n+1}\alpha$ for x in F. The case where $A_i = \emptyset$ or $B_i = \emptyset$ is left as an exercise.

B. The series $\Phi_0 + \Phi_1 + \cdots + \Phi_n + \cdots$ is next proved to converge absolutely for each x in X. Consider the series $\Phi_0 + \Phi_1 + \cdots + \Phi_n + \cdots$. $|\Phi_n(x)| \leq (1/3)\cdot(2/3)^n\cdot\alpha$ for all x in X. Since $(1/3)\alpha[1 + 2/3 + (2/3)^2 + \cdots + (2/3)^n + \cdots]$ converges, the series $\Phi_0 + \Phi_1 + \cdots + \Phi_n + \cdots$, by the comparison test, converges absolutely for all x and hence converges for each x in X to a unique limit L_x. Define $s(x) = L_x$. Two things must be established about s; first that s is an extension of g to all of X and second that s is continuous.

C. First it is shown that S is an extension of g. Let x be any element in F. $|g(x) - \Phi_0(x) - \cdots - \Phi_n(x)| \leq (2/3)^{n+1}\alpha$. For each $\epsilon > 0$, there exists a natural number M such that $n > M$ implies $(2/3)^n\alpha < \epsilon/2$. Hence, since $|g(x) - \Phi_0(x) - \cdots - \Phi_n(x)| \leq (2/3)^{n+1}\alpha$, if $n > M$, $|g(x) - \Phi_0(x) - \cdots - \Phi_n(x)| < \epsilon/2$ for all x in F. Also since the series $\Phi_0 + \Phi_1 + \cdots + \Phi_n + \cdots$ converges for each x to $s(x)$, there exists for each x in F a natural number N_x such that if $n > N_x$ then $|\Phi_0(x) + \Phi_1(x) + \cdots + \Phi_n(x) - s(x)| < \epsilon/2$. So if $n > M$ and $n > N_x$, then $|g(x) - \Phi_0(x) - \cdots - \Phi_n(x)| < \epsilon/2$ and $|\Phi_0(x) + \cdots + \Phi_n(x) - s(x)| < \epsilon/2$. Hence $|g(x) - \Phi_0(x) - \cdots - \Phi_n(x)| + |\Phi_0(x) + \cdots + \Phi_n(x) - s(x)| < \epsilon/2 + \epsilon/2$. Thus for any x in F, $|g(x) - s(x)| < \epsilon$. This implies that for any positive real number ϵ and for each x in F, $|g(x) - s(x)| < \epsilon$. Thus, $|g(x) - s(x)| = 0$ for all x in F and $s(x)$ is an extension of g to all of X.

D. It is next shown that s is continuous. In chapter 4, a theorem on uniform convergence will imply the continuity of s. Here, however, to prove continuity of s at a point a in X, it will be established directly that for each $\epsilon > 0$, there exists a basic neighborhood U of a in X such that if x is in U, $|s(x) - s(a)| < \epsilon$. Denote $\Phi_0(x) + \cdots + \Phi_n(x)$ by $s_n(x)$. $|s(x) - s(a)|$ can be written as $|s(x) - s_n(x) + s_n(x) - s_n(a) + s_n(a) - s(a)|$. This latter expression is less than or equal to $|s(x) - s_n(x)| + |s_n(x) - s_n(a)| + s_n(a) - s(a)|$. $|s(x) - s_n(x)| = |\sum_{i=0}^{\infty}\Phi_i(x) - \sum_{i=0}^{n}\Phi_i(x)| = |\sum_{n+1}^{\infty}\Phi_i(x)|$ and $|\sum_{i=n+1}^{\infty}\Phi_i(x)| \leq \sum_{i=n+1}^{\infty}|\Phi_i(x)| \leq \sum_{i=n+1}^{\infty}(2/3)^i\alpha$, for all x in X. $\sum_{i=n+1}^{\infty}(2/3)^i\alpha$ is equal to $\alpha(2/3)^{n+1}[1 + 2/3 + \cdots + (2/3)^i + \cdots]$. This last expression is equal to $3\alpha(2/3)^{n+1}$. For each $\epsilon > 0$, there exists a natural number M such that $m > M$ implies $3\alpha(2/3)^{m+1} < \epsilon/3$. Hence if $m > M$, $|s(x) - s_m(x)| < \epsilon/3$ for all x in X, including a. Since s_m is continuous, there exists a neighborhood U of a in X such that x in U implies that $|s_m(x) - s_m(a)| < \epsilon/3$. This neighborhood U establishes continuity, since for x in U, $|s(x) - s_m(x)| + |s_m(x) - s_m(a)| + |s_m(a) - s(a)| < \epsilon/3 + \epsilon/3 + \epsilon/3$. Hence for x in U, $|s(x) - s(a)| < \epsilon$ and s is continuous at a. ▮

18.30 Definition. A subset A in a space X is called *C^*-embedded* in X if and only if every continuous function from A into E^1 with bounded range can be extended continuously to all of X. A subset A in a space X is called *C-embedded* if and only if every continuous function from A into E^1 can be extended continuously to all of X.

18.31 Corollary. *Every closed subset of a T_4-space is C^*-embedded and C-embedded.*

Proof: Theorem 18.29 establishes the C^*-embedding. Next, let f be any continuous function from a closed subset F of X into E^1. The composite function $\arctan \circ f$ from F into E^1 is continuous and has a bounded range contained in $\{y \mid -\pi/2 < y < \pi/2\}$. Hence $\arctan \circ f$ has a continuous extension, f^*, to the whole of X. If $|f^*(x)| < \pi/2$ for all x in X, then the composite function $\tan \circ f^*$ is continuous on all of X and agrees with f on F. If for some x in X, $|f^*(x)| \geq \pi/2$, let $B = f^{*-1}\{y \mid |y| \geq \pi/2\}$. B is closed in X and is disjoint from F since $f^*[F] \subseteq \{y \mid -\pi/2 < y < \pi/2\}$. Hence, since X is T_4, there exists a continuous function g from X into $[0, 1]$ such that $g[F] = \{1\}$ and $g[B] = \{0\}$. The product function $g \boxtimes f^*$ which assigns $g(x) \times f^*(x)$ to x in X agrees with f^* on F. Further $|g(x) \times f^*(x)| < \pi/2$, for all x in X, since $g[B] = \{0\}$. Thus for x in X, $\tan\big(g(x) \times f^*(x)\big)$ is a single real number, and for a in F, $\tan\big(g(a) \times f^*(a)\big) = f(a)$. Hence the composite function $\tan \circ (g \boxtimes f^*)$ is a continuous extension of f to all of X. ▮

Completely Regular Spaces

The set of continuous functions from a space X into the space E^1 determines another class of spaces—the class of completely regular spaces. It will be shown that these spaces carry the weak topology determined by the set of all continuous functions from the space, X, into E^1.

18.32 Definition. A space X is a *$T_{3+1/2}$-space* if and only if for every point x in X and every non-empty closed set F not containing x, there exists a continuous function, f, from X into the closed interval $[0, 1]$ in E^1 such that $f(x) = 0$ and $f[F] = \{1\}$.

EXERCISE 6. Prove that a space $\{X, \mathfrak{J}\}$ is a $T_{3+1/2}$-space if and only if for every point x in X and every closed set F not containing x, there exists a continuous function, f, from X into the closed unit interval $[0, 1]$ such that $f[F] = \{0\}$ and $f(x) = 1$.

18.33 Definition. A space X is *completely regular* if and only if x is T_1 and $T_{3+1/2}$.

18.34 Theorem. *Any normal space, X, is completely regular and any completely regular space, X, is regular.*

Proof: A. Since a normal space, X, is a T_1-space, singletons are closed. Hence, by the Urysohn lemma, the set of continuous functions from X into $[0, 1]$ in E^1 separates any point and any closed set not containing the point. Thus X is completely regular.

B. If X is a completely regular space, then X is a T_1-space. Let x be any point in X and let F be any closed subset of X which does not contain x. Since X is completely regular, there exists at least one continuous function, f, from X into $[0, 1]$ in E^1 such that $f(x) = 0$ and $f[F] = \{1\}$. Let $U = \{y \mid 0 \leq y < 1/4; y \text{ is in } f[X]\}$ and let $V = \{y \mid 3/4 < y \leq 1; y \text{ is in } f[X]\}$. $f^{-1}[U]$ is open and contains x; $f^{-1}[V]$ is open and contains F and $f^{-1}[U] \cap f^{-1}[V] = \emptyset$. Thus, X is T_3. ▮

18.35 Example. Let $S = \{a, b, c\}$; let $\mathfrak{I} = \{S, \emptyset, \{a\}\}$. $\{S, \mathfrak{I}\}$ is T_4. However, $\{S, \mathfrak{I}\}$ is not $T_{3+1/2}$ since the only closed set containing $\{a\}$ is S. For $f(a) = 0$, $f^{-1}(0) = S$, for any continuous function f from S into E^1.

18.36 Example. Let X be the space consisting of the set of real numbers with the usual basic neighborhoods except at 0. The basic neighborhoods for 0 are sets $N_\epsilon = \{x \mid |x| < \epsilon;\ \epsilon > 0 \text{ and } x \neq 1/n$, for n any natural number$\}$. X is Hausdorff, but X is not completely regular, since there exists no continuous function, f, which maps 0 onto 0 and $\{x \mid x = 1/n$, for n a natural number$\}$ onto 1. Let $U = \{x \mid 0 \leq x < 1/4\}$ and let $V = \{x \mid 3/4 < x \leq 1\}$. $f^{-1}[U]$ and $f^{-1}[V]$, where $f^{-1}[U]$ and $f^{-1}[V]$ are, by definition, $f^{-1}[U \cap f[X]]$ and $f^{-1}[V \cap f[X]]$, respectively, would be open and disjoint; 0 would be in $f^{-1}[U]$ and $\{x \mid x = 1/n$ for n a natural number$\}$ would be in $f^{-1}[V]$. No such open sets exists in X.

There exist non-trivial but complicated examples of spaces which are regular but not completely regular (see Bibliography, Hewitt [1] and Novak [1]); none will be included here. However, an example of a completely regular but non-normal space is given below.

The next theorem establishes that the topology for any completely regular space, X, is the weak topology induced by the set, $C(X)$, of all continuous functions from X into E^1.

18.37 Definition. Let X be a space. A zero-set of X is a subset A of X such that $A = f^{-1}(0)$ for some continuous function f from X into E^1, i.e., $A = \{x \mid f(x) = 0$ for some f in $C(X)\}$. It is immediate, since singletons are closed in E^1, that all zero sets are closed in the original space, X. A *zero* of a function with range in E^1 is an element z in the domain of f such that $f(z) = 0$.

18.38 Lemma. *A space X is a $T_{3+1/2}$-space if and only if the family $Z(X)$ of all zero sets in X is a base for the closed sets in X.*

Proof: A. Let X be a $T_{3+1/2}$-space, let F be any non-empty closed set in X and let x be a point not in F. Since X is a $T_{3+1/2}$-space, there exists a continuous function f from X into E^1 such that $f(x) = 1$ and $f[F] = \{0\}$. Hence x is not in $Z_f = f^{-1}(0)$. Since x was any point in the complement, $\sim F$, of F, F is the intersection of all the zero sets which contain it. This means (definition 3.53) that the zero sets in X constitute a base for the closed sets in X.

B. Let the zero sets in X constitute a base for the cotopology on X. Let p be a point, F a closed set and let p be in the complement, $\sim F$, of F. Since the zero sets constitute a base for the closed sets, there exists a zero set Z_f in X such that $F \subseteq Z_f$ and p is not in Z_f. This means that $f[F] = \{0\}$ and $f(p) = a \neq 0$. For x in X, let $g(x) = f(x) \cdot a^{-1}$. Then $g[F] = \{0\}$ and $g(p) = 1$. Define $h(x) = 0$ if $g(x) \leq 0$, $h(x) = g(x)$, if $0 \leq g(x) \leq 1$, and $h(x) = 1$ if $g(x) \geq 1$. Then, $h[F] = \{0\}$, $h(p) = 1$ and for x in X, $0 \leq h(x) \leq 1$. h is continuous; hence, X is a $T_{3+1/2}$-space. ▮

18.39 Corollary. *A space X is completely regular if and only if it is T_1 and the set of all zero sets constitutes a base for the closed sets in X.*

18.40 Theorem. *A space $\{X, \mathfrak{J}\}$ is a $T_{3+1/2}$-space if and only if the topology, $\mathfrak{J}$, on X is the weak topology induced by the set $C(X)$ of all continuous functions from X into E^1.*

Proof: Let $\{X, \mathfrak{J}\}$ be a $T_{3+1/2}$-space. Let F be any closed set in the weak cotopology. By definition 10.2, exercise 8 in section 10 and definition 10.9, $F = \bigcap_\nu \bigcup_{i=1}^{k\nu} f_i^{-1}[A_i]$, where A_i is closed in E^1. By definition of $C(X)$, each f_i is continuous in the given topology; hence, F is closed with the given topology and the weak topology induced by $C(X)$ on X is contained in the given topology. Conversely, let F be closed with the given topology. By lemma 18.38, F is the intersection of zero sets. Let $F = \bigcap_{f \in \mathfrak{A}} Z_f$, where each Z_f is a zero set for a function f in $\mathfrak{A} \subseteq C(X)$. $Z_f = f^{-1}[\{0\}]$, where $\{0\}$ is closed in E^1. Hence by definition (10.9) of the weak topology, F belongs to the weak cotopology. ▮

18.41 Corollary. *A space $\{X, \mathfrak{J}\}$ is completely regular if and only if it is T_1 and the given topology, $\mathfrak{J}$, is the weak topology induced by $C(X)$, the set of all continuous functions from X into E^1.*

Quotient Spaces, Subspaces and Products of Completely Regular Spaces

In example 17.5, a Hausdorff space, X, is defined which is neither T_3, $T_{3+1/2}$ nor T_4. The set $\{0\}$ is closed and the set $F = \{x \mid x = 1/n$, for n a natural number$\}$ is closed. There exist no disjoint open sets U and V such that 0 is in U and $F \subseteq V$. The space X can be defined as a quotient space of a subspace, S, of E^2. Let S denote the complement in E^2 of the set $\{(0, 0)\} \cup \{(x, y) \mid x = 1/n$ for n a natural number and $y \neq 0\}$. Define f from S onto the real numbers by $f((x, y)) = x$. Next, define the equivalence relation R as $(a, b)\ R\ (c, d)$ if and only if $f((a, b)) = f((c, d))$. Thus points of S are in the same class if and only if they have the same x-coordinate. S/R with the quotient topology becomes a quotient space of S. By the next theorem, S is completely regular, since E^2 is. Thus a quotient space of a completely regular space is not necessarily completely regular.

18.42 Theorem. *A subspace of a $T_{3+1/2}$-space is a $T_{3+1/2}$-space.*

Proof: Let M be a subspace of the $T_{3+1/2}$-space X. Let m be a point in M and let F be a closed subset of M which does not contain m. By definition of the relative topology, there exists a closed set F^* of X such that $F = F^* \cap M$. F^* does not contain m. Since X is a $T_{3+1/2}$-space, there exists a continuous function f whose domain is X and such that $f(m) = 0$, $f[F^*] = \{1\}$ and $0 \leq f(x) \leq 1$ for x in X. Consider the function $g\colon M \to [0, 1]$ such that $g(a) = f(a)$ for a in M. By lemma 9.21, g is continuous from M into $[0, 1]$, $g(m) = 0$ and $g[F] = \{1\}$. ▮

18.43 Lemma. *Let $\{f_1, f_2, \ldots, f_k\}$ denote a finite set of continuous functions from a space X into E^1. For x in X, let $g(x) =$ maximum $\{f_1(x), f_2(x), \ldots, f_k(x)\}$. Then g is continuous from X into E^1.*

Proof: Let a be a point in X. Let $V_\epsilon^* = \{y \mid |y - g(a)| < \epsilon\}$. Let $V_\epsilon^i = \{y \mid |y - f_i(a)| < \epsilon\}$ for $i = 1, 2, \ldots, k$. Since each f_i is continuous at a in X, there exist neighborhoods $U_1, \ldots, U_i, \ldots, U_k$ of a in X such that $f_i[U_i] \subseteq V_\epsilon^i$. Consider $U^* = U_1 \cap \cdots \cap U_i \cap \cdots \cap U_k$. U^* is a neighborhood of a in X such that $f_i[U^*] \subseteq V_\epsilon^i$ for each $i = 1, \ldots, k$. Let $g(a) = f_j(a)$, i.e., $f_j(a)$ is the maximum of $\{f_1(a), \ldots, f_i(a), \ldots, f_k(a)\}$. Then for x in U^*, $f_j(x)$ is in $V_\epsilon^j = V_\epsilon^*$. Further, if x is in U^* and $f_i(x)$ is not in V_ϵ^j, then $f_i(a) < f_j(a)$, and since V_ϵ^i and V_ϵ^j are intervals of real numbers, $f_i(x) < f_j(x)$. Hence, $f_i(x) \neq g(x)$. Thus for x in U^*, $g(x)$ is in V_ϵ^* and so g is continuous. ▮

18.44 Theorem. *A product space $\prod_\nu X_\nu$, where each X_ν is completely regular, is completely regular; and conversely, if $\prod_\nu X_\nu \neq \emptyset$ is completely regular, then each X_ν is.*

Proof: By theorem 16.18, $\prod_\nu X_\nu$ is a T_1-space. Let x^* be a point in $\prod_\nu X_\nu$ which is not contained in the closed set F of $\prod_\nu X_\nu$. There exists an open set B of the defining base for the product topology such that x^* is in B and $B \cap F = \emptyset$. Let $B = V_{\nu_1}^* \cap V_{\nu_2}^* \cap \cdots \cap V_{\nu_k}^*$, where each $V_{\nu_i}^*$ is a set in the usual subbase, i.e., $V_{\nu_i}^* = p_{\nu_i}^{-1}[U_{\nu_i}]$, where U_{ν_i} is an open set in X_{ν_i} and p_{ν_i} is the projection function. Now $x^* \in V_{\nu_i}^*$ for $i = 1, 2, \ldots, k$; hence, $x_{\nu_i} = p_{\nu_i}(x^*)$ is in U_{ν_i} for $i = 1, 2, \ldots, k$. Since X_{ν_i} is completely regular, there are continuous functions f_{ν_i} from X_{ν_i} into $[0, 1]$, for $i = 1, 2, \ldots, k$ such that $f_{\nu_i}(x_{\nu_i}) = 0$ and $f_{\nu_i}[\sim U_{\nu_i}] = \{1\}$. Now consider the composite functions $f_{\nu_i} \circ p_{\nu_i}$ from $\prod_\nu X_\nu$ into $[0, 1]$. $f_{\nu_i} \circ p_{\nu_i}(x^*) = 0$ for $i = 1, 2, \ldots, k$ and each $f_{\nu_i} \circ p_{\nu_i}$ is continuous for $i = 1, 2, \ldots, k$. Define $g\colon \prod_\nu X_\nu \to [0, 1]$ as follows: $g(x) =$ maximum $\{f_{\nu_1} \circ p_{\nu_1}(x), f_{\nu_2} \circ p_{\nu_2}(x), \ldots, f_{\nu_k} \circ p_{\nu_k}(x)\}$. By lemma 18.43, g is a continuous function of X into $[0, 1]$. Also $g(x^*) = 0$. Further, if x is not in $B = V_{\nu_1}^* \cap V_{\nu_2}^* \cap \cdots \cap V_{\nu_k}^*$, x is not in $V_{\nu_i}^*$ for some i, and so $p_{\nu_i}(x)$ is not in U_{ν_i}. Thus $f_{\nu_i} \circ p_{\nu_i}(x) = 1$ for this i. This means that $g(x) = 1$ for x in $\sim B$ and so $g[F] = \{1\}$ and $\prod_\nu X_\nu$ is completely regular.

The converse is left as an exercise. ▮

18.45 Corollary. *Let A be any set. The function space I^A of all functions from A into the closed unit interval I with the product topology is completely regular.*

Proof: The closed unit interval [0, 1] in E^1 with the relative topology along with all metrizable spaces will be proved to be completely regular in chapter 4 (theorem 19.20). By theorem 18.44, I^A is then completely regular. ▮

18.46 Theorem. *A space X is completely regular if and only if it is homeomorphic to a subspace of the product space I^C, where I denotes the closed unit interval with the relative topology and C denotes the set of continuous functions from X into I.*

Proof: A. If X is homeomorphic to a subspace of I^C, then by corollary 18.45 and theorem 18.42, X is homeomorphic to a completely regular space and hence is completely regular.

B. If X is completely regular, define the mapping Φ from X into the space I^C as follows: $\Phi(x)$ is the element of I^C whose f-th coordinate is $f(x)$ (f is a continuous function from X into [0, 1]). By theorem 12.13, Φ is continuous since the composite $p_f \circ \Phi(x) = f(x)$ is continuous, where p_f is a projection function. Since X is completely regular, if x and y are two distinct points of X, there exists a continuous function f from X into [0, 1] such that $f(x) = 0$ and $f(y) = 1$. This means that the f-th coordinate of $\Phi(x)$ is 0 and the f-th coordinate of $\Phi(y)$ is 1. Hence Φ is 1:1. Lastly, it must be shown that Φ is open. Let G be an open set in X and consider $\Phi[G]$. Let $\Phi(x)$ be any point in $\Phi[G]$ and let g denote a function from X into [0, 1] such that $g(x) = 0$ and $g[\sim G] = \{1\}$. Such a function exists by the complete regularity of X. By the definition of the product topology, the set $V = p_g^{-1}[\{t \mid 0 \leq t < 1\}]$ is open in I^C; hence, $V \cap \Phi[X]$ is open in $\Phi[X]$. Further, since $g(x) = 0$, $\Phi(x)$ is in $V \cap \Phi[X]$. Now let α^* be any element in $V \cap \Phi[X]$. There is an element z in X such that $\Phi(z) = \alpha^*$, and so $0 \leq g(z) < 1$. This implies that $g(z) \neq 1$ and hence z is in G. Thus, $\Phi(z) = \alpha^*$ is in $\Phi[G]$, and so $V \cap \Phi[X]$ is contained in $\Phi[G]$. $\Phi(x)$ is then an interior point of $\Phi[G]$ and Φ is open. Thus the theorem is proved. ▮

The standard example for showing that a subspace of a normal space is not necessarily normal is the so-called "Tychonoff Plank" discussed in chapter 6. This space is a product space of the space of ordinal numbers up to and including the first infinite ordinal ω_0 with the space of all ordinals up to and including the first uncountable ordinal ω_1; each space has the interval topology.

18.47 Theorem. *Any closed subspace of a normal space is normal.*

Proof: Exercise.

The product space of two normal spaces may fail to be a normal space. Example 18.4 contains an example of a space which is completely regular but not normal. This space can be obtained as a product of normal spaces as follows.

18.48 Example. Let X be the set of real numbers with basic neighborhoods $U(x, \epsilon) = \{y \mid x \leq y < x + \epsilon;\ \epsilon > 0\}$. Thus, the basic neighborhoods of a real number p are the so-called "half-open" intervals for which p is the left-hand end point. Since each such basic neighborhood is closed, the resulting space $\{X, \mathfrak{J}\}$ is regular. Further, $\{X, \mathfrak{J}\}$ has the additional property that any open covering of X contains a countable subcovering. For let $\mathcal{G}$ be any open covering of X. We define from $\mathcal{G}$ the covering $\mathscr{g}$ as follows. Let G_α be a set in $\mathcal{G}$ and let x be a point in G_α. Then there exists $I_x = \{y \mid x \leq y < x + \epsilon;\ \epsilon > 0\}$ and $I_x \subseteq G_\alpha$. Choose such as I_x for each x in X. The collection of these sets, I_x, is also a covering for X. Let M denote $\{z \mid z$ is in no I_x for $x \neq z\}$. Then if z_1 is in M and z_2 is in M, $I_{z_1} \cap I_{z_2} = \emptyset$. Since the intervals in the collection $\{I_z\}$ for z in M are disjoint, the collection is countable. Let $[I_{z_1}, I_{z_2}, \ldots, I_{z_k}, \ldots]$ denote this collection. Next let N denote $\{q \mid q$ is in some I_x for $x \neq q\}$. Now the collection $\{I_x^-\}$ of the intervals I_x minus their end points, covers N. The proofs of theorems 5.10 and 18.15 combine to give the procedure for establishing that a countable number of these intervals, say, $\{I_{x_1}^-, I_{x_2}^-, \ldots, I_{x_n}^-, \ldots\}$ cover N. It follows that the collection $\{I_{x_1}, I_{x_2}, \ldots, I_{x_n}, \ldots\}$ will also cover N. Hence the collection $\{I_{z_1}, I_{z_2}, \ldots, I_{z_n}, \ldots\} \cup \{I_{x_1}, I_{x_2}, \ldots, I_{x_j}, \ldots\}$ covers $M \cup N$; i.e., the whole of X. Thus a countable number of intervals $\{I_{t_1}, I_{t_2}, \ldots, I_{t_n}, \ldots\}$ covers X. Now each I_n is contained entirely in some G_n of the covering $\mathcal{G}$; so for each I_{t_n} we choose a G_n in $\mathcal{G}$. The collection $\{G_1, G_2, \ldots, G_n, \ldots\}$ covers X and is countable. Hence by theorem 18.14, X is normal. Consider now the product space $X \times X$. The product topology can be identified by the basic neighborhood relation that assigns to each point (p, q) in $X \times X$ the sets $\{(x, y) \mid p \leq x < p + \epsilon$ and $q \leq y < q + \epsilon\}$. This space $X \times X$ is then homeomorphic to the space S of example 18.4. The topological equivalence can be set up geometrically by a rotation of

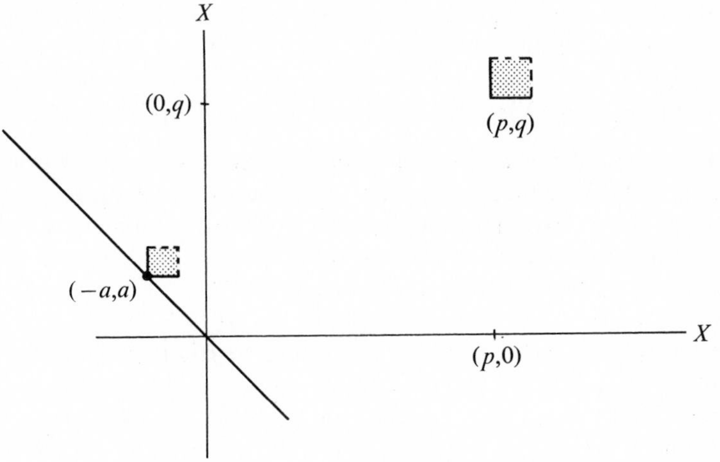

FIGURE 19

$X \times X$ of $+45°$ about the origin; a rotation is 1:1, continuous, and has a continuous inverse. Since S is not normal, $X \times X$ is not normal. Thus, a product of normal spaces is not necessarily normal.

18.49 Example. Since the space X of the preceding example is normal, it is completely regular. By theorem 18.44, $X \times X$ is completely regular but not normal.

EXERCISE 7. Prove that if a non-empty product space $\prod_\nu X_\nu$ is T_4, then each X_ν is.

An Algebraic Topological Invariant—The Ring $C(X)$

In corollary 18.41, the set, $C(X)$, of all continuous functions from a space X into the usual space E^1 of real numbers was established as having an important relation to the topology on a completely regular space. It will next be shown that a ring can be defined on $C(X)$ which is in a certain sense a topological invariant.

18.50 Definition. An algebraic system, Σ_X, uniquely defined for a topological space X will be called an *algebraic topological invariant* if and only if for any space Y, which is homeomorphic to X, if a system Σ_Y is defined in the same manner as Σ_X is defined for X, then Σ_Y is isomorphic to Σ_X.

18.51 Theorem. *Let $C(X)$ denote the set of continuous functions from a space X into E^1. Define $f \boxplus g = \{(x, y) \mid f(x) + g(x) = y\}$ and $f \boxtimes g = \{(x, y) \mid f(x) \cdot g(x) = y\}$. $\{C(X), \boxplus, \boxtimes\}$ is a commutative ring with unit.*

Proof: Exercise.

NOTATION: The ring $\{C(X), \boxplus, \boxtimes\}$ is usually denoted by $C(X)$ when no confusion seems likely.

18.52 Theorem. *The ring $C(X)$ is an algebraic topological invariant.*

Proof: A. Let h be a homeomorphism from X onto Y. Let g be an element in $C(Y)$. Define the function ϕ from $C(Y)$ into $C(X)$ as follows: for g in $C(Y)$, let $\phi(g) = g \circ h$. $\phi(g)$ as the composite of the two continuous functions h and g is continuous and so is an element of $C(X)$.

B. ϕ is onto. Let f be any element in $C(X)$. Consider the composite function $f \circ h^{-1}$. $f \circ h^{-1}$ is in $C(Y)$. Further, $\phi(f \circ h^{-1}) = f \circ h^{-1} \circ h = f$ by definition of ϕ. Hence, $\phi(f \circ h^{-1}) = f$, and so f is in the range of ϕ.

C. ϕ is 1:1. Let $\phi(g_1) = \phi(g_2)$. $\phi(g_1) = g_1 \circ h$ and $\phi(g_2) = g_2 \circ h$. Hence $g_1(h(x)) = g_2(h(x))$ for all x in X. Since h is onto, $g_1(y) = g_2(y)$ for every y in Y. Thus, $g_1 = g_2$ and ϕ is 1:1.

D. ϕ is a ring homomorphism. Let g_1 and g_2 again denote elements in $C(Y)$. $\phi(g_1 \boxplus g_2) = (g_1 \boxplus g_2) \circ h = \phi(g_1) \boxplus \phi(g_2)$ by definition of $\boxplus$. Similarly, $\phi(g_1 \boxtimes g_2) = \phi(g_1) \boxtimes \phi(g_2)$ by definition of $\boxtimes$. ▮

The previous theorem introduces for the first time an algebraic topological invariant, $C(X)$. Algebraic topological invariants have become extremely important in modern topology. Other examples are homotopy and homology groups. The invariance is established, as it is in theorem 18.52, by assigning to each homeomorphism between the topological spaces X and Y an isomorphism between the algebraic structures. The generalization of this step is the cornerstone on which all of modern algebraic topology is based.

In the case of a compact (chapter 6) Hausdorff space, X, it can be established that the ring, $C(X)$, is a complete set of topological invariants, i.e., $C(X)$ completely characterizes the space X, so that if $C(X)$ and $C(Y)$ are isomorphic, a homeomorphism between X and Y can be established. The next theorem shows that for general spaces the ring $C(X)$ does not completely characterize the space X; the theorem also establishes another important relation between $C(X)$ and completely regular spaces.

18.53 Theorem. *Let X be any topological space and let $C(X)$ denote the ring of continuous functions from X into E^1. There exists a completely regular space whose ring of continuous functions is isomorphic to $C(X)$.*

Proof: A space must be defined which has two qualifications: it must be completely regular and its ring of continuous functions must be isomorphic to $C(X)$. An equivalence relation, a quotient set and a quotient mapping will help with the latter and theorem 18.40 will help with the former.

A. First, a ring which is isomorphic to $C(X)$ is defined. Let R denote the equivalence relation, $\{(a, b) \text{ in } X \times X \mid f(a) = f(b) \text{ for all } f \text{ in } C(X)\}$. X/R again denotes the set of equivalence classes determined by R and q again denotes the quotient mapping which sends each element of X onto the equivalence class containing it. Now, let f be any element in $C(X)$. f is constant on the equivalence classes determined by R, by definition of R, and so determines uniquely a function f^* from X/R into E^1 defined by $f^*(D) = f(x)$, where D is an equivalence class and x is in D. Further, f is equal to the composite function $f^* \circ q$. Conversely, any function g from X/R into E^1 determines uniquely a function $g \circ q$ from X into E^1. Thus the set, A, of functions, g, from X/R into E^1 such that $g \circ q$ is in $C(X)$, i.e., continuous from X into E^1, can be put into 1:1 correspondence with $C(X)$. Let Ψ denote this correspondence from A onto $C(X)$. $\Psi(g) = g \circ q$. The set A becomes a ring with operations $\boxplus$ and $\boxtimes$ defined in the usual way. For if g_1 and g_2 are in A, then $g_1 \circ q$ and $g_2 \circ q$ are in $C(X)$ and so $g_1 \circ q \boxminus g_2 \circ q$, where $\boxminus g$ is the additive inverse of g are in the ring $C(X)$ (theorem 18.51). However, $g_1 \circ q \boxminus g_2 \circ q = (g_1 \boxminus g_2) \circ q$ and so $g_1 \boxminus g_2$ is in A. Similarly, $g_1 \boxtimes g_2$ is in A. Thus Ψ is an isomorphism from $\{A, \boxplus, \boxtimes\}$ onto $C(X)$.

B. A completely regular space is now defined on X/R. Let ω-$\mathfrak{I}$ denote the weak topology for X/R determined by the set A of functions from X/R into E^1 defined in part A, above. Since for g in A, $g \circ q$ is continuous, by theorem 13.4, g is continuous from $\{X/R, \mathfrak{I}_Q\}$ into E^1, where $\mathfrak{I}_Q$ is the quotient topology. Hence, by theorem 10.10, $\mathfrak{I}_Q \supseteq \omega$-$\mathfrak{I}$. Also, by definition of the quotient topology and by theorem 10.12, q is continuous from X onto $\{X/R, \omega\text{-}\mathfrak{I}\}$. Hence, if h is any continuous function from $\{X/R, \omega\text{-}\mathfrak{I}\}$ into E^1, then $h \circ q$ as the composite of two continuous functions is a continuous function and h is in A, by definition of A. Thus, A is exactly the set of continuous functions from $\{X/R, \omega\text{-}\mathfrak{I}\}$ into E^1. $\{X/R, \omega\text{-}\mathfrak{I}\}$ is then a $T_{3+1/2}$-space, by theorem 18.40. Lastly, it is shown that $\{X/R, \omega\text{-}\mathfrak{I}\}$ is Hausdorff. Let D_1 and D_2 be two points in X/R, i.e., two equivalence classes determined by the relation R. There exists, by definition of R, a function f in $C(X)$ such that $f(a) \neq f(b)$, where a is in D_1 and b is in D_2. As shown above f can be expressed as $f^* \circ q$ where f^* is continuous from $\{X/R, \omega\text{-}\mathfrak{I}\}$ into E^1. Further, $f^*[D_1] = f(a) \neq f(b) = f^*[D_2]$. Since E^1 is Hausdorff, there exist disjoint open sets U and V in E^1 such that $f^*[D_1]$ is in U and $f^*[D_2]$ is in V. Hence $(f^*)^{-1}[U]$ and $(f^*)^{-1}[V]$ are the disjoint open sets required to make $\{X/R, \omega\text{-}\mathfrak{I}\}$ Hausdorff. Hence, $\{X/R, \omega\text{-}\mathfrak{I}\}$ is a completely regular space and $C(X/R)$ is isomorphic to $C(X)$. ▌

18.54 Example. A. To illustrate the procedure in the proof of the preceding theorem and to emphasize that the topology ω-$\mathfrak{I}$ is not necessarily a quotient topology even though a quotient mapping is used indirectly to define the topology, the space of example 17.5 is used. This space $\{X, \mathfrak{I}\}$ is determined on the set of real numbers when each real number except 0 is assigned the usual neighborhoods. The basic neighborhoods of 0 are the sets, V^ϵ, where $V^\epsilon = \{x \mid |x| < \epsilon$ and $x \neq 1/n$ for n a natural number, and ϵ a positive real number$\}$. This space was shown to be Hausdorff but not regular and so it is not completely regular. Further, $\{x \mid x = 1/n$, for n a natural number$\}$, as well as all infinite subsets of it, is closed in this space, $\{X, \mathfrak{I}\}$. These same sets are not closed in E^1, since 0 is a limit point. This is the basic difference between this unusual topology $\mathfrak{I}$ and the usual topology on the real numbers. Thus $\mathfrak{I}$ is larger than the usual topology.

B. Now, it will be shown that $C(E^1) = C(X)$. There exist no disjoint open sets U and V in $\{X, \mathfrak{I}\}$ such that $M \subseteq U$, where M contains an infinite subset of $\{x \mid x = 1/n$, for n a natural number$\}$ and 0 is in V; hence, there can exist no continuous function from $\{X, \mathfrak{I}\}$ into E^1 such that $f(0)$ is not a point in the closure of $f[M]$. For let G be a usual basic open interval which contains $f(0)$ and no point of $f[M]$. Say $G = \{y \mid |f(0) - y| < \epsilon\}$. Then $G_1 = \{y \mid |f(0) - y| < \epsilon/2\}$ and $G_2 = \{y \mid |f(0) - y| > \epsilon\}$ are disjoint open sets in E^1. f is continuous from $\{X, \mathfrak{I}\}$ into E^1; hence, $f^{-1}[G_1]$ and $f^{-1}[G_2]$ are disjoint open sets in $\{X, \mathfrak{I}\}$ such that 0 is in $f^{-1}[G_1]$ and $M \subseteq f^{-1}[G_2]$. This is a contradiction. Now, consider f continuous from

$\{X, \mathfrak{J}\}$ into E^1 and F closed in E^1. $f^{-1}[F]$ is, of course, closed in $\{X, \mathfrak{J}\}$. $f^{-1}[F]$ is also closed in E^1 if $f^{-1}[F]$ does not contain an infinite subset of $\{x \mid x = 1/n$, for n a natural number$\}$. So let $f^{-1}[F]$ contain an infinite subset of $\{x \mid x = 1/n$, for n a natural number$\}$. By the above, $f(0)$ is in the closure of $f[f^{-1}[F]] = F$. Hence, since F is closed in the range, $f(0)$ is in F and 0 is in $f^{-1}[F]$. This means that $f^{-1}[F]$ is also closed in E^1 and that f is continuous from E^1 into E^1. Since $\mathfrak{J}$ is larger than the usual topology, every function which is continuous from E^1 into E^1 is continuous from $\{X, \mathfrak{J}\}$ into E^1. Hence $C(X) = C(E^1)$.

C. Lastly, it will be shown that E^1 is the space $\{X/R, \omega\text{-}\mathfrak{J}\}$ of the preceding theorem and that $\omega\text{-}\mathfrak{J}$ is not the quotient topology. Since the topology $\mathfrak{J}$, above, is larger than the topology on the usual space E^1, the identity mapping $i(x) = x$ is continuous and so belongs to $C(X)$. This means that the relation R of the previous theorem is the identity relation $\{(a, b) \mid a = b\}$. This means $q(x) = \{x\}$. Thus X/R can be considered to be the set and q the identity mapping $i(x) = x$. Since $f \circ i = f$, it follows that $\Psi(f) = f$ and $A = C(X)$, with the notation of the previous theorem. Since $C(X) = C(E^1)$, the topology $\omega\text{-}\mathfrak{J}$ for X/R is the topology for the real numbers determined by $C(E^1)$. By corollary 18.41, this is the usual topology for the real numbers and $\{X/R, \omega\text{-}\mathfrak{J}\}$ is E^1. E^1, however, does not carry the quotient topology determined by the mapping $i(x) = x$. The quotient topology is the largest topology for the range with which i is continuous; hence, this would be the original topology $\mathfrak{J}$ which is larger than the topology on E^1.

SUMMARY FOR CHAPTER 3

The separation axioms endow the general topological space with additional properties which are useful both for abstract considerations and for applications. The standard separation axioms are:

1. **T_0-Axiom:** Of any two points in the space, at least one has a neighborhood which does not contain the other point.
2. **T_1-Axiom:** Of any two points in the space, each has a neighborhood which does not contain the other point.
3. **T_2-Axiom:** If p and q denote two distinct points in the space, there exists a neighborhood U of p and a neighborhood V of q such that $U \cap V = \emptyset$.
4. **T_3-Axiom:** If p is any point and F is any closed set not containing p, then there exist disjoint open sets G_1 and G_2 such that p is in G_1 and $F \subseteq G_2$. T_1 and T_3 yield a regular space.
5. **$T_{3+1/2}$-Axiom:** For each point p and non-empty closed set F not containing p, there exists a continuous function f from the space into the unit interval $[0, 1]$ such that $f(p) = 0$ and $f[F] = \{1\}$. T_1 and $T_{3+1/2}$ yield a completely regular space.

6. **T_4-Axiom:** For each two disjoint closed sets F_1 and F_2, there exist disjoint open sets G_1 and G_2 such that $F_1 \subseteq G_1$ and $F_2 \subseteq G_2$. T_1 and T_4 yield a normal space. Normality $\Rightarrow$ Complete Regularity $\Rightarrow$ Regularity $\Rightarrow$ Hausdorff $\Rightarrow T_1 \Rightarrow T_0$.

The main basic theorem brought in by the T_0-axiom is that different singletons have different closures. The main theorem brought in by the T_1-axiom is that singletons, and hence finite sets, are closed. The main basic theorems brought in by the T_2 (Hausdorff)-axiom are (1) that sequential and net limits, when they exist, are unique, and (2) that continuous extensions of continuous functions defined on dense subsets, when they exist, are unique. The main basic theorem brought in by regularity is that under certain conditions continuous extensions do exist for continuous functions defined on dense subsets. The main basic theorems brought in by complete regularity are that (1) a space is completely regular if and only if it is homeomorphic to a subspace of a product space $\prod_\nu Y_\nu$, where $Y_\nu = [0, 1]$ with the relative topology, (2) a space X is completely regular if and only if the topology is the weak topology determined by the set $C(X)$ of all continuous functions from X into E^1, and (3) completely regular spaces determine all possible rings $C(X)$ of continuous functions from X into E^1. In addition, each homeomorphism between two completely regular spaces X and Y determines an isomorphism between the rings $C(X)$ and $C(Y)$. The ring $C(X)$ is then an algebraic topological invariant. The main basic theorems brought in by the T_4-axiom are (1) that disjoint closed sets are separated by the continuous functions from the space into E^1, and (2) that closed subsets are C^*-embedded in the space, i.e., any continuous, bounded function defined on a closed subset can be extended continuously to the whole space.

CHAPTER 4

Metrizable Spaces and Uniformizable Spaces

One of the most useful special classes of topological spaces is the class of metrizable spaces. The topology for these spaces is or can be given in terms of a distance function just as it is for E^1 and for E^2. The distance function, called a metric, identifies a special and useful collection of basic neighborhoods called spherical neighborhoods. Most of the spaces of modern analysis can be defined by a basic neighborhood relation determined by a metric.

19. METRICS AND METRIZABLE SPACES.

METRICS

19.1 Definition. Let X be any set. A function ρ from $X \times X$ into the set of real numbers is called a *metric for* X if and only if for x, y, z in X,

(a) $\rho(x, y) = 0$ if and only if $x = y$;
(b) $\rho(x, y) = \rho(y, x)$; and
(c) $\rho(x, y) + \rho(y, z) \geq \rho(x, z)$ (triangle inequality).

19.2 Lemma. *For any metric* ρ *on a set* X, $\rho(x, y) \geq 0$ *for* x, y *in* X.

Proof: Exercise.

EXERCISE 1. Let X be any set and let d be a function from $X \times X$ into the set of real numbers. Further, let d satisfy the following conditions:

a'. $d(x, y) = 0$ if and only if $x = y$, and

b'. $d(x, y) + d(z, y) \geq d(x, z)$. Prove (1) that d is a metric, and (2) that any metric satisfies a' and b'.

EXERCISE 2. Prove that ρ, where $\rho(a, b) = |a - b|$, is a metric on the set of real numbers.

EXERCISE 3. Let X be any set; let $\rho(x, y) = 1$ for every ordered pair (x, y) in $X \times X$ such that $x \neq y$. Let $\rho(x, x) = 0$ for every x in X. Prove that ρ is a metric on X.

The previous exercise shows that a metric can be defined on any set.

EXERCISE 4. Show that the function d defined by $d((x_0, y_0), (x_1, y_1))$ = maximum $\{|x_0 - x_1|, |y_0 - y_1|\}$ is a metric on X, where X is the set of all ordered pairs of real numbers.

EXERCISE 5. Again, let X be the set of all ordered pairs of real numbers and define $w(((a, b), (c, d))) = |a - c| + |b - d|$. Prove that w is a metric for X.

EXERCISE 6. Let f be any function from a set X into E^1. Let $\delta(x, y) = |f(x) - f(y)|$. Which properties of a metric does δ possess?

A non-empty set M of real numbers is said to be *bounded* if and only if there exists a positive real number β such that for x in M, $|x| \leq \beta$. A non-empty set M of real numbers is said to be *bounded from below* if and only if there exists a real number α, called a *lower bound*, such that for x in M, $\alpha \leq x$; and it is called *bounded from above* if and only if there exists a real number γ, called an *upper bound*, such that for x in M, $x \leq \gamma$. It is a fundamental characteristic of the real number structure that every non-empty set M of real numbers bounded from below has a lower bound, called a *greatest lower bound*, that is greater than all other lower bounds; similarly, every non-empty set M of real numbers bounded from above has an upper bound, called a *least upper bound*, that is less than all other upper bounds of M. These properties of the real number structure together with the existence of a metric on a set X make possible the following definitions.

19.3 Definition. Let X be a non-empty set with a metric ρ, and let A and B be any two non-empty subsets of X. $\rho[A \times B]$ is a non-empty set of non-negative real numbers and hence is bounded from below by 0. It then has a greatest lower bound, $d_\rho(A, B)$, called the *ρ-distance between A and B.*

19.4 Definition. If X is a set with a metric ρ, if x is a point of X and if B is a non-empty subset of X, the *ρ-distance from the point x to the subset B* is defined to be $d_\rho(\{x\}, B)$ and is usually denoted by $d_\rho(x, B)$.

19.5 Definition. The *ρ-diameter*, Δ, of a non-empty subset A of a set X with metric ρ is defined to be the least upper bound, if it exists, of the set $\rho[A \times A]$. If the diameter exists, A is called *bounded with respect to ρ*; otherwise A is called *unbounded* or *not bounded with respect to ρ.*

METRIZABLE SPACES

19.6 Lemma. *Let X be a set with metric ρ. The relation $R = \{(x, U) \mid x$ is in X and $U = \{y \mid y$ is in X and $\rho(x, y) < \epsilon$, for ϵ real and positive$\}\}$ is a basic neighborhood relation for X.*

Proof: BN-I. Let x be in X; let $U = \{y \mid \rho(x, y) < 1\}$. $U \neq \emptyset$. (x, U) is in R and so the domain of R is X. If (x, U) is in R, then, since $\rho(x, x) = 0$, x belongs to U; thus, every basic neighborhood of x contains x. BN-II. Let (x, U) and (x, V) both belong to R. Let $U = \{y \mid \rho(x, y) < \epsilon_1\}$ and let $V = \{y \mid \rho(x, y) < \epsilon_2\}$. Let δ^* be the minimum of ϵ_1 and ϵ_2. Let $W = \{y \mid \rho(x, y) < \delta^*\}$. (x, W) is in R; also, $W \subseteq U \cap V$. BN-III. Let (x, U) be in R, let t be any point in U and let $U = \{y \mid \rho(x, y) < \epsilon^*\}$. Then let $\delta^* = \epsilon^* - \rho(x, t)$. Let $N = \{y \mid \rho(t, y) < \delta^*\}$. (t, N) is in R. Further, if z is in N, $\rho(t, z) < \epsilon^* - \rho(x, t)$. Therefore, $\rho(t, z) + \rho(x, t) < \epsilon^*$, which implies that $\rho(x, z) < \epsilon^*$, and so z is in U. Thus, $N \subseteq U$. ▮

19.7 Example. If X is the set of all real numbers and if $\rho(x, y) = |x - y|$, then R, defined in lemma 19.6, is $\{(a, U) \mid U = \{y \mid |y - a| < \epsilon \text{ for } \epsilon \text{ real and positive}\}\}$.

19.8 Example. If X is the set of all ordered pairs of real numbers and if $\rho[(x, y), (p, q)] = \sqrt{(x - p)^2 + (y - q)^2}$ then R, defined in lemma 19.6, is the set $\{((a, b), U) \mid a, b \text{ are real and } U = \{(x, y) \mid \sqrt{(x - a)^2 + (y - b)^2} < \epsilon \text{ for } \epsilon \text{ real and positive}\}\}$. Thus the range of R is the set of all "interiors" of circles in the plane. The proof that ρ is a metric is contained in the proof of theorem 21.3.

19.9 Definition. Let X be a set with metric ρ and let $R = \{(x, U) \mid x \text{ is in } X \text{ and } U = \{y \mid \rho(x, y) < \epsilon \text{ for some positive, real } \epsilon\}\}$. R is called a *spherical neighborhood relation* and the sets in the range of R are called *spherical neighborhoods*. The spherical neighborhood $\{y \mid \rho(x, y) < \epsilon\}$ is sometimes denoted by $U_\rho(x, \epsilon)$. ϵ is sometimes referred to as the *radius* and x as the *center* of $U_\rho(x, \epsilon)$. Spherical neighborhoods are also sometimes referred to as *ϵ-neighborhoods*. By theorem 3.46, the range of any basic neighborhood relation is a base for a topology. The range of a spherical neighborhood relation will be called a *spherical base* for the topology which it determines.

19.10 Definition. A topological space $\{X, \mathfrak{I}\}$ is called a *metrizable space* if and only if there exists a metric ρ such that the spherical base determined by ρ is a base for $\mathfrak{I}$. The symbol $\{X, \mathfrak{I}_\rho\}$ is sometimes used to denote the metrizable space determined by a given metric ρ on X. ρ is then called an *admissible metric* for $\mathfrak{I}_\rho$ or for $\{X, \mathfrak{I}_\rho\}$.

EXERCISE 7. Prove that in any metrizable space $\{X, \mathfrak{I}_\rho\}$,
(a) $F_1 = \{y \mid \rho(y, a) \geq \epsilon\}$ is closed;
(b) $F_2 = \{y \mid \rho(y, a) \leq \epsilon\}$ is closed; and
(c) the boundary of the spherical neighborhood $U_\rho(p, \epsilon)$ is $\{x \mid \rho(p, x) = \epsilon\}$.

19.11 Lemma. *E^1 is a metrizable space.*

Proof: By definition of E^1. ▮

19.12 Example. Let X be any set and let $\rho(x, y) = 1$ if $x \neq y$ and let $\rho(x, x) = 0$. ρ is a metric and determines the discrete topology. Thus any discrete space is metrizable.

19.13 Example. Let X be any set and let Y be a metrizable space with admissible metric ρ. Let Y be bounded with respect to ρ and let Y^X, as usual, denote the set of all functions from X into Y. Define $\sigma(f, g) = \text{l.u.b.}_{x \in X}\,\{\rho(f(x), g(x))\}$. σ is a metric on Y^X.

The following example shows that not all spaces are metrizable.

19.14 Example. Let X be the set of real numbers; let one basic neighborhood, U_x, be defined for each x in X: $U_x = \{y \mid y \leq x\}$. The set of all ordered pairs (x, U_x) is a basic neighborhood relation, R, for X. $\{X, R\}$ then determines a topological space. This space is not a metrizable space; for assume ρ is any metric defined on X and let $\overline{R}$ be the spherical neighborhood relation determined for X by ρ. Let x^* and y^* be two distinct points of X, and let $\rho(x^*, y^*) = \delta > 0$. Let $x^* < y^*$; then $V_\rho(y^*, \delta/2)$ is a spherical neighborhood of y^*, determined by ρ. If R and $\overline{R}$ are to be equivalent, then $V_\rho(y^*, \delta/2)$ would have to contain $U_{y^*} = \{y \mid y \leq y^*\}$. Hence, $V_\rho(y^*, \delta/2)$ would have to contain x^*. This would mean that $\rho(x^*, y^*) < \delta/2$. This is a contradiction. Hence the original space is not metrizable.

19.15 Lemma. *Let X be metrizable with metric ρ. Let x^* be a given point of X. The function $f{:}x \to \rho(x, x^*)$ is a continuous function from X into the subspace of E^1 consisting of the non-negative real numbers.*

Proof: Let x_0 be any point of X. For each $\epsilon > 0$, a spherical neighborhood $U(x_0, \delta)$ must be found such that if y is in $U(x_0, \delta)$ then $|\rho(y, x^*) - \rho(x_0, x^*)| < \epsilon$; i.e., $|f(y) - f(x_0)| < \epsilon$. By the triangle inequality, $\rho(x_0, y) + \rho(y, x^*) \geq \rho(x_0, x^*)$ and $\rho(y, x_0) + \rho(x_0, x^*) \geq \rho(y, x^*)$. Hence, $\rho(x_0, y) \geq \rho(x_0, x^*) - \rho(y, x^*)$ and $\rho(y, x_0) \geq \rho(y, x^*) - \rho(x_0, x^*)$. Thus, $\rho(x_0, y) \geq |\rho(x_0, x^*) - \rho(y, x^*)| = |f(x_0) - f(y)|$. Hence, if y is in $U(x_0, \epsilon)$, i.e., if $\rho(x_0, y) < \epsilon$, then $|f(x_0) - f(y)| < \epsilon$. Thus, f is continuous at every point of X. ▮

19.16 Lemma. *If M is a non-empty subset of a metrizable space X with metric ρ, then the function $f{:}x \to d_\rho(x, M)$ from X into the subspace of E^1 consisting of the non-negative reals is continuous.*

Proof: $f(x) = d_\rho(x, M)$. Let t_0 be any point of X. For each $\epsilon > 0$, consider the neighborhood $U_\rho(t_0, \epsilon)$ of t_0 in X. Let y be any element in $U_\rho(t_0, \epsilon)$; then, $\rho(t_0, y) < \epsilon$. $f(t_0) = d_\rho(t_0, M)$ and $f(y) = d_\rho(y, M)$. Now, $\rho(t_0, m) \leq$

$\rho(t_0, y) + \rho(y, m)$ and $\rho(y, m) \leq \rho(y, t_0) + \rho(t_0, m)$ for every m in M. Hence, $\text{g.l.b.}_{m \in M} \{\rho(t_0, m)\} \leq \rho(t_0, y) + \text{g.l.b.}_{m \in M} \{\rho(y, m)\}$ and $\text{g.l.b.}_{m \in M} \{\rho(y, m)\} \leq \rho(y, t_0) + \text{g.l.b.}_{m \in M} \{\rho(t_0, m)\}$. Hence, $d_\rho(t_0, M) \leq \rho(t_0, y) + d_\rho(y, M)$ and $d_\rho(y, M) \leq \rho(y, t_0) + d_\rho(t_0, M)$. Therefore, $|d_\rho(t_0, M) - d_\rho(y, M)| \leq \rho(t_0, y) < \epsilon$. Hence, $|f(t_0) - f(y)| < \epsilon$ and so for any ϵ-neighborhood V of $f(t_0)$ in E^1, there exists a neighborhood U of t_0 in X such that $f[U] \subseteq V$. So, $f: x \to d_\rho(x, M)$ is continuous. ▮

19.17 Lemma. *If X is a metrizable space with metric ρ and if M is a non-empty subset of X, then $d_\rho(t, M) = 0$ if and only if t is in $\overline{M}$.*

Proof: A. Let $t \in \overline{M}$. If $t \in M$, then $d_\rho(t, M) = 0$ by definition of $d_\rho(t, M)$. If t is a limit point of M, then for any $\epsilon > 0$ there is a point m of M that lies in $U_\rho(t, \epsilon)$. Hence, $\rho(m, t) < \epsilon$ and $d_\rho(t, M) < \epsilon$. Hence, since ϵ was arbitrary, $d_\rho(t, M)$ is less than any positive number; therefore, $d_\rho(t, M) = 0$.

B. Let $d_\rho(t, M) = 0$. Let $U_\rho(t, \epsilon)$ be any spherical neighborhood of t in X. Since $d_\rho(t, M) = 0 < \epsilon$, there exists a point m of M that is in $U_\rho(t, \epsilon)$. Hence every neighborhood of t contains a point of M; so, $t \in \overline{M}$. ▮

19.18 Corollary. *If F is a non-empty closed subset of a metrizable space X with metric ρ and if x is a point of X which is not in F, then $d_\rho(x, F)$ is positive.*

19.19 Theorem. *If X is a metrizable space with admissible metric ρ, then the function $f: (x, y) \to \rho(x, y)$ of $X \times X$ into E^1 is continuous.*

Proof: Let (x_0, y_0) be any point of $X \times X$. Let N be an ϵ-neighborhood of $\rho(x_0, y_0)$ in E^1. Consider the set $U \times V$ containing (x_0, y_0) in $X \times X$, where $U = \{x \mid \rho(x, x_0) < \epsilon/2\}$ and $V = \{y \mid \rho(y, y_0) < \epsilon/2\}$. $U \times V$ is certainly a basic neighborhood of (x_0, y_0) in the product topology on $X \times X$. Now, let (a, b) be any point of $X \times X$ that lies in $U \times V$.

$$\rho(a, b) \leq \rho(a, x_0) + \rho(x_0, y_0) + \rho(y_0, b)$$

and

$$\rho(x_0, y_0) \leq \rho(x_0, a) + \rho(a, b) + \rho(b, y_0).$$

Hence,

$$|\rho(a, b) - \rho(x_0, y_0)| \leq \rho(a, x_0) + \rho(b, y_0).$$

Since (a, b) is in $U \times V$, $\rho(a, x_0) < \epsilon/2$ and $\rho(b, y_0) < \epsilon/2$; hence $|\rho(a, b) - \rho(x_0, y_0)| < \epsilon$. Therefore, $|f(a, b) - f(x_0, y_0)| < \epsilon$ and so f is continuous at every point of $X \times X$. ▮

EXERCISE 8. Let X be a metrizable space with metric ρ and let F_1 and F_2 be any two disjoint closed sets in X. Prove or find a counterexample for: $d_\rho(F_1, F_2)$ is always positive.

19.20 Theorem. *Every metrizable space, X, is normal; hence, completely regular, regular, Hausdorff, T_1, and T_0.*

Proof: A. Let z be any point in X and let ρ be an admissible metric for X. Let b be an element of the complement of $\{z\}$; i.e., b is in $\sim\{z\}$. Let $\rho(z, b) = \delta$. Consider $U = \{y \mid \rho(b, y) < \delta\}$. U is a spherical neighborhood of b in X and U does not contain z. Hence, every point of $\sim\{z\}$ is interior and so $\sim\{z\}$ is open. Therefore, $\{z\}$ is closed and X is T_1.

B. Next it must be shown that X is a T_4-space. Let F_1 and F_2 be any two non-empty disjoint closed sets in X. Let a be in F_1. Then a is not in F_2 and so $d_\rho(a, F_2) = \delta_a \neq 0$, by lemma 19.17. Consider the spherical neighborhood $U_\rho(a, \delta_a/2)$ of a in X. $U_\rho(a, \delta_a/2)$ is open by lemma 19.6 and the definition of a basic neighborhood relation; further, $U_\rho(a, \delta/2)$ contains no point of F_2 by definition of $d_\rho(a, F_2)$. For each element a in F_1, there is then defined a spherical neighborhood U_a which is $U_\rho(a, \delta_a/2)$ as defined above. $\bigcup_{a\in F_1} U_a$ is the union of open sets and hence is open. Also, $F_1 \subseteq \bigcup_{a\in F_1} U_a$. Similarly, spherical neighborhoods, V_b, for b in F_2 are defined; $\bigcup_{b\in F_2} V_b$ is open and $F_2 \subseteq \bigcup_{b\in F_2} V_b$. Now let z be an element in $\bigcup_{a\in F_1} U_a$ and let z be also in $\bigcup_{b\in F_2} V_b$. For some x in F_1, z is in U_x by definition of $\bigcup$; similarly, for some y in F_2, z is in V_y. Now by the triangle inequality for a metric, $\rho(x, y) \leq \rho(x, z) + \rho(z, y)$. Also, $\rho(x, z) < \delta_x/2$ and $\rho(z, y) < \delta_y/2$ by definition of U_x and V_y respectively. Hence, $\rho(x, y) < \delta_x/2 + \delta_y/2$. Let $\delta_y \geq \delta_x$. Then $\rho(x, y) < \delta_y$. This contradicts the definition of δ_y as the greatest lower bound of $\{r \mid$ there exists x in F_1 such that $\rho(x, y) = r\}$. Hence, no such z can exist and $(\bigcup_{a\in F_1} U_a) \cap (\bigcup_{b\in F_2} V_b) = \emptyset$. This implies that any metrizable space is a T_4-space. ▮

Topologically Equivalent Metrics

19.21 Definition. Let X be a set and let ρ and σ be two metrics on X. ρ and σ are called *topologically equivalent metrics* for X if and only if they determine the same topological space on X; i.e., if and only if the basic neighborhood relations R_ρ and R_σ determined respectively by ρ and σ are equivalent basic neighborhood relations for X.

The next theorems show that in general for any one metrizable space there exist many topologically equivalent metrics.

19.22 Theorem. *If X is a set with metric ρ and σ is the mapping $(x, y) \to f(\rho(x, y))$, where f is a strictly increasing, real-valued function defined on the non-negative reals such that $f(0) = 0$ and $f(a + b) \leq f(a) + f(b)$, then σ is a metric on X which is topologically equivalent to ρ.*

Proof: First it must be shown that σ is a metric on X. $\sigma(x, x) = f(\rho(x, x)) = 0$. If $\sigma(x, y) = 0$, then $f(\rho(x, y)) = 0$. Since f is strictly increasing, it is 1:1; hence, if $f(\rho(x, y)) = 0$, then $\rho(x, y) = 0$ and so $x = y$. $\sigma(y, x) = f(\rho(y, x)) = f(\rho(x, y)) = \sigma(x, y)$. $\sigma(x, y) + \sigma(y, z) = f(\rho(x, y)) + f(\rho(y, z))$. By definition of f, $f(\rho(x, y)) + f(\rho(y, z)) \geq f(\rho(x, y) + \rho(y, z))$. Since f is strictly increasing and since $\rho(x, y) + \rho(y, z) \geq \rho(x, z)$, then $f(\rho(x, y) + \rho(y, z)) \geq f(\rho(x, z)) =$

$\sigma(x, z)$. Hence, $\sigma(x, y) + \sigma(y, z) \geq \sigma(x, z)$. Next it must be shown that σ and ρ are topologically equivalent metrics. Let $U_\rho(x_0, \epsilon)$ be a spherical neighborhood from the metric ρ. Consider the spherical neighborhood $V_\sigma(x_0, f(\epsilon))$ from the metric σ. If y is in $V_\sigma(x_0, f(\epsilon))$, then $\sigma(x_0, y) < f(\epsilon)$. Hence, $f(\rho(x_0, y)) < f(\epsilon)$. Since f is strictly increasing, $\rho(x_0, y) < \epsilon$ and $V_\sigma(x_0, f(\epsilon)) \subseteq U_\rho(x_0, \epsilon)$. Conversely, let $W_\sigma(x_0, \epsilon)$ be any spherical neighborhood of x_0 from the metric σ. Let z be in $W_\sigma(x_0, \epsilon)$. Then $\sigma(x_0, z) = \delta < \epsilon$ and $\delta = f(\rho(x_0, z))$. Further $W_\sigma(x_0, \delta) \subseteq W_\sigma(x_0, \epsilon)$. Next, $f^{-1}(\delta)$ is a real number; so, consider $N_\rho(x_0, f^{-1}(\delta))$. Let y be in $N_\rho(x_0, f^{-1}(\delta))$. $\rho(x_0, y) < f^{-1}(\delta)$; therefore, $\sigma(x_0, y) = f(\rho(x_0, y)) < \delta$, since f is strictly increasing. Thus, $N_\rho(x_0, f^{-1}(\delta)) \subseteq W_\sigma(x_0, \delta) \subseteq W_\sigma(x_0, \epsilon)$. Since the spherical neighborhood relations R_ρ and R_σ are equivalent, ρ and σ are topologically equivalent metrics and hence determine the same topological space on X. ▮

Among the topologically equivalent metrics for any metrizable space, there always exist metrics relative to which the space is bounded. The next theorem establishes this, but first an elementary lemma is needed.

19.23 Lemma. *If a and b are any non-negative real numbers such that $a \geq b$, then $a/(1 + a) \geq b/(1 + b)$. If further, $m \geq n \geq 0$, then $(b + m)/(a + n) \geq b/a$ for $a \neq 0$.*

Proof: $a \geq b$ implies that $ab + a \geq ab + b$. Hence, $a(b + 1) \geq b(a + 1)$ and so, $a/(a + 1) \geq b/(b + 1)$. Secondly, $ma \geq nb$. Hence, $ab + ma \geq ab + nb$ and $a(b + m) \geq b(a + n)$. Thus $(b + m)/(a + n) \geq b/a$. ▮

19.24 Theorem. *If X is a metrizable space with admissible metric ρ, then there exists a metric σ for X which is topologically equivalent to ρ and relative to which X is bounded.*

Proof: Let $f(t) = t/(1 + t)$ for t real and $t \geq 0$, $0 \leq f(t) < 1$. Also, f is strictly increasing by the previous lemma (19.23) and $f(0) = 0$. Further,

$$f(s + t) = \frac{s + t}{1 + s + t} \leq f(s) + f(t) = \frac{s}{1 + s} + \frac{t}{1 + t}$$

$$= \frac{s + st + t + st}{(1 + s)(1 + t)} \leq \frac{s + t + 2st}{1 + s + t + st},$$

again, by the previous lemma. Now let

$$\sigma(a, b) = f(\rho(a, b)) = \frac{\rho(a, b)}{1 + \rho(a, b)}$$

for all a and b in X. By theorem 19.22, σ is a metric on X and σ is topologically equivalent to ρ. Further, since for all a and b in X, $0 \leq \sigma(a, b) < 1$, X is bounded relative to σ. ▮

19.25 Example. Let X be a set with metric ρ and let $\sigma(x, y) = \sqrt{\rho(x, y)}$. By theorem 19.22, ρ is a metric for X which is equivalent to ρ.

19.26 Example. Let X be a set with metric ρ and let $\sigma(x, y) = \log(\rho(x, y) + 1)$. By theorem 19.22, σ is also a metric for X which is equivalent to ρ.

EXERCISE 9. Let X denote the set of all sequences of real numbers. Define $\rho[(a_1, a_2, \ldots, a_n, \ldots), (b_1, b_2, \ldots, b_n, \ldots)] = 1/k$, where $a_i = b_i$ for $i < k$, $a_k \neq b_k$, and $\rho[(a_1, a_2, \ldots, a_n, \ldots), (b_1, b_2, \ldots, b_n, \ldots)] = 0$ if and only if $a_i = b_i$ for all i.

(a) Prove that ρ is a metric on X.

(b) Using ρ to define a topology on X, find a subset of X which is not closed in the resulting metrizable space, $\{X, \mathfrak{J}_\rho\}$.

(c) Prove that the relative topology on the subset $A_5 = \{(a_1, \ldots, a_i, \ldots) \mid a_i = 1$ for $i \neq 5\}$ is the discrete topology.

(d) Prove that the metrizable space $\{X, \mathfrak{J}_\rho\}$ is not separable.

EXERCISE 10. Using the metrizable space in the previous exercise, find the set of all points on the unit circle with center $(0, 0, 0, \ldots, 0, \ldots)$.

EXERCISE 11. Let S denote the set of all bounded sequences of real numbers. Define $\omega((a_1, a_2, \ldots, a_n, \ldots)(b_1, \ldots, b_n, \ldots)) = \text{l.u.b.}_n |a_n - b_n|$.

(a) Prove that ω is a metric for S.

(b) Prove that $A_5 = \{(a_1, a_2, \ldots, a_i, \ldots) \mid a_i = 1$ for $i \neq 5\}$ does not have the discrete topology as a subspace of the metrizable space determined by ω.

(c) Prove that this metrizable space is not separable.

20. COUNTABILITY AND SEPARABILITY FOR METRIZABLE SPACES.

The following theorem establishes that the special class of metrizable spaces is a subclass of the special class of first countable spaces.

20.1 Theorem. *Every metrizable space satisfies the first axiom of countability.*

Proof: Let X be a metrizable space with admissible metric ρ and let x_0 be any point in X. Consider the sequence $U_1, U_{1/2}, \ldots, U_{1/n}, \ldots$, where $U_{1/n} = \{x \mid x$ is in X and $\rho(x, x_0) < 1/n$ for $n = 1, 2, \ldots\}$. Let W be any open set in X which contains x_0. Since the set of all spherical neighborhoods determined by ρ forms a base for the topology on X, there exists $\epsilon^* > 0$ such that $U_\rho(x_0, \epsilon^*) \subseteq W$. By the archimedean order on the real numbers, there exists a natural number n^* such that $1/n^* < \epsilon^*$. Hence, U_{1/n^*} in the given sequence is contained in W. Since x_0 was any point of X, X is a first countable space. ∎

20.2 Corollary. *If X is a metrizable space and $A \subseteq X$, then x is a limit point of A if and only if x is a sequential limit point of some sequence in $A \sim \{x\}$.*

Proof: The corollary is an immediate consequence of theorems 20.1, 7.8 and 7.10. ∎

20.3 Corollary. *If X is a metrizable space and f is a function from X into a space Y, then f is continuous at x_0 if and only if the sequence (x_n) converging to x_0 implies that the sequence $(f(x_n))$ converges to $f(x_0)$.*

Proof: The corollary is an immediate consequence of theorems 20.1, 7.11, and 7.12. ▌

Thus, all metrizable spaces are first countable. However, not all first countable spaces are metrizable, as example 19.14 shows.

20.4 Example. Let X be any set containing a non-countable number of points. Let $\rho(x, y) = 1$ for every pair (x, y) in $X \times X$ such that $x \neq y$ and let $\rho(x, x) = 0$. ρ is a metric on X. Any base, $\mathcal{B}$, for the topology on X determined by ρ must contain $\{U \mid U = \{x\}$ for x in $X\}$. Hence, $\mathcal{B}$ is not countable. Thus, a metrizable space need not be second countable.

EXERCISE 1. Let X be the set of all bounded sequences of real numbers. Let $\mathfrak{J}_\rho$ be the topology determined by the metric $\rho(\alpha, \beta) = \text{l.u.b.}\ \{|a_i - b_i| \mid \alpha = (a_1, a_2, \ldots, a_i, \ldots)$ and $\beta = (b_1, b_2, \ldots, b_i, \ldots)\}$. Prove that $\{X, \mathfrak{J}_\rho\}$ is not second countable.

It has been established in section 5 that a second countable space always possesses a countable dense subset; in other words, that every second countable space is separable. It was also established in section 5, by providing a counterexample, that a separable space is not necessarily second countable. For metrizable spaces, however, the situation is different. The following theorem and theorem 5.14 imply that in a metrizable space, second countability and separability are equivalent properties; one cannot occur without the other.

20.5 Theorem. *If X is a separable, metrizable space, then X is second countable.*

Proof: Let $D = \{d_1, d_2, \ldots, d_n, \ldots\}$ be a countable dense subset of X. Since X is a metrizable space with metric ρ, say, the spherical neighborhoods from ρ can be used to discuss topological questions for X. Consider the collection $\mathcal{B} = \{N \mid N = U_\rho(d_i, r)$ for d_i in D and r a positive rational$\}$. $\mathcal{B}$ is countable, since it can be expressed as the union of a countable number of countable sets. Also, each element of $\mathcal{B}$ is an open subset of X. Now, let G be any open set in X. It must be shown that G is the union of sets in $\mathcal{B}$. Let x be any element in G. Since G is open, there is a spherical neighborhood $V_\rho(x, \epsilon)$ that is contained in G. Since the rationals are dense in the reals, there exists a rational number, r, such that $0 < r < \epsilon$. Hence, $U_\rho(x, r)$ is also contained in G. Since D is dense in X, there exists an element d_i of D that lies in $U_\rho(x, r/2)$. Now, $\rho(x, d_i) < r/2$. Hence, x lies in $U_\rho(d_i, r/2)$, an element of $\mathcal{B}$. Let z be any element in $U_\rho(d_i, r/2)$. $\rho(x, z) \leq \rho(x, d_i) + \rho(d_i, z) < r/2 + r/2 = r$. Hence, $U_\rho(d_i, r/2) \subseteq G$ and so G is the union of sets in $\mathcal{B}$. ▌

20.6 Theorem. *Every open covering of a separable, metrizable space X contains a countable subcovering of X.*

Proof: By the previous theorem X is second countable and hence by theorem 18.15, X is Lindelöf. ▮

It has been established that every metrizable space is normal (theorem 19.20) and first countable (theorem 20.1). The following example shows that not every normal, first countable space is metrizable.

20.7 Example. Let X be the set of real numbers. Let the basic neighborhood relation, R, for X be defined as follows:

$$R = \{(x, U) \mid U = \{y \mid a < y \leq x \text{ for some real } a < x\}\}.$$

A. $\{X, R^+\}$ is normal, where R^+ is again the unique neighborhood relation for X determined by R. For, every point z of $\sim\{x\}$ for x in X, is interior to $\sim\{x\}$; hence, $\sim\{x\}$ is open, $\{x\}$ is closed and $\{X, R^+\}$ is T_1. Further, let F_1 and F_2 be two disjoint closed sets of $\{X, R^+\}$ and let t be a point in F_1. t is not a limit point of F_2, hence, there exists a basic neighborhood U_t of t such that $U_t = \{y \mid a < y \leq t \text{ for } a \text{ real}\}$ and $U_t \cap F_2 = \emptyset$. Let $G_1 = \bigcup_{t \in F_1} U_t$. G_1 is open, contains F_1 and contains no point of F_2. Similarly, there is an open set $G_2 = \bigcup_{s \in F_2} V_s$ that contains F_2 and contains no point of F_1. Consider now $G_1 \cap G_2$ and assume z is in $G_1 \cap G_2$. z must be in U_t for some real t in F_1, and in V_s for some real s in F_2, by definition of G_1 and G_2. Say $t < s$; $U_t = \{y \mid a < y \leq t\}$ and $V_s = \{w \mid b < w \leq s\}$. Hence, $a < z < t$ and $b < z < s$. This means that $b < t$ and, since $t < s$, that t is in V_s. This is a contradiction since $F_1 \cap G_2 = \emptyset$. Thus, $\{X, R^+\}$ is a normal space.

B. $\{X, R^+\}$ is first countable. Let x be any point in X. The sets $U_x = \{y \mid r < y \leq x \text{ for } r \text{ rational}\}$ form a countable local base at x.

C. $\{X, R^+\}$ is not second countable. Let $\mathcal{B}$ be any base for $\{X, R^+\}$. For a fixed $\epsilon > 0$, consider the collection of all sets V_x^ϵ for x in X such that $V_x^\epsilon = \{y \mid x - \epsilon < y \leq x\}$. Each set V_x^ϵ is open in $\{X, R^+\}$ and so must contain a set B_x that contains x and is in this base $\mathcal{B}$. Since $B_x \subseteq V_x^\epsilon$, B_x contains no real number larger than x. So, let B_x and B_y be two such sets and let $x < y$. By definition, B_y contains y and y is not in B_x. Thus $B_x \neq B_y$. Thus the collection $\{B_x\}$ has cardinal number c; hence, since B_x is in $\mathcal{B}$ for each real number x, $\mathcal{B}$ is not countable.

D. $\{X, R^+\}$ is separable. Let x be any real number and consider the neighborhood $V_x^\epsilon = \{y \mid x - \epsilon < y \leq x, \text{ for } \epsilon > 0\}$. There is a rational number, r, such that $x - \epsilon < r \leq x$, by definition of the real numbers. Hence the countable set of rationals is dense in $\{X, R^+\}$.

E. Since $\{X, R^+\}$ is separable and not second countable, it cannot be a metrizable space by theorem 20.5.

20.8 Example. Let X denote the set of rational numbers. Let R be the following basic neighborhood relation for X: $R = \{(x, U) \mid x \text{ is in } X \text{ and } U = \{y \mid y \leq x\}\}$. Since $\mathcal{B}$, the range of R, is countable, $\{X, R^+\}$ is second countable. However, as shown in example 19.14, $\{X, R^+\}$ is not metrizable.

The counterexamples have gone as far as they can go in this direction. Urysohn established that a normal, second countable space is metrizable. In order to prove this theorem by Urysohn, we need to know about a subspace of a metrizable space and a product of metrizable spaces. These we investigate first; afterwards, the famous Urysohn imbedding theorem will be proved.

Subspaces, Quotient Spaces and Products of Metrizable Spaces

20.9 Theorem. *If X is a metrizable space and S is a subspace of X, then S is metrizable.*

Proof: Let p be any point of S, let G be any open set of S that contains p, and let ρ be an admissible metric for X. $G = G^* \cap S$, where G^* is open in X, by definition of the relative topology. There exists a real number $\epsilon > 0$ such that $U = \{x \mid x \text{ is in } X \text{ and } \rho(x, p) < \epsilon\}$ is contained in G^*. Hence $U \cap S = \{x \mid x \text{ is in } S \text{ and } \rho(x, p) < \epsilon\}$ is contained in $G = G^* \cap S$. Hence σ defined by $\sigma(x, y) = \rho(x, y)$, for x and y in S, is a metric on S. σ is then the restriction of ρ to $S \times S$. The sets $U(p, \epsilon) = \{x \mid \sigma(p, x) < \epsilon \text{ for real } \epsilon > 0 \text{ and } p \text{ in } S\}$ form a base for the relative topology. Hence the subspace S is a metrizable space. ∎

20.10 Example. If X is a metrizable space and X/D is a quotient space defined from X, then X/D is not necessarily a metrizable space. In example 13.8 for instance, a subspace X of E^2 is defined and a quotient space X/D is then defined. X/D is not first countable and hence cannot be a metrizable space. X, as a subspace of E^2, is a metrizable space by example 19.8 and theorem 20.9.

20.11 Theorem. *Let $\prod_{\nu \in \mathfrak{A}} X_\nu$ denote a product space where each X_ν is a metrizable space with more than one point and $\mathfrak{A}$ is uncountable. $\prod_{\nu \in \mathfrak{A}} X_\nu$ is not metrizable.*

Proof: If $\prod_{\nu \in \mathfrak{A}} X_\nu$ were metrizable, it would be first countable. If $\prod_{\nu \in \mathfrak{A}} X_\nu$ were first countable, the factor spaces, X_ν, except for at most a countable number, would have the trivial topology, by theorem 12.31. This contradicts the definition of X_ν for each ν. ∎

20.12 Theorem. *If M_i, for $i = 1, 2, \ldots, n, \ldots$, is a metrizable space, then $\prod_{i=1}^{n} M_i$, for n a natural number, and $\prod_{i=1}^{\infty} M_i$ are metrizable spaces, i.e., the product space of a countable number of metrizable spaces is a metrizable space.*

Proof: Let ρ_i be an admissible metric for M_i. It was established in theorem 19.24 that the metric

$$\overline{\rho_i}:\overline{\rho_i}(x_i, y_i) = \frac{\rho_i(x_i, y_i)}{1 + \rho_i(x_i, y_i)}$$

for M_i is equivalent to ρ_i. It was further established in theorem 19.22 that

$$\sigma_i:\sigma_i(x_i, y_i) = \frac{1}{2^i}\,\frac{\rho_i(x_i, y_i)}{1 + \rho_i(x_i, y_i)}$$

is also equivalent to ρ_i. Thus the σ_i-diameter of M_i is less than or equal to $1/2^i$. Next, define $\sigma(\alpha, \beta) = \sum_{i=1}^{n} \sigma_i(x_i, y_i)$ for $\prod_{i=1}^{n} M_i$, where $\alpha = (x_1, x_2, \ldots, x_n)$ and $\beta = (y_1, y_2, \ldots, y_n)$ and $\sigma(\alpha, \beta) = \sum_{i=1}^{\infty} \sigma_i(x_i, y_i)$ for $\prod_{i=1}^{\infty} M_i$, where $\alpha = (x_1, x_2, \ldots, x_i, \ldots)$ and $\beta = (y_1, y_2, \ldots, y_i, \ldots)$. Since $\sigma_i(x_i, y_i) < 1/2^i$, $\sum_{i=1}^{n} \sigma_i(x_i, y_i) < 1/2 + 1/4 + \cdots + 1/2^n$. Hence, $\sum_{i=1}^{\infty} \sigma_i(x_i, y_i)$ converges by comparison with the geometric series $\sum_{i=1}^{\infty} 1/2^i$. Thus, σ is a mapping from $(\prod_{i=1}^{n} M_i) \times (\prod_{i=1}^{n} M_i)$ or $(\prod_{i=1}^{\infty} M_i) \times (\prod_{i=1}^{\infty} M_i)$ into the non-negative real numbers. It must be shown that in both cases σ is a metric. Obviously, $\sigma(\alpha, \alpha) = 0$ and if $\sigma(\alpha, \beta) = 0$, $\alpha = \beta$. Further, $\sigma(\alpha, \beta) = \sigma(\beta, \alpha)$. Next, consider $\sigma(\alpha, \beta) + \sigma(\beta, \gamma)$ for α, β, γ in $\prod_{i=1}^{n} M_i$ or $\prod_{i=1}^{\infty} M_i$. In $\prod_{i=1}^{n} M_i$,

$$\sigma(\alpha, \beta) + \sigma(\beta, \gamma) = \sum_{i=1}^{n} \sigma_i(x_i, y_i) + \sum_{i=1}^{n} \sigma_i(y_i, z_i) \geq \sum_{i=1}^{n} \sigma_i(x_i, z_i) = \sigma(\alpha, \gamma),$$

where α and β are defined as above and $\gamma = (z_1, z_2, \ldots, z_n)$, and so in the case of a finite product σ satisfies the triangle inequality. In the case of an infinite product,

$$\sigma(\alpha, \beta) + \sigma(\beta, \gamma) = \sum_{i=1}^{\infty} \sigma_i(x_i, y_i) + \sum_{i=1}^{\infty} \sigma_i(y_i, z_i),$$

where $\alpha = (x_1, x_2, \ldots, x_i, \ldots)$, $\beta = (y_1, y_2, \ldots, y_i, \ldots)$ and $\gamma = (z_1, z_2, \ldots, z_i, \ldots)$. Now,

$$\begin{aligned}
\sum_{i=1}^{\infty} \sigma_i(x_i, y_i) + \sum_{i=1}^{\infty} \sigma_i(y_i, z_i) &= \lim_{n\to\infty} \sum_{i=1}^{n} \sigma_i(x_i, y_i) + \lim_{n\to\infty} \sum_{i=1}^{n} \sigma_i(y_i, z_i) \\
&= \lim_{n\to\infty} \left[\sum_{i=1}^{n} \sigma_i(x_i, y_i) + \sum_{i=1}^{n} \sigma_i(y_i, z_i)\right] \\
&= \lim_{n\to\infty} \left\{\sum_{i=1}^{n} [\sigma_i(x_i, y_i) + \sigma_i(y_i, z_i)]\right\}.
\end{aligned}$$

Now
$$\sum_{i=1}^{n} [\sigma_i(x_i, y_i) + \sigma_i(y_i, z_i)] \geq \sum_{i=1}^{n} \sigma_i(x_i, z_i).$$

Hence,
$$\lim_{n\to\infty} \sum_{i=1}^{n} [\sigma_i(x_i, y_i) + \sigma_i(y_i, z_i)] \geq \lim_{n\to\infty} \sum_{i=1}^{n} \sigma_i(x_i, z_i) = \sigma(\alpha, \gamma)$$

and so $\sigma(\alpha, \beta) + \sigma(\beta, \gamma) \geq \sigma(\alpha, \gamma)$. σ is then a metric for $\prod_{i=1}^{\infty} M_i$. It remains to be shown that σ gives a basic neighborhood relation equivalent to one from the product topology. Let α be any point in the product space $\prod_{i=1}^{\infty} M_i$ (the case for the finite product will be left as an exercise). Let $G_1 \times G_2 \times \cdots \times G_k \times M_{k+1} \times \cdots \times M_n \times \cdots$ be a base element from the product topology that contains $\alpha = (x_1, x_2, \ldots, x_n, \ldots)$. By definition of the topology on M_i, each set G_i, $i = 1, 2, \ldots, k$, contains a spherical neighborhood, $N_\sigma^i(x_i, \epsilon_i)$. Let δ be the minimum value in $(\epsilon_1, \epsilon_2, \ldots, \epsilon_k)$. Consider the spherical neighborhood $W_\sigma(\alpha, \delta)$ of α in the product space. If γ is in $W_\sigma(\alpha, \delta)$ then $\sigma(\gamma, \alpha) < \delta$. If $\alpha = (x_1, x_2, \ldots, x_i, \ldots)$ and $\gamma = (z_1, z_2, \ldots, z_i, \ldots)$ then $\sum_{i=1}^{\infty} \sigma_i(z_i, x_i) < \delta$. Therefore, $\sigma_i(z_i, x_i) < \delta$ for each i and so $\sigma_i(z_i, x_i) < \epsilon_i$ for $i = 1, 2, \ldots, k$. Hence z_i is in G_i for $i = 1, 2, \ldots, k$ and γ is in $G_1 \times G_2 \times \cdots \times G_k \times M_{k+1} \times \cdots \times M_n \times \cdots$. Thus, $W_\sigma(\alpha, \delta) \subseteq G_1 \times G_2 \times \cdots \times G_k \times M_{k+1} \times \cdots \times M_n \times \cdots$ and so every neighborhood of α from the product topology contains a σ-spherical neighborhood. Conversely, let $V_\sigma(\alpha, \delta)$ be any σ-spherical neighborhood for α, where again $\alpha = (x_1, x_2, \ldots, x_n, \ldots)$. Choose a natural number k, such that $1/2^{k+1} + 1/2^{k+2} + \cdots < \delta/2$; this is possible since the series $\sum_{i=1}^{\infty} 1/2^i$ converges. Define G as $U_1 \times U_2 \times \cdots \times U_k \times M_{k+1} \times \cdots \times M_n \times \cdots$ where $U_i = \{z_i \mid z_i \text{ is in } M_i \text{ and } \sigma_i(z_i, x_i) < \delta/2^k\}$. Then if $\beta = (y_1, y_2, \ldots, y_n, \ldots)$ is in G, $\sigma(\alpha, \beta) < \delta/2^k + \delta/2$. So, β is in $V(\alpha, \delta)$ and $G \subseteq V_\sigma(\alpha, \delta)$. ▌

20.13 Corollary. *If $\prod_{i=1}^{n} X_i$ and $\prod_{i=1}^{\infty} X_i$ are product spaces where X_i is a metrizable space with metric ρ_i for each natural number i then σ, where*

$$\sigma(\alpha, \beta) = \sum_{i=1}^{n} \frac{\rho_i(x_i, y_i)}{1 + \rho_i(x_i, y_i)} \cdot \frac{1}{2^i}$$

for $\alpha = (x_1, x_2, \ldots, x_n)$ and $\beta = (y_1, y_2, \ldots, y_n)$, is an admissible metric for $\prod_{i=1}^{n} X_i$ and σ, where

$$\sigma(\alpha, \beta) = \sum_{i=1}^{\infty} \frac{\rho_i(x_i, y_i)}{1 + \rho_i(x_i, y_i)} \cdot \frac{1}{2^i}$$

for $\alpha = (x_1, x_2, \ldots, x_n, \ldots)$ and $\beta = (y_1, y_2, \ldots, y_n, \ldots)$, is an admissible metric for $\prod_{i=1}^{\infty} X_i$.

Proof: The proof of the corollary is contained in the proof of the preceding theorem. ▌

20.14 Definition. The metric

$$\sigma:\sigma(\alpha, \beta) = \sum_{i=1}^{n \text{ or } \infty} \frac{\rho_i(x_i, y_i)}{1 + \rho_i(x_i, y_i)} \cdot \frac{1}{2^i}$$

will be called the *product metric.*

An Imbedding Theorem

20.15 Lemma. *If X is a metrizable space and if $\{Y, \mathfrak{I}\}$ is homeomorphic to X, then $\{Y, \mathfrak{I}\}$ is a metrizable space.*

Proof: Exercise.

20.16 Theorem (Urysohn Imbedding). *Any second countable, normal space X is a separable, metrizable space.*

Proof: Since X is second countable it is separable. The rest of the proof consists of four parts: in part A, a function F is defined from X into $E^1 \times E^1 \times \cdots \times E^1 \times \cdots$; in part B, F is shown to be 1:1; in part C, F is shown to be continuous; in part D, F^{-1} is shown to be continuous.

A. Let $U_1, U_2, \ldots$ denote a countable base, $\mathfrak{B}$, for X. Consider a set U_i in this base and let x be a point in U_i. Since X is regular, there exists an open set V containing x such that $\overline{V} \subseteq U_i$. By definition of a base, V must contain some set, say U_j, from $\mathfrak{B}$ such that x is in U_j and $U_j \subseteq V$. Hence $\overline{U}_j \subseteq \overline{V}$ and $\overline{U}_j \subseteq U_i$. Thus for any set U_i in the base, $\mathfrak{B}$, there is at least one set U_j in the base $\mathfrak{B}$ such that $\overline{U}_j \subseteq U_i$. Consider now the set of all pairs (U_m, U_n) in $\mathfrak{B} \times \mathfrak{B}$ such that $\emptyset \neq \overline{U}_m \subseteq U_n$. This set is countable; hence, its elements may be listed: $(A_1, B_1), (A_2, B_2), \ldots, (A_n, B_n), \ldots$, where $\overline{A}_n \subseteq B_n$ for every n and for every n, A_n and B_n are open sets in $\mathfrak{B}$. Since X is normal, by Urysohn's lemma, for each pair (A_n, B_n), there are continuous functions defined on X with range in $[0, 1]$ such that the image of $\overline{A_n}$ is 0 and the image of $\sim B_n$ is 1. Choose one such function for each pair (A_n, B_n) to obtain a sequence $(f_1, f_2, \ldots, f_n, \ldots)$. Each f_n has X for its domain and its range is contained in $[0, 1]$; further $f_n[\overline{A_n}] = 0$ and $f_n[\sim B_n] = 1$. Now let x be any element in X; consider the sequence of real numbers identified by $(f_1(x), f_2(x), \ldots, f_n(x), \ldots)$. Such a sequence denotes a point in $E^1 \times E^1 \times \cdots \times E^1 \times \cdots$ with $0 \leq f_n(x) \leq 1$ for all n. By theorem 20.12, $E^1 \times E^1 \times \cdots \times E^1 \times \cdots$ is a metrizable space. Let F denote the function: $x \to (f_1(x), f_2(x), \ldots, f_n(x), \ldots)$. The domain of F is X and the range is contained in the metrizable space $E^1 \times E^1 \times \cdots \times E^1 \times \cdots$.

B. F is 1:1. Let s, t be two distinct points in X. Since X is a T_0-space, there exists a base element U_e, say, that contains s and does not contain t. Also there exists U_k, say, such that s is in U_k and $\overline{U}_k \subseteq U_e$. Hence t is not in $\overline{U}_k$. Consider the function f_i that goes with the pair (U_k, U_e). $f_i(s) = 0$ since s is in $\overline{U}_k$ and $f_i(t) = 1$ since t is in $\sim U_e$. Hence $F(s) \neq F(t)$ and F is 1:1.

C. F is continuous. F is a function from the space X into a product space. $p_i[F(x)] = f_i(x)$ where p_i is the projection function from $E_1 \times E_2 \times \cdots$. $E_i \times \cdots$ onto E_i. Since each f_i is continuous the composite functions $p_i \circ F$ are continuous. Hence, by theorem 12.13, F is continuous.

D. F^{-1} is continuous. Let $(y_1, y_2, \ldots, y_j, \ldots) = y^*$ denote any point in the domain of F^{-1}. X is the range of F^{-1}. Let $F^{-1}(y^*)$ be denoted by x and let B_k be a base element in the countable base $\mathcal{B}$ that contains x. There exists a base element A_k that contains x and such that $\overline{A}_k \subseteq B_k$. Let f_k be the function chosen for the pair (A_k, B_k) in part A. $f_k(x) = 0$, by definition of f_k. Let G denote $\{t \mid t < 1\}$ in E^1. Let $G^* = \prod_{i=1}^{\infty} G_i$ where $G_i = E^1$ for $i \neq k$ and $G_k = G$. G^* is open in $E^1 \times E^1 \times \cdots \times E^1 \times \cdots$; hence $G^* \cap F[X]$ is open in $F[X]$. Since $f_k(x) = 0$, $f_k(x)$ is in G; hence $F(x) = y^*$ is in $G^* \cap F[X]$. Thus $G^* \cap F[X]$ is a neighborhood of y^*. By definition of f_k, $f_k[\sim B_k] = 1$; hence, $\{F^{-1}[G^* \cap F[X]]\} \cap (\sim B_k) = \emptyset$. So, $F^{-1}[G^* \cap F[X]] \subseteq B_k$. Thus for any neighborhood N of x, there is a neighborhood N^* of y^* that is mapped into N by F^{-1}. Thus F^{-1} is continuous and F is, then, a homeomorphism. Since X is homeomorphic to the metric space $F[X]$, X is a metrizable space by lemma 20.15. ▮

The previous theorem is the basic classical result relating to the problem of finding sufficient conditions for a topological space to be metrizable.

20.17 Corollary. *Every separable, metrizable space, X, is homeomorphic to a subspace of $E^1 \times E^1 \times \cdots \times E^1 \times \cdots$.*

Proof: By theorems 19.20 and 20.5, X is normal and second countable. By the proof of theorem 20.16, X can be imbedded topologically in $E^1 \times E^1 \times \cdots \times E^1 \times \cdots$. ▮

20.18 Corollary. *Every second countable, regular space is metrizable.*

Proof: By theorem 18.22, every second countable, regular space is normal. ▮

In the next section every separable metrizable space will also be imbedded in the Hilbert cube, a special subspace of Hilbert space.

EXERCISE 2. Prove that if a non-empty product space $\prod_\nu X_\nu$ is metrizable, then each of the spaces X_ν is metrizable.

21. EXAMPLES OF IMPORTANT METRIZABLE SPACES.

EUCLIDEAN SPACES

The most basic and useful metrizable spaces are the Euclidean n-spaces, E^n. These have already been defined as product spaces of E^1 itself. The following corollary is a restatement of corollary 20.13, an immediate result of theorem 20.12.

21.1 Corollary. *The Euclidean n-spaces, E^n, topologically, are metrizable spaces with admissible metric, σ_n, where*

$$\sigma_n((x_1, x_2, \ldots, x_n), (y_1, y_2, \ldots, y_n)) = \sum_{i=1}^{n} \frac{|x_i - y_i|}{1 + |x_i - y_i|} \cdot \frac{1}{2^i}.$$

Proof: Corollary 20.13. ▌

The above metrics, σ_n, for $n = 1, 2, \ldots$, define the product topology on E^n and hence can be used, wherever convenient, for the topological study of E^n. However, σ_n is not the usual metric for E^n; the so-called Euclidean (usual) metric defined below is topologically equivalent to σ_n for E^n.

21.2 Lemma (Cauchy-Schwarz Inequality). *If u_i and v_i, for $i = 1, 2, \ldots, n$ where n is a natural number, are real numbers then*

$$\left(\sum_{i=1}^{n} u_i^2\right) \cdot \left(\sum_{i=1}^{n} v_i^2\right) \geq \left(\sum_{i=1}^{n} u_i v_i\right)^2.$$

Proof: Consider

$$\sum_{i=1}^{n} (u_i + \lambda v_i)^2$$

where λ also is a real number.

$$\sum_{i=1}^{n} (u_i + \lambda v_i)^2 \geq 0,$$

for all real λ, u_i and v_i; hence,

$$\sum_{i=1}^{n} (u_i^2 + 2\lambda u_i v_i + \lambda^2 v_i^2) \geq 0$$

and so

$$\sum_{i=1}^{n} u_i^2 + 2\lambda \sum_{i=1}^{n} u_i v_i + \lambda^2 \sum_{i=1}^{n} v_i^2 \geq 0.$$

Let

$$\sum_{i=1}^{n} v_i^2 = A, \qquad \sum_{i=1}^{n} u_i^2 = C \qquad \text{and} \qquad \sum_{i=1}^{n} u_i v_i = B.$$

Then $A\lambda^2 + 2B\lambda + C \geq 0$ and $A \geq 0$, $C \geq 0$, for all real λ. If $A = 0$ then $v_i = 0$ for every i and so

$$\left(\sum_{i=1}^{n} u_i v_i\right)^2 = 0 = \sum_{i=1}^{n} u_i^2 \sum_{i=1}^{n} v_i^2.$$

If $A \neq 0$, then $A > 0$ and we can divide by A to get $\lambda^2 + 2B/A\lambda + C/A \geq 0$.

Hence $(\lambda + B/A)^2 + C/A - B^2/A^2 \geq 0$ for all λ and so, in particular, when $\lambda = -B/A$. Hence, $C/A - B^2/A^2 \geq 0$ and so, $AC - B^2 \geq 0$. This implies $AC \geq B^2$ or

$$\left(\sum_{i=1}^{n} u_i^2\right) \cdot \left(\sum_{i=1}^{n} v_i^2\right) \geq \left(\sum_{i=1}^{n} u_i v_i\right)^2 . \blacksquare$$

21.3 Theorem. *The Euclidean n-spaces, E^n, for n a natural number, can also be defined, topologically, by using the metrics*

$$\rho_n : \rho_n[(x_1, x_2, \ldots, x_n), (y_1, y_2, \ldots, y_n)] = \sqrt{\sum_{i=1}^{n} (x_i - y_i)^2}.$$

Proof: A. ρ_n for each n is a metric. (i) $\rho_n(\alpha, \beta) = 0$ if and only if $\alpha = \beta$, by definition. (ii) $\rho_n(\alpha, \beta) = \rho_n(\beta, \alpha)$ by definition. (iii) Let $\alpha = (x_1, x_2, \ldots x_n)$, $\beta = (y_1, y_2, \ldots, y_n)$ and $\gamma = (z_1, z_2, \ldots, z_n)$ be any three points in E^n.

$$\rho_n(\alpha, \beta) + \rho_n(\beta, \gamma) = \sqrt{\sum_{i=1}^{n} (x_i - y_i)^2} + \sqrt{\sum_{i=1}^{n} (y_i - z_i)^2}$$

and

$$\rho_n(\alpha, \gamma) = \sqrt{\sum_{i=1}^{n} (x_i - z_i)^2}.$$

Let $u_i = x_i - y_i$, $v_i = y_i - z_i$; then $u_i + v_i = x_i - z_i$,

$$\rho_n(\alpha, \beta) + \rho_n(\beta, \gamma) = \sqrt{\sum_{i=1}^{n} u_i^2} + \sqrt{\sum_{i=1}^{n} v_i^2}$$

and

$$\rho_n(\alpha, \gamma) = \sqrt{\sum_{i=1}^{n} (u_i + v_i)^2}.$$

$$[\rho_n(\alpha, \beta) + \rho_n(\beta, \gamma)]^2 = \sum_{i=1}^{n} u_i^2 + 2\sqrt{\sum_{i=1}^{n} (u_i)^2 \cdot \sum_{i=1}^{n} (v_i)^2} + \sum_{i=1}^{n} v_i^2$$

and

$$[\rho_n(\alpha, \gamma)]^2 = \sum_{i=1}^{n} (u_i + v_i)^2 = \sum_{i=1}^{n} u_i^2 + 2\sum_{i=1}^{n} u_i v_i + \sum_{i=1}^{n} v_i^2.$$

So, $[\rho_n(\alpha, \beta) + \rho_n(\beta, \gamma)]^2$ and $[\rho_n(\alpha, \gamma)]^2$ differ on the middle terms

$$2\sqrt{\sum_{i=1}^{n} (u_i)^2 \sum_{i=1}^{n} v_i^2} \quad \text{and} \quad 2\sum_{i=1}^{n} u_i v_i.$$

By the previous lemma 21.2,

$$\left(\sum_{i=1}^{n} u_i^2\right)\left(\sum_{i=1}^{n} v_i^2\right) \geq \left(\sum_{i=1}^{n} u_i v_i\right)^2.$$

Hence,

$$\sqrt{\left(\sum_{i=1}^{n} u_i^2\right)\left(\sum_{i=1}^{n} v_i^2\right)} \geq \sum_{i=1}^{n} u_i v_i$$

and $\rho_n(\alpha, \beta) + \rho_n(\beta, \gamma) \geq \rho_n(\alpha, \gamma)$. ρ_n is then a metric.

B. ρ_n defines the product topology on the set of ordered n-tuples of real numbers. Let y^* be any point in E^n. Let G^* be any basic open set which contains y^*. If $y^* = (y_1, y_2, \ldots, y_i, \ldots, y_n)$ and $G^* = \prod_{i=1}^{n} G_i$ where $G_i = \{x_i \mid |x_i - y_i| < \epsilon_i\}$ then let ϵ^* denote the minimum of $\{\epsilon_1, \ldots, \epsilon_i, \ldots, \epsilon_n\}$. Next let

$$V_{\rho_n}(y^*, \epsilon^*) = \left\{(a_1, \ldots, a_i, \ldots, a_n) \;\middle|\; \sqrt{\sum_{i=1}^{n} (a_i - y_i)^2} < \epsilon^*\right\}.$$

If $(a_1, \ldots, a_i, \ldots, a_n)$ is in $V_{\rho_n}(y^*, \epsilon^*)$, then $|a_i - y_i| < \epsilon^* \leq \epsilon_i$. Hence $V_{\rho_n}(y^*, \epsilon^*) \subseteq G^*$. Conversely if $W_{\rho_n}(y^*, \delta)$ is any spherical neighborhood of y^* from the metric ρ_n, let $G^* = \prod_{i=1}^{n} G_i$ where $G_i = \{t_i \mid |t_i - y_i| < \delta/\sqrt{n}\}$. Now, if $(s_1, \ldots, s_i, \ldots, s_n)$ is in G^*, then $|s_i - y_i| < \delta/\sqrt{n}$ and $(s_i - y_i)^2 < \delta^2/n$ for $i = 1, 2, \ldots, n$. Hence $\sum_{i=1}^{n} (s_i - y_i)^2 < \delta^2$ and $(s_1, \ldots, s_i, \ldots, s_n)$ is in G^*. Thus, $G^* \subseteq W_{\rho_n}(y^*, \delta)$. ▮

The following definition is a geometric not a topological one.

21.4 Definition. "*Euclidean metric*" is the name given to the metric

$$\rho_n : \rho_n[(x_1, x_2, \ldots, x_n), (y_1, y_2, \ldots, y_n)] = \sqrt{\sum_{i=1}^{n} |x_i - y_i|^2}$$

for E^n for each natural number n. For each such n, ρ_n defines the Euclidean n-space of Euclidean geometry.

EXERCISE 1. Prove that the mapping $\sigma(\alpha, \beta) = |x_\alpha - x_\beta| + |y_\alpha - y_\beta|$ where $\alpha = (x_\alpha, y_\alpha)$ and $\beta = (x_\beta, y_\beta)$ and the mapping $\rho(\alpha, \beta) = \sqrt{(x_\alpha - x_\beta)^2 + (y_\alpha - y_\beta)^2}$ are topologically equivalent metrics for the set of all ordered pairs of real numbers.

It is to be observed that

$$\sigma_n(p, q) = \sum_{i=1}^{n} \frac{|p_i - q_i|}{1 + |p_i - q_i|} \cdot \frac{1}{2^i} < \sum_{i=1}^{n} \frac{1}{2^i} = 1/2 + 1/4 + \cdots + 1/2^n$$

$$= \frac{1}{2} \cdot \frac{1 - (1/2)^n}{1/2} = 1 - (1/2)^n < 1.$$

Hence, E^n is a bounded space using metric σ_n and is not a bounded space using metric ρ_n even though the metrics are topologically equivalent. Thus boundedness has no purely topological meaning.

Two topologically equivalent metrics for the product space E^n are, then,

$$\rho_n : \rho_n\big((x_1, x_2, \ldots, x_n), (y_1, y_2, \ldots, y_n)\big) = \sqrt{\sum_{i=1}^{n} (x_i - y_i)^2}$$

and

$$\sigma_n : \sigma_n\big((x_1, x_2, \ldots, x_n), (y_1, y_2, \ldots, y_n)\big) = \sum_{i=1}^{n} \frac{|x_i - y_i|}{1 + |x_i - y_i|} \cdot \frac{1}{2^i}.$$

In the case of the infinite product $\prod_{i=1}^{\infty} X_i$, where $X_i = E^1$ for every natural number i,

$$\sigma_\infty : \sigma_\infty[(x_1, x_2, \ldots), (y_1, y_2, \ldots)] = \sum_{i=1}^{\infty} \frac{|x_i - y_i|}{1 + |x_i - y_i|} \cdot \frac{1}{2^i}$$

has been shown in corollary 20.13 to be an admissible metric for this product space. So, the product space $E^1 \times E^1 \times \cdots \times E^1 \times \cdots$ is a metrizable space with admissible metric σ_∞. The elements of $E^1 \times E^1 \times \cdots \times E^1 \times \cdots$ are infinite sequences of real numbers.

21.5 Lemma. *The product space $E^1 \times E^1 \times \cdots \times E^1 \times \cdots$ is second countable and hence separable.*

Proof: Since E^1 is second countable, $E^1 \times E^1 \times \cdots \times E^1 \times \cdots$, as the product of a countable number of second countable spaces, is second countable and hence separable. ▮

EXERCISE 2. Find a countable, dense subset in $E^1 \times E^1 \times \cdots \times E^1 \times \cdots$.

Hilbert Space

A natural question now would be "is there an analogous ρ_∞ equivalent to σ_∞ for $E^1 \times E^1 \times \cdots \times E^1 \times \cdots$." The answer is "no," since if $p = (1, 1, \ldots, 1, \ldots)$ and $q = (2, 2, \ldots, 2, \ldots)$ then $\rho_\infty(p, q)$ would be, symbolically,

$$\sqrt{\sum_{i=1}^{\infty} (p_i - q_i)^2} = \sqrt{1 + 1 + 1 \ldots}$$

which does not identify a real number. Thus, the Euclidean metric does not generalize to the case of the infinite product space, $E^1 \times E^1 \times \cdots \times E^1 \times \cdots$. However, since the Euclidean metric is important geometrically in its own right, it is natural to seek a generalization of it for infinite sequences. The next definition gives the basic generalization of the Euclidean metric to a set of infinite sequences to give Hilbert space. First, however, two lemmas are needed.

21.6 Lemma. *If* $(x_1, x_2, \ldots)$ *and* $(y_1, y_2, \ldots)$ *are two sequences of real numbers such that*

$$\sum_{i=1}^{\infty} x_i^2 \quad \text{and} \quad \sum_{i=1}^{\infty} y_i^2$$

both converge, then $\sqrt{\sum_{i=1}^{\infty} (x_i - y_i)^2}$ *exists as a unique real number.*

Proof: For k any natural number,

$$\sqrt{\sum_{i=1}^{k} (x_i - 0)^2} + \sqrt{\sum_{i=1}^{k} (0 - y_i)^2} \geq \sqrt{\sum_{i=1}^{k} (x_i - y_i)^2}$$

by the Cauchy-Schwarz inequality of lemma 21.2 and the proof of theorem 21.3. Since the sequences

$$\left\{\sum_{i=1}^{k} (x_i)^2\right\} \quad \text{and} \quad \left\{\sum_{i=1}^{k} (y_i)^2\right\}$$

both converge, the sequences

$$\left\{\sqrt{\sum_{i=1}^{k} (x_i)^2}\right\} \quad \text{and} \quad \left\{\sqrt{\sum_{i=1}^{k} (y_i)^2}\right\}$$

converge. Hence, the sequence

$$\left\{\sqrt{\sum_{i=1}^{k} (x_i)^2} + \sqrt{\sum_{i=1}^{k} (y_i)^2}\right\}$$

is bounded above. By the above-mentioned inequality, the set

$$\left\{\sqrt{\sum_{i=1}^{k} (x_i - y_i)^2}\right\}$$

is also bounded from above. Since the sequence is monotonically increasing with k, it converges. Hence,

$$\lim_{k \to \infty} \sqrt{\sum_{i=1}^{k} (x_i - y_i)^2}$$

exists as a unique real number denoted by

$$\sqrt{\sum_{i=1}^{\infty} (x_i - y_i)^2}. \quad \blacksquare$$

21.7 Lemma. *If H denotes the set of all sequences, $(x_1, x_2, \ldots, x_i, \ldots)$, of real numbers such that $\sum_{i=1}^{\infty}(x_i^2)$ converges, then the function*

$$\rho_\infty : \rho_\infty[(x_1, x_2, \ldots), (y_1, y_2, \ldots)] = \sqrt{\sum_{i=1}^{\infty} (x_i - y_i)^2}$$

is a metric on H.

Proof: $\rho_\infty[(x_1, x_2, \ldots), (y_1, y_2, \ldots)] = 0$ if and only if $x_i = y_i$ for every i and $\rho_\infty[(x_1, x_2, \ldots), (y_1, y_2, \ldots)] = \rho_\infty[(y_1, y_2, \ldots), (x_1, x_2, \ldots)]$ by definition of ρ_∞. If $(x_1, x_2, \ldots)$, $(y_1, y_2, \ldots)$ and $(z_1, z_2, \ldots)$ are three points in H then for every k,

$$\sqrt{\sum_{i=1}^{k} (x_i - y_i)^2} + \sqrt{\sum_{i=1}^{k} (y_i - z_i)^2} \geq \sqrt{\sum_{i=1}^{k} (x_i - z_i)^2}$$

again by lemma 21.2 and theorem 21.3. Hence,

$$\lim_{k\to\infty}\left[\sqrt{\sum_{i=1}^{k} (x_i - y_i)^2} + \sqrt{\sum_{i=1}^{k} (y_i - z_i)^2}\right] \geq \lim_{k\to\infty}\sqrt{\sum_{i=1}^{k} (x_i - z_i)^2}.$$

Now

$$\lim_{k\to\infty}\left[\sqrt{\sum_{i=1}^{k} (x_i - y_i)^2} + \sqrt{\sum_{i=1}^{k} (y_i - z_i)^2}\right]$$

$$= \lim_{k\to\infty}\sqrt{\sum_{i=1}^{k} (x_i - y_i)^2} + \lim_{k\to\infty}\sqrt{\sum_{i=1}^{k} (y_i - z_i)^2}.$$

Hence,

$$\lim_{k\to\infty}\sqrt{\sum_{i=1}^{k} (x_i - y_i)^2} + \lim_{k\to\infty}\sqrt{\sum_{i=1}^{k} (y_i - z_i)^2} \geq \lim_{k\to\infty}\sqrt{\sum_{i=1}^{k} (x_i - z_i)^2}.$$

Let $\{\sqrt{a_k}\}$, for $a_k \geq 0$, converge to A. $|a_k - A^2| = |(\sqrt{a_k} - A)(\sqrt{a_k} + A)| = |\sqrt{a_k} - A|\,|\sqrt{a_k} + A|$. Now $\{\sqrt{a_k}\}$ is bounded, hence $\sqrt{a_k} < B$, say, for all k. Hence for each $\epsilon > 0$ there is a natural number N such that if $k > N$, $|\sqrt{a_k} - A| < \epsilon/(B + A)$. So if $k > N$, $|a_k - A^2| < \epsilon/(B + A)$. $|\sqrt{a_k} + A| < \epsilon$. Hence,

$$\lim_{k\to\infty}\{a_k\} = A^2 \quad \text{or} \quad \lim_{k\to\infty}\sqrt{a_k} = \sqrt{\lim_{k\to\infty} a_k}\,.$$

Thus

$$\sqrt{\lim_{k\to\infty}\sum_{i=1}^{k} (x_i - y_i)^2} + \sqrt{\lim_{k\to\infty}\sum_{i=1}^{k} (y_i - z_i)^2} \geq \sqrt{\lim_{k\to\infty}\sum_{i=1}^{k} (x_i - z_i)^2}$$

or $$\sqrt{\sum_{i=1}^{\infty}(x_i - y_i)^2} + \sqrt{\sum_{i=1}^{\infty}(y_i - z_i)^2} \geq \sqrt{\sum_{i=1}^{\infty}(x_i - z_i)^2}.$$

Thus the triangle inequality also holds and ρ_∞ is a metric. ▮

21.8 Definition. The set of all sequences of real numbers, $(x_1, x_2, \ldots, x_i, \ldots)$, such that $\sum_{i=1}^{\infty}(x_i)^2$ converges, with the topology defined by the metric

$$\rho_\infty : \rho_\infty[(x_1, x_2, \ldots), (y_1, y_2, \ldots)] = \sqrt{\sum_{i=1}^{\infty}(x_i - y_i)^2}$$

is called *Hilbert space* and is sometimes denoted by H.

21.9 Lemma. *Hilbert space, H, is separable.*

Proof: Consider the set D of all infinite sequences $(r_1, r_2, \ldots, r_i, \ldots)$ such that r_i is rational for every i and such that there exists a natural number N with the property that for $i > N$, $r_i = 0$. This collection can be put into 1:1 correspondence with the set of all ordered k-tuples of rational numbers and, hence, is countable. Further, each sequence in this set D is in H. Next, let $(y_1, y_2, \ldots, y_i, \ldots)$ be any point in H. For any $\epsilon > 0$, there exists a natural number $N > 1$ such that $\sum_{i=N}^{\infty}(y_i)^2 < \epsilon^2/2$, since the series $\sum_{i=1}^{\infty}(y_i)^2$ converges. Since the rationals are dense in E^1, there exists, for each $i < N$, a rational number, r_i, such that

$$|r_i - y_i| < \frac{\epsilon}{\sqrt{2(N-1)}}.$$

Consider then the sequence, $(r_1, r_2, \ldots, r_{n-1}, 0, \ldots, 0, \ldots)$.

$$\rho_\infty^2[(r_1, r_2, \ldots, r_{n-1}, 0, \ldots, 0, \ldots), (y_1, y_2, \ldots, y_i, \ldots)] = \sum_{i=1}^{N-1}(r_i - y_i)^2 + \sum_{i=N}^{\infty}(y_i)^2.$$

Now $$\sum_{i=1}^{N-1}(r_i - y_i)^2 + \sum_{i=N}^{\infty}(y_i)^2 < \epsilon^2/2 + \epsilon^2/2 = \epsilon^2.$$

Hence, $\rho_\infty[(r_1, r_2, \ldots, r_{n-1}, 0, \ldots, 0, \ldots), (y_1, y_2, \ldots, y_i, \ldots)] < \epsilon$ and the countable collection D is dense in H. ▮

21.10 Lemma. *Hilbert space, H, is second countable.*

Proof: Since H is metrizable and separable, it is second countable. ▮

21.11 Lemma. *Let S be the subspace of* $E^1 \times E^1 \times \cdots \times E^1 \times \cdots$ *consisting of all sequences* $(x_1, x_2, \ldots)$ *such that* $\sum_{i=1}^{\infty}(x_i)^2$ *converges in* E^1. *Let* $\mathfrak{I}_\sigma$ *denote the relative product topology on this subset; let* $\mathfrak{I}_\rho$ *denote the Hilbert space topology for this set. Then* $\mathfrak{I}_\sigma \subsetneqq \mathfrak{I}_\rho$.

Proof: A. $\mathfrak{J}_\sigma \subseteq \mathfrak{J}_\rho$. Let $\alpha = (x_1, x_2, \ldots)$ be a sequence of real numbers such that $\sum_{i=1}^{\infty} (x_i)^2$ converges in E^1. Let $V_\sigma(\alpha, \epsilon)$ denote a σ-spherical neighborhood of α; i.e.,

$$V_\sigma(\alpha, \epsilon) = \left\{\beta = (y_1, y_2, \ldots) \;\middle|\; \sum_{i=1}^{\infty} (y_i)^2 \text{ converges and } \sum_{i=1}^{\infty} \frac{|x_i - y_i|}{1 + |x_i - y_i|} \cdot \frac{1}{2^i} < \epsilon\right\}.$$

Consider the ρ-spherical neighborhood

$$U_\rho(\alpha, \epsilon) = \left\{\gamma = (c_1, c_2, \ldots) \;\middle|\; \sum_{i=1}^{\infty} (c_i)^2 \text{ converges and } \sqrt{\sum_{i=1}^{\infty} |x_i - c_i|^2} < \epsilon\right\}.$$

Let $\gamma = (c_1, c_2, \ldots)$ be any element in $U_\rho(\alpha, \epsilon)$; then,

$$\sqrt{\sum_{i=1}^{\infty} (x_i - c_i)^2} < \epsilon.$$

Hence $|x_i - c_i| < \epsilon$, for every i. Therefore,

$$\sum_{i=1}^{\infty} \frac{|x_i - c_i|}{1 + |x_i - c_i|} \cdot \frac{1}{2^i} < \sum_{i=1}^{\infty} \epsilon \cdot \frac{1}{2^i} = \epsilon.$$

Hence γ is in $V_\sigma(\alpha, \epsilon)$. Now if G is in $\mathfrak{J}_\sigma$, then α in G implies that there exists a spherical neighborhood $V_\sigma(\alpha, \epsilon)$ that is contained in G. However, since the spherical neighborhood $U_\rho(\alpha, \epsilon)$ is contained in $V_\sigma(\alpha, \epsilon)$, it also is contained in G. Thus every point of G is interior with $\mathfrak{J}_\rho$ and so G is in $\mathfrak{J}_\rho$. Since G was any set in $\mathfrak{J}_\sigma$, $T_\sigma \subseteq \mathfrak{J}_\rho$.

B. $\mathfrak{J}_\sigma \neq \mathfrak{J}_\rho$. Consider the set M of the sequences $e_1 = (1, 0, \ldots, 0, \ldots)$; $e_2 = (0, 1, 0, \ldots, 0, \ldots)$; $e_3 = (0, 0, 1, 0, \ldots, 0, \ldots)$, $\ldots$, $e_i = (0, 0, \ldots, 0, a_i = 1, 0, \ldots)$, $\ldots$. Consider $U_\rho(0^*, 1/2)$, where $0^* = (0, 0, \ldots, 0, \ldots)$. $\rho(0^*, e_i) = \sqrt{0 + 0 + \cdots + 0 + 1 + 0 \cdots} = 1$. Hence $U_\rho(0^*, 1/2)$ contains no point of M and 0^* is not a limit point of M with $\mathfrak{J}_\rho$, i.e., in Hilbert space. However, let $V_\sigma(0^*, \epsilon)$ be any σ-spherical neighborhood of 0^*. There exists a natural number n, such that $1/2^n < \epsilon$. Consider the point e_n of M.

$$\sigma(0^*, e_n) = \frac{1}{(1 + 1)2^n} = \frac{1}{2^{n+1}} < \epsilon.$$

Hence e_n is in $V_\sigma(0^*, \epsilon)$. Since $V_\sigma(0^*, \epsilon)$ was any σ-spherical neighborhood of 0^*, 0^* is a limit point of M in $\{S, \mathfrak{J}_\sigma\}$. Since $Cl_\rho(M)$, the closure assigned to M by $\mathfrak{J}_\rho$, contains only M and the $\mathfrak{J}_\rho$ limit points of M, $Cl_\rho(M)$ does not contain 0^*; therefore $Cl_\rho(M)$ is not closed in $\{S, \mathfrak{J}_\sigma\}$. Thus $\mathfrak{J}_\sigma \neq \mathfrak{J}_\rho$. ▮

EXERCISE 3. Show that the function $i(x) = x$ of H into $E^1 \times E^1 \times \ldots$ is continuous but that its inverse is not.

21.12 Definition. The *Hilbert cube* is the subspace H^* of H consisting of those sequences $(x_1, x_2, \ldots, x_i, \ldots)$ of H such that $0 \leq x_i \leq 1/_i$ for each natural number i.

21.13 Theorem. *The Hilbert cube, H^*, is homeomorphic to the subspace, I^ω, of $E^1 \times \cdots \times E^1 \times \cdots$ defined by $\prod_{i=1}^{\infty} X_i$, where for every i, $X_i = I$, the unit interval subspace of E^1.*

Proof: A. The mapping h. Let $(x_1, x_2, \ldots)$ denote any point in I^ω. Define $h((x_1, x_2, \ldots))$ to be $(x_1, x_2/2, x_3/3, \ldots, x_i/i, \ldots)$. The image is in H^* and h is 1:1 by definition of H^* and I^ω. Further, h is onto; for, if $(y_1, y_2, \ldots, y_i, \ldots)$ is in H^*, $0 \leq y_i \leq 1/i$ and $0 \leq i \cdot y_i \leq 1$.

B. h is continuous. Let $\alpha:(x_1, x_2, \ldots)$ be any point in I^ω and let $\beta:(y_1, y_2, \ldots, y_i, \ldots) = (x_1, x_2/2, \ldots, x_i/i, \ldots)$ be its image in H^*. Let

$$V_\rho(\beta, \epsilon) = \left\{\gamma = (c_1, c_2, \ldots, c_i, \ldots) \;\middle|\; \sqrt{\sum_{i=1}^{\infty} (y_i - c_i)^2} < \epsilon\right\}$$

be any spherical neighborhood of $(y_1, y_2, \ldots, y_i, \ldots)$ in H^*. Since the series $\sum_{i=1}^{\infty} 1/i^2$ converges, there exists a natural number, N, such that

$$\sum_{i=N+1}^{\infty} \frac{1}{i^2} < \frac{\epsilon^2}{2}.$$

Consider the neighborhood $U^* = U_1 \times U_2 \times \cdots \times U_n \times I \times I \ldots$ of $(x_1, x_2, \ldots, x_n, \ldots)$ in I^ω, where $U_j = \{z_j \text{ in } I \mid |z_j - x_j| < \epsilon/\sqrt{2N}\}$ for $j = 1, 2, \ldots, N$. If $(z_1, z_2, \ldots, z_i, \ldots)$ is in U^*,

$$\sum_{i=1}^{N} \left(\frac{x_i}{i} - \frac{z_i}{i}\right)^2 < \sum_{i=1}^{N} (x_i - z_i)^2 < \frac{\epsilon^2}{2}$$

and

$$\sum_{i=N+1}^{\infty} \left(\frac{x_i}{i} - \frac{z_i}{i}\right)^2 < \frac{\epsilon^2}{2}.$$

Hence, if $(z_1, z_2, \ldots, z_i, \ldots)$ is in U^*, $h((z_1, z_2, \ldots, z_i, \ldots))$ is in $V_\rho(\beta, \epsilon)$ and h is continuous.

C. h^{-1} is continuous. $h^{-1}:H^* \to I^\omega$. Let $U^* = U_1 \times U_2 \times \cdots \times U_n \times I \times I \times \cdots$ be any basic neighborhood of $(x_1, x_2, \ldots, x_i, \ldots)$ in I^ω where $U_j = \{a_j \text{ in } I \mid |a_j - x_j| < \epsilon_j\}$, for $j = 1, 2, \ldots, N$. Let $\delta =$ minimum $\{\epsilon_1, \epsilon_2/2, \ldots, \epsilon_N/N\}$. Consider $V_\rho(\beta, \delta)$ where $\beta = (x_1, x_2/2, \ldots, x_i/i, \ldots)$ and

$$V_\rho(\beta, \delta) = \left\{(c_1, c_2, \ldots, c_i, \ldots) \text{ in } H^* \;\middle|\; \sqrt{\sum_{i=1}^{\infty} \left(c_i - \frac{x_i}{i}\right)^2} < \delta\right\}.$$

If $\sum_{i=1}^{\infty} (c_i - x_i/i)^2 < \delta^2$, $|c_j - x_j/j| < \delta < \epsilon_j/j$ for $j = 1, 2, \ldots, N$. Hence

$|jc_j - x_j| < \epsilon_j$ for $j = 1, 2, \ldots, N$ and $(c_1, 2c_2, \ldots, ic_i, \ldots) = h^{-1}((c_1, c_2, \ldots, c_i, \ldots))$ is in U^*. h^{-1} is then continuous. ▮

21.14 Corollary. *Any second countable, normal space, S, is homeomorphic to a subspace of the Hilbert cube, H^*.*

Proof: In the proof of the Urysohn imbedding theorem 20.16, any second countable, normal space is imbedded topologically in I^∞ by a mapping, F. The composite mapping $h \circ F: S \to H^*$ is then a homeomorphism from S onto a subspace of the Hilbert cube, H^*. ▮

21.15 Corollary. *Any separable, metrizable space is homeomorphic to a subspace of the Hilbert cube H^*.*

Proof: Any separable, metrizable space is normal and second countable. ▮

Metrizable Function Spaces

Certain function spaces constitute useful instances of metrizable spaces. In section 12, some function spaces were defined as product spaces. The set, Y^X, of all functions with domain X and with range in Y is the product set $\prod_{\nu \in X} Y_\nu$, where $Y_\nu = Y$ for every ν. Thus it follows that if Y is a topological space, then the set Y^X can be topologized with the product topology and a space whose elements or points are functions is defined. The product topology turns out to be only one of several useful topologies for spaces whose elements are functions. If Y is a metrizable space, a significant question to ask is "is Y^X, the product space, a metrizable space?" In theorems 12.30 and 12.31 it was established that a product space was first countable if and only if all but a countable number of the factor spaces had the trivial topology. Thus, theorems 12.30, 12.31 and 20.12 establish that Y^X with the product topology is metrizable along with Y if and only if X is countable. Since the useful spaces of analysis are not countable, other topologies for Y^X become important. One such topology is a topology for Y^X determined by an admissible metric for Y relative to which Y is bounded. Since for every metrizable space there exists an admissible metric relative to which the space is bounded the problem is solved topologically. However, analysis, both real and complex, is concerned at times with the determination of a topological space by a particular metric, e.g. the Euclidean metrics for $E^1$and E^2 (geometric considerations) as well as with the space itself (topological considerations). Thus, the question becomes "from any admissible metric for a space Y can a topology for all or part of Y^X, where X is a space, be defined?" The answer, worked out below, is that ρ, any admissible metric for Y, determines uniquely first a set $B_\rho(X, Y) \subseteq Y^X$ consisting of those functions whose range is ρ-bounded in Y and then a topology for $B_\rho(X, Y)$.

21.16 Lemma. *If X is any set and Y is a metrizable space with admissible metric ρ, then for f and g in $B_\rho(X, Y)$, $\text{l.u.b.}_{x \in X} \{\rho(f(x), g(x))\}$ is a unique real number.*

Proof: Let f and g be in $B_\rho(X, Y)$. Choose a in X. Then for any x in X, $\rho(f(x), g(x)) \leq \rho(f(x), f(a)) + \rho(f(a), g(a)) + \rho(g(a), g(x))$. Since f is bounded, $\rho(f(x), f(a)) \leq M_1$, say, for all x in X. Similarly, g is bounded and $\rho(g(a), g(x)) \leq M_2$, say, for all x in X. $\rho(f(a), g(a))$ is a unique real number. Thus for any x in X, $\rho(f(x), g(x)) \leq M_1 + \rho(f(a), g(a)) + M_2$. $\{r \mid r = \rho(f(x), g(x))$ for some x in $X\}$ is then bounded and so has a least upper bound. ∎

21.17 Lemma. *Let* $\sigma(f, g) = \text{l.u.b.}_{x \in X}\{\rho(f(x), g(x))\}$. σ *is a metric for* $B_\rho(X, Y)$, *where* ρ *is a metric on* Y *and so determines a metrizable function space,* $\{B_\rho(X, Y), \mathfrak{J}_\sigma\}$.

Proof: Exercise.

To illustrate one important aspect of the difference between the product topology and the topology $\mathfrak{J}_\sigma$ of lemma 21.17, the following example is included.

21.18 Example. Let X and Y both be the closed unit interval, [0, 1], of real numbers and let Y have the usual relative topology from E^1. Thus, Y is bounded relative to the metric ρ, where $\rho(x, y) = |x - y|$. Thus $B_\rho(X, Y) = Y^X$ and so Y^X has two topologies, the product topology $\mathfrak{J}_P$ and the metrizable topology $\mathfrak{J}_\sigma$. Consider the sequence of elements (functions) $(f_1, f_2, \ldots, f_n, \ldots)$ in $\{Y^X, \mathfrak{J}_P\}$ and in $\{Y^X, \mathfrak{J}_\sigma\}$, where $f_n(x) = x^n$. This is a sequence of functions from [0, 1] onto [0, 1] and hence is a sequence of elements in Y^X. Now, in $\{Y^X, \mathfrak{J}_P\}$, (f_n) converges to the function f^* of Y^X where $f^*(x) = 0$ for $x \neq 1$ and $f^*(1) = 1$. For, by theorem 12.9, we only have to check that the sequences $(f_1(x), f_2(x), \ldots, f_n(x), \ldots)$ of real numbers converge for each x in [0, 1] to $f^*(x)$. If $x = 1$, then $f_n(1) = 1$ for all n and $(1, 1, \ldots, 1, \ldots)$ converges to $1 = f^*(1)$. Similarly, if $x = 0$, then $f_n(0) = 0$ for all n and $(0, 0, \ldots, 0, \ldots)$ converges to $0 = f^*(0)$. In general, $(f_1(x), f_2(x), \ldots, f_n(x), \ldots)$ is $(x^1, x^2, \ldots, x^n, \ldots)$ and $\lim_{n \to \infty} x^n = 0$ for $0 \leq x < 1$. Thus for each x in [0, 1], $(f_1(x), f_2(x), \ldots, f_n(x), \ldots)$ converges to $f^*(x)$. So in $\{Y^X, \mathfrak{J}_P\}$, the sequence of points $(f_1, f_2, \ldots, f_n, \ldots)$ converges to the point f^*. In $\{Y^X, \mathfrak{J}_\sigma\}$, the situation is different, however. By the definition of convergence, $(f_1, f_2, \ldots, f_n, \ldots)$ converges to f^* in $\{Y^X, \mathfrak{J}_\sigma\}$ if and only if for each σ-spherical neighborhood, U, of f^* in Y^X, there exists a natural number, N, such that if $n > N$, then f_n is in U. So, consider for any natural number N, $\sigma(f_N, f^*)$. Since f_N is continuous on [0, 1], for each $\epsilon > 0$, there exists $\delta > 0$ such that if $|x - 1| < \delta$, then $|f_N(x) - 1| < \epsilon$. Thus $|1| - |f_N(x)| < \epsilon$ and $1 - \epsilon < |f_N(x)|$. So $|f_N(x)| = |f_N(x) - 0| > 1 - \epsilon$. Thus, for each $\epsilon > 0$, there always exists an x such that $0 < x < 1$ and $|x^N - 0| = |f_N(x) - f^*(x)| > 1 - \epsilon$. Hence, $\text{l.u.b.}_{x \text{ in } X} |f_N(x) - f^*(x)| = 1$ or $\sigma(f_N, f^*) = 1$ for any natural number N. This means that every point f_n from the sequence $(f_1, f_2, \ldots, f_n, \ldots)$ is at a σ-distance 1 from the point f^*. So, for $\epsilon = 1/2$, say, no point f_n lies in $U = \{g \mid \text{l.u.b.}_{x \text{ in } X} |g(x) - f^*(x)| < 1/2\}$ and the sequence $(f_1, f_2, \ldots, f_n, \ldots)$ does not converge to

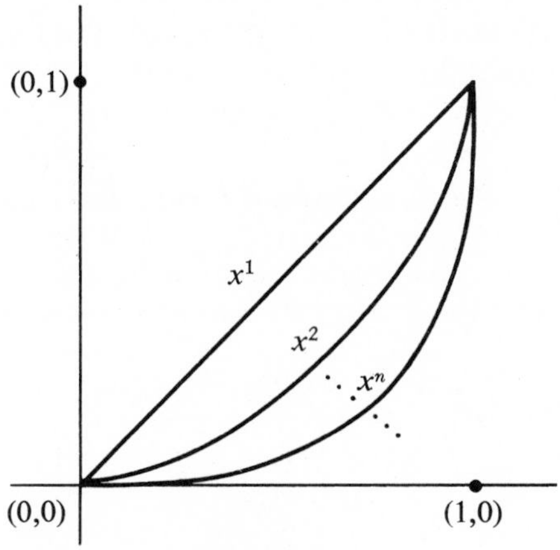

FIGURE 20

f^* in $\{Y^X, \mathfrak{J}_\sigma\}$. Now, it so happens that f_n, for each n, is a continuous function from [0, 1] onto [0, 1], but f^* is not continuous at $x = 1$. Thus, the product topology in this instance allows a sequence of continuous functions to converge to a discontinuous function. The metrizable topology determined by lemma 21.17 does not allow this and actually never does. Thus, for studies of sequences of real-valued functions whose ranges are bounded, the metrizable topology seems to be more sensitive. It preserves continuity in "passing to the sequential limit."

21.19 Lemma. *If Y is a metrizable space with admissible metric ρ, and X is any infinite set, then the relative product topology for $B_\rho(X, Y)$ is contained in the metrizable topology, defined in lemma 21.17, and is unequal to it if Y contains more than one point.*

Proof: Let $G^* = \prod_{x \text{ in } X} G_x$, where G_x is open in Y and $G_x = Y$ except for at most a finite number of values, $\alpha_1, \alpha_2, \ldots, \alpha_k$ of x. G^*, then, denotes a base element of the product topology on Y^X. Let f^* be any element in $G^* \cap B_\rho(X, Y)$. $f^*(x)$ is in G_x for every x in X. Since $G_{\alpha_1}, G_{\alpha_2}, \ldots, G_{\alpha_k}$ are all open subsets of Y, $f^*(\alpha_i)$ is contained in some spherical neighborhood, $U_\rho(f^*(\alpha_i), \epsilon_i) = \{y \mid \rho(y, f^*(\alpha_i)) < \epsilon_i\}$ in G_{α_i} for $i = 1, 2, \ldots, k$. Let ϵ be the minimum of $\{\epsilon_1, \epsilon_2, \ldots, \epsilon_k\}$. Then $V = \{g \mid \text{l.u.b.}_{x \text{ in } X}\, \rho(f^*(x), g(x)) < \epsilon\}$ is a σ-spherical neighborhood of f^* and is contained in G^*. Thus $U \cap B_\rho(X, Y) \subseteq G^* \cap B_\rho(X, Y)$. $G^* \cap B_\rho(X, Y)$, then, is open in the metrizable topology since all of its points are interior. The metrizable topology then contains the relative product topology for $B_\rho(X, Y)$. Now, consider a constant function f^* such that $f^*(x) = a$ for every x in X. Since Y contains more than one point, let ϵ be positive and less than one-fourth $\rho(a, b)$ for some point b in Y. Then the set $U = \{g \mid \text{l.u.b.}_{x \text{ in } X}\, \rho[f^*(x), g(x)] < \epsilon\} \cap B_\rho(X, Y)$, which is in $\mathfrak{J}_\sigma$, is not in the relative product topology. For let $G^* = \prod_{x \text{ in } X} G_x$, where G_x is open in Y and $G_x = Y$ except for $x = \alpha_1, \alpha_2, \ldots, \alpha_k$, and let $f^* \in G^*$. The element g in $B_\rho(X, Y)$ such that $g(x) = b$ for $x \neq \alpha_i$ and $g(\alpha_i) = a$ for $i = 1, 2, \ldots, k$ lies in $G^* \cap B_\rho(X, Y)$ but does not lie in U. Thus U is not in the relative product topology. ▮

21.20 Theorem. *If X is any topological space, if Y is a metrizable space with metric ρ and if C denotes the subset of $B_\rho(X, Y)$ consisting of all continuous ρ-bounded functions from X into Y, then C is closed in the metrizable space $\{B_\rho(X, Y), \mathfrak{I}_\sigma\}$, defined in 21.17.*

Proof: Let f^* in $\{B_\rho(X, Y), \mathfrak{I}_\sigma\}$ be a limit point of a set M of continuous functions in $B_\rho(X, Y)$. Since $\{B_\rho(X, Y), \mathfrak{I}_\sigma\}$ is a metrizable space, there exists a sequence $(f_1, f_2, \ldots, f_n, \ldots)$ of functions in $M - \{f^*\}$ that converges to f^* in $\{B_\rho(X, Y), \mathfrak{I}_\sigma\}$. Let q be any point in X. Consider $\rho(f^*(x), f^*(q))$. $\rho(f^*(x), f^*(q)) \leq \rho(f^*(x), f_n(x)) + \rho(f_n(x), f_n(q)) + \rho(f_n(q), f^*(q))$ for every n, by the triangle inequality. Now, for each $\epsilon > 0$, there exists a natural number N such that if $m > N$, then $\sigma(f^*, f_m) < \epsilon/3$ or $\text{l.u.b.}_{x \text{ in } X}\, \rho(f^*(x), f_m(x)) < \epsilon/3$. This implies that $\rho(f^*(x), f_m(x)) < \epsilon/3$ for all x in X, in particular $\rho(f^*(q), f_m(q)) < \epsilon/3$. Further, since f_m is continuous for all m, for each $\epsilon > 0$, there is a neighborhood U of q in X such that if x is in U, then $\rho(f_m(x), f_m(q)) < \epsilon/3$. Thus for each $\epsilon > 0$, there is a neighborhood U of q in X such that if x is in U, $\rho(f^*(x), f^*(q)) \leq \rho(f^*(x), f_m(x)) + \rho(f_m(x), f_m(q)) + \rho(f_m(q), f^*(q)) < \epsilon/3 + \epsilon/3 + \epsilon/3$, or for x in U, $\rho(f^*(x), f^*(q)) < \epsilon$. Hence, f^* is continuous at every point of X and so is in C. Hence, C contains all its limit points in $\{B_\rho(X, Y), \mathfrak{I}_\sigma\}$ and so is closed. ▮

Returning to example 21.18, one sees that in order for a sequence $(f_1, f_2, \ldots, f_n, \ldots)$ to converge to a function f^* in the product topology on Y^X all that was needed was for each sequence $(f_1(x), f_2(x), \ldots, f_n(x), \ldots)$ to converge to $f^*(x)$ at its own rate, i.e., for each $\epsilon > 0$, *for each* x, there must exist a natural number N_x such that if $n > N_x$, then $\rho(f_n(x), f^*(x)) < \epsilon$. However, in the case of the metrizable topology $\mathfrak{I}_\sigma$ on $B_\rho(X, Y)$, if the sequence $(f_1, f_2, \ldots, f_n, \ldots)$ is to converge to f^*, then for each $\epsilon > 0$, there must exist a natural number N such that if $n > N$, $\sigma(f_n, f^*) < \epsilon$. This latter means something much stronger than the former condition. $\text{l.u.b.}_{x \text{ in } X} \{\rho(f_n(x), f^*(x))\} < \epsilon$, for $n > N$, implies that *for every x in X*, $\rho(f_n(x), f^*(x)) < \epsilon$ if $n > N$. Thus, before $(f_1, f_2, \ldots, f_n, \ldots)$ can converge to f^* in $\{B_\rho(X, Y), \mathfrak{I}_\sigma\}$ there must exist one natural number N that "works" for all of the sequences $(f_1(x), f_2(x), \ldots, f_n(x), \ldots)$. So if these numbers N_x and N are considered to be a measure of how "fast" the sequences $(f_1(x), f_2(x), \ldots, f_n(x), \ldots)$ converge, then, in the product space, each sequence has its own rate and there is no relation among the rates. However, in $\{B_\rho(X, Y), \mathfrak{I}_\sigma\}$, the sequences $(f_1(x), f_2(x), \ldots, f_n(x), \ldots)$ must all converge at the same "rate" for each ϵ, namely N. In other words in $\{B_\rho(X, Y), \mathfrak{I}_\sigma\}$ the sequences $(f_1(x), f_2(x), \ldots, f_n(x), \ldots)$ must converge to $f^*(x)$ at a "uniform rate."

21.21 Definition. The metrizable topology, $\mathfrak{I}_\sigma$, for $B_\rho(X, Y)$, where $\sigma(f, g) = \text{l.u.b.}_{x \text{ in } X} \{\rho(f(x), g(x))\}$ and ρ is an admissible metric on Y, is called the *topology of uniform convergence* and the product topology on Y^X is called the *topology of pointwise convergence.*

An analogous topology of uniform convergence can also be defined for a set of functions, Y^X, where Y is a space with an admissible "uniform structure"—a uniformizable space. Such spaces, studied in section 23, are topological spaces but not all are metrizable.

21.22 Definition. Let X be a topological space and Y a metrizable space. Let $f_1, f_2, \ldots, f_n, \ldots$ and f^* be functions from X into Y. The sequence $(f_1, f_2, \ldots, f_n, \ldots)$ is said to *converge uniformly to* f^* in X relative to the admissible metric ρ for Y if and only if for each $\epsilon > 0$, there exists a natural number N such that if $n > N$, then $\rho(f_n(x), f^*(x)) < \epsilon$ for all x in X.

In example 21.18, the sequence $(x^1, x^2, x^3, \ldots, x^n, \ldots)$, for $0 \leq x \leq 1$, converges to the function f^* in the usual sense of convergence of sequences of functions but it does not converge uniformly to f^*.

21.23 Corollary. *If the sequence, $(f_1, f_2, \ldots, f_n, \ldots)$ of continuous functions from a space X into a metrizable space Y converges uniformly, relative to some admissible metric, to the function f^* from X into Y, then f^* is continuous on X.*

Proof: Let ρ be an admissible metric for Y and a any point in X; consider $\rho(f^*(a), f^*(x))$ for x in X. $\rho(f^*(a), f^*(x)) \leq \rho(f^*(a), f_n(a)) + \rho(f_n(a), f_n(x)) + \rho(f_n(x), f^*(x))$ for every n. Now if ϵ is real and positive, there exists a natural number N^* such that if $m > N^*$, $\rho(f^*(a), f_m(a)) < \epsilon/3$ and $\rho(f_m(x), f^*(x)) < \epsilon/3$. This follows from the uniform convergence of $(f_1, f_2, \ldots, f_n, \ldots)$ to f^*. Further, since f_m is continuous for any m, there exists a neighborhood U of a in X such that if x is in U, $\rho(f_m(a), f_m(x)) < \epsilon/3$. Thus if x is in U, $\rho(f^*(a), f^*(x)) < \epsilon/3 + \epsilon/3 + \epsilon/3 = \epsilon$ and f^* is continuous. ▮

EXERCISE 4. Let X be a space and Y a metrizable space. Let ρ be an admissible metric for Y and let $(f_1, f_2, \ldots, f_n, \ldots)$ be a sequence of functions in $B_\rho(X, Y)$. Prove that the sequence $(f_1, f_2, \ldots, f_n, \ldots)$ converges uniformly to f^* in X relative to ρ if and only if the sequence $(f_1, f_2, \ldots, f_n, \ldots)$ converges to f^* in the metrizable space $\{B_\rho(X, Y), \mathfrak{I}_\sigma\}$, where $\mathfrak{I}_\sigma$ is the topology of uniform convergence.

EXERCISE 5. Let X be a set and Y a topological space. Let $\mathfrak{V}_U^x = \{f \mid f(x)$ is in U, U is an open set in Y and x is a point in $X\}$. Prove that the sets $\mathfrak{V}_U^x$ form a subbase for the product topology on Y^X.

EXERCISE 6. Let X be a set and Y a metrizable space with admissible metric ρ. Show that the relation $\{(f, U) \mid U = \{g \mid \rho(f(x), g(x)) < \alpha(x)$, where α is a function from X into the positive reals$\}$ is a basic neighborhood relation for the set Y^X. Call the resulting topology the m-topology for Y^X.

EXERCISE 7. Show that if Y is a metrizable space with admissible metric ρ, then the metrizable topology for $B_\rho(X, Y)$ is contained in the relative m-topology for $B_\rho(X, Y)$ (see the preceding exercise).

21.24 Example. The set s of all sequences of real numbers with metric

$$\sum_{i=1}^{\infty} \frac{|a_i - b_i|}{1 + |a_i - b_i|} \cdot \frac{1}{2^i} = \sigma(\alpha, \beta),$$

where $\alpha = (a_1, a_2, \ldots, a_n)$ and $\beta = (b_1, b_2, \ldots, b_n, \ldots)$, determines the product space $\prod_{\nu \in \mathfrak{N}} X_\nu$, where X_ν is E^1 for every ν and $\mathfrak{N}$ is the set of natural numbers (corollary 20.13).

EXERCISE 8. Show that if M is the set of bounded sequences of real numbers and if the metric $\omega(a, b) = \text{l.u.b.}_{i \text{ in } I} |a_i - b_i|$ is defined on M, then the relative product topology is contained in this metrizable topology, $\mathfrak{I}_\omega$, for M (see example 21.24).

22. METRIC SPACES. CATEGORY. A FIXED POINT THEOREM.

Metric Spaces

In the previous section 21, two concepts were introduced which were defined in terms of—and hence were dependent on—a metric: boundedness and the set $B_\rho(X, Y)$ of all ρ-bounded functions from X into Y, where ρ was a metric on Y. Both of these concepts were used, however, as means to topological ends, i.e., the metric, relative to which a metrizable space Y was bounded, determined a (topological) function space and the ρ-boundedness of the ranges of certain functions was used first to identify the set $B_\rho(X, Y)$ and then to determine a topology for this set. The resulting topological spaces were studied for their topological properties. There is, however, an area of modern mathematics which is concerned with "metric properties" for themselves and not just as means for topological ends. Such an area might be called "metrology"; this term however is not standard. In this section concepts and theorems in "metrology" as well as topology will appear.

22.1 Definition. A pair $\{\{X, \mathfrak{I}\}, \rho\}$ is called a *metric space* if and only if $\{X, \mathfrak{I}\}$ is a metrizable space and ρ is an admissible metric for $\mathfrak{I}$.

NOTE: For brevity's sake, expressions like "second countable metric space" and "separable metric space" will be used throughout to denote a metric space whose topological part is separable or second countable, etc.

22.2 Example. $\{E^n, \rho_n\}$, where n is a positive integer, where E^n is, topologically, Euclidean n-space and where ρ_n is the Euclidean metric (definition 21.4), is a metric space. The term "Euclidean n-space" is used ambiguously to denote both the metrizable space (topology) and the metric space ("metrology"). When the only concern is topology the Euclidean or product or any other convenient, admissible metric can be used; when the concern is "metrology," then the Euclidean metric is understood.

22.3 Example. $\{H, \rho_\infty\}$, where H is the Hilbert (topological) space and ρ_∞ is the generalized Euclidean metric (definition 21.8) is a metric space.

With each such structure, i.e., a metric space, modern mathematics associates a 1:1 function which preserves the basic properties of the structure. The 1:1 function associated with metric spaces is an "isometric" function or an "isometry."

22.4 Definition. Let $\{\{X, \mathfrak{I}_1\}, \rho\}$ and $\{\{Y, \mathfrak{I}_2\}, \sigma\}$ be metric spaces. A function f from $\{\{X, \mathfrak{I}_1\}, \rho\}$ into $\{\{Y, \mathfrak{I}_2\}, \sigma\}$ is called *isometric* or an *isometry* if and only if $\sigma(f(a), f(b)) = \rho(a, b)$ for all a and b in X.

22.5 Lemma. *If f from $\{\{X, \mathfrak{I}_1\}, \rho\}$ into $\{\{Y, \mathfrak{I}_2\}, \sigma\}$ is an isometry, then f is a homeomorphism from $\{X, \mathfrak{I}_1\}$ into $\{Y, \mathfrak{I}_2\}$.*

Proof: Exercise.

Thus if two metric spaces are "metrologically" equivalent, i.e., isometric, their topological parts are homeomorphic.

22.6 Definition. A metric space $\{S, \rho'\}$ is called a metric subspace of a metric space $\{X, \rho\}$ if and only if S is a subspace of X and ρ' is $\rho \mid S \times S$, i.e., the restriction of ρ to $S \times S$.

22.7 Definition. If $\{X_i, \rho_i\}$ is a countable set of metric spaces, the *metric product space*, $\prod_i \{X_i, \rho_i\}$, is defined to be the metric space $\{\prod_i X_i, \sigma_P\}$, where σ_P is the product metric (definition 20.14).

22.8 Definition. A sequence $(a_1, a_2, \ldots, a_n, \ldots)$ in a metric space $\{\{X, \mathfrak{I}\}, \rho\}$ is called *Cauchy* or *fundamental* if and only if for every $\epsilon > 0$, there exists a natural number M such that if $n > M$ and if $m > M$, then $\rho(a_n, a_m) < \epsilon$. A sequence $(a_1, a_2, \ldots, a_n, \ldots)$ in a metric space $\{\{X, \mathfrak{I}\}, \rho\}$ is said to *converge* if and only if it converges in $\{X, \mathfrak{I}\}$.

22.9 Lemma. *Every sequence which converges in a metric space is Cauchy.*

Proof: Exercise.

The previous lemma represents a blend of "metrology" and topology, since convergence is strictly topological and Cauchyness is strictly "metrological," as the following examples show.

22.10 Example. Consider the sequence $(e_1, e_2, \ldots, e_i, \ldots)$, where $e_1 = (1, 0, \ldots, 0, \ldots)$, $e_2 = (0, 1, 0, \ldots, 0, \ldots), \ldots$, $e_i = (0, 0, \ldots, 0, 1, 0, \ldots)$, first in the metric Hilbert space $\{H, \rho_\infty\}$ and then in $\{E^1 \times E^1 \times \cdots \times E^1 \times \cdots, \sigma\}$. In the metric Hilbert space, $\rho_\infty(e_i, e_j) = \sqrt{2}$ for all i, j, with $i \neq j$. Hence, the sequence $(e_1, e_2, \ldots, e_i, \ldots)$ is not Cauchy in $\{H, \rho_\infty\}$. However in $E^1 \times \cdots \times E^1 \times \cdots$ with the product metric σ defined by

$$\sigma(e_i, e_j) = \frac{1}{2^i} \cdot \frac{1}{1+1} + \frac{1}{1+1} \cdot \frac{1}{2^j} = \frac{1}{2^{i+1}} + \frac{1}{2^{j+1}}.$$

For each $\epsilon > 0$, there exists a natural number M such that if $i + 1 > M$ and if $j + 1 > M$, then $1/2^{i+1} < \epsilon/2$ and $1/2^{j+1} < \epsilon/2$. Hence, if i and j are both greater than M, then $\sigma(e_i, e_j) < \epsilon$ and the sequence $(e_1, e_2, \ldots, e_i, \ldots)$ is a Cauchy sequence in the metric space $\{E^1 \times \cdots \times E^1 \times \cdots, \sigma\}$.

22.11 Definition. A metric space $\{\{X, \mathfrak{I}\}, \rho\}$ is called *complete* if and only if every Cauchy sequence converges to a point in the space.

22.12 Example. Let X be the metric space, E^1, of real numbers with the usual metric $\rho(x, y) = |x - y|$; let $\{Y, \rho'\}$ be the metric subspace of E^1 determined by $\{y \mid -1 < y < +1\}$ and ρ. Let $f{:}x \to 1/(1 + |x|)$. f is a homeomorphism from E^1 onto the subspace Y. $\{E^1, \rho\}$ is complete. Consider the sequence $(1/2, 2/3, 3/4, \ldots, n/(n + 1, \ldots)$ in Y. This is a Cauchy sequence in $\{Y, \rho'\}$, but does not converge to any real number in Y. $\{E^1, \rho\}$ is complete; $\{Y, \rho'\}$ is not complete; E^1 and Y are homeomorphic. Further, the sequence $(1/2, 2/3, 3/4, \ldots, n/(n + 1), \ldots)$ in $\{Y, \rho'\}$ is Cauchy but its image $(1, 2, \ldots, n, \ldots)$ assigned by the homeomorphism $f^{-1}{:}y \to y/(1 - |y|)$ is not a Cauchy sequence in $\{E^1, \rho\}$. Thus neither completeness nor Cauchyness is a topological property.

22.13 Lemma. *Cauchyness and completeness are preserved by isometries.*

Proof: Exercise.

22.14 Example. Let X denote the subspace of E^1 consisting of the points $1, 1/2, 1/3, \ldots, 1/n, \ldots$, where n is a natural number. The relative topology is given by the metric $\rho(x, y) = |x - y|$. This metric identifies the discrete topology for X. The sequence $(1, 1/2, \ldots, 1/n, \ldots)$ is Cauchy and so the metric space $\{X, \rho\}$ is not complete. Consider, now, the metric $\sigma(x, y) = 1$ for $x \neq y$ and $\sigma(x, x) = 0$ for the set $\{1, 1/2, \ldots, 1/n, \ldots\}$. This metric determines the same (discrete) topology for $\{1, 1/2, \ldots, 1/n, \ldots\}$ as does ρ above. However, the sequence $(1, 1/2, \ldots, 1/n, \ldots)$ is not Cauchy in the metric space $\{X, \sigma\}$. Further, the metric space $\{X, \sigma\}$ is complete.

22.15 Theorem. *Any metric subspace $\{F, \rho'\}$ of a complete metric space $\{X, \rho\}$ is complete whenever F is closed in X.*

Proof: Exercise.

Since the metric subspace determined by $\{x \mid 0 < x < 1\}$ in E^1 is not complete, not every metric subspace of a complete metric space is complete. However, the metric product space (definition 22.7) of a countable number of complete metric spaces is complete.

22.16 Lemma. *A sequence $(f_1, f_2, \ldots, f_n, \ldots)$ in a metric product space $\{\prod_i X_i, \sigma_P\}$ is Cauchy if and only if the images $f_1(i), f_2(i), \ldots, f_n(i), \ldots$ assigned by the projection functions are Cauchy.*

Proof: A. Let $(f_1, f_2, \ldots, f_n, \ldots)$ be a Cauchy sequence in the metric product space $\{\prod_i X_i, \sigma_P\}$. Then for $\epsilon > 0$ and k a positive integer, there exists a positive integer, N, such that if $n > N$ and $m > N$, then

$$\sigma_P(f_n, f_m) < \frac{\epsilon}{1+\epsilon} \cdot \frac{1}{2^k}.$$

This means, by definition (20.14) of σ_P, that

$$\sum_i \frac{\rho_i(f_n(i), f_m(i))}{1 + \rho_i(f_n(i), f_m(i))} \cdot \frac{1}{2^i} < \frac{\epsilon}{1+\epsilon} \cdot \frac{1}{2^k}.$$

Hence,

$$\frac{\rho_k(f_n(k), f_m(k))}{1 + \rho_k(f_n(k), f_m(k))} \cdot \frac{1}{2^k} < \frac{\epsilon}{1+\epsilon} \cdot \frac{1}{2^k}.$$

It follows that $\rho_k(f_n(k), f_m(k)) < \epsilon$, and thus $(f_1(k), f_2(k), \ldots, f_n(k), \ldots)$ is a Cauchy sequence in $\{X_k, \rho_k\}$.

B. Conversely, for each positive integer i let $(f_1(i), f_2(i), \ldots, f_n(i), \ldots)$ be a Cauchy sequence in $\{X_i, \rho_i\}$. For any $\epsilon > 0$, there exists a positive integer N^* such that

$$\sum_{i=N^*+1}^{\infty} \frac{1}{2^i} < \frac{\epsilon}{2}.$$

This follows from the convergence of the series $1 + 1/2 + 1/4 + \cdots + 1/2^i + \cdots$. Hence,

$$\sum_{i \geq N^*+1}^{\infty} \frac{\rho_i(f_m(i), f_n(i))}{1 + \rho_i(f_m(i), f_n(i))} \cdot \frac{1}{2^i} < \frac{\epsilon}{2}.$$

Now, since $(f_1(i), f_2(i), \ldots, f_n(i), \ldots)$ is Cauchy for all i, there exists for each $i \leq N^*$, a natural number M_i such that if $m > M_i$ and $n > N_i$, $\rho_i(f_m(i), f_n(i)) < \epsilon/2N^*$. Thus

$$\frac{\rho_i(f_m(i), f_n(i))}{1 + \rho_i(f_m(i), f_n(i))} \cdot \frac{1}{2^i} < \frac{\epsilon}{2N^*}.$$

Now if $n > M_1 + M_2 + \cdots + M_{N*}$ and $m > M_1 + M_2 + \cdots + M_{N*}$, then

$$\sum_{i=1}^{N^*} \frac{\rho_i(f_m(i), f_n(i))}{1 + \rho_i(f_m(i), f_n(i))} \cdot \frac{1}{2^i} < \frac{\epsilon}{2}.$$

Thus if $n > M_1 + \cdots + M_{N*}$ and if $m > M_1 + \cdots + M_{N*}$, then

$$\sigma_P(f_m, f_n) = \sum_i \frac{\rho_i(f_m(i), f_n(i))}{1 + \rho_i(f_m(i), f_n(i))} \cdot \frac{1}{2^i} < \epsilon$$

and so $(f_1, f_2, \ldots, f_n, \ldots)$ is Cauchy. ∎

22.17 Theorem. *The metric product space of a countable number of complete metric spaces is complete.*

Proof: Let $(f_1, f_2, \ldots, f_n, \ldots)$ be a Cauchy sequence in the metric product space $\{\prod_i X_i, \sigma_P\}$. By the previous lemma, the projected sequences, $(f_1(i), f_2(i), \ldots, f_n(i), \ldots)$, for $i = 1, 2, \ldots$ are Cauchy. Since each space X_i is complete, the projected sequences converge. Hence, by theorem 12.9, $(f_1, f_2, \ldots, f_n, \ldots)$ converges in $\prod_i X_i$ and so $(f_1, f_2, \ldots, f_n, \ldots)$ converges in $\{\prod_i X_i, \sigma_P\}$ (definition 22.7). Thus $\{\prod_i X_i, \sigma_P\}$ is complete. ∎

22.18 Lemma. *A sequence $(f_1, f_2, \ldots, f_j, \ldots)$ in (metric) Euclidean n-space $\{E^n, \rho_n\}$ is Cauchy if and only if the projected sequences $(f_1(k), f_2(k), \ldots, f_j(k), \ldots)$ are Cauchy in $\{E^1, \rho_1\}$. ρ_n is the Euclidean metric.*

Proof: A. Let $(f_1, f_2, \ldots, f_n, \ldots)$ be a Cauchy sequence in $\{E^n, \rho_n\}$. Then let k be any positive integer such that $1 \le k \le n$ and let $\epsilon > 0$. Since $(f_1, f_2, \ldots, f_j, \ldots)$ is Cauchy in $\{E^n, \rho_n\}$, there exists a positive integer N^* such that if $i > N^*$ and $j > N^*$, $\rho_n(f_i, f_j) < \epsilon$. Hence

$$\sqrt{\sum_{t=1}^{n} (f_i(t) - f_j(t))^2} < \epsilon.$$

It follows then that $|f_i(k) - f_j(k)| < \epsilon$ and that $(f_1(k), f_2(k), \ldots, f_j(k), \ldots)$ is Cauchy.

B. Conversely, let $(f_1, f_2, \ldots, f_n, \ldots)$ be a sequence in $\{E^n, \rho_n\}$ and for each positive integer k such that $1 \le k \le n$, let $(f_1(k), f_2(k), \ldots, f_j(k), \ldots)$ be Cauchy in $\{E^1, \rho_1\}$. Then for $\epsilon > 0$ and for each such k, there exists a positive integer N_k^* such that if $i > N_k^*$ and $j > N_k^*$, then $|f_i(k) - f_j(k)| < \epsilon/\sqrt{n}$. Thus if $M^* = N_1^* + N_2^* + \cdots + N_n^*$ and if $j > M^*$ and $i > M^*$, then

$$\sqrt{\sum_{k=1}^{n} (f_i(k) - f_j(k))^2} < \epsilon.$$

Thus, $(f_1, f_2, \ldots, f_n, \ldots)$ is Cauchy. ∎

22.19 Theorem. *Euclidean n-space, $\{E^n, \rho_n\}$ with the Euclidean metric, ρ_n, is a complete metric space.*

Proof: Let $(f_1, f_2, \ldots, f_j, \ldots)$ be a Cauchy sequence in $\{E^n, \rho_n\}$. By the previous lemma, the projected sequences $(f_1(k), \ldots, f_j(k), \ldots)$, for $1 \leq k \leq n$, are Cauchy sequences in $\{E^1, \rho_1\}$. Since $\{E^1, \rho_1\}$, the space of real numbers with the usual metric, is complete, the projected sequences, then, all converge. By theorem 12.9, the sequence $(f_1, f_2, \ldots, f_j, \ldots)$ converges in E^n. Thus, $\{E^n, \rho_n\}$ is complete. ▮

22.20 Theorem. *$\{H, \rho_\infty\}$, where H is the Hilbert space and ρ_∞ is the generalized Euclidean metric for H, is complete.*

Proof: Any element in H is a sequence, f, whose domain is the set of positive integers and whose range is a subset of the real numbers, such that $f(1)^2 + f(2)^2 + \cdots + f(i)^2 + \cdots$ converges in E^1. So, let $(f_1, f_2, \ldots, f_n, \ldots)$ be a Cauchy sequence in $\{H, \rho_\infty\}$.

$$\begin{aligned} f_1 &= (f_1(1),\, f_1(2),\, \ldots,\, f_1(i),\, \ldots) \\ f_2 &= (f_2(1),\, f_2(2),\, \ldots,\, f_2(i),\, \ldots) \\ &\vdots \\ f_n &= (f_n(1),\, f_n(2),\, \ldots,\, f_n(i),\, \ldots). \end{aligned}$$

An element f^* in H must be found to which the sequence $(f_1, f_2, \ldots, f_n, \ldots)$ converges in H. Now for each $\epsilon > 0$, there exists a natural number N such that if m and n are greater than N, then $\rho_\infty(f_m, f_n) < \epsilon$. Hence,

$$\sqrt{\sum_{i=1}^{\infty} (f_m(i) - f_n(i))^2} < \epsilon \quad \text{and} \quad \sum_{i=1}^{\infty} (f_m(i) - f_n(i))^2 < \epsilon^2.$$

Hence if m, n are both greater than N, $|f_m(i) - f_n(i)| < \epsilon$ for each i and so, for any fixed i, $(f_1(i), f_2(i), \ldots, f_n(i), \ldots)$ is a Cauchy sequence of real numbers. This means that the sequence $(f_1(i), f_2(i), \ldots, f_n(i), \ldots)$ converges in E^1 to a real number which will be denoted by $f^*(i)$. Consider the sequence, $(f^*(1), f^*(2), \ldots, f^*(i), \ldots)$. It will be shown that this sequence is an element in H and that the sequence $(f_1, f_2, \ldots, f_n, \ldots)$ converges to it in H. The proof rests mainly on the definitions of "infinite sums $\sum_{i=1}^{\infty}$" as the limits of sequences of finite sums. For each $\epsilon > 0$, there exists a natural number N such that if n and m are natural numbers both greater than N, then

$$\sqrt{\sum_{i=1}^{\infty} (f_n(i) - f_m(i))^2} < \sqrt{\epsilon/2}.$$

Hence,
$$\sum_{i=1}^{\infty} [f_n(i) - f_m(i)]^2 < \epsilon/2, \quad \text{for } n > N \text{ and } m > N.$$

Now by definition, $\sum_{i=1}^{\infty} (f_n(i) - f_m(i))^2$ is the limit of a sequence of partial sums

$$\sum_{i=1}^{q} (f_n(i) - f_m(i))^2,$$

i.e., $$\sum_{i=1}^{\infty} (f_n(i) - f_m(i))^2 = \lim_{q\to\infty} \sum_{i=1}^{q} (f_n(i) - f_m(i))^2 = \lim_{q\to\infty} s(q),$$

say, where $$s(q) = \sum_{i=1}^{q} (f_n(i) - f_m(i))^2.$$

Now

$$\sum_{i=1}^{q} (f_n(i) - f_m(i))^2$$

is a function of ordered triples of natural numbers, (q, n, m). Let

$$S(q, n, m) = \sum_{i=1}^{q} (f_n(i) - f_m(i))^2.$$

For any q, if $n > N$ and $m > N$, then $S(q, n, m) < \epsilon/2$. Thus the sequence $S(q, n, 1), S(q, n, 2), \ldots, S(q, n, m), \ldots$ for fixed q and $n > N$ approaches

$$\lim_{m\to\infty} \sum_{i=1}^{q} (f_n(i) - f_m(i))^2.$$

By the basic properties of limits of sequences,

$$\lim_{m\to\infty} \sum_{i=1}^{q} (f_n(i) - f_m(i))^2 = \sum_{i=1}^{q} (f_n(i) - \lim_{m\to\infty} f_m(i))^2 = \sum_{i=1}^{q} (f_n(i) - f^*(i))^2,$$

by definition of $f^*(i)$. Hence, since $S(q, n, m) < \epsilon/2$ for all q and $n > N$ and $m > N$, then for $n > N$,

$$\sum_{i=1}^{q} (f_n(i) - f^*(i))^2 \leq \epsilon/2.$$

So, for $n > N$,

$$\lim_{q\to\infty} \sum_{i=1}^{q} (f_n(i) - f^*(i))^2 \leq \epsilon/2.$$

Thus

$$\sqrt{\sum_{i=1}^{\infty} [f_n(i) - f^*(i)]^2}$$

is defined and for $n > N$ is less than $\sqrt{\epsilon/2}$. Now,

$$\sqrt{\sum_{i=1}^{q} f^*(i)^2} = \sqrt{\sum_{i=1}^{q} (0 - f^*(i))^2}.$$

By the Cauchy-Schwarz inequality, lemma 21.2,

$$\sqrt{\sum_{i=1}^{q} (0 - f^*(i))^2} \leq \sqrt{\sum_{i=1}^{q} (0 - f_n(i))^2} + \sqrt{\sum_{i=1}^{q} (f_n(i) - f^*(i))^2}.$$

The first term on the right is bounded by

$$\sqrt{\sum_{i=1}^{q} f_n(i)^2}$$

which exists, since f_n is in H. The second term on the right is less than or equal to $\sqrt{\epsilon/2}$ if $n > N$, by above. Hence

$$\sqrt{\sum_{i=1}^{q} f^*(i)^2}$$

is bounded above and is monotonically increasing with respect to q. Thus, $\sum_{i=1}^{\infty} f^*(i)$ exists, f^* is in H and $\rho_\infty(f_n, f^*) < \epsilon$ for $n > N$. Thus every Cauchy sequence in $\{H, \rho_\infty\}$ converges to an element of H. This establishes that $\{H, \rho_\infty\}$ is complete. ▮

Thus Hilbert space H is a metrizable, separable and hence second countable space; and $\{H, \rho_\infty\}$ is complete.

22.21 Theorem. *If $\{Y, \rho\}$ is a complete metric space then $\{\{B_\rho(X, Y), \mathfrak{I}_\sigma\}, \sigma\}$ is complete, where $\mathfrak{I}_\sigma$ is the topology of uniform convergence and σ is the metric determining it (definition 21.21).*

Proof: Let $(f_1, f_2, \ldots, f_n, \ldots)$ be a Cauchy sequence in $\{\{B_\rho(X, Y), \mathfrak{I}_\sigma\}, \sigma\}$. For each real $\epsilon > 0$, there exists a natural number N such that if $n > N$ and $m > N$, then $\sigma(f_n, f_m) < \epsilon$. Hence, if $n > N$ and $m > N$, $\rho(f_n(x), f_m(x)) < \epsilon$ for all x in X. Hence, for each x in X, the sequence $(f_1(x), f_2(x), \ldots, f_n(x), \ldots)$ is a Cauchy sequence in $\{Y, \rho\}$ and so converges to an element of Y, say $f^*(x)$. The function $f^*: x \to f^*(x)$ is an element of Y^X. It is also in $B_\rho(X, Y)$. For, let a and b be any two points of X. $\rho(f^*(a), f^*(b)) \leq \rho(f^*(a), f_n(a)) + \rho(f_n(a), f_n(b)) + \rho(f_n(b), f^*(b))$, for any natural number n. Since $(f_1(a), f_2(a), \ldots, f_n(a), \ldots)$ converges to $f^*(a)$ in Y and $(f_1(b), f_2(b), \ldots, f_n(b), \ldots)$ converges to $f^*(b)$ in Y, there exists a natural number N such that if $m > M$, $\rho(f_m(a), f^*(a)) < 1/2$ and $\rho(f_m(b), f^*(b)) < 1/2$. Since f_m is in $B_\rho(X, Y)$, it is ρ-bounded and $\rho(f_m(a), f_m(b)) < \beta$, where β is some positive real number.

Thus, $\rho(f^*(a), f^*(b)) < 1/2 + \beta + 1/2 = \beta + 1$ and so f^* is in $B_\rho(X, Y)$. Now assume that $(f_1, f_2, \ldots, f_n, \ldots)$ does not converge to f^* in $\{B_\rho(X, Y), \mathfrak{I}_\sigma\}$. Then there exists a positive real number ϵ^* such that for every natural number N, there exists a point p in X and a natural number $k \geq N$ such that $\rho((f_k(p), f^*(p))) \geq \epsilon^*$. By definition of a Cauchy sequence, there exists a natural number M such that if $n > M$ and $m > M$, then $\sigma(f_n, f_m) < \epsilon/4$. This implies that if $n > M$ and $m > M$, then $\rho(f_n(x), f_m(x)) < \epsilon/4$ for every x in X. By the assumption above, there exists a point p in X and a natural number $k > M$ such that $\rho(f_k(p), f^*(p)) \geq \epsilon^*$. Since $(f_1(p), f_2(p), \ldots, f_n(p), \ldots)$ converges to $f^*(p)$ in Y, there exists a natural number $j > M$ such that $\rho(f_j(p), f^*(p)) < \epsilon/4$. Further, since $k > M$ and $j > M$, $\rho(f_k(p), f_j(p)) < \epsilon/4$. Thus $\rho(f_j(p), f^*(p)) + \rho(f_j(p), f_k(p)) < \epsilon/4 + \epsilon/4$. Hence, $\rho(f_k(p), f^*(p)) < \epsilon/2$. This contradicts the definition of k and p given above. Hence, $(f_1, f_2, \ldots, f_n, \ldots)$ converges to f^* and so $\{\{B_\rho(X, Y), \mathfrak{I}_\sigma\}, \sigma\}$ is complete. ∎

Completion of a Metric Space

22.22 Theorem. *Every metric space $\{X, \xi\}$ can be imbedded isometrically in a complete metric space $\{X^*, \xi^*\}$ in such a way that the image of X is dense in X^*.*

Proof: Let $B_\rho(X)$ denote the set (definition 21.21) of bounded functions from X into $\{E^1, \rho\}$ where, as usual, $\rho(a, b) = |a - b|$. Since $\{E^1, \rho\}$ is complete, $\{\{B_\rho(X), \mathfrak{I}_\sigma\}, \sigma\}$ is complete by theorem 22.21. Let a be some point in X. Define $\alpha(x) = F_x$, where $F_x: z \to \xi(z, x) - \xi(z, a)$ for z in X. Since for all z in X, $\xi(z, x) - \xi(z, a) \leq \xi(a, x)$ by the triangle inequality, F_x is in $B_\rho(X)$. Now let x_1 and x_2 be in X and consider $\sigma(F_{x_1}, F_{x_2})$ where σ denotes the metric on $B_\rho(X)$. $\sigma(F_{x_1}, F_{x_2}) = \text{l.u.b.}_{z\in X} |F_{x_1}(z) - F_{x_2}(z)| = \text{l.u.b.}_{z\in X_2} |\xi(z, x_1) - \xi(z, a) - \xi(z, x_2) + \xi(z, a)| = \text{l.u.b.}_{z\in X} |\xi(z, x_1) - \xi(z, x_2)| \leq \xi(x_1, x_2)$. Therefore, $\sigma(F_{x_1}, F_{x_2}) = \sigma(\alpha(x_1), \alpha(x_2)) \leq \xi(x_1, x_2)$. Also, $\xi(x_1, x_2) = |\xi(x_1, x_2) - \xi(x_2, x_2)| \leq \text{l.u.b.}_{z\in X} |\xi(x_1, z) - \xi(x_2, z)|$. However, from the above, $\text{l.u.b.}_{z\in X} |\xi(x_1, z) - \xi(x_2, z)| = \sigma(\alpha(x_1), \alpha(x_2))$. Thus $\xi(x_1, x_2) \leq \sigma(\alpha(x_1), \alpha(x_2))$ and so α is isometric. Since $\{B_\rho(X), \mathfrak{I}_\sigma\}, \sigma\}$ is complete, the metric subspace determined by $\overline{\alpha[X]}$, the closure of $\alpha[X]$ in $\{B_\rho(X), \mathfrak{I}_\sigma\}$, is a complete metric space, by theorem 22.15. Since $\alpha[X]$ is dense in $\overline{\alpha[X]}$, this is the desired space $\{X^*, \xi^*\}$. ∎

Category

In section 16, the word "category" was introduced. It is used here with a different meaning.

Category, like other concepts in this chapter, has applications in analysis. The next theorem is referred to in example 18.4. In definition 5.11, a subset M of a space X is defined to be "dense" in X if and only if $\overline{M} = X$. By lemma 12.21, a set M in a space X is "nowhere dense" in X if and only if $\overline{M}$ contains no non-empty open sets of X.

22.23 Definition. A subset M of a space X is called of the *first category in X* if and only if M is the union of a countable collection of sets that are nowhere dense in X. A subset M of a space X is said to be of the *second category in X* if and only if it is not of the first category in X.

22.24 Lemma. *The set of rational numbers is a set of the first category in* E^1.

Proof: Since any set, $\{x\}$, containing a single real number x is closed and not open in E^1, any set $\{r_i\}$ containing a single rational number r_i is nowhere dense in E^1. Hence the set of rational numbers is the union of a countable number of sets nowhere dense in E^1. ▌

22.25 Lemma. *The union of any countable collection of sets of the first category in a space X is a set of the first category in X.*

Proof: The union of a countable collection of countable sets is countable. ▌

22.26 Example. Let $\{X, \mathfrak{I}\}$ be the subspace of E^1 consisting of the numbers $1, 1/2, \ldots, 1/n, \ldots$, for n a natural number. This space is countable; however, it is of the second category in itself. For assume $X = \bigcup_{i=1}^{\infty} A_i$, where A_i, for each i, is a subset of X. Let 1 be in A_j, say. Then, since $\{1\} \subseteq A_j$ and $\{1\}$ is open, A_j is not nowhere dense in E^1.

The next lemma is needed for the theorem which follows it.

22.27 Lemma. *The union of any finite number of closed sets in a space X, no one of which contains a non-empty open set, also contains no non-empty open set of X.*

Proof: Let F_1 be closed and contain no non-empty open set. Assume that the union of any k (a natural number) such sets contains no non-empty open set. Let $F_1 \cup F_2 \cup \cdots \cup F_k \cup F_{k+1}$ denote the union of any $k + 1$ closed sets no one of which contains a non-empty open set. Let G be a non-empty open set contained in $F_1 \cup F_2 \cup \cdots \cup F_k \cup F_{k+1}$. F_{k+1} does not contain G; hence, $(\sim F_{k+1}) \cap G$ is a non-empty open set in X. Since $G \subseteq F_1 \cup F_2 \cup \cdots \cup F_k \cup F_{k+1}$, $(\sim F_{k+1} \cap G) \subseteq F_1 \cup F_2 \cup \cdots \cup F_k$. This contradicts the induction assumption. Hence a non-empty open set $G \subseteq F_1 \cup F_2 \cup \cdots \cup F_{k+1}$ cannot exist. ▌

22.28 Theorem (Baire Category Theorem). *If* $\{\{X, \mathfrak{I}_\rho\}, \rho\}$ *is a complete metric space, then* $\{X, \mathfrak{I}_\rho\}$ *is of the second category in itself.*

Proof: Let $\bigcup_{i=1}^{\infty} B_i$ be any union of a countable number of nowhere dense sets of $\{X, \mathfrak{I}_\rho\}$. Let the closure of each B_i be denoted, as usual, by $\overline{B}_i$. By definition of B_i, each $\overline{B}_i$ contains no non-empty open set. Hence $\overline{B}_1 \neq X$ and so there exists a point x_1 in $\sim\overline{B}_1$. Since $\sim\overline{B}_1$ is open, there exists a neighborhood W of x_1 such that $W \subseteq \sim\overline{B}_1$; further, the intersection of W with the spherical neighborhood $N_\rho(x_1, 1/2)$ of x_1 of radius 1/2 contains a neighborhood V of x_1 such that the diameter of V is less than or equal to 1 and $V \subseteq \sim\overline{B}_1$. By the regularity of $\{X, \mathfrak{I}_\rho\}$, V contains a neighborhood U_1 of x_1 such that $\overline{U}_1 \subseteq V$ and hence $U_1 \subseteq \sim\overline{B}_1$ and $\overline{U}_1$ has a diameter less than or equal to 1. Now it will be assumed that the points $x_1, x_2, \ldots, x_k$ and the corresponding neighborhoods $U_1, U_2, \ldots, U_k$ have been defined such that

1. $U_{i+1} \subseteq U_i$ 2. $\operatorname{diam}(\overline{U}_i) \leq 1/i$ 3. $\overline{U}_i \cap [\overline{B}_1 \cup \overline{B}_2 \cup \cdots \cup \overline{B}_i] = \emptyset$

for $i = 1, 2, \ldots, k$. Next consider $\overline{B}_1 \cup \overline{B}_2 \cup \cdots \cup \overline{B}_k \cup \overline{B}_{k+1}$. This set is closed; hence its complement is open. Further, by lemma 22.27, $\overline{B}_1 \cup \cdots \cup \overline{B}_k \cup \overline{B}_{k+1}$ contains no non-empty open set. Hence, there exists a point, say x_{k+1}, in U_k that is not contained in $\overline{B}_1 \cup \overline{B}_2 \cup \cdots \cup \overline{B}_k \cup \overline{B}_{k+1}$ and there exists a neighborhood W' of x_{k+1} that contains no point of $\overline{B}_1 \cup \overline{B}_2 \cup \cdots \cup \overline{B}_{k+1}$ and is contained in U_k. As above, the intersection of the spherical neighborhood $N_\rho\big(x_{k+1}, 1/2(k+1)\big)$ and the neighborhood W' contains a neighborhood, V, of x_{k+1}. By regularity of $\{X, \mathfrak{I}_\rho\}$, V contains a neighborhood U_{k+1} of x_{k+1} such that $\overline{U}_{k+1} \subseteq V \subseteq W' \cap N_\rho\big(x_{k+1}, 1/2(k+1)\big)$. Hence the neighborhood U_{k+1} of the point x_{k+1} has the following properties:

1. $\overline{U}_{k+1} \cap [\overline{B}_1 \cup \overline{B}_2 \cup \cdots \cup \overline{B}_{k+1}] = \emptyset$
2. $U_{k+1} \subseteq U_k$
3. $\operatorname{diam}(\overline{U}_{k+1}) \leq 1/(k+1)$.

Thus a sequence of points $x_1, x_2, \ldots, x_i, \ldots$ has been constructed such that x_i is in $\sim[\overline{B}_1 \cup \overline{B}_2 \cup \cdots \cup \overline{B}_i]$ for each i. Now, for each $\epsilon > 0$, there exists a natural number Q such that $1/Q < \epsilon$. Hence, if $n > Q$ and $m > Q$, x_m is in U_Q and x_n is in U_Q. Hence, $\rho(x_m, x_n) \leq 1/Q < \epsilon$. This means that the sequence $(x_1, x_2, \ldots, x_n, \ldots)$ constructed above is a Cauchy sequence in the complete metric space $\big\{\{X, \mathfrak{I}_\rho\}, \rho\big\}$ and so converges to a point x^* in X. Now x^* must be shown to be outside every $\overline{B}_i$. Since x^* is a sequential limit of $(x_1, x_2, \ldots, x_n, \ldots)$, x^* is in the closure of the set of elements $\{x_1, x_2, \ldots, x_n, \ldots\}$. Further, by theorem 7.7, x^* is in the closure of the set $\{x_i, x_{i+1}, \ldots, x_n, \ldots\}$ for every natural number i.

Thus, x^* is in $\overline{U}_i$ for every i, by definition of the sets U_i and the sequence $(x_1, x_2, \ldots, x_n, \ldots)$. Now assume that x^* is in $\overline{B}_k$ for some natural number k. Then since x^* is in $\overline{U}_k$ and since $\overline{U}_k \cap [\overline{B}_1 \cup \cdots \cup \overline{B}_k] = \emptyset$, a contradiction results. Therefore, x^* is in X but is in no $\overline{B}_k$. Hence, $X \neq \bigcup_{i=1}^{\infty} \overline{B}_i$ and $X \neq \bigcup_{i=1}^{\infty} B_i$. Since $\bigcup_{i=1}^{\infty} B_i$ denotes any union of a countable number of nowhere dense sets in $\{X, \mathfrak{I}_\rho\}$, $\{X, \mathfrak{I}_\rho\}$ is not of the first category in itself. ∎

The previous theorem illustrates another combination of "metrology" and topology. Second category is a topological concept and completeness is a "metrological" concept. Yet, the theorem states that the completeness of a metric space implies the second category property for its topological part.

22.29 Corollary. *The subset of irrational numbers is of the second category in* E^1.

Proof: By lemma 22.24, the rational numbers form a set of the first category in E^1. If the irrationals formed a set of the first category in E^1, then E^1, by lemma 22.25 would be of the first category in E^1. Since $\{E^1, \rho\}$, where $\rho(x, y) = |x - y|$, is complete, theorem 22.28 is contradicted. ▮

The previous corollary is used in example 18.4 in chapter 3.

22.30 Corollary. *All Euclidean spaces, Hilbert space and any closed subspaces of these spaces are of the second category in themselves.*

Proof: The spaces and their usual metrics are all complete metric spaces.

22.31 Example. The rationals with the relative topology from E^1 form a space S of the first category in S.

22.32 Example. The Cantor ternary set is of the first category in E^1 since it is closed and contains no non-empty open sets of E^1. However, as a closed subset of E^1, it determines a complete metric space; hence, it is of the second category in itself.

A Fixed Point Theorem

The following theorem establishes the existence of fixed points for contractions of complete metric spaces.

22.33 Theorem. *Let* $\{\{X, \mathfrak{I}_\rho\}, \rho\}$ *be a complete metric space and let* f *be a continuous function from* $\{X, \mathfrak{I}_\rho\}$ *into itself such that for all* x, y *in* X, $\rho(f(x), f(y)) \leq \alpha \cdot \rho(x, y)$, *where* $0 \leq \alpha < 1$. *Then there exists exactly one point* b *in* X *such that* $f(b) = b$.

Proof: Let x be in X; let $x_1 = f(x)$; let $x_2 = f(x_1)$; . . . ; let $x_n = f(x_{n-1})$; . . . . $\rho(x_1, x_2) = \rho(f(x), f(x_1)) \leq \alpha\rho(x, x_1) = \alpha \cdot \rho(x, f(x))$; $\rho(x_2, x_3) = \rho(f(x_1), f(x_2)) \leq \alpha \cdot \rho(x_1, x_2) \leq \alpha^2 \cdot \rho(x, f(x); \ldots ;)$ $\rho(x_n, x_{n+1}) \leq \alpha^n \cdot \rho(x, f(x))$. $\rho(x_n, x_{n+p}) \leq \rho(x_n, x_{n+1}) + \cdots + \rho(x_{n+p-1}, x_{n+p}) \leq (\alpha^n + \alpha^{n+1} + \cdots + \alpha^{n+p-1}) \cdot \rho(x, f(x)) = ((\alpha^n - \alpha^{n+p}) / (1 - \alpha))\rho(x, f(x))$. Hence, $\rho(x_n, x_{n+p}) < (\alpha^n/(1 - \alpha)) \cdot \rho(x, f(x))$ and $\rho(x_n, x_{n+p}) \to 0$ as $n \to \infty$. Thus $(x_1, x_2, \ldots, x_n, \ldots)$ is a Cauchy sequence in the complete metric space $\{\{X, \mathfrak{I}_\rho\}, \rho\}$ and so converges to b, say, in X. $\rho(b, f(b)) \leq \rho(b, x_n) + \rho(x_n, f(b)) = \rho(b, x_n) + \rho(f(x_{n-1}), f(b)) \leq \rho(b, x_n) + \alpha \cdot \rho(b, x_{n-1})$. Now for $\epsilon > 0$, choose n so large that $\rho(b, x_{n-1}) < \epsilon/2\alpha$ and $\rho(b, x_n) < \epsilon/2$. Then $\rho(b, f(b)) < \epsilon$ and so $f(b) = b$. If, also, $f(d) = d$, then $\rho(b, d) = \rho(f(b), f(d)) \leq \alpha \cdot \rho(b, d)$. This is a contradiction. ▮

23. METRIC UNIFORM CONTINUITY. UNIFORMIZABLE SPACES. UNIFORM CONVERGENCE. UNIFORM SPACES.

Metric Uniform Continuity

A theorem concerning the extension of functions defined on dense subsets of metric spaces will serve to introduce the next concept, that of uniform continuity. This latter, in turn, will serve to introduce a new structure, the most general structure on which uniform continuity can usefully be defined—the uniform space. Metric uniform continuity is a "metrological" property, always defined in terms of and dependent on a particular metric.

23.1 Example. Consider the identity function $f(x) = x$ of E^1 onto E^1. For each a in the domain and each real $\epsilon > 0$, there exists a real number $\delta > 0$ such that if $|x - a| < \delta$, then $|f(x) - f(a)| < \epsilon$, e.g., let $\delta = \epsilon$. Now if x^* is another real number, then $|y - x^*| < \delta(=\epsilon)$ implies that $|f(y) - f(x^*)| < \epsilon$. Hence, for a given $\epsilon > 0$, the same number, δ, "works" at x^* that "worked" at a. Thus given a positive real number ϵ, one can find a positive real number δ such that if $|x - y| < \delta$, then $|f(x) - f(y)| < \epsilon$.

23.2 Example. Consider, now, the function $g(x) = x^2$ from the metric subspace, S, of E^1 consisting of the positive real numbers onto itself. By the rules for order on the positive real numbers, $x^2 > a^2$ if $x > a$. Hence, g is a strictly increasing function. Any interval $\{x \mid a - \delta < x < a + \delta\}$ in S will have its image in the interval $\{y \mid (a - \delta)^2 < y < (a + \delta)^2\}$. The diameter of this latter interval is $(a + \delta)^2 - (a - \delta)^2 = 4\delta a$. Hence if $\delta = \epsilon/4$ and if $|x - a| < \delta$, $|g(x) - g(a)| < 4(\epsilon/4a)a = \epsilon$. Thus, at a point a, for each $\epsilon > 0$, $\delta = \epsilon/4a$ "works." These values for δ vary with a. Further, it will be shown that no single value for δ will "work" at all points of the domain. Let x denote a point in the domain of g. Let $N = \{z \mid x - \delta' < z < x + \delta'$, for δ' a positive real number$\}$ be any basic neighborhood of x in S, the domain of g. $x + \delta'/2$ denotes a real number in N. Now $|g(x + \delta'/2) - g(x)| = |(x + \delta'/2)^2 - (x)^2| = (\delta')^2/4 + \delta' x$. There exists, for any fixed $\delta' > 0$, a real number $x^* > 0$, by the archimedean order on the reals, such that $\delta' \cdot x^* > \epsilon$. Hence at this point x^*, in the domain of g, $|x^* + \delta'/2 - x^*| < \delta'$ but $|g(x) - g(x^*)| = |(x^* + \delta'/2)^2 - x^{*2}| = \delta' x^* + (\delta')^2/4 > \epsilon$. Hence, δ' does not "work" at x^*. So, for a given $\epsilon > 0$, there is no one value for δ that "works" at all points of the domain.

If we consider this number δ to measure the "rate of continuity" in the sense of a "rate of convergence" of the functional values, near a given point a in the domain, we see that the function $f(x) = x$ has a uniform rate at each point. In other words, an upper bound, ϵ, on the amount of deviation being given, x can "deviate" from any point a in the domain by an amount up to δ, without changing the image value by "too much," (ϵ). On the other hand, in the case of the function $g(x) = x^2$, described above, there is no fixed amount of deviation in the domain that is "safe" for a given deviation in the range. Hence the continuity of $f(x) = x$ is called uniform continuity.

23.3 Definition. A function f from a metric space $\{\{X, \mathfrak{J}_\rho\}, \rho\}$ into a metric space $\{\{Y, \mathfrak{J}_\xi\}, \xi\}$ is called uniformly continuous if and only if for every $\epsilon > 0$, there exists $\delta > 0$ such that if $\rho(a, b) < \delta$, then $\xi(f(a), f(b)) < \epsilon$ for all a, b in X.

23.4 Lemma. *If f is uniformly continuous from the metric space $\{\{X, \mathfrak{J}_\rho\}, \rho\}$ into the metric space $\{\{Y, \mathfrak{J}_\xi\}, \xi\}$, then f is continuous from $\{X, \mathfrak{J}_\rho\}$ into $\{Y, \mathfrak{J}_\xi\}$.*

Proof: Exercise.

One of the useful implications of uniform continuity is the existence of extensions of certain functions; this fact has applications in real and complex analysis.

23.5 Lemma. *Let $(a_1, a_2, \ldots, a_n, \ldots)$ be a Cauchy sequence in the metric space $\{\{X, \mathfrak{J}_\rho\}, \rho\}$. Let f be uniformly continuous from $\{\{X, \mathfrak{J}_\rho\}, \rho\}$ into $\{\{Y, \mathfrak{J}_\xi\}, \xi\}$. Then $(f(a_1), f(a_2), \ldots, f(a_n), \ldots)$ is Cauchy.*

Proof: For $\epsilon > 0$, there exists $\delta > 0$ such that if $\rho(a, b) < \delta$, $\xi(f(a), f(b)) < \epsilon$. Further, there exists a natural number N such that if $n > N$ and $m > N$, $\rho(a_m, a_n) < \delta$. Thus, if $n > M$ and $m > N$, $\xi(f(a_m), f(a_n)) < \epsilon$. Hence, $(f(a_1), f(a_2), \ldots, f(a_n), \ldots)$ is Cauchy. ∎

It is to be recalled that the continuous image of a Cauchy sequence is not necessarily Cauchy (see example 22.12).

23.6 Theorem. *If f is uniformly continuous from a dense metric subspace of a metric space $\{\{X, \mathfrak{J}_\rho\}, \rho\}$ into a complete metric space $\{\{Y, \mathfrak{J}_\xi\}, \xi\}$, then f can be extended to a uniformly continuous function on $\{\{X, \mathfrak{J}_\rho\}, \rho\}$ with range in $\{\{Y, \mathfrak{J}_\xi\}, \xi\}$.*

Proof: Let $\{\{D, \mathfrak{J}_{\rho'}\}, \rho'\}$ denote the dense metric subspace of $\{\{X, \mathfrak{J}_\rho\}, \rho\}$. Let a be any point in $\sim D$, the complement of D in X. Since $\{D, \mathfrak{J}_{\rho'}\}$ is dense in $\{X, \mathfrak{J}_\rho\}$, a is a limit point of D. Hence, by corollary 20.2, there exists a sequence $(d_1, d_2, \ldots, d_n, \ldots)$ in D which converges to a. It follows from lemma 22.9 that $(d_1, d_2, \ldots, d_n, \ldots)$ is Cauchy in $\{\{X, \mathfrak{J}_\rho\}, \rho\}$ and hence, by lemma 23.5, that $(f(d_1), f(d_2), \ldots, f(d_n), \ldots)$ is Cauchy in $\{\{Y, \mathfrak{J}_\xi\}, \xi\}$. Since $\{\{Y, \mathfrak{J}_\xi\}, \xi\}$ is complete, $(f(d_1), f(d_2), \ldots, f(d_n), \ldots)$ converges to some point of Y, say, α. Define $f^*(a) = \alpha$ for a in $\sim D$ and $f^*(d) = f(d)$ for d in D. To show that f^* is a function, let $(e_1, e_2, \ldots, e_n, \ldots)$ in D also converge to a in

$\{X, \mathfrak{I}_\rho\}$. Then $(d_1, e_1, d_2, e_2, \ldots, d_n, e_n, \ldots)$ converges to a in $\{D, \mathfrak{I}_{\rho'}\}$, and so is Cauchy. Thus by the previous lemma, $(f(d_1), f(e_1), f(d_2), f(e_2), \ldots, f(d_n), f(e_n), \ldots)$ is Cauchy in $\{\{Y, \mathfrak{I}_\xi\}, \xi\}$. Since $\{\{Y, \mathfrak{I}_\xi\}, \xi\}$ is complete, $(f(d_1), f(e_1), f(d_2), f(e_2), \ldots, f(d_n), f(e_n), \ldots)$ must converge to some point β in $\{Y, \mathfrak{I}_\xi\}$. Thus $(f(d_1), f(d_2), \ldots, f(d_n), \ldots)$ as a subsequence of a converging sequence must converge to β and, similarly, $(f(e_1), f(e_2), \ldots, f(e_n), \ldots)$ must converge to β. Since $\{Y, \mathfrak{I}_\xi\}$ is Hausdorff, $\beta = \alpha$ and f^* is a function. To prove uniform continuity, let $\epsilon > 0$, and let a and b be points in X. Since $\{D, \mathfrak{I}_{\rho'}\}$ is dense in $\{X, \mathfrak{I}_\rho\}$, there exists a sequence $(a_1, a_2, \ldots, a_n, \ldots)$ in D which converges to a and a sequence $(b_1, b_2, \ldots, b_n, \ldots)$ which converges to b. Now for any positive integer n, $\rho(a_n, b_n) \leq \rho(a_n, a) + \rho(a, b) + \rho(b, b_n)$. Also, since f is uniformly continuous on $\{\{X, \mathfrak{I}_\rho\}, \rho\}$, there exists a positive, real δ such that if $\rho(a_n, b_n) < \delta$, $\xi(f(a_n), f(b_n)) < \epsilon/3$. In addition, by convergence and by definition of f^*, there exist N_1 and N_2 such that if $n > N_1$, $\rho(a_n, a) < \delta/3$ and $\rho(b_n, b) < \epsilon/3$, and if $n > N_2$, $\xi(f^*(a_n), f^*(a)) < \epsilon/3$ and $\xi(f^*(b_n), f^*(b)) < \epsilon/3$. Now, since $\xi(f^*(a), f^*(b)) \leq \xi(f^*(a), f^*(a_n)) + \xi(f^*(a_n), f^*(b_n)) + \xi(f^*(b_n), f^*(b))$, for all n, if $\rho(a, b) < \delta/3$, $\xi(f^*(a), f^*(b)) < \epsilon$. Thus, f^* is uniformly continuous from $\{\{X, \mathfrak{I}_\rho\}, \rho\}$ into $\{\{Y, \mathfrak{I}_\xi\}, \xi\}$. ∎

The previous theorem implies, in particular, that any real-valued function that is uniformly continuous on the usual metric subspace of rational numbers can be extended to a function that is uniformly continuous on the whole metric space E^1.

Uniform Structures

In chapter 1, the "ϵ" and "δ" of introductory calculus were seen, on close scrutiny, to identify sets of real numbers. This observation led to the general topological structure and a general definition of continuity. A careful look at the "ϵ" and "δ" of uniform continuity may prove to be as fruitful. If $\{\{X, \mathfrak{I}_\rho\}, \rho\}$

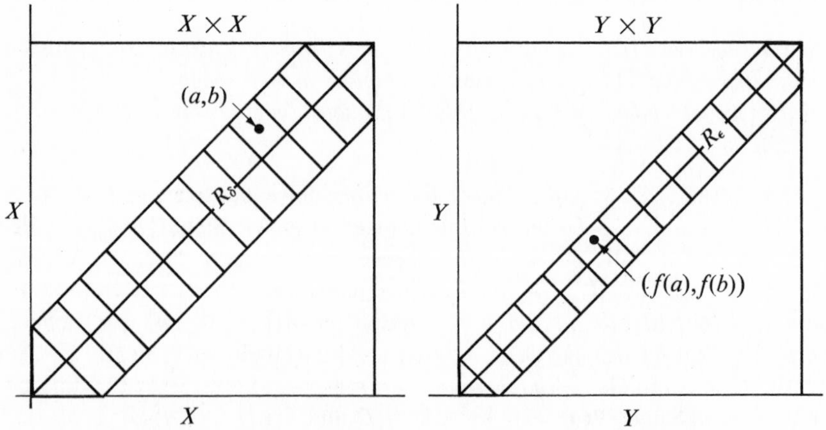

FIGURE 21 Uniform continuity: (a,b) in $R_\delta \Rightarrow (f(a),f(b))$ in R_ϵ

is a metric space with metric ρ, and if $\{\{Y, \mathfrak{I}_\xi\}, \xi\}$ is a metric space with metric ξ, then $f: X \to Y$ is uniformly continuous if and only if for each $\epsilon > 0$, there is a $\delta > 0$ such that if $\rho(x, y) < \delta$, then $\xi[f(x), f(y)] < \epsilon$. This situation can be described as follows: ϵ identifies a subset R_ϵ of $Y \times Y$, i.e., a relation on Y; $R_\epsilon = \{(y_1, y_2) \mid \xi(y_1, y_2) < \epsilon\}$. Similarly, δ identifies a subset R_δ of $X \times X$, i.e., a relation on X; $R_\delta = \{(x_1, x_2) \mid \rho(x_1, x_2) < \delta\}$. Uniform continuity states that for every such relation R_ϵ on Y, there is a relation R_δ on X such that if (a, b) is in R_δ, then $(f(a), f(b))$ is in R_ϵ.

It is in this latter form that uniform continuity can be generalized to spaces other than metric spaces. The general definition depends on a set of relations defined on the domain and a set of relations defined on the range of the function. This latter realization leads to the definition of a structure called a "uniform structure." A uniform structure is a set of relations on a set X. In order that the resulting definition of uniform continuity be a true generalization of metric uniform continuity, this set of relations must also yield a usual continuity, and hence, must lead to a topology on the set X. Thus this collection of relations on X, analogous to the collection $\{R_\delta\}$ for a metric space, must satisfy certain conditions. These conditions are included in the definition of a uniform structure for a set X. With these conditions on the collection, a resulting topology can be defined on X as well as continuity and uniform continuity which are generalizations of metric continuity and metric uniform continuity.

23.7 Definition. A collection $\mathfrak{U}$ of relations on a set X is said to be a *uniform structure* or *uniformity* for X if and only if

1. the collection $\mathfrak{U}$ is a filter on $X \times X$;
2. every set A in $\mathfrak{U}$ contains the diagonal Δ of $X \times X$, i.e., the set of all ordered pairs (x, x);
3. if A is in $\mathfrak{U}$, then A^{-1} is in $\mathfrak{U}$ where $A^{-1} = \{(x, y) \mid (y, x) \text{ is in } A\}$;
4. if A is in $\mathfrak{U}$, then there is a B in $\mathfrak{U}$ such that $B \circ B \subseteq A$, where $B \circ A = \{(x, z) \mid \text{there exists } y \text{ in } X \text{ such that } (x, y) \text{ is in } A \text{ and } (y, z) \text{ is in } B\}$.

NOTE: $B \circ A$ is the analogue of the composite of two functions.

EXERCISE 1. Prove that $(A \circ B)^{-1} = B^{-1} \circ A^{-1}$.

23.8 Lemma. *Let X be a set. Let $\mathfrak{B}$ denote the collection of all subsets, R_δ, of $X \times X$, where $R_\delta = \{(a, b) \mid \rho(a, b) < \delta$ for ρ a metric on X and δ a positive real number$\}$. Then $\mathfrak{B}$ is a filter base for a uniform structure $\mathfrak{U}$ for X.*

Proof: Since ρ is a metric and $\rho(x, x) = 0 < \delta$ for every x in X, the diagonal of $X \times X$ is contained in every R_δ. Thus $\mathfrak{B}$ is not empty and it does not contain the null set as an element. Further, if R_{δ_1} and R_{δ_2} are two distinct relations in $\mathfrak{B}$, then $\delta_1 < \delta_2$, say; so, if (x, y) is in R_{δ_1}, then (x, y) is in R_{δ_2} or $R_{\delta_1} \subseteq R_{\delta_2}$. Thus the intersection of two sets in $\mathfrak{B}$ contains a set in $\mathfrak{B}$. Hence the collection

$\mathcal{U}$ of all sets in $X \times X$ that contain a set of $\mathcal{B}$ is a filter on $X \times X$. Further, if V is in $\mathcal{U}$, then V contains an R_δ in $\mathcal{B}$; hence, V^{-1} contains R_δ^{-1}, $\{(x, y) \mid \rho(y, x) < \delta\} = R_\delta$. Thus V^{-1} contains R_δ and so belongs to $\mathcal{U}$. Lastly, if V is any relation in $\mathcal{U}$, V contains a relation R_δ, say, in $\mathcal{B}$; hence, V contains $R_{\delta/2}$ in $\mathcal{B}$, since $R_{\delta/2} \subseteq R_\delta$. Now if (x, y) is in $R_{\delta/2}$ and if (y, z) is in $R_{\delta/2}$, then $\rho(x, y) < \delta/2$ and $\rho(y, z) < \delta/2$; hence, $\rho(x, z) \leq \rho(x, y) + \rho(y, z) < \delta/2 + \delta/2 = \delta$. (x, z) is then in R_δ. Thus $R_{\delta/2} \circ R_{\delta/2}$ is contained in V. ▌

The first part of establishing a generalization has been completed; the new definition includes the old. The second part of the task is to exhibit examples described by the new but not the old. Two such examples follow. Example 23.26 which comes further on contains a more complicated example of a non-metric uniform structure.

23.9 Example. Let $\mathcal{U}$ consist of the one set $X \times X$. This one set constitutes a filter on $X \times X$ which is a uniform structure. This uniform structure differs from a uniform structure defined by a metric in the following respect: every point in $X \times X$ belongs to every set of the uniform structure. In any uniform structure defined from a metric, ρ, if (x, y) is in $X \times X$ and $\rho(x, y) = \delta^* \neq 0$, then (x, y) is not in $R_{\delta^*/2}$. Thus, in any uniform structure, $\mathcal{U}$, defined from a metric no point (x, y) off the diagonal lies in every relation in $\mathcal{U}$.

23.10 Example. Let X be the set of real-valued functions defined on the closed unit interval, $[0, 1]$, of E^1, that are continuous at all but a finite number of points of $[0, 1]$. For any such function, f, the integral $\int_0^1 f(x)\, dx$ exists. Define the uniform structure $\mathcal{U}$ for X as follows: the collection $\{R_\delta\}$, where $R_\delta = \{(f, g) \mid \int_0^1 |f - g|\, dx < \delta\}$ is a filter base for $\mathcal{U}$. By using the basic properties of the definite integral, one can establish that the filter $\mathcal{U}$ has all the properties of a uniform structure. However, $\mathcal{U}$ does not have the property described in the previous example which is possessed by all metric uniform structures. For, if f is any function in X, let f^* be the following function: $f^*(x) = f(x)$ for $x \neq 1/2$ and $f^*(1/2) = f(1/2) + 1$. f^* is in X and $\int_0^1 |f - f^*|\, dx = 0$. Hence, (f, f^*) lies in every relation R_δ in $\mathcal{U}$ and so in every relation V in $\mathcal{U}$ but (f, f^*) is not on the diagonal of $X \times X$.

Uniformizable Spaces

Uniform structures lead in a natural way to the most general structures on which uniform continuity and Cauchy sequences can usefully be defined. The following discussion establishes first the path from a uniform structure to a topological space called a uniformizable space. The uniformizable space is an instance of the topology being defined by a neighborhood relation.

NOTATION: If R is any relation on a set X, then $R[x]$, as usual, will denote $\{y \mid (x, y) \text{ is in } R\}$, i.e., the set of images assigned to x by R.

23.11 Lemma. *Let $\mathfrak{U}$ be a uniform structure for a non-empty set X. The collection $R^+ = \{(x, N) \mid x \text{ is in } X \text{ and } N = W[x] \text{ for } W \text{ a relation in } \mathfrak{U}\}$ is a neighborhood relation for X. N is, as defined above, the set of images of x assigned by W.*

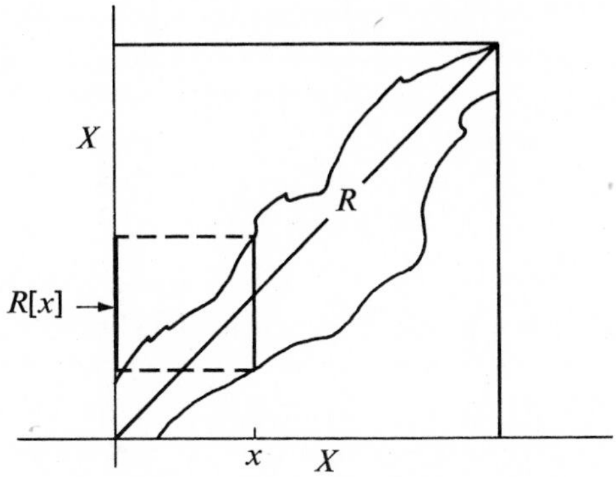

FIGURE 22 $R \subseteq X \times X$; $R[x]$ for x in X

Proof: 1. Since $\mathfrak{U}$ is not empty and since every relation in $\mathfrak{U}$ contains the diagonal of $X \times X$, each point x in X has at least one neighborhood and each neighborhood of x contains x. 2. Let M be any subset of X that contains $W[x]$. Let $W^* = \{(a, b) \mid (a, b) \text{ is in } W \text{ or } b \text{ is in } M\}$. $W^* \supseteq W$; hence, W^* is in $\mathfrak{U}$ since W is in $\mathfrak{U}$ and $\mathfrak{U}$ is a filter. Now if z is in M, (x, z) is in W^* and z is in $W^*[x]$. Therefore, $M \subseteq W^*[x]$. Conversely, if z is in $W^*[x]$, then (x, z) is in W^*. This means that z is in M. Hence, $W^*[x] \subseteq M$. So, $M = W^*[x]$ for W^* a relation in $\mathfrak{U}$ and (x, M) is in R^+. 3. Consider $W[x]$ and $V[x]$ for W and V in $\mathfrak{U}$ and x in X. $W \cap V$ is a relation in $\mathfrak{U}$, since $\mathfrak{U}$ is a filter. Now $(W \cap V)[x] \subseteq W[x]$ and $(W \cap V)[x] \subseteq V[x]$. Hence, $(W \cap V)[x] \subseteq W[x] \cap V[x]$. 4. Let W be a relation in $\mathfrak{U}$ and, as above, let $W[x]$ denote the set of images of x assigned by W. Let G denote the set of all points z in $W[x]$ with the property that there exists a relation N in $\mathfrak{U}$ such that $N[z] \subseteq W[x]$. x is in G and $G \subseteq W[x]$. Now let z be any point in G. There exists a relation N in $\mathfrak{U}$ such that $N[z] \subseteq W[x]$, by definition of G. Further, there exists a relation V in $\mathfrak{U}$ such that $V \circ V \subseteq N$. Consider, then, $V[z]$. Let y be any point in $V[z]$. $V[y] \subseteq (V \circ V)[z] \subseteq N[z] \subseteq W[x]$. Hence, y is in G, by definition of G. This means that $V[z] \subseteq G$. By part 2, above, (z, G) is in R^+ for every z in G, including, in particular, x and axiom N-IV is satisfied.

Since R^+ satisfies axioms N-I, N-II, N-III and N-IV of definition 2.5, R^+ is a neighborhood relation for X and so by theorem 2.6 determines a topological space on X. ▌

23.12 Definition. A *uniformizable space* is a topological space for which the neighborhood relation can be defined from a uniform structure. The symbol $\{X, \mathfrak{I}_{\mathfrak{U}}\}$ will sometimes be used to denote a uniformizable space determined by the uniform structure $\mathfrak{U}$ on X. $\mathfrak{U}$ will be called an *admissible uniform structure* or *uniformity* for $\mathfrak{I}_{\mathfrak{U}}$ or for $\{X, \mathfrak{I}_{\mathfrak{U}}\}$.

23.13 Theorem. *Any metrizable space* $\{X, \mathfrak{I}_{\rho}\}$ *is a uniformizable space.*

Proof: Let $\mathfrak{U}$ be the uniformity determined by $\{W \mid W = \{(x, y) \mid \rho(x, y) < \delta$ for positive, real $\delta\}\}$ as base, where ρ is an admissible metric for $\{X, \mathfrak{I}_{\rho}\}$. Now let G be any open set in $\{X, \mathfrak{I}_{\rho}\}$. For each x in G, there exists a spherical neighborhood $U_{\rho}(x, \delta) = \{y \mid \rho(x, y) < \delta\}$ which is contained in G. Hence, the set $W[x]$ of images of x assigned by W in $\mathfrak{U}$, where $W = \{(x, y) \mid \rho(x, y) < \delta\}$, lies entirely in G. So, G is open in $\{X, \mathfrak{I}_{\mathfrak{U}}\}$.

Conversely, if H is open in $\{X, \mathfrak{I}_{\mathfrak{U}}\}$, then for any y in H, there is a relation W in $\mathfrak{U}$ such that the set $W[y]$ of images of y assigned by W lies in H. By definition of $\mathfrak{U}$, W must contain a relation $N_{\delta} = \{(a, b) \mid \rho(a, b) < \delta\}$. Hence the spherical neighborhood $U_{\rho}(y, \delta)$ is contained in H and y is interior to G in $\{X, \mathfrak{I}_{\rho}\}$. G is then open in $\{X, \mathfrak{I}_{\rho}\}$ and the two topologies are the same. ▮

EXERCISE 2. Let the diagonal Δ of $X \times X$ belong to a uniform structure $\mathfrak{U}$ for X. What does this imply about the topology $\mathfrak{I}_{\mathfrak{U}}$ for X?

23.14 Lemma. *If there is a subset M of $X \times X$, which is not the diagonal but which is also contained in every relation W of a uniform structure $\mathfrak{U}$ for X, then the topology $\mathfrak{I}_{\mathfrak{U}}$ is not T_0.*

Proof: Exercise. [*Hint:* M^{-1} is also contained in every W.]

23.15 Lemma. *If $\mathfrak{U}$ is a uniform structure for a set X and W is any set in $\mathfrak{U}$, then there exists a relation U of $\mathfrak{U}$ such that $U \circ U^{-1} \subseteq W$. Further, U can be chosen to be symmetric, i.e., $U^{-1} = U$.*

Proof: Exercise. [*Hint:* $R = V \cap V^{-1}$ is symmetric. $R \subseteq V$; $R^{-1} \subseteq V$. $R \circ R^{-1} \subseteq V \circ V$.]

23.16 Lemma. *If $\mathfrak{U}$ is a uniformity for a set X such that the intersection of all sets in $\mathfrak{U}$ is exactly the diagonal of $X \times X$, then the uniform topology $\mathfrak{I}_{\mathfrak{U}}$ for X is Hausdorff.*

Proof: Let x and y be distinct points in X. (x, y) is not on the diagonal of $X \times X$. Hence, there exists a relation V in $\mathfrak{U}$ such that (x, y) is not in V. There exists a relation N in $\mathfrak{U}$ such that $N \circ N \subseteq V$. Consider the neighborhoods $N \cap N^{-1}[x]$ and $N \cap N^{-1}[y]$ and let q be in $(N \cap N^{-1}[x]) \cap (N \cap N^{-1}[y])$. (x, q) is then in N and (y, q) is in N^{-1}. Hence, (q, y) is in N, (x, y) is in $N \circ N$

and so (x, y) is in V. This is a contradiction and so the neighborhoods $N \cap N^{-1}[x]$ and $N \cap N^{-1}[y]$ are disjoint. ▌

23.17 Example. Let X be any infinite set. Define on X the minimal T_1-topology, $\mathfrak{J}$, i.e., the topology consisting of the null set and all complements of finite sets. $\{X, \mathfrak{J}\}$ is a T_1-space but X is not a Hausdorff (T_2-) space. By the previous lemmas, a uniformizable space is either Hausdorff or not T_0. Thus, no T_1-space that is not Hausdorff can be a unformizable space. Hence, $\{X, \mathfrak{J}\}$ is a topological space that is not a uniformizable space.

The next theorems will completely characterize T_0-uniformizable spaces from the point of view of their separation properties. A space is a T_0-uniformizable space if and only if it is completely regular.

23.18 Theorem. *Every uniformizable space* $\{X, \mathfrak{J}_{\mathfrak{U}}\}$ *is a* $T_{3+1/2}$*-space (Pontrjagin-Kakutani-Weil).*

Proof: The proof is similar in parts to the proof of Urysohn's lemma, theorem 18.23. The same countable, dense subset D—the dyadic fractions—of the unit interval $[0, 1]$ is used.

A. A function, d, from this set D into $X \times X$ is first defined. Let p be any point in the space $\{X, \mathfrak{J}_{\mathfrak{U}}\}$ and let F be any non-empty closed subset of X which does not contain p. There exists a neighborhood, $N[p]$, of p such that $N[p] \cap F = \emptyset$. Hence, $F \subseteq {\sim}N[p]$. By definition of a uniformizable space, $N[p] = \{q \mid (p, q)$ is in N for N a relation in the uniform structure $\mathfrak{U}$ on $X\}$. By definition of a uniform structure and lemma 23.15, there exists a symmetric relation V_0 such that $V_0 \subseteq N$. Again, by lemma 23.15, there exists a symmetric relation V_1 such that $V_1 \circ V_1 \subseteq V_0$. Assume, then, that symmetric relations $V_0, V_1, \ldots, V_n$ have thus been chosen for n a natural number. There exists a symmetric relation V_{n+1} such that $V_{n+1} \circ V_{n+1} \subseteq V_n$. Hence, a sequence $V_0, V_1, \ldots, V_n, \ldots$ of symmetric relations in $\mathfrak{U}$ can be chosen such that $V_{n+1} \circ V_{n+1} \subseteq V_n$. Next, let t be any dyadic rational number such that $0 \leq t \leq 1$, i.e., $t = k/2^n$, where k and n are non-negative integers and $k \leq 2^n$. Let $M_n = \{0/2^n\} \cup \{1/2^n\} \cup \cdots \cup \{1/2^n\} \cup \cdots \cup \{2^n/2^n\}$ as in the proof of Urysohn's lemma, theorem 18.23. Define, now, a function, d_1, from M_1 into $\mathfrak{U} \cup \{\Delta\}$, as follows: $d_1(0/2^1) = \Delta$; $d_1(1/2^1) = V_1$ and $d_1(2/2^1) = V_0$, where $M_1 = \{0/2^1\} \cup \{1/2^1\} \cup \{2/2^1\}$. Next, assume that d_n has been defined from M_n into $\mathfrak{U} \cup \{\Delta\}$. Consider, now, $M_{n+1} = \{0/2^{n+1}\} \cup \{1/2^{n+1}\} \cup \cdots \cup \{i/2^{n+1}\} \cup \cdots \cup \{2^{n+1}/2^{n+1}\}$. If i is even, i.e., $i = 2k$, define $d_{n+1}(i/2^{n+1}) = d_{n+1}(2k/2^{n+1}) = d_{n+1}(k/2^n) = d_n(k/2^n)$. By the induction assumption, $d_n(k/2^n)$ is already defined. If i is odd, i.e., $i = 2k + 1$, then $i/2^{n+1} = (2k + 1)/2^{n+1} = 2k/2^{n+1} + 1/2^{n+1} = k/2^n + 1/2^{n+1}$. Define, then, $d_{n+1}(i/2^{n+1}) = V_{n+1} \circ d_n(k/2^n)$. Now for any t in D, define $d(t) = d_n(t)$, where $t = k/2^n$. d is then defined from D into $\mathfrak{U} \cup \{\Delta\}$. Denote $d(t)$ by U_t. $U_0 = \Delta$; for $t \neq 0$, U_t is in $\mathfrak{U}$.

B. Next, certain inclusion relations must be shown to hold for the relations U_t. Let $t_1 = k/2^n$ and let $t_2 = (k+1)/2^n$, where $0 \leq t_1 < t_2 \leq 1$. If $n = 0$, then $k = 0$, $t_1 = 0$ and $t_2 = 1$. Hence, $U_1 \supseteq V_0 \circ U_0$ since, by definition above, $U_1 = V_0$ and $U_0 = \Delta$. Assume, then, that $U_{t_2} \supseteq V_n \circ U_{t_1}$ for n some non-negative integer and all k. Consider then $n + 1$. If k is even, where $q_1 = k/2^{n+1}$, and $q_2 = (k+1)/2^{n+1}$ then $U_{q_2} = V_{n+1} \circ U_{q_1}$, by definition of U_{q_2} in part A. If k is odd, let $k = 2j + 1$. Let $q_0 = 2j/2^{n+1}$. Then, $q_0 = 2j/2^{n+1}$, $q_1 = (2j+1)/2^{n+1}$ and $q_2 = (2j+2)/2^{n+1}$. Since $q_0 = j/2^n$ and $q_2 = (j+1)/2^n$, by the induction assumption, $U_{q_2} \supseteq V_n \circ U_{q_0}$. By definition of the relations, $V_0, V_1, \ldots, V_n, \ldots, V_{n+1} \circ V_{n+1} \subseteq V_n$. Therefore, $U_{q_2} \supseteq V_{n+1} \circ V_{n+1} \circ U_{q_0}$. Again, by definition, $U_{q_1} = V_{n+1} \circ U_{q_0}$. Hence, by substitution, $U_{q_2} \supseteq V_{n+1} \circ U_{q_1}$. Further, since $V_{n+1} \supseteq \Delta$, it follows that $U_{q_2} \supseteq U_{q_1}$. By transitivity, if s_1 and s_2 are any dyadic rationals such that $s_1 \leq s_2$, then $U_{s_1} \subseteq U_{s_2}$.

C. A function f from X into $[0, 1]$ is now defined. Let x be any point in X and let $A_x = \{s \mid s$ is negative and real or x is not in $U_s[p]$, where $U_s[p]$ is the set of images of p determined by the relation $U_s\}$. If x is in $U_t[p]$ for every t, then A_x is the set of negative reals. If there exists one t in D such that x is not in $U_t[p]$, then t is in A_x and A_x is not empty. Thus, A_x, for every x in X, is a non-empty set of real numbers bounded above by 1. Hence, A_x determines uniquely a real number in $[0, 1]$; namely, its least upper bound. Define $f(x)$ to be this least upper bound of A_x. Since $U_0 = \Delta$, $U_0[p] = \{p\}$. Since $U_0 \subseteq U_t$ for all t in D, A_p is the set of negative real numbers and $f(p) = 0$. Also, since $F \subseteq {\sim}V_0[p]$ and $U_1[p] = V_0[p]$, it follows that $f[F] = 1$.

D. f is next shown to be continuous. Let a be any point in X and let $\epsilon > 0$. By the archimedean order on the real numbers, there exists a natural number n such that $1/2^{n-1} < \epsilon$. Consider the neighborhood $V_n[a]$ of a in the uniformizable space $\{X, \mathfrak{I}_{\mathfrak{U}}\}$, where V_n is as defined above. $f(a)$ is a real number such that $0 \leq f(a) \leq 1$. Since $1 = 2^n/2^n$ is greater than or equal to $f(a)$, $\{j \mid j$ is a natural number and $j/2^n \geq f(a)\}$ is not empty and so has a smallest element k. Then $(k-1)/2^n < f(a) \leq k/2^n$. If $k \geq 2^n - 1$, then for any b in X, $f(b) \leq (k+1)/2^n$ and $(f(b) - f(a)) \leq 1/2^{n-1} < \epsilon$. So let $k < 2^n - 1$. Now, $f(a) < k/2^n$ or $f(a) = k/2^n$. First, let $f(a) < k/2^n$. Then, a is in $U_{k/2^n}[p]$, i.e., (p, a) is in $U_{k/2^n}$, by definition of f. Now if b is in $V_n[a]$, i.e., (a, b) is in V_n, then (p, b) is in $V_n \circ U_{k/2^n}$. Since $V_n \circ U_{k/2^n} \subseteq U_{(k+1)/2^n}$ by part B, above, (p, b) is in $U_{(k+1)/2^n}$. Hence $f(b) \leq (k+1)/2^n$, by definition of f, and $(f(b) - f(a)) < 2/2^n < \epsilon$. Next, if $f(a) = k/2^n$, then $f(a) < (k+1)/2^n$ and, as above, it can be proved that $f(b) \leq (k+2)/2^n$. In all cases, then, $(f(b) - f(a)) \leq 2/2^n < \epsilon$. Similarly, it is shown that if $f(b) < (k-2)/2^n$ and a is in $V_n[b]$, then $f(a) \leq (k-1)/2^n$. The contrapositive of this statement yields that for a in $V_n[b]$, $f(a) > (k-1)/2^n$ implies $f(b) \geq (k-2)/2^n$, i.e., for a in $V_n[b]$, $(f(a) - f(b)) \leq 2/2^n < \epsilon$. Since V_n was chosen to be symmetric, a being in $V_n[b]$ is equivalent to b being in $V_n[a]$ is equivalent to (a, b) being in V_n. Hence, if b is in $V_n[a]$ or if (a, b) is in V_n then $|f(a) - f(b)| < \epsilon$. ∎

23.19 Corollary. *Any uniformizable space is either completely regular or not T_0.*

Proof: By theorem 23.18 and lemmas 23.14 and 23.16.

23.20 Corollary. *Any Hausdorff uniformizable space is completely regular.*

The converse of corollary 23.20 is also true and will now be established after a relative uniform structure for a subspace and a product uniform structure for a product space have been introduced.

23.21 Theorem. *If $\{X_\nu\}$ is a collection of uniformizable spaces, then the non-empty product space $\prod_\nu X_\nu$ is a uniformizable space.*

Proof: Let X^* denote the product space $\prod_\nu X_\nu$ and let $\mathcal{V}^*$ denote the collection of all relations $V^* = \{(x^*, y^*) \mid x^*, y^*$ are in X^* and (x_ν, y_ν) is in U_ν for some ν, where x_ν and y_ν are the ν-th coordinates of x^* and y^*, respectively, and U_ν is a relation in $\mathcal{U}_\nu$, an admissible uniformity for $X_\nu\}$. Let $\mathcal{U}^*$ denote the collection of all relations on X^* which contain any intersection of finitely many sets in $\mathcal{V}^*$. $\mathcal{V}^*$ is said to generate $\mathcal{U}^*$. $\mathcal{U}^*$ is called the *product uniformity*.

A. $\mathcal{U}^*$ is a filter on $X^* \times X^*$. Each relation in $\mathcal{V}^*$ contains the diagonal Δ^* of $X^* \times X^*$ because each relation U_ν in $\mathcal{U}_\nu$ on X_ν does. Hence, no set U^* in $\mathcal{U}^*$ is empty. Further, the intersection of finitely many sets in $\mathcal{U}^*$ contains the intersection of finitely many sets in $\mathcal{V}^*$ and hence belongs to $\mathcal{U}^*$ by definition. Lastly, if a set A^* contains a set in $\mathcal{U}^*$ it automatically contains the intersection of finitely many sets in $\mathcal{V}^*$ and hence is in $\mathcal{U}^*$ by definition.

B. $\mathcal{U}^*$ is a uniform structure for X^*. In part A it was established that every relation in $\mathcal{U}^*$ contains the diagonal Δ^*. Next let U^* be any relation in $\mathcal{U}^*$. U^* contains an intersection $V_1^* \cap V_2^* \cap \cdots \cap V_k^*$ of sets in $\mathcal{V}^*$. By definition of $\mathcal{V}^*$, above, V_i^{*-1}, for $i = 1, \ldots, k$, is in $\mathcal{V}^*$. Hence, $V_1^{*-1} \cap V_2^{*-1} \cap \cdots \cap V_k^{*-1}$ is in $\mathcal{U}^*$. Since U^{*-1} contains $V_1^{*-1} \cap V_2^{*-1} \cap \cdots \cap V_k^{*-1}$, U^{*-1} is in $\mathcal{U}^*$. Lastly, let U^* again denote any relation in $\mathcal{U}^*$. Let $U^* \supseteq V_1^* \cap \cdots \cap V_k^*$. Let $V_i^* = \{(x^*, y^*) \mid (x_{\nu_i}, y_{\nu_i})$ is in U_{ν_i}, where x_{ν_i} and y_{ν_i} are the ν_i-th coordinates of x^* and y^*, respectively, and U_{ν_i} is in the uniform structure $\mathcal{U}_{\nu_i}$ for $X_{\nu_i}\}$. For each $i = 1, \ldots, k$, there exists a relation W_{ν_i} in $\mathcal{U}_{\nu_i}$ such that $W_{\nu_i} \circ W_{\nu_i} \subseteq U_{\nu_i}$, by definition of a uniform structure. Let $W_i^* = \{(x^*, y^*) \mid (x_{\nu_i}, y_{\nu_i})$ is in W_{ν_i}, where x_{ν_i} and y_{ν_i} are the ν_i-th coordinates of x^* and $y^*\}$. W_i^* belongs to $\mathcal{U}^*$ by definition of $\mathcal{U}^*$. Hence, since $W_i^* \circ W_i^* \supseteq W_i^*$, $W_i^* \circ W_i^*$ belongs to $\mathcal{U}^*$. Further, since $W_i^* \circ W_i^* = \{(x^*, y^*) \mid$ there exists z^* in X^* such that (x^*, z^*) is in W_i^* and (z^*, y^*) is in $W_i^*\}$. This set is equal to $\{(x^*, y^*) \mid$ there exists a z^* in X^* such that (x_{ν_i}, z_{ν_i}) and (z_{ν_i}, y_{ν_i}) are both in $W_{\nu_i}\}$, by definition of W_i^*. However, this latter set is contained in $\{(x^*, y^*) \mid (x_{\nu_i}, y_{\nu_i})$ is in $W_{\nu_i} \circ W_{\nu_i}\} = (W_{\nu_i} \circ W_{\nu_i})^*$. Since $W_{\nu_i} \circ W_{\nu_i} \subseteq U_{\nu_i}$, $W_i^* \circ W_i^* \subseteq$

V_i^*, for $i = 1, \ldots, k$. This last inclusion implies that $(W_1^* \circ W_1^*) \cap \cdots \cap (W_k^* \circ W_k^*) \subseteq V_1^* \cap \cdots \cap V_k^* \subseteq U^*$. Also, $(W_1^* \circ W_1^*) \cap \cdots \cap (W_k^* \circ W_k^*) \supseteq (W_1^* \cap \cdots \cap W_k^*) \circ (W_1^* \cap \cdots \cap W_k^*)$ by definition of $\cap$ and $\circ$. Hence, $(W_1^* \cap \cdots \cap W_k^*) \circ (W_1^* \cap \cdots \cap W_k^*) \subseteq U^*$ and $W_1^* \cap \cdots \cap W_k^*$ belongs to $\mathfrak{U}^*$ by definition. Thus $\mathfrak{U}^*$ is a uniform structure for the product set $\prod_\nu X_\nu$.

C. The topology determined by $\mathfrak{U}^*$ is the product topology. Let x^* be any point in the product space X^*. Basic neighborhoods for x^* determined by the product topology are product sets $G^* = \prod_\nu G_\nu$, where each G_ν is open in X_ν and $G_\nu = X_\nu$ for $\nu \neq \alpha_1, \alpha_2, \ldots, \alpha_k$. Since each X_{α_i} is a uniformizable space by hypothesis, G_{α_i} can be considered to be a set $U_{\alpha_i}[x_{\alpha_i}]$, where U_{α_i} is a relation in $\mathfrak{U}_{\alpha_i}$ the uniform structure for X_{α_i}, x_{α_i} is the α_i-th coordinate of x^* and $U_{\alpha_i}[x_{\alpha_i}]$ is the set of images assigned to x_{α_i} by U_{α_i}. Hence, if $V_i^* = \{(x^*, y^*) \mid (x_{\alpha_i}, y_{\alpha_i})$ is in $U_{\alpha_i}\}$, $G^* = V_1^*[x] \cap V_2^*[x] \cap \cdots \cap V_k^*[x] = \{y^* \mid (x^*, y^*)$ is in $V_1^* \cap V_2^* \cap \cdots \cap V_k^*\}$. Thus the neighborhoods from the product topology are exactly the neighborhoods from the product uniformity $\mathfrak{U}^*$. ∎

Just as any topology, $\mathfrak{J}$, on a space $\{X, \mathfrak{J}\}$ induces a relative topology r-$\mathfrak{J}$ on a subset S of X, so a uniform structure on X induces a relative uniform structure on a subset S of X.

23.22 Lemma. *If X is a set, $\mathfrak{U}$ is a uniform structure for X and S is a non-empty subset of X, then $\mathfrak{U} \mid S = \{W \cap (S \times S) \mid W$ is in $\mathfrak{U}\}$ is a uniform structure on S and is called the* relative uniformity.

Proof: Exercise.

23.23 Theorem. *If X is a set, S is a non-empty subset of X and $\mathfrak{U}$ is a uniform structure on X, then the topology $\mathfrak{J}_{\mathfrak{U}|S}$ for S, where $\mathfrak{U} \mid S$ is the uniform structure induced on S by $\mathfrak{U}$, is the relative topology r-$\mathfrak{J}_{\mathfrak{U}}$ for S as a subspace of $\{X, \mathfrak{J}_{\mathfrak{U}}\}$.*

Proof: A. Let G be in $\mathfrak{J}_{\mathfrak{U}|S}$ and let x be in G. There exists W in $\mathfrak{U}$ such that $(W \cap (S \times S))[x] \subseteq G$, by definition of $\mathfrak{J}_{\mathfrak{U}|S}$. Now $(W \cap (S \times S))[x] = W[x] \cap S$. Hence, x is interior to G in the relative topology r-$\mathfrak{J}_{\mathfrak{U}}$, and so G is in r-$\mathfrak{J}_{\mathfrak{U}}$.

B. Let G be in r-$\mathfrak{J}_{\mathfrak{U}}$ and again let x be any point in G. There exists a neighborhood $W[x]$ of x, where W is in $\mathfrak{U}$, such that $W[x] \cap S \subseteq G$, by definition of r-$\mathfrak{J}_{\mathfrak{U}}$. Now, $W[x] \cap S = (W \cap (S \times S))[x]$. Hence, $(W \cap (S \times S))[x] \subseteq G$. $(W \cap (S \times S))[x]$ is a neighborhood of x assigned by the uniform structure $\mathfrak{U} \mid S$ on S, and, so, G is in $\mathfrak{J}_{\mathfrak{U}|S}$. ∎

23.24 Corollary. *Any product space I^X, where I denotes the closed unit interval,* [0, 1], *with the usual topology is a uniformizable space.*

Proof: I is a metrizable space and, hence, by theorem 23.13, is a uniformizable space. By theorem 23.21, I^X, for any set X, is then a uniformizable space. ▌

23.25 Theorem. *Every completely regular space, X, is a uniformizable space, i.e., there exists a uniform structure for X whose topology is the given topology.*

Proof: By theorem 18.46, every completely regular space is topologically indistinguishable from a subspace of a product space, I^A. Hence, by theorem 23.23 and corollary 23.24, every completely regular space is a uniformizable space. ▌

Thus, theorem 23.25 and corollary 23.20 establish that a space is completely regular if and only if it is Hausdorff and uniformizable.

23.26 Example. Since every completely regular space is a uniformizable space and since every metrizable space is normal, the product space in example 18.48, which is completely regular and not normal, is an example of a Hausdorff uniformizable space which is not metrizable.

Uniform Spaces, Completeness and an Extension Theorem

The uniform generalization of a metrizable space is a uniformizable space and the uniform generalization of a metric space is a uniform space.

23.27 Definition. A pair $\{\{X, \mathfrak{J}\}, \mathfrak{U}\}$ is called a uniform space if and only if $\{X, \mathfrak{J}\}$ is a uniformizable space and $\mathfrak{U}$ is an admissible uniformity for $\mathfrak{J}$. The briefer symbol $\{X, \mathfrak{U}\}$ is also used.

23.28 Definition. A function f from a uniform space $\{\{X, \mathfrak{J}\}, \mathfrak{U}\}$ into a uniform space $\{\{Y, \mathfrak{J}'\}, \mathfrak{U}'\}$ is called *uniformly continuous* if and only if for each relation V' in $\mathfrak{U}'$, there exists a relation V in $\mathfrak{U}$ such that if (x, y) is in V, $(f(x), f(y))$ is in V'. If f is 1:1 and if f and f^{-1} are both uniformly continuous, f is called *iso-uniform*.

The above definition can be restated in terms of the function $(f, f)\colon (x, y) \to (f(x), f(y))$. Thus, f is uniformly continuous if and only if $(f, f)^{-1}[V']$ is in the uniform structure $\mathfrak{U}$, for every V' in $\mathfrak{U}'$. f is then iso-uniform if also it is 1:1 and $(f, f)[V]$ is in $\mathfrak{U}'$ for every V in $\mathfrak{U}$. Thus, it follows from the definition that the larger the uniformity on the domain the more chance a function has to be uniformly continuous.

23.29 Lemma. *If f is uniformly continuous from the uniform space $\{\{X, \mathfrak{J}\}, \mathfrak{U}\}$ into the uniform space $\{\{Y, \mathfrak{J}'\}, \mathfrak{V}\}$, then f is continuous from $\{X, \mathfrak{J}\}$ into $\{Y, \mathfrak{J}'\}$.*

Proof: Exercise.

EXERCISE 3. Let f be a continuous function from a space $\{X, \mathfrak{I}\}$ into the space E^1 of real numbers. Let $V_f(\epsilon) = \{(x, y) \mid |f(x) - f(y)| < \epsilon\}$. Let $\mathcal{V}$ denote the set of all $V_f(\epsilon)$ for ϵ positive and real. Prove that the collection $\mathcal{U}_f$ of all relations on X which contain at least one set $V_f(\epsilon)$ is a uniform structure for X.

EXERCISE 4. Let $\mathcal{U}$ be the usual uniform structure on E^1, i.e., the collection of all relations on the real numbers which contain relations $V_i(\epsilon) = \{(x, y) \mid |i(x) - i(y)| < \epsilon$ for i the identity function, $i(x) = x$, and ϵ positive and real$\}$. Let $g(x) = x^2$. Let $\mathcal{U}_g$ denote the uniform structure described in exercise 3. Prove that $\mathcal{U} \not\subseteq \mathcal{U}_g$ and $\mathcal{U}_g \not\subseteq \mathcal{U}$.

23.30 Theorem. *If $\{X, \mathfrak{I}_{\mathcal{U}}\}$ is a completely regular space, then the uniform structure generated by all the uniform structures $\mathcal{U}_f$ for f in $C(X)$, the ring of continuous functions from X into E^1, is admissible. $\mathcal{U}_f$ is the uniform structure consisting of the collection of all relations which contain a relation $V_f(\epsilon) = \{(x, y) \mid |f(x) - f(y)| < \epsilon$ for ϵ positive and real$\}$.*

Proof: A. It must be shown that the collection $\bigcup_{f \in C(X)} \mathcal{U}_f$ does determine a uniform structure uniquely. The filter generated by the filters $\mathcal{U}_f$ consists of all relations which contain any intersection of finitely many sets in $\bigcup_{f \in C(X)} \mathcal{U}_f$. Since all relations in $\bigcup_{f \in C(X)} \mathcal{U}_f$ contain the diagonal Δ of $X \times X$, the empty set does not belong to the collection and no intersection of finitely many sets in $\bigcup_{f \in C(X)} \mathcal{U}_f$ is empty. Thus the collection $\bigcup_{f \in C(X)} \mathcal{U}_f$ generates a filter, $\mathcal{U}$, on $X \times X$. Next, if U is in $\mathcal{U}$, then U contains an intersection $V_{f_1}(\epsilon_1) \cap V_{f_2}(\epsilon_2) \cap \cdots \cap V_{f_k}(\epsilon_k)$, where $V_{f_i}(\epsilon_i) = \{(x, y) \mid |f_i(x) - f_i(y)| < \epsilon_i$ for ϵ_i positive and real$\}$. Since $V_{f_i}^{-1}(\epsilon_i) = V_{f_i}(\epsilon_i)$, $U^{-1} \supseteq V_{f_1}(\epsilon_1) \cap V_{f_2}(\epsilon_2) \cap \cdots \cap V_{f_k}(\epsilon_k)$ and U^{-1} is in $\mathcal{U}$. Lastly, let U be in $\mathcal{U}$ and again let $U \supseteq V_{f_1}(\epsilon_1) \cap V_{f_2}(\epsilon_2) \cap \cdots \cap V_{f_k}(\epsilon_k)$ where, as above, $V_{f_i}(\epsilon_i) = \{(x, y) \mid |f_i(x) - f_i(y)| < \epsilon_i\}$. Consider for each $i = 1, \ldots, k$, $W_i = \{(x, y) \mid |f_i(x) - f_i(y)| < \epsilon_i/2\}$. $W_i \circ W_i = \{(x, y) \mid$ there exists z such that $|f_i(x) - f_i(z)| < \epsilon_i/2$ and $|f_i(z) - f_i(y)| < \epsilon_i/2\}$. Thus if (x, y) is in $W_i \circ W_i$, $|f_i(x) - f_i(y)| < \epsilon_i$ and (x, y) is in $V_{f_i}(\epsilon_i)$. Hence, $W_i \circ W_i \subseteq V_{f_i}(\epsilon_i)$. This means that $(W_1 \circ W_1) \cap \cdots \cap (W_k \circ W_k) \subseteq V_{f_1}(\epsilon_1) \cap \cdots \cap V_{f_k}(\epsilon_k)$ and since $(W_1 \cap \cdots \cap W_k) \circ (W_1 \cap \cdots \cap W_k) \subseteq (W_1 \circ W_1) \cap \cdots \cap (W_k \circ W_k)$, then $(W_1 \cap \cdots \cap W_k) \circ (W_1 \cap \cdots \cap W_k) \subseteq U$. Thus the collection of all continuous functions in $C(X)$, as described above, determines uniquely a uniform structure—the smallest uniform structure containing all relations $V_f(\epsilon) = \{(x, y) \mid |f(x) - f(y)| < \epsilon$ for ϵ positive and real and f in $C(X)\}$.

B. Now, consider the topology $\mathfrak{I}_{\mathcal{U}}$ determined by $\mathcal{U}$ on X. Let x be any point; a local base at x consists of all finite intersections $V_1[x] \cap V_2[x] \cap \cdots \cap V_k[x]$, where V_i is an abbreviation for $\{(x, y) \mid |f_i(x) - f_i(y)| < \epsilon_i$ for ϵ_i real and positive and f_i in $C(X)\}$. Since X is completely regular, by corollary 18.41, the topology on X is the weak topology determined by $C(X)$. By definition of the weak topology, a local base at a point x in X consists of all intersections $G_1 \cap G_2 \cap \cdots \cap G_k$, where $G_i = \{y \mid |f_i(x) - f_i(y)| < \epsilon_i$, for f_i in $C(X)$ and ϵ_i real and positive$\}$. Thus the neighborhoods determined by $\mathcal{U}$ are exactly the neighborhoods determined by the original completely regular topology and hence $\mathfrak{U}$ is admissible. ▌

Thus, theorems 23.25 and 23.30 establish that a single topology can be determined by different uniform structures. Hence, since the uniform continuity of a function depends on a uniform structure, the topology on a uniformizable space again does not, in general, determine a unique set of uniformly continuous functions.

The next aim of this section will be to generalize theorem 23.6 to Hausdorff uniform spaces. However, in theorem 23.6 the necessary functional values were obtained as limits of Cauchy sequences in the range space. In a general topological space, "Cauchyness" has no meaning, and in a non-first countable space, not all limit points are sequential limits in the sense of theorem 7.8. However, the idea of "Cauchyness" generalizes to nets in uniform spaces.

23.31 Definition. A net $n: D \to X$ in a uniform space $\{\{X, \mathfrak{I}_{\mathfrak{U}}\}, \mathfrak{U}\}$ is called *Cauchy* if and only if for each relation U in $\mathfrak{U}$, there is an α in the domain D of n such that if $d_1 > \alpha$ and $d_2 > \alpha$, $(n(d_1), n(d_2))$ is in U. A net n *converges* in $\{\{X, \mathfrak{I}_{\mathfrak{U}}\}, \mathfrak{U}\}$ if and only if it converges in $\{X, \mathfrak{I}_{\mathfrak{U}}\}$.

23.32 Lemma. *If a net $n: D \to X$ in a uniform space $\{\{X, \mathfrak{I}_{\mathfrak{U}}\}, \mathfrak{U}\}$ converges to any point p in X, then n is Cauchy.*

Proof: Let U be any relation in $\mathfrak{U}$. By lemma 23.15, there exists a relation W in $\mathfrak{U}$ such that $W^{-1} \circ W \subseteq U$. Since n converges to p, there is an α in D such that if $d > \alpha$, $n(d)$ is in $W[p]$, where again $W[p]$ is the neighborhood of p determined by the relation W. Let $e > \alpha$ be in the domain of n. Then $n(e)$ is also in $W[p]$. Thus $(p, n(d))$ and $(p, n(e))$ are both in W. Hence, $(n(d), p) \circ (p, n(e))$ is in $W \circ W^{-1}$. Thus $(n(d), n(e))$ is in U and so n is Cauchy. ▌

23.33 Definition. A uniform space $\{\{X, \mathfrak{I}_{\mathfrak{U}}\}, \mathfrak{U}\}$ is called *complete* if and only if every Cauchy net in $\{\{X, \mathfrak{I}_{\mathfrak{U}}\}, \mathfrak{U}\}$ converges to a point of $\{\{X, \mathfrak{I}_{\mathfrak{U}}\}, \mathfrak{U}\}$.

In example 22.12, two different models of the same topological space are given. Both models are uniform spaces with the uniform structures determined by the usual metrics. However, one model—the usual space of real numbers—is complete and the other model—the open interval $\{x \mid -1 < x < 1$ and x is real$\}$—is not complete. Thus completeness and Cauchyness, like uniform continuity, depend on a particular uniform structure and are not in general determined by the topology.

23.34 Lemma. *If f is a uniformly continuous function from the uniform space $\{X, \mathfrak{U}\}$ into the uniform space $\{Y, \mathfrak{V}\}$ and if n is a Cauchy net in $\{X, \mathfrak{U}\}$, then $f \circ n$ is Cauchy in $\{Y, \mathfrak{V}\}$.*

Proof: Let V be any relation in $\mathcal{V}$. Since f is uniformly continuous, there is a relation U in $\mathcal{U}$ such that if (a, b) is in U, then $(f(a), f(b))$ is in V. Since n is Cauchy, there exists an element δ_0 in the domain of n such that if $\alpha > \delta_0$ and $\beta > \delta_0$, then (a_α, a_β) is in U. Hence, if $\alpha > \delta_0$ and $\beta > \delta_0$, then $(f(a_\alpha), f(a_\beta))$ is in V and $f \circ n$ is Cauchy. ∎

EXERCISE 5. If f is uniformly continuous from the uniform space $\{X, \mathcal{U}\}$ into the uniform space $\{Y, \mathcal{V}\}$ and if n is a net in $\{X, \mathcal{U}\}$ such that $f \circ n$ is Cauchy in $\{Y, \mathcal{V}\}$, then is n Cauchy in $\{X, \mathcal{U}\}$?

The necessary definitions and lemmas for the generalization of theorem 23.6 to Hausdorff uniform spaces have now been established.

23.35 Theorem. *If f is a uniformly continuous function from a dense uniform subspace $\{D, \mathcal{U}'\}$ of a uniform space $\{X, \mathcal{U}\}$ into a complete Hausdorff uniform space $\{Y, \mathcal{V}\}$, then f can be extended to a function, f^*, defined on all of X and uniformly continuous.*

Proof: A. For the definition of f^*, let x be any point in X. If x is in D, then let $f^*(x) = f(x)$. If x is in $\sim D$, the complement of D, then x is a limit point of D and so there is a net, n, in D which converges to x in X. By lemma 23.32, n is Cauchy. By lemma 23.34, then, $f \circ n$ is Cauchy in $\{Y, \mathcal{V}\}$. Since $\{Y, \mathcal{V}\}$ is complete, $f \circ n$ converges. Let $f \circ n$ converge to y. Define $f^*(x)$ to be y. Since $\{Y, \mathcal{V}\}$ is Hausdorff, $f \circ n$ determines y uniquely. Assume, however, that a net n' in D also converges to x in $\{X, \mathcal{U}\}$. As above, $f \circ n'$ determines its limit y' in $\{Y, \mathcal{V}\}$ uniquely. It must be shown that $y = y'$. Let V be any relation in $\mathcal{V}$, the uniform structure on Y. By the definition of a uniform structure, there exists a relation N in $\mathcal{V}$ such that $N \circ N \subseteq V$ and by lemma 23.15, there exists a relation M in $\mathcal{V}$ such that $M \circ M^{-1} \subseteq N$. Hence $(M \circ M^{-1}) \circ (M \circ M^{-1}) \subseteq V$ and so $(M \circ \Delta) \circ (M \circ M^{-1}) \subseteq V$, where Δ is the diagonal subset of M. However, $(M \circ \Delta) \circ (M \circ M^{-1}) = M \circ (M \circ M^{-1})$, so there is a relation M in $\mathcal{V}$ such that $M \circ (M \circ M^{-1}) \subseteq V$. Since f is uniformly continuous, there is a relation B in $\mathcal{U}$ such that if (a, b) is in B, $(f(a), f(b))$ is in M. Again by lemma 23.15, there is a relation C in $\mathcal{U}$ such that $C^{-1} \circ C \subseteq B$. Further, since n and n' both converge to x, there is a δ in the domain of n and a δ' in the domain of n' such that if $\alpha > \delta$ and $\alpha' > \delta'$, then $(n(\alpha), x)$ and $(n'(\alpha'), x)$ are both in C. Hence, $(n(\alpha), n'(\alpha'))$ is in $C^{-1} \circ C$ and so is in B. Hence $(f \circ n(\alpha), f \circ n'(\alpha'))$ is in M. Further, since $f \circ n$ converges to y and $f \circ n'$ converges to y', there exists δ_1 and δ_1' such that if $\alpha > \delta_1$ and $\alpha' > \delta_1'$, then $(f \circ n(\alpha), y)$ and $(f \circ n'(\alpha'), y')$ are in M. By definition of the direct ordering on the domains of nets, there exist δ_* such that $\delta_* > \delta$ and $\delta_* > \delta_1$ and δ_*' such that $\delta_*' > \delta'$ and $\delta_*' > \delta_1'$. Hence, if $\alpha > \delta_*$ and $\alpha' > \delta_*'$, then $(f \circ n(\alpha), y)$, $(f \circ n'(\alpha'), y')$ and $(f \circ n(\alpha), f \circ n'(\alpha'))$ will all be in M. Thus $(f \circ n'(\alpha'), y') \circ (f \circ n(\alpha), f \circ n'(\alpha')) \circ (y, f \circ n(\alpha))$ will be in $M \circ M \circ M^{-1}$ and so in V. Thus (y, y') is in V. Since V was any relation in Hausdorff $\mathcal{V}$, by lemma 23.14, $y = y'$ and hence f^* is a function.

B. f^* is uniformly continuous. Let V be any relation in $\mathcal{V}$. Since $\mathcal{V}$ is a uniform structure, there exists a relation W in $\mathcal{V}$ such that $W \circ W \subseteq V$ and by lemma 23.15, there exists a relation A in $\mathcal{V}$ such that $A^{-1} \circ A \subseteq W$. Hence, $(A^{-1} \circ A) \circ (A^{-1} \circ A) \subseteq W \circ W \subseteq V$. Since f is uniformly continuous on D, there exists a relation U^* in $\mathcal{U}$, such that if (d_1, d_2) is in U^* for d_1, d_2 in D, then $(f(d_1), f(d_2))$ is in A or (d_1, d_2) in $U^* \cap (D \times D)$ implies that $(f(d_1), f(d_2))$ is in A. This follows from theorem 23.23. As above, there exists a relation N in $\mathcal{U}$ such that $N \circ N \subseteq U^*$ and there exists also a relation M in $\mathcal{U}$ such that $M \circ M^{-1} \subseteq N$. Hence, $(M \circ M^{-1}) \circ (M \circ M^{-1}) \subseteq U^*$. Now, let α and β be any points of X such that (α, β) is in M. It will be shown that $(f^*(\alpha), f^*(\beta))$ is in V. There exist nets n and m in D such that n converges to α and m converges to β. Hence, there exists δ_0 in the domain of n and e_0 in the domain of m such that if $\delta > \delta_0$ and $e > e_0$, then $(\alpha, n(\delta))$ and $(\beta, m(e))$ are both in M, where, of course, $n(\delta)$ and $m(e)$ are in D. Further, by definition of $f^*(\alpha)$ and $f^*(\beta)$, there exist δ_1 in the domain of n and e_1 in the domain of m such that if $\delta > \delta_1$ and $e > e_1$, then $(f^*(\alpha), f \circ n(\delta))$ and $(f^*(\beta), f \circ m(e))$ are in A. By definition of nets, their domains are directly ordered; hence, there exists δ_2 such that $\delta_2 > \delta_1$ and $\delta_2 > \delta_0$ and there exists e_2 such that $e_2 > e_1$ and $e_2 > e_0$ in the domains of n and m, respectively. Hence if $\delta > \delta_2$ and if $e > e_2$, then $(\alpha, n(\delta))$, (α, β), $(\beta, m(e))$ will all be in M, and further, $(f^*(\alpha), f \circ n(\delta))$ and $(f^*(\beta), f \circ m(e))$ will be in A. This means that $(n(\delta), m(e))$ is in $M \circ M \circ M^{-1}$. $M \circ M \circ M^{-1} = M \circ \Delta \circ M \circ M^{-1}$, where Δ is the diagonal of $X \times X$. Hence, $M \circ M \circ M^{-1}$ is contained in $(M \circ M^{-1}) \circ (M \circ M^{-1})$. Hence, $M \circ M \circ M^{-1} \subseteq U^*$, by definition of M. Thus $(n(\delta), m(e))$ is in U^* and so $(f \circ n(\delta), f \circ m(e))$ is in A by the uniform continuity of f on $\{D, \mathcal{U}'\}$ and by the definition of U^* and A. Further, $(f^*(\alpha), f^*(\beta))$ is in $A^{-1} \circ A \circ A = (A^{-1} \circ A) \circ (\Delta \circ A) \subseteq (A^{-1} \circ A) \circ (A^{-1} \circ A) \subseteq V$. Hence, $(f^*(\alpha), f^*(\beta))$ is in V, if (α, β) is in M. Thus f^* is uniformly continuous on $\{X, \mathcal{U}\}$. ▮

Thus the pattern of the proof of theorem 23.6 has been reconstructed without the use of a metric and the analogous extension theorem for uniform spaces has been established.

Completeness for uniform spaces can also be defined in terms of filters.

23.36 Definition. A filter $\mathfrak{F}$ on a uniform space $\{X, \mathcal{U}\}$ is called *Cauchy* if and only if for every relation U^* in $\mathcal{U}$, there exists a set A in $\mathfrak{F}$ such that $A \times A \subseteq U^*$.

23.37 Theorem. *A uniform space $\{X, \mathcal{U}\}$ is complete if and only if every Cauchy filter converges.*

Proof: A. Let $\{X, \mathcal{U}\}$ be complete and let $\mathfrak{F}$ be a Cauchy filter on $\{X, \mathcal{U}\}$. By the choice axiom, a net η is defined with domain $\mathfrak{F}$ and range in $\bigcup \mathfrak{F}$ such that $\eta(F)$ is in F for F in $\mathfrak{F}$. Let U^* be any relation in $\mathfrak{U}$. Since $\mathfrak{F}$ is Cauchy, there is a set F in $\mathfrak{F}$ such that $F \times F \subseteq U^*$. Hence if $A \subseteq F$ and $B \subseteq F$, then $\eta(A) \in F$ and $\eta(B) \in F$. Therefore, $(\eta(A), \eta(B)) \in U^*$. Thus η is Cauchy and converges to, say, p. Now let N be any neighborhood of p in $\{X, \mathfrak{U}\}$. Since η converges to p, there is an element α in the domain of η such that if $\beta \geq \alpha$, $\eta(\beta) \in N$. N is defined by a relation W^* in $\mathfrak{U}$. $N = W^*[p]$. Now there exists a relation V^* in $\mathfrak{U}$ such that $V^* \circ V^* \subseteq W^*$. Since η converges to p, $p \in \overline{F}$ for every F in $\mathfrak{F}$. Further since $\mathfrak{F}$ is Cauchy there exists A in $\mathfrak{F}$ such that $A \times A \subseteq V^*$. Hence $A \cap V^*[p] \neq \emptyset$. Now let q be in $A \cap V^*[p]$ and let x be any point in A. $(q, x) \in A \times A$ and $(p, q) \in V^*$. Thus $(p, x) \in V^* \circ V^* \subseteq W^*$ and so $x \in W^*[p]$. Consequently, $A \subseteq W^*[p]$ and $\mathfrak{F}$ converges to p.

B. Conversely, let every Cauchy filter on $\{X, \mathfrak{U}\}$ converge and let η be any Cauchy net in $\{X, \mathfrak{U}\}$. Consider for each α in the domain of η the set $T_\alpha = \{\eta(\nu) \mid \nu \text{ is in the domain of } \eta \text{ and } \nu \geq \alpha\}$. $\{T_\alpha \mid \alpha \text{ is in the domain of } \eta\}$ is then the base of a filter, $\mathfrak{F}$, on X. Since η is Cauchy, for each relation W^* in $\mathfrak{U}$, there exists an element α^* in the domain of η such that $\mu \geq \alpha^*$ and $\nu \geq \alpha^*$ imply that $(\eta(\mu), \eta(\nu)) \in W^*$. Hence, if $\alpha \geq \alpha^*$, $T_\alpha \times T_\alpha \subseteq W^*$. Thus $\mathfrak{F}$ is Cauchy and converges to some point p of $\{X, \mathfrak{U}\}$. Now let $V^*[p]$ be any neighborhood of p in $\{X, \mathfrak{U}\}$, let ν be in the domain of η and let $\nu \geq \alpha^*$. Since $\mathfrak{F}$ converges to p, $V^*[p]$ contains a base element T_α of $\mathfrak{F}$. Hence, if $\nu \geq \alpha$, $\eta(\nu) \in V^*[p]$. So, η converges to p and $\{X, \mathfrak{U}\}$ is complete. ▮

Thus theorem 23.37 establishes an alternate definition for complete uniform spaces in terms of Cauchy filters.

EXERCISE 6. Prove that if $\mathfrak{F}_1$ and $\mathfrak{F}_2$ are filters on a uniform space $\{X, \mathfrak{U}\}$ and if $\mathfrak{F}_2$ is Cauchy and $\mathfrak{F}_1 \supseteq \mathfrak{F}_2$, then $\mathfrak{F}_1$ is Cauchy.

EXERCISE 7. Prove that if $\mathfrak{F}$ is a Cauchy filter on the uniform space $\{X, \mathfrak{U}_1\}$, if $\mathfrak{U}_2$ is a uniform structure for X and if $\mathfrak{U}_2 \subseteq \mathfrak{U}_1$, then $\mathfrak{F}$ is a Cauchy filter on the uniform space $\{X, \mathfrak{U}_2\}$.

EXERCISE 8. Let f be a uniformly continuous function from a uniform space $\{X, \mathfrak{U}\}$ onto a uniform space $\{Y, \mathfrak{V}\}$. Let $\mathfrak{F}$ be a Cauchy filter on $\{X, \mathfrak{U}\}$. Prove that $f^\#[\mathfrak{F}]$, the set of images of sets in $\mathfrak{F}$ assigned by f, is a Cauchy filter on $\{Y, \mathfrak{V}\}$, the range space.

EXERCISE 9. Give an example of a Cauchy filter whose image assigned by a continuous function is not Cauchy.

A Metrization Theorem and a Completion Theorem

The next goal is the generalization of two theorems: theorem 20.16 (Urysohn's imbedding theorem)—every second countable, normal space is metrizable; and theorem 22.22—every metric space can be imbedded in a complete metric space by a function which is isometric. Several definitions, lemmas and theorems will be needed.

23.38 Definition. A *completion* of a uniform space $\{X, \mathfrak{U}\}$ is a complete uniform space $\{X^*, \mathfrak{U}^*\}$ into which $\{X, \mathfrak{U}\}$ can be mapped by a 1:1 function f which along with f^{-1} is uniformly continuous, i.e., which is iso-uniform, and whose range is dense in $\{X^*, \mathfrak{U}^*\}$. This definition amounts to saying that a completion of $\{X, \mathfrak{U}\}$ is a complete uniform space $\{X^*, \mathfrak{U}^*\}$ in which $\{X, \mathfrak{U}\}$ is a dense subspace and $\mathfrak{U}$ is the relative uniform structure.

23.39 Theorem. *Any Hausdorff uniform space has at most one completion except for iso-uniform images.*

Proof: Let $\{X, \mathfrak{U}\}$ be a Hausdorff uniform space. Let X^* and Y^* denote completions of X. $X \subseteq X^*$ and $X \subseteq Y^*$ and X is dense in both X^* and Y^*. The identity function $i: X \to X$ is uniformly continuous from $\{X, \mathfrak{U}\}$ onto $\{X, \mathfrak{U}\}$, and hence by theorem 23.35 can be extended to a uniformly continuous function, f, from X^* into Y^*. Similarly, $i^{-1}: X \to X$ can be extended to a uniformly continuous function, g, from Y^* into X^*. Now, $g^{-1} \circ f$ is a uniformly continuous function from X^* into itself which is an extension of i. By theorem 16.24, there is just one extension of i to all of X^*; hence, $g^{-1} \circ f$ must be the identity of X^* onto X^*. Similarly, $f^{-1} \circ g$ is the identity of Y^* onto Y^*. This means that f and g are onto. Also f is 1:1; for, let $f(a) = f(b)$. Then $g^{-1}(f(a)) = g^{-1}(f(b))$ and since $g^{-1} \circ f$ is the identity of X onto X, $a = b$. Since f is 1:1 and onto, it is the desired function and X^* and Y^* are essentially the same uniform space. ∎

23.40 Theorem. *Any closed subspace of a complete uniform space together with the relative uniformity yields a complete uniform space.*

Proof: Let F be a closed subspace of a complete uniform space, $\{X, \mathfrak{U}\}$. Let (a_d) be a Cauchy net in $\{F, \mathfrak{U} \mid F\}$. By definition of the relative uniform structure and topology, (a_d) is a Cauchy net in $\{X, \mathfrak{U}\}$. Since $\{X, \mathfrak{U}\}$ is complete, (a_d) converges to b, say, in $\{X, \mathfrak{U}\}$. By corollary 7.24, b is in F. Thus F is complete. ∎

23.41 Theorem. *Every uniform product space $\{X^*, \mathfrak{U}_P\}$ of complete uniform spaces is a complete uniform space, where $\mathfrak{U}_P$ is the product uniformity.*

Proof: By theorem 23.21, $\{X^*, \mathfrak{U}_P\}$ is a uniform space. Let $X^* = \prod_\nu X_\nu$ and let (a_d) be a Cauchy net in this product space X^*. If p_ν denotes the projection function from X^* onto X_ν, then the symbol $(p_\nu(a_y))$ denotes the net in X_ν of ν-th coordinates of the a_d. Let $\mathfrak{U}_\nu$ denote the uniformity on X_ν and for each ν, let U_ν be a relation in $\mathfrak{U}_\nu$. Define $U^* = \{(x^*, y^*) \mid (x_\nu, y_\nu)$ is in U_ν, where x_ν and y_ν are the ν-th coordinates of x^* and y^*, respectively$\}$. By theorem 23.21, U^* is a relation in the product uniformity $\mathfrak{U}_P$ on X^*. Since (a_d) is a Cauchy net in X^*, there exists a d^* in the domain of the net such that if $d_1 \geq d^*$ and if $d_2 \geq d^*$, then the ordered pair (a_{d_1}, a_{d_2}) is in U^*. This means that the ordered pair $(p_\nu(a_{d_1}), p_\nu(a_{d_2}))$ is in U_ν, by definition of U^*. Hence the net $(p_\nu(a_d))$ in X_ν is Cauchy. Since X_ν is complete, the net $(p_\nu(a_d))$ converges to α_ν, say, in X_ν. Let α^* denote the point of X^* whose ν-th coordinate is α_ν. By theorem 12.9, the net (a_d) converges to α^* and so $\{X^*, \mathcal{U}_P\}$ is complete. ∎

A completion for a Hausdorff uniform space will be established by imbedding the space iso-uniformly into a uniform product of complete Hausdorff uniform spaces. However, first it will be established that any uniform structure can be described "numerically" in a certain sense and the metrization theorem will follow.

Let $\{X, \mathfrak{I}_\mathcal{U}\}$ be a uniformizable space. The proof of theorem 23.18 (Pontrjagin-Kakutani-Weil) established that for any sequence $(V_0, V_1, \ldots, V_n, \ldots)$ of symmetric relations in $\mathcal{U}$ such that $V_{n+1} \circ V_{n+1} \subseteq V_n$, there could be defined a collection $\{U_t\}$ of relations, one for each dyadic rational in [0, 1], such that: (1) U_t is in the uniform structure for $t \neq 0$ and $U_0 = \Delta$, and (2) for $t_1 \leq t_2$, $U_{t_1} \subseteq U_{t_2}$. A function f from X into [0, 1] was defined in terms of the relations U_t and a particular point p. At the end of the proof in part D it was established that if (a, b) is in V_n, then $|f(a) - f(b)| \leq 1/2^{n-1}$. Thus f is uniformly continuous relative to $\mathcal{U}$. Another similar function given by Weil will now be defined for the sequence $(V_0, V_1, \ldots, V_n, \ldots)$ using the same associated relations, U_t, referred to above and defined in the proof of theorem 23.18.

23.42 Definition. Let $V_0, V_1, \ldots, V_n, \ldots$ be symmetric relations in an admissible uniform structure $\mathcal{U}$ on a space X such that $V_{n+1} \circ V_{n+1} \subseteq V_n$. For each dyadic rational t in [0, 1], let U_t be defined as in the proof of theorem 23.18. For (x, y) in $X \times X$, define $A_{(x,y)} = \{t \mid t$ is negative or (x, y) is not in $U_t \circ U_t^{-1}\}$. Define $F((x, y)) = \text{l.u.b. } A_{(x,y)}$.

23.43 Lemma. *F is a uniformly continuous function from $\{X \times X, \mathcal{U}_P\}$ into* [0, 1]. $F((x, y)) = F((y, x))$ *and* $F((x, x)) = 0$.

Proof: A. If $y = x$, then (x, y) is in the diagonal Δ and hence (x, y) is in $U_0 \circ U_0^{-1}$. Since $U_{t_1} \circ U_{t_1}^{-1} \subseteq U_{t_2} \circ U_{t_2}^{-1}$, if $t_1 \leq t_2$, (x, y) is in every relation $U_t \circ U_t^{-1}$. Therefore, $A_{(x,y)} =$ the set of negative reals and $F((x, y)) = 0$.

B. Since $U_t \circ U_t^{-1}$ is symmetric, (x, y) in $U_t \circ U_t^{-1}$ implies that (y, x) is in $U_t \circ U_t^{-1}$.

C. The proof here is again analogous to the part of the proof of theorem 23.18 relating to the continuity of the function f mentioned above. Let $\epsilon > 0$ and choose a natural number m such that $1/2^{m-1} < \epsilon$. Consider now the uniformity on $X \times X$. $W^* = \{((p, q), (r, s)) \mid (p, r) \in V_m \text{ and } (q, s) \in V_m\}$ is a relation in the product uniformity $\mathcal{U}_p$ on $X \times X$. It will be shown that if $((p, q), (r, s)) \in W^*$, $|F((p, q)) - F((r, s))| < \epsilon$ and, hence, that F is uniformly continuous. So let $((p, q), (r, s)) \in W^*$. For some $k = 0, \ldots, 2^m$, $(k - 1)/2^m <$

$F((p, q)) \leq k/2^m$. Let $F((p, q)) < k/2^m$. Then $(p, q) \in U_{k/2^m} \circ U_{k/2^m}^{-1}$. Now since $(p, r) \in V_m$ and $(q, s) \in V_m$, $(r, s) \in V_m \circ U_{k/2^m} \circ U_{k/2^m}^{-1} \circ V_m^{-1} = (V_m \circ U_{k/2^m}) \circ (V_m \circ U_{k/2^m})^{-1}$. However, by the proof of theorem 23.18, $V_m \circ U_{k/2^m} \subseteq U_{(k+1)/2^m}$. Therefore, $(r, s) \in U_{(k+1)/2^m} \circ U_{(k+1)/2^m}^{-1}$ and $F((r, s)) \leq (k + 1)/2^m$. This means that $F((r, s)) - F((p, q)) < (k + 1)/2^m - (k - 1)/2^m = 1/2^{m-1}$. If $F((p, q)) = k/2^m$, then $F((p, q)) < (k + 1)/2^m$ and it follows analogously that $F((r, s)) \leq (k + 2)/2^m$. Hence, $F((r, s)) - F((p, q)) \leq 1/2^{m-1}$. Thus in all cases, $F((r, s)) - F((p, q)) < \epsilon$. By the exact same procedure it follows that $F((p, q)) - F((r, s)) < \epsilon$. Hence, if $((p, q), (r, s)) \in W^*$, $|F((p, q)) - F((r, s))| < \epsilon$ and F is uniformly continuous. ▮

The previous theorem leads to a very useful procedure mentioned previously: the procedure for describing the sets in a uniform structure "numerically."

23.44 Definition. Let X be any set; a *pseudo-metric* on X is a function d from $X \times X$ into the non-negative reals such that for every x, y, p in X, (1) $d(x, x) = 0$, (2) $d(x, y) = d(y, x)$, and (3) $d(x, p) + d(p, y) \geq d(x, y)$.

EXERCISE 10. Give an example of a pseudo-metric on a set X which is not a metric on X.

EXERCISE 11. Let X be any set and let f be any function from X into E^1, the usual space of reals. Prove that $d(x, y) = |f(x) - f(y)|$ is a pseudo-metric on X.

23.45 Lemma. *Let d denote a pseudo-metric on a non-empty set X. The collection of all relations on X which contain any relation $R_\epsilon = \{(x, y) \mid d(x, y) < \epsilon$ for $0 < \epsilon < 1\}$ is a uniform structure for X.*

Proof: Exercise.

NOTATION: Let d be a pseudo-metric on a set X. Denote by $\mathfrak{U}_d$ the uniform structure determined in lemma 23.45 by the pseudo-metric d.

23.46 Theorem. *If $(V_0, V_1, \ldots, V_n, \ldots)$ is a sequence of symmetric relations on a set X such that $V_{n+1} \circ V_{n+1} \subseteq V_n$ for $n = 0, 1, 2, \ldots$, then there is a pseudo-metric, d, on X such that for each $\delta > 0$, there is a V_n such that $V_n \subseteq \{(x, y) \mid d(x, y) < \delta\}$ and for every relation V_m, there is an $\epsilon > 0$ such that $\{(x, y) \mid d(x, y) < \epsilon\} \subseteq V_m$. Further, $0 \leq d(x, y) \leq 1$ for all (x, y) in $X \times X$.*

Proof: A. Let $d(p, q) = \text{l.u.b.}_{r \in X} |F(p, r) - F(r, q)|$, where F is the function defined in definition 23.42. By the properties of the absolute value function and by lemma 23.43, d is a pseudo-metric and $0 \leq d(x, y) \leq 1$.

B. Further, at the end of the proof of lemma 23.43, it was established that if (p, r) and (q, s) are in V_m, then $|F(p, q) - F(r, s)| \leq 1/2^{m-1}$. Now, for every q, (q, q) is in V_m, hence for $s = q$, if (p, r) is in V_m, $|F(p, q) - F(r, q)| \leq 1/2^{m-1}$. Thus if $1/2^{m-1} < \epsilon$, for (p, r) in V_m, $d(p, r) < \epsilon$. This establishes that $V_m \subseteq \{(x, y) \mid d(x, y) < \epsilon\}$.

C. Conversely, let $d(p, q) < 1/2^{m+1}$. Then, by definition of $d(p, q)$, $|F(p, r) - F(r, q)| < 1/2^{m+1}$ for all r, including $r = q$. Hence $|F(p, q)| < 1/2^{m+1}$. This means that (p, q) is in $U_{1/2^{m+1}} \circ U_{1/2^{m+1}} = V_{m+1} \circ V_{m+1}$. Since $V_{m+1} \circ V_{m+1} \subseteq V_m$, (p, q) is in V_m. Thus $\{(p, q) \mid d(p, q) < 1/2^{m+1}\} \subseteq V_m$. ∎

23.47 Theorem. *Every uniform structure on a set X can be determined by a set of pseudo-metrics.*

Proof: Let $\mathcal{U}$ be any uniform structure on a set X. Let N be any relation in $\mathcal{U}$. It was established in the proof of theorem 23.18, part A, that a sequence $(V_0, V_1, \ldots, V_n, \ldots)$ of symmetric relations could be chosen so that (1) $V_0 \subseteq N$ and (2) $V_{n+1} \circ V_{n+1} \subseteq V_n$ for $n = 0, 1, 2, \ldots$. Thus there exists a family $\{\Sigma_\nu\}$ of sequences $(V_0^\nu, V_1^\nu, \ldots, V_n^\nu, \ldots)$ of symmetric relations such that for every ν, $V_{n+1}^\nu \circ V_{n+1}^\nu \subseteq V_n^\nu$ for $n = 0, 1, 2, \ldots$, with the property that $\bigcup_\nu \Sigma_\nu$ is a base for the filter $\mathcal{U}$. By theorem 23.46, for each sequence Σ_ν a pseudo-metric d_ν can be defined such that the collection of all relations $R_{d_\nu}^\epsilon = \{(x, y) \mid d_\nu(x, y) < \epsilon$ for ϵ positive and real$\}$ is equivalent to the sequence $(V_0^\nu, V_1^\nu, \ldots, V_n^\nu, \ldots)$ in the sense that any filter which contains $\{V_0^\nu, V_1^\nu, \ldots, V_n^\nu, \ldots\}$ must contain all relations $R_{d_\nu}^\epsilon$, and conversely. Thus the collection $\{R_{d_\nu}^\epsilon\}$ for all positive, real ϵ and all ν constitutes a base for $\mathcal{U}$. ∎

EXERCISE 12. Prove that a function f from a uniform space $\{X, \mathcal{U}\}$ into the real number space, E^1, is uniformly continuous if and only if the uniform structure determined by the pseudo-metric $d(x, y) = |f(x) - f(y)|$ is contained in the original structure $\mathcal{U}$. See lemma 23.45.

23.48 Definition. A uniform structure, $\mathcal{U}$, will also be called (*pseudo*-) *metrizable* if and only if $\mathcal{U}$ can be determined as in the previous theorem by one (pseudo-) metric.

On the road to the completion theorem lies the metrization theorem. If the uniformity $\mathcal{U}$ is given the additional property that one of the families, Σ_ν, described in the last theorem, alone, constitutes a base for $\mathcal{U}$ then the associated pseudo-metric, d_ν, alone determines $\mathcal{U}$.

23.49 Theorem. *A uniformity, $\mathcal{U}$, is pseudo-metrizable if and only if the uniformity $\mathcal{U}$ has a countable base.*

Proof: A. Let the relations, $U_1, U_2, \ldots, U_n, \ldots$ constitute a countable base for $\mathcal{U}$. Then the relations $W_1 = U_1$, $W_2 = U_1 \cap U_2, \ldots, W_n =$

$U_1 \cap \cdots \cap U_n, \ldots$ constitute a base for $\mathfrak{U}$. Also, $W_1 \supseteq W_2 \supseteq \cdots \supseteq W_n \supseteq \cdots$. By lemma 23.15, W_1 contains a symmetric relation V_1 in $\mathfrak{U}$. Again by lemma 23.15, $V_1 \cap W_2$ contains a symmetric relation V_2 in $\mathfrak{U}$ such that $V_2 \circ V_2 \subseteq V_1 \cap W_1$. Assume that symmetric relations $V_1, V_2, \ldots, V_n$ have been defined such that V_i is in $\mathfrak{U}$ and $V_{i+1} \circ V_{i+1} \subseteq V_i \cap W_{i+1}$ for $i = 1, \ldots, n-1$. Again by lemma 23.15, $V_n \cap W_{n+1}$ contains a symmetric relation V_{n+1} from $\mathfrak{U}$ such that $V_{n+1} \circ V_{n+1} \subseteq V_n \cap W_{n+1}$. Thus an infinite sequence $V_1, V_2, \ldots, V_n, \ldots$ of relations in $\mathfrak{U}$ has been defined such that $V_{n+1} \circ V_{n+1} \subseteq V_n$. Further, let U be any relation in $\mathfrak{U}$. Since $U_1, U_2, \ldots, U_n, \ldots$ constitute a base for $\mathfrak{U}$, $U \supseteq U_n$, say. Hence, $U \supseteq W_n$ and so $U \supseteq V_n$. Thus the relations $V_1, V_2, \ldots, V_n, \ldots$ constitute a base for $\mathfrak{U}$. By theorem 23.46, there is a pseudo-metric, d, such that the relations, $R_\epsilon = \{(x, y) \mid d(x, y) < \epsilon$ for ϵ positive and real$\}$ also constitute a base for $\mathfrak{U}$.

B. If the uniform structure $\mathfrak{U}$ is pseudo-metrizable with pseudo-metric d, then the relations $R_{1/n} = \{(x, y) \mid d(x, y) < 1/n$ for n a natural number$\}$ constitute a countable base for $\mathfrak{U}$. ▮

23.50 Corollary. *A Hausdorff uniformity $\mathfrak{U}$ is metrizable if and only if $\mathfrak{U}$ has a countable base.*

Proof: A. If $\mathfrak{U}$ is metrizable, then a metric ρ determines $\mathfrak{U}$ through the base of all relations $R_\epsilon = \{(x, y) \mid \rho(x, y) < \epsilon$ for ϵ positive and real$\}$. Hence the collection of relations $R_{1/n} = \{(x, y) \mid \rho(x, y) < 1/n$ for n a natural number$\}$ is a countable base.

B. If $\mathfrak{U}$ has a countable base, by theorem 23.49, $\mathfrak{U}$ is pseudo-metrizable. Let (x, y) be in $X \times X$ and let $x \neq y$. Then since $\{X, \mathfrak{J}_\mathfrak{U}\}$ is Hausdorff, by lemma 23.14, there is a relation U in $\mathfrak{U}$ such that (x, y) is not in U. Hence there is an $\epsilon > 0$ such that $d(x, y) > \epsilon$, where d is the chosen pseudo-metric. Thus for $x \neq y$, $d(x, y) \neq 0$ and d is a metric. ▮

The completion theorem now follows.

23.51 Theorem. *Any Hausdorff uniform space $\{X, \mathfrak{U}\}$ has a completion.*

Proof: A. First a product space is defined. In the proof of theorem 23.47, it was established that a family $\{\Sigma_\nu\}$ of sequences $(V_0^\nu, V_1^\nu, \ldots, V_n^\nu, \ldots)$ for ν in some indexing set $\mathfrak{A}$ and $n = 0, 1, 2, \ldots$, can be chosen such that $\bigcup_\nu \Sigma_\nu$ is a base for $\mathfrak{U}$, each V_n^ν is symmetric and $V_{n+1}^\nu \circ V_{n+1}^\nu \subseteq V_n^\nu$. Now let C denote the metric space of continuous functions from X into the unit interval $[0, 1]$ with metric $\sigma(f, g) = \text{l.u.b.}_{x \in X} |f(x) - g(x)|$. Since the usual space E^1 of real numbers is a complete metric space, by theorem 22.15, $[0, 1]$ is a complete metric space. By theorems 21.20, 22.15 and 22.21, C is a complete metric space. Next, consider the product space $\prod_{\nu \in \mathfrak{A}} Y_\nu$, where $Y_\nu = C$ for each ν in the indexing set $\mathfrak{A}$ defined above. By theorem 23.41, $\{\prod_{\nu \in \mathfrak{A}} Y_\nu, \mathfrak{V}_P\}$, for $\mathfrak{V}_P$

the product uniformity, is a complete uniform space and by theorem 16.18, $\prod_{\nu \in \mathfrak{A}} Y_\nu$ is Hausdorff.

B. Next, a function Ψ from $\{X, \mathfrak{U}\}$ into $\{\prod_{\nu \in \mathfrak{A}} Y_\nu, \mathfrak{V}_P\}$ is defined. Let a be any point in X. $\Psi(a)$ will be identified through its coordinates in $\prod_{\nu \in \mathfrak{A}} Y_\nu$. Each ν in $\mathfrak{A}$ corresponds to a sequence $(V_0^\nu, V_1^\nu, \ldots, V_n^\nu, \ldots)$ of symmetric relations in $\mathfrak{U}$ such that $V_{n+1}^\nu \circ V_{n+1}^\nu \subseteq V_n^\nu$. By theorem 23.46, for each ν in $\mathfrak{A}$, a pseudo-metric, d_ν, can be chosen such that $0 \leq d_\nu(x, y) \leq 1$ for all x, y in X; $V_n^\nu \subseteq \{(x, y) \mid d_\nu(x, y) \leq 1/2^{n-1}\}$ and $\{(x, y) \mid d_\nu(x, y) < 1/2^{n+1}\} \subseteq V_n^\nu$. $\Psi(a)$ is defined to be the point whose ν-th coordinate is the function $x \to d_\nu(a, x)$. Since the ν-th coordinate is a point in $Y_\nu = C$, it must be a continuous function from X into $[0, 1]$. $x \to d_\nu(a, x)$ is continuous, since $d_\nu(a, x) \leq d_\nu(a, y) + d_\nu(y, x)$ and $d_\nu(a, y) \leq d_\nu(a, x) + d_\nu(x, y)$. For, then, $|d_\nu(a, x) - d_\nu(a, y)| \leq d_\nu(x, y)$. Hence, for ϵ positive and real, choose a natural number n such that $1/2^{n-1} < \epsilon$, then, if (x, y) is in V_n^ν, $d_\nu(x, y) \leq 1/2^{n-1} < \epsilon$ and $|d_\nu(a, x) - d_\nu(a, y)| < \epsilon$. Thus, $x \to d_\nu(a, x)$ is uniformly continuous on $\{X, \mathfrak{U}\}$. Again by theorem 23.46, the range of d_ν is contained in $[0, 1]$.

C. Ψ is 1:1. Let a and b denote distinct points in X. Since X is Hausdorff and since $\bigcup_\nu \Sigma_\nu$, defined in part A, is a base for $\mathfrak{U}$, by lemma 23.14, there is a ν in the indexing set $\mathfrak{A}$ and a natural number n such that (a, b) is not in V_n^ν. Hence, by the proof of theorem 23.46, $d_\nu(a, b) \geq 1/2^{n+1}$. Now, the ν-th coordinate of $\Psi(a)$ is the function $x \to d_\nu(a, x)$, which, of course, assigns to a the image 0; while the ν-th coordinate of $\Psi(b)$ is $x \to d_\nu(b, x)$ and assigns to a an image $\geq 1/2^{n+1}$. Thus, $\Psi(a) \neq \Psi(b)$ and Ψ is 1:1.

D. Ψ^{-1} is uniformly continuous. For let U be any relation in $\mathfrak{U}$. There is a μ in $\mathfrak{A}$ and a natural number n such that $V_n^\mu \subseteq U$ since again $\bigcup_\nu \Sigma_\nu$ is a base for $\mathfrak{U}$. Consider, now, the relation U^* in the relative product uniform structure from $\prod_\nu Y_\nu$ such that $U^* = \{(\alpha^*, \beta^*) \text{ in } \Psi[X] \times \Psi[X] \mid \sigma(\alpha_\mu, \beta_\mu) < 1/2^{n+1}\}$, where α_μ and β_μ are the μ-th coordinates of $\alpha^* = \Psi(a)$ and $\beta^* = \Psi(b)$, respectively, and σ is the metric on $Y_\mu = C$. α_μ is the function $x \to d_\mu(a, x)$ and β_μ is $x \to d_\mu(b, x)$ and $\sigma(\alpha_\mu, \beta_\mu) = \text{l.u.b.}_{x \in X} |d_u(a, x) - d_\mu(b, x)|$. Hence, if (α^*, β^*) is in U^*, $|d_\mu(a, x) - d_u(b, x)| < 1/2^{n+1}$ for all x in X. Hence if $x = b$, for (α^*, β^*) in U^*, $|d_\mu(a, b) - d_\mu(b, b)| < 1/2^{n+1}$, and so, $d_\mu(a, b) < 1/2^{n+1}$. This implies, by the proof of theorem 23.46, as mentioned above, that (a, b) is in V_n^μ. Thus if (α^*, β^*) is in U^*, $(\Psi^{-1}(\alpha^*), \Psi^{-1}(\beta^*))$ is in $V_n^\mu \subseteq U$ and so Ψ^{-1} is uniformly continuous on $\Psi[X]$ with the relative product uniformity.

E. Ψ is uniformly continuous on $\{X, \mathfrak{U}\}$. Let U^*, now, denote any basic relation in the relative, product, uniform structure on $\Psi[X]$. $U^* = \{(\alpha^*, \beta^*) \text{ in } \Psi[X] \times \Psi[X] \mid \sigma(\alpha_{\nu_i}, \beta_{\nu_i}) < \epsilon_i$ for ϵ_i positive and real and for $i = 1, 2, \ldots, k\}$, where α_{ν_i} and β_{ν_i} are the ν_i-th coordinates of α^* and β^*. $\sigma(\alpha_{\nu_i}, \beta_{\nu_i}) = \text{l.u.b.}_{x \in X} |d_{\nu_i}(a, x) - d_{\nu_i}(b, x)|$, where $\Psi(a) = \alpha^*$ and $\Psi(b) = \beta^*$. Let $1/2^n <$ minimum $\{\epsilon_1, \epsilon_2, \ldots, \epsilon_k\}$ and let V in $X \times X$ be a relation of $\mathfrak{U}$ which is contained in $V_{n+1}^{\nu_1} \cap V_{n+1}^{\nu_2} \cap \cdots \cap V_{n+1}^{\nu_k}$. If (a, b) is in V, then $d_{\nu_i}(a, b) \leq 1/2^n$ for $i = 1, 2, \ldots, k$, by theorem 23.46. Now, for any x in X,

$d_{\nu_i}(a, x) \leq d_{\nu_i}(a, b) + d_{\nu_i}(b, x)$ and $d_{\nu_i}(b, x) \leq d_{\nu_i}(b, a) + d_{\nu_i}(a, x)$ for $i = 1, \ldots, k$, since each d_{ν_i} is a pseudo-metric. Therefore, $|d_{\nu_i}(a, x) - d_{\nu_i}(b, x)| \leq d_{\nu_i}(a, b)$ and $\sigma(\alpha_{\nu_i}, \beta_{\nu_i}) \leq 1/2^n < \epsilon_i$ for $i = 1, \ldots, k$. Thus if (a, b) is in V, $(\Psi(a), \Psi(b))$ is in U^* and so Ψ is uniformly continuous on $\{X, \mathcal{U}\}$.

Since $\{\prod_{\nu\in\mathfrak{A}} Y_\nu, \mathcal{V}_P\}$, where $Y_\nu = C$, is a complete, Hausdorff, uniform space, the uniform subspace determined by $\overline{\Psi[X]}$ is a complete, Hausdorff, uniform space by theorem 23.40. In addition, $\Psi[X]$, of course, is dense in $\overline{\Psi[X]}$ and since Ψ is iso-uniform $\{\overline{\Psi[X]}, \mathcal{V}'_P\}$, where $\mathcal{V}'_P$ is the relative product uniformity, is by definition 23.38, the unique completion of $\{X, \mathcal{U}\}$. ∎

Thus, it has been established that every Hausdorff uniform space for which the given uniformity has a countable base is metrizable and that every Hausdorff uniform space can be imbedded in a unique complete uniform space in a way that "preserves" the uniform structure, and so the analogues for uniformizable and uniform spaces of theorems 20.16 and 22.22 have been obtained.

Uniform Convergence

A generalized version of uniform convergence will now be introduced and will serve to close the discussion on uniform spaces. Definitions 21.21 and 21.22 introduce the concept of "uniform convergence" related to a function space $B_\rho(X, Y)$, where ρ is a metric for Y. These latter definitions will now be generalized to the case where Y is a uniformizable space.

NOTATION: Let Y be a uniformizable space with uniform structure $\mathcal{U}$ and topology $\mathfrak{I}_{\mathcal{U}}$. Let X be a set and let Y^X be the set of all functions with domain X whose range is in Y. For each U in $\mathcal{U}$, define $U^* = \{(f, g) \mid f$ and g are in Y^X and $(f(x), g(x))$ is in U for all x in $X\}$. $\mathcal{U}^*$ will denote the collection of all relations on Y^X which contain such a relation, U^*. It will be shown that $\mathcal{U}^*$ is a uniform structure for Y^X.

23.52 Lemma. *The collection $\mathcal{U}^*$ defined above constitutes a uniform structure for Y^X.*

Proof: A. $\mathcal{U}^*$ is a filter on $Y^X \times Y^X$. (a) First, $\mathcal{U}^*$ is not empty since $\mathcal{U}^*$ contains $Y^X \times Y^X$. (b) Next, if $\tilde{G}_1 \supseteq \tilde{G}_2$ and $\tilde{G}_2$ belongs to $\mathcal{U}^*$, then $\tilde{G}_2$ contains some set U^*, by definition of $\mathcal{U}^*$. Hence $\tilde{G}_1 \supseteq U^*$ and so $\tilde{G}_1$ belongs to $\mathcal{U}^*$. (c) Let $\tilde{G}_1$ and $\tilde{G}_2$ belong to $\mathcal{U}^*$. Consider $\tilde{G}_1 \cap \tilde{G}_2$. First $\tilde{G}_1 \supseteq U_1^*$ and $\tilde{G}_2 \supseteq U_2^*$ by definition of $\mathcal{U}^*$, and so $\tilde{G}_1 \cap \tilde{G}_2 \supseteq U_1^* \cap U_2^*$. Let U_1 and U_2 be relations in $\mathcal{U}$ corresponding to U_1^* and U_2^* as defined above. $U_1 \cap U_2$ belongs to $\mathcal{U}$ since $\mathcal{U}$ is a uniformity on Y. Hence $(U_1 \cap U_2)^*$ is in $\mathcal{U}^*$. Now, $(U_1 \cap U_2)^* = \{(f, g) \mid (f(x), g(x))$ is in $U_1 \cap U_2$ for all x in $X\}$. Hence if (f, g) is in $(U_1 \cap U_2)^*$, $(f(x), g(x))$ is in U_1 for all x and $(f(x), g(x))$ is in U_2 for all x. Hence (f, g) is in $U_1^* \cap U_2^*$ and $(U_1 \cap U_2)^* \subseteq U_1^* \cap U_2^*$. By definition of $\mathcal{U}^*$, $\tilde{G}_1 \cap \tilde{G}_2$ belongs to $\mathcal{U}^*$. (d) The null set does not belong to $\mathfrak{U}^*$ since any $\tilde{G}$ in $\mathfrak{U}^*$ must contain a relation $U^* = \{(f, g) \mid (f(x), g(x))$ is in U for all x in X and for some U in $\mathfrak{U}\}$. Hence $U^* \supseteq \{(f, g) \mid f = g\}$ since U contains the diagonal in $Y \times Y$. Thus $\tilde{G}$ is not empty.

B. $\mathfrak{U}^*$ has the additional properties of a uniform structure. (a) It was shown in A, part (d), that every relation in $\mathfrak{U}^*$ contains the diagonal Δ of $Y^X \times Y^X$. (b) Let $\tilde{G}$ be any relation in $\mathfrak{U}^*$, let $\tilde{G} \supseteq U^*$ and let U denote a defining relation in $\mathfrak{U}$ for U^*. $(U^*)^{-1} = \{(g, f) \mid (f(x), g(x))$ is in U for all x in $X\}$. Hence $(U^*)^{-1} = \{(g, f) \mid (g(x), f(x))$ is in U^{-1} for all x in $X\}$. Since $\mathfrak{U}$ is a uniform structure, U^{-1} is in $\mathfrak{U}$ and so $(U^*)^{-1} = (U^{-1})^*$. Thus $(U^*)^{-1}$ is in $\mathfrak{U}^*$. (c) Again let $\tilde{G}$ be any relation in $\mathfrak{U}^*$, let $\tilde{G} \supseteq U^*$ and let U denote a defining relation in $\mathfrak{U}$ for U^*. There exists a relation W in $\mathfrak{U}$ such that $W \circ W \subseteq U$. Consider $W^* \circ W^*$. $W^* \circ W^* = \{(f, h) \mid$ there exists g in Y^X such that $(f(x), g(x))$ and $(g(x), h(x))$ are in W for all x in $X\}$. Thus $W^* \circ W^* \subseteq \{(f, h) \mid (f(x), h(x))$ is in $W \circ W$ for all x in $X\}$. Hence $W^* \circ W^* \subseteq (W \circ W)^*$. Further, since $W \circ W \subseteq U$, $(W \circ W)^* \subseteq U^*$ and so $W^* \circ W^* \subseteq U^*$. Thus it has been established that the collection $\mathfrak{U}^*$ of relations on Y^X is a uniform structure for Y^X. ▮

23.53 Definition. If X is any set and Y is a uniformizable space with uniform structure $\mathfrak{U}$ and topology $\mathfrak{I}_{\mathfrak{U}}$, then the uniform structure $\mathfrak{U}^*$ induced on Y^X by $\mathfrak{U}$, as described in lemma 23.52, defines the topology for Y^X called the *topology of uniform convergence.*

23.54 Theorem. *If X is an infinite set and Y is a uniformizable space, then the topology of uniform convergence for Y^X contains the product topology for Y^X and, except in the special case that Y has the trivial topology, is unequal to it.*

Proof: A. Let B be any base element in the product topology for Y^X. $B = \prod_{x \in X} G_x$, where $G_x = Y$ for $x \neq \alpha_1, \alpha_2, \ldots, \alpha_k$. Let f be any element in B, i.e., $f(x)$ is in G_x for every x in X. The factors $G_{\alpha_1}, G_{\alpha_2}, \ldots, G_{\alpha_k}$ of B are all open sets in Y; hence, $f(\alpha_i)$, for $i = 1, 2, \ldots, k$, is contained in some neighborhood $U_i[f(\alpha_i)]$ in G_{α_i}, where U_i denotes a relation in the uniformity $\mathfrak{U}$ on Y and $U_i[f(\alpha_i)]$ denotes again the set of images of $f(\alpha_i)$ assigned by U_i. Since $\mathfrak{U}$ is a uniform structure on Y, $U_1 \cap U_2 \cap \cdots \cap U_k$ is a relation in $\mathfrak{U}$ and $(U_1 \cap U_2 \cap \cdots \cap U_k) \subseteq U_i$ for $i = 1, 2, \ldots, k$. Hence the neighborhood $(U_1 \cap U_2 \cap \cdots \cap U_k)[f(\alpha_i)]$ of $f(\alpha_i)$ in Y is contained in G_{α_i}. Further, the neighborhood $(U_1 \cap U_2 \cap \cdots \cap U_k)[f(x)]$ is contained in $G_x = Y$ for $x \neq \alpha_i$, $i = 1, 2, \ldots, k$. Hence, the neighborhood $(U_1 \cap U_2 \cap \cdots \cap U_k)^*[f] = \{g \mid (f, g)$ is in $(U_1 \cap U_2 \cap \cdots \cap U_k)^*$ in the uniformity $\mathfrak{U}^*$ on $Y^X\} = \{g \mid (f(x), g(x))$ is in $(U_1 \cap U_2 \cap \cdots \cap U_k)$ for all x in $X\}$ is contained in B. Thus B is open in the uniform topology and $\mathfrak{I}_{\mathfrak{U}^*} \supseteq \mathfrak{I}_P$, where $\mathfrak{I}_{\mathfrak{U}^*}$ is the uniform topology and $\mathfrak{I}_P$ is the product topology.

B. If the uniform topology on Y is not trivial, then there exist two points a and b in Y and an open set A containing a and not containing b. This means that there exists a neighborhood $U[a]$ from the relation U in the uniformity $\mathcal{U}$ on Y such that b is not in $U[a]$. Consider, now, the element f in Y^X such that $f(x) = a$ for every x in X. Consider the relation U^* on Y^X corresponding to the relation U on Y and the neighborhood $U^*[f]$ that U^* assigns to f. $U^*[f] = \{g \mid (f(x), g(x)) \text{ is in } U \text{ for all } x \text{ in } X\}$. Next, let B be any base element from the product topology that contains f. $B = \prod_{x \in X} G_x$, where $G_x = Y$ for $x \neq \alpha_1, \alpha_2, \ldots, \alpha_k$ and G_{α_i} is open in Y for $i = 1, 2, \ldots, k$. Further a is in G_{α_i} for $i = 1, 2, \ldots, k$, since f is in B. Now, consider g in Y^X such that $g(x) = b$ for $x \neq \alpha_1, \alpha_2, \ldots, \alpha_k$ and $g(\alpha_i) = a$ for $i = 1, 2, \ldots, k$. g is in B. Since for $x \neq \alpha_1, \ldots, \alpha_k$, $(f(x), g(x)) = (a, b)$, $(f(x), g(x))$ is not in U for $x \neq \alpha_1, \alpha_2, \ldots, \alpha_k$ and g is then not in $U^*[f]$. Thus $U^*[f]$ contains no base element from the product topology. Hence, it is not a neighborhood of f in the product space. Since the two topologies identify different neighborhood relations for Y^X, $\mathfrak{J}_P \neq \mathfrak{J}_{\mathcal{U}^*}$. ∎

The previous theorem and definition are generalizations to uniformizable spaces of the analogous lemma (21.19) and definition (21.21) for metrizable spaces. Further, the concept of "uniform convergence" (definition 21.22) will be generalized to have meaning relative to uniformizable spaces. Also, theorem 21.20 concerning the subset C of continuous functions will be generalized to the case of a uniformizable space, Y. As in the case of a metrizable space Y, the convergence of nets in $\{Y^X, \mathfrak{J}_{\mathcal{U}^*}\}$ is called uniform convergence relative to the uniformity, $\mathcal{U}$, on Y which determines $\mathcal{U}^*$.

23.55 Definition. Let $\{Y, \mathfrak{J}_{\mathcal{U}}\}$ be a uniformizable space and let (f_d) denote a net of functions in Y^X. This net (f_d) is said to *converge uniformly relative to* $\mathcal{U}$ to the function g in the set Y^X if and only if for each relation U in the uniform structure $\mathcal{U}$ on Y, there is an element a in the domain of (f_d) such that if $d > a$, then $(f_d(x), g(x))$ is in U for every x in X. This definition does not refer directly to a topology on Y^X.

23.56 Theorem. *If (f_d) is a net in the uniformizable space $\{Y^X, \mathfrak{J}_{\mathcal{U}^*}\}$, then (f_d) converges to g if and only if the net (f_d) converges uniformly to g relative to the uniform structure $\mathcal{U}$ for Y which determines $\mathcal{U}^*$.*

Proof: A. Let (f_d) converge to g in the space $\{Y^X, \mathfrak{J}_{\mathcal{U}^*}\}$. By definition of convergence, for any neighborhood $U^*[g]$, where U^* is a relation in $\mathcal{U}^*$ and $U^*[g]$ denotes the set of images of g assigned by U^*, there is an a in the domain of the net (f_d) such that if $d > a$, then f_d is in $U^*[g]$ or (g, f_d) is in U^* or $(g(x), f_d(x))$ is in U for every x in X. U and U^* have the meaning assigned to them in lemma 23.52. Thus, for each relation V in the uniform structure $\mathcal{U}$ on Y, consider the corresponding relation V^* in $\mathcal{U}^*$ on Y^X. There is an a in the domain of (f_d) such that if $d > a$, then (g, f_d) is in V^*, by above. Hence, if $d > a$, $(g(x), f_d(x))$ is in V for every x in X, by definition of V^* and V. Thus (f_d) converges uniformly to g.

B. Let the net (f_d) in Y^X converge uniformly to g. Let $\tilde{G}[g]$ be any neighborhood of g in Y^X. $\tilde{G}$ is a relation in the uniform structure $\mathcal{U}^*$ induced on Y^X by $\mathcal{U}$; $\tilde{G} \supseteq V^*$, say, for V^* a basic relation in $\mathcal{U}^*$. Consider the defining relation V in $\mathcal{U}$ on Y corresponding to V^*, as described in definition 23.53. There exists an a in the domain of (f_d) such that if $d > a$, then $(g(x), f_d(x))$ is in V for all x in X, by definition of uniform convergence. Hence if $d > a$, (g, f_d) is in V^* by definition of V^*, and so (g, f_d) is in $\tilde{G}$. Thus, f_d is in $\tilde{G}[g]$ and (f_d) converges to g in $\mathfrak{I}_{\mathcal{U}^*}$ on Y^X. ∎

23.57 Theorem. *If X is a topological space, $\{Y, \mathfrak{I}_{\mathcal{U}}\}$ is a uniformizable space, $\mathfrak{I}_{\mathcal{U}^*}$ is the topology of uniform convergence for Y^X and C is the set of continuous functions in Y^X, then C is closed in $\{Y^X, \mathfrak{I}_{\mathcal{U}^*}\}$.*

Proof: Let g be a limit point of C in $\{Y^X, \mathfrak{I}_{\mathcal{U}^*}\}$. There is a net (f_d) in $C \sim \{g\}$ that converges to g in $\{Y^X, \mathfrak{I}_{\mathcal{U}^*}\}$. Let p be any point in X and let $g(p)$ be its image in Y assigned by g. Let $V[g(p)]$ be any neighborhood of $g(p)$ in $\{Y, \mathfrak{I}_{\mathcal{U}}\}$, where V is a relation in $\mathcal{U}$. Since $\mathcal{U}$ is a uniform structure on Y, there exists a relation W in $\mathcal{U}$ such that $W \circ W \subseteq V$ and by lemma 23.15, there exists in $\mathcal{U}$ a symmetric relation N such that $(N \circ N) \subseteq W$. Hence $(N \circ N) \circ (N \circ N) \subseteq V$. Since f_d is continuous for every d, there exists for each d a neighborhood G_d of p in X such that if x is in G_d, $f_d(x)$ is in $N[f_d(p)]$ or $(f_d(p), f_d(x))$ is in N. Further, since the net (f_d) converges to g in the topology of uniform convergence on Y^X, there is an a in the domain of (f_d) such that if $d > a$, then $(g(x), f_d(x))$ is in N for every x in X, including of course $x = p$. So, let $d^* > a$ and consider G_{d^*}. If x is in G_{d^*}, then $(g(p), f_{d^*}(p))$, $(g(x), f_{d^*}(x))$ and $(f_{d^*}(p), f_{d^*}(x))$ are all in the symmetric relations N, and so $(g(p), g(x))$ is in $(N) \circ (N \circ N) \subseteq (N \circ N) \circ (N \circ N) \subseteq V$. So $(g(p), g(x))$ is in V or $g(x)$ is in $V[g(p)]$ if x is in G_{d^*}. g is continuous at every point of X. This means that g belongs to C. Hence C is closed in $\{Y^X, \mathfrak{I}_{\mathcal{U}^*}\}$. ∎

23.58 Corollary. *Let X be any space; let Y be a uniformizable space and let (f_d) be a net of continuous functions from X into Y that converges uniformly, relative to an admissible uniformity, to the function g from X into Y. Then g is continuous.*

Proof: The corollary is a rephrasing of theorem 23.57. ∎

SUMMARY FOR CHAPTER 4

A metrizable space is a special type of topological space in which the topology can be described "numerically" in the sense that basic neighborhoods can be identified by positive real numbers. Metrizable spaces are normal, first countable topological spaces. Uniform continuity, Cauchy sequences and uniform convergence can be defined for metric spaces, i.e., spaces with an assigned metric, and are metric properties, not topological properties.

The Euclidean n-spaces, E^n, and, in particular, the spaces E^1 of real numbers and E^2 for the topology on the complex numbers, as well as Hilbert space, H, are second countable; hence, first countable, separable, metrizable spaces. Further, each covering of E^n or H by open sets contains a countable subcovering. Since any subspace of E^n or H is a second countable, metrizable space, it is also first countable and separable and any covering of it by open sets contains a countable subcovering.

Urysohn's imbedding theorem establishes that every second countable, normal space is metrizable. Since every regular, second countable space is normal; every second countable regular space is metrizable.

A uniformizable space is a generalization of a metrizable space; its topology is or can be defined from a uniform structure on a set just as the topology for a metrizable space is or can be defined in terms of a metric on a set. A uniform structure on a set X is a filter on $X \times X$ with some additional properties. Each uniform structure can be described "numerically" by certain sets of pseudo-metrics. The topology determined by a uniform structure is either Hausdorff or it is not T_0. Further, every T_0-uniformizable space is completely regular and conversely, every completely regular space is a T_0-uniformizable space.

Just as there is not a unique admissible metric for a given topology on a set, so there is, in general, not a unique admissible uniform structure for a topological space. Compact spaces, which will be defined in chapter 6, do have unique admissible uniform structures. For any completely regular space $\{X, \mathfrak{J}\}$ the uniform structure determined by the set of all continuous functions from $\{X, \mathfrak{J}\}$ into E^1 always yields the original topology. With this uniform structure, every continuous function from $\{X, \mathfrak{J}\}$ into E^1 is uniformly continuous. Thus uniform continuity is not a topological concept in the sense that it is not determined by the topologies on the domain and range. Similarly, Cauchyness and completeness are properties of uniform spaces, i.e., spaces with a given uniformity.

A uniformity is metrizable if and only if it is T_0 and has a countable base. Every T_0-uniform space can be imbedded in a complete uniform space in a way which preserves the uniform structure.

If X is a set and $\{Y, \mathfrak{J}_{\mathfrak{U}}\}$ is a uniformizable space, then a uniform structure $\mathfrak{U}^*$ for the set Y^X of all mappings from X into Y can be defined from $\mathfrak{U}$ in a natural way. The resulting topology for Y^X is called the topology of uniform convergence and it always contains the product topology.

CHAPTER 5

Connectedness

In section 6, the concept of topological invariant was introduced. A topological invariant is any property, P, of spaces such that if the space S possesses P and if h is any homeomorphism whose domain is S, then $h[S]$ possesses P. The properties described in the separation axioms are topological invariants; metrizability is a topological invariant; separability and first and second countability are topological invariants. Another fundamental topological invariant is "connectedness." As the name implies, connectedness is related to the number of pieces into which the space somehow or other falls. For example, two disjoint discs in the plane, E^2, say $\{(x, y) \mid x^2 + y^2 \leq 1\}$ and $\{(x, y) \mid (x - 4)^2 + (y - 4)^2 \leq 1\}$, with the relative topology, ought to constitute a "disconnected" space. A single disc in E^2, say $\{(x, y) \mid x^2 + y^2 \leq 1\}$, with the relative topology, ought to constitute a connected space. The problem is to try to describe this property using only basic topological terms. An example from the usual space R_0 of rational numbers may help to push us further along toward the desired definition. In the space of rational numbers with the usual topology defined by the basic neighborhood relation $\{(r^*, U) \mid U = \{r \mid |r - r^*| < \epsilon\}$, for ϵ rational and positive$\}$, the topology is defined in terms of the natural order relation, $<$, on the rationals. For any two rationals r_1 and r_2, either $r_1 < r_2$ or $r_2 < r_1$ but not both. Further, every rational number, r, has a square, r^2, which is also rational; and 2 is a rational number. Hence, if $A = \{r \mid r$ is rational and $r^2 < 2$ or $r < 0\}$ and if $B = \{r \mid r$ is rational and $r^2 > 2$ and $r > 0\}$, then $R_0 = A \cup B$ and $A \cap B = \emptyset$. Thus R_0 falls into two disjoint sets. Since there is no rational number r such that $r^2 = 2$, A and B are somehow or other separated by this "gap" in the rationals. It appears that neither A nor B contains a limit point of the other, and hence that both sets are closed in R_0. Since $B = {\sim}A$ and $A = {\sim}B$, both sets would then also be open. Thus A and B are both open and both closed; $A \neq \emptyset$ and $B \neq \emptyset$; $A \cup B = R_0$ and $A \cap B = \emptyset$. Connectedness, then, seems to preclude the existence of non-empty, proper subsets that are both open and closed.

24. DEFINITIONS OF CONNECTEDNESS. BASIC THEOREMS.

24.1 Definition. A space $\{S, \mathfrak{I}\}$ is *connected* if and only if S contains no subsets, except S and $\emptyset$, which are both open and closed. A space is called *disconnected* or *non-connected* if and only if it is not connected.

EXERCISE 1. Prove that any space $\{S, \mathfrak{D}\}$, where S contains more than one point and $\mathfrak{D}$ denotes the discrete topology for S, is not connected. Prove also that any space $\{S, \mathfrak{L}\}$, where $\mathfrak{L}$ is the trivial topology, is connected.

EXERCISE 2. Let X be an infinite set and let $\mathfrak{I}$ be the minimal T_1-topology, i.e., the only closed sets are X, $\emptyset$ and all finite sets. Prove that $\{X, \mathfrak{I}\}$ is connected.

24.2 Lemma. *A space $\{S, \mathfrak{I}\}$ is connected if and only if S is not the union of two non-empty, disjoint, open sets.*

Proof: Exercise.

24.3 Corollary. *A space $\{S, \mathfrak{I}\}$ is connected if and only if $\{S, \mathfrak{I}\}$ cannot be represented as the union of two non-empty, disjoint, closed sets.*

Proof: Exercise.

NOTATION: $X = A \cup B$ separation or $X = A \cup B$ sep is written when (1) $X = A \cup B$ and (2) $A \cap B = \emptyset$ and (3) $A \neq \emptyset \neq B$ and (4) A and B are both open in X.

EXERCISE 3. Let $\{S, \mathfrak{I}\}$ be the space defined on the set of real numbers by the basic neighborhood relation $\{(q, U) \mid U = \{x \mid x \geq q\}\}$. Prove that $\{S, \mathfrak{I}\}$ is connected.

24.4 Lemma. *Let $\{S, \mathfrak{I}\}$ be a connected topological space. Let $\mathfrak{I}^*$ be a topology for S that is contained in $\mathfrak{I}$. Then $\{S, \mathfrak{I}^*\}$ is connected.*

Proof: Exercise.

24.5 Lemma. *Let $\mathfrak{I}$ and $\mathfrak{I}^*$ be two topologies for a set S; let $\mathfrak{I} \supset \mathfrak{I}^*$ and let $\{S, \mathfrak{I}^*\}$ be disconnected. $\{S, \mathfrak{I}\}$ is, then, disconnected.*

Proof: Exercise.

24.6 Lemma. *A subset B of a space $\{S, \mathfrak{I}\}$ is open and closed in $\{S, \mathfrak{I}\}$ if and only if B has empty boundary.*

Proof: A. Let B be open and closed in $\{S, \mathfrak{I}\}$ and let b be any boundary point of B. By definition of boundary, b is in $\overline{B} \cap \overline{\sim B}$. Since B is closed, $\overline{B} = B$ and b is in B. Since B is open, $\sim B$ is closed, $\overline{\sim B} = \sim B$ and b is in $\sim B$. Thus b is in $B \cap \sim B = \emptyset$. This is a contradiction. Hence B has no boundary points.

B. Let B have no boundary in $\{S, \mathfrak{I}\}$. Then $\overline{B} \cap \overline{\sim B} = \emptyset$. If p is a limit point of B, then p is in $\overline{B}$ and hence p is not in $\overline{\sim B}$. Thus p is not in $\sim B$, so p is in B and B is closed. Similarly, $\sim B$ is closed. Hence B is both open and closed. ▮

24.7 Corollary. *A space $\{S, \mathfrak{I}\}$ is connected if and only if S contains no non-empty proper subsets with empty boundary.*

Proof: By lemma 24.6, a set with empty boundary is both open and closed. ▮

24.8 Theorem. *No countable metrizable space $\{S, \mathfrak{I}\}$ which contains more than one point is connected.*

Proof: Let $\{p_1, p_2, \ldots, p_i, \ldots\}$ denote the set of elements of $\{S, \mathfrak{I}\}$. Let $s_i = \rho(p_1, p_i)$, where ρ is an admissible metric for $\mathfrak{I}$. $\{s_1, s_2, \ldots, s_i, \ldots\}$ is a countable set of real numbers. There exists a positive real number ϵ which is unequal to s_i for $i = 1, 2, \ldots$ and such that $\epsilon < s_2$, say. Let $F_1 = \{x \mid \rho(p_1, x) \leq \epsilon\}$. F_1 is non-empty and closed in $\{S, \mathfrak{I}\}$. Let $F_2 = \{x \mid \rho(p_1, x) \geq \epsilon\}$. F_2 is non-empty and closed in $\{S, \mathfrak{I}\}$. $F_1 \cap F_2$ is empty and $F_1 \cup F_2 = S$. ▮

24.9 Corollary. *The space of rational numbers with the usual topology is not connected.*

Proof: The rationals with the usual topology constitute a countable, metrizable space with more than one point. ▮

EXERCISE 4. Prove that all connected T_1-spaces with more than one point are infinite.

EXERCISE 5. Give an example of a finite T_0-space which is connected.

24.10 Definition. A space $\{S, \mathfrak{I}\}$ is said to have *dimension* 0 at a point q if and only if q has a local base in which each set is both open and closed. A space has dimension 0 if and only if it has dimension 0 at every point.

24.11 Theorem. *Every non-empty, countable metrizable space $\{S, \mathfrak{I}\}$ is* 0-*dimensional.*

Proof: Let q be any point of $\{S, \mathfrak{I}\}$. Let $\{x_1, x_2, \ldots, x_n, \ldots\}$ denote the set of other points in S. Let $s_i = \rho(q, x_i)$, where ρ is an admissible metric for $\mathfrak{I}$. The set $\{s_1, s_2, \ldots, s_i, \ldots\}$ is a countable set of real numbers; hence, there exist real numbers not in this set. So if $U_\rho(q, \epsilon)$ is any spherical neighborhood of q from ρ, there exists a positive real number δ which is less than ϵ and which is unequal to s_i for $i = 1, 2, \ldots$. Thus $U_\rho(q, \delta) \subseteq U_\rho(q, \epsilon)$ and there are no points of S at a distance δ from q. By lemma 24.6, and exercise 7 after definition 19.10,

$U(q, \delta)$ is then both open and closed. q, then, has a local base consisting of sets which are both open and closed. Since q was any point of S, $\{S, \mathfrak{J}\}$ is 0-dimensional. ▮

24.12 Corollary. *The set of rational numbers and the usual topology constitute a 0-dimensional space.*

Proof: The space is non-empty, countable and metrizable. ▮

EXERCISE 6. Find an example of an uncountable, non-discrete, metrizable space which is 0-dimensional.

24.13 Theorem. *If f is a continuous function of a space $\{S, \mathfrak{S}\}$ on to a space $\{T, \mathfrak{J}\}$ and if $\{S, \mathfrak{S}\}$ is connected, then $\{T, \mathfrak{J}\}$ is connected.*

Proof: Let A be a non-empty, proper, open subset in the space $\{T, \mathfrak{J}\}$. f is continuous; therefore, $f^{-1}[A]$ is open in $\{S, \mathfrak{S}\}$. Since A is non-empty and proper, $\emptyset \neq f^{-1}[A] \neq S$. Since $\{S, \mathfrak{S}\}$ is connected, $f^{-1}[A]$ is not also closed. Thus A cannot be closed. Hence $\{T, \mathfrak{J}\}$ contains no non-empty, proper subsets which are both open and closed and so is connected. ▮

24.14 Corollary. *Connectedness is a topological invariant.*

Proof: Exercise.

EXERCISE 7. Let f be a continuous function of a space S onto a connected space T. Prove or find a counterexample to: S is connected.

EXERCISE 8. Prove or find a counterexample to: non-connectedness is a topological invariant.

24.15 Corollary. *If S is a connected space and if S/D is a quotient (decomposition) space of S, then S/D is connected.*

Proof: Exercise.

24.16 Definition. Let $\{S, \mathfrak{J}\}$ be a space and M a subset of S. M is called a *connected (disconnected) subset* in $\{S, \mathfrak{J}\}$ if and only if $\{M, r\text{-}\mathfrak{J}\}$, where $r\text{-}\mathfrak{J}$ denotes the relative topology, is a connected (disconnected) space.

24.17 Theorem. *Let $\{S, \mathfrak{J}\}$ be a space; let $S = A \cup B$ separation, and let C be a connected subset of S. Then $C \subseteq A$ or $C \subseteq B$.*

Proof: Since A and B are open in S, $C \cap A$ and $C \cap B$ are in the relative topology for C. Hence, $C \cap A$ and $C \cap B$ are both open in the subspace $\{C, r\text{-}\mathfrak{J}\}$. Further, $(C \cap A) \cup (C \cap B) = C$ and $(C \cap A) \cap (C \cap B) = \emptyset$. Since C is connected, $C \cap A = \emptyset$ or $C \cap B = \emptyset$. Hence $C \subseteq B$ or $C \subseteq A$. ▮

24.18 Lemma. *If $\{S, \mathfrak{I}\}$ is a space, $M \subseteq S$, M is connected in $\{S, \mathfrak{I}\}$ and $\{X, r\text{-}\mathfrak{I}\}$ is a subspace of $\{S, \mathfrak{I}\}$ such that $M \subseteq X$, then M is a connected subset of $\{X, r\text{-}\mathfrak{I}\}$. $r\text{-}\mathfrak{I}$ denotes the relative topology.*

Proof: By theorem 9.27, the relative topology for M from $\{S, \mathfrak{I}\}$ is the same as the relative topology for M from $\{X, r\text{-}\mathfrak{I}\}$. Thus, there is just one subspace $\{M, r\text{-}\mathfrak{I}\}$ based on M and one relative topology. By hypothesis, this topology contains no proper, non-empty, closed sets. ▌

24.19 Theorem. *If M is a connected subset of a space $\{S, \mathfrak{I}\}$ and if $M \subseteq N \subseteq \overline{M}$, then N is a connected subset of $\{S, \mathfrak{I}\}$.*

Proof: By the previous lemma, M is a connected subset of N. Let $N = A \cup B$ sep. By theorem 24.17, $M \subseteq A$, say. A is closed in N; hence the closure of M in the subspace $\{N, r\text{-}\mathfrak{I}\}$ is contained in A. By theorem 9.7, the closure of M in $\{N, r\text{-}\mathfrak{I}\}$ is $\overline{M} \cap N$, where as usual $\overline{M}$ denotes the closure of M in $\{S, \mathfrak{I}\}$. However, since $N \subseteq \overline{M}$ by hypothesis, $\overline{M} \cap N = N$. Hence, $N \subseteq A$ and $B = \emptyset$. So there exists no separation of N. ▌

24.20 Corollary. *If M is a connected subset of $\{S, \mathfrak{I}\}$, then so is $\overline{M}$.*

Proof: By previous theorem. ▌

24.21 Definition. A finite sequence $\{M_1, M_2, \ldots, M_k\}$ of distinct sets in a set X is called a *bridge between M_1 and M_k* if and only if $M_i \cap M_j \neq \emptyset$ is equivalent to $|i - j| \leq 1$ for $1 \leq i, j \leq k$. A collection, K, of sets in a set X is called *bridged* or a *bridged system* if and only if for any two sets A and B in K, there is a bridge between A and B whose sets are all in K.

N.B.: In some places in the literature the word "chain" is used instead of "bridge" in the previous definition.

24.22 Theorem. *Let $\{S, \mathfrak{I}\}$ be a space and let $\{C_\nu\}$ be a collection of connected subsets of S which form a bridged system. Then $\bigcup_\nu C_\nu$ is connected.*

Proof: Let $\bigcup_\nu C_\nu = A \cup B$ sep. Let C_ν be any set in the collection $\{C_\nu\}$. Since C_ν is connected then by theorem 24.17, C_ν is contained in A, say. Let C_α be any other set in $\{C_\nu\}$. There exists a bridge $C_\nu = C_{i_1}, C_{i_2}, \ldots, C_{i_k} = C_\alpha$ in $\{C_\nu\}$. Let P consist of the subset of natural numbers which are greater than k along with the subset of all natural numbers m, such that $C_{i_m} \subseteq A$. 1 belongs to P since $C_{i_1} = C_\nu \subseteq A$. Assume j is in P for $j < k$. Then $C_{i_j} \subseteq A$. Hence, since $C_{i_j} \cap C_{i_{j+1}} \neq \emptyset$, $C_{i_{j+1}} \subseteq A$. If $j \geq k$, $j + 1$ is in P, by definition of P. Hence all natural numbers are in P and $C_\alpha \subseteq A$. Since C_α was any other set in $\{C_\nu\}$, $\bigcup_\nu C_\nu \subseteq A$ and $B = \emptyset$. This contradicts the definition of $A \cup B$ separation. Hence $\bigcup_\nu C_\nu$ is connected. ▌

24.23 Theorem. *Let $\{C_\nu\}$ be a collection of connected subsets in a space $\{S, \mathfrak{I}\}$ such that $\bigcap_\nu C_\nu \neq \emptyset$. Then $\bigcup_\nu C_\nu$ is connected.*

Proof: Let C_α and C_β be any two sets in $\{C_\nu\}$. $\{C_\alpha, C_\beta\}$ is a bridge from C_α to C_β. Hence, $\{C_\nu\}$ is a bridged system of connected sets, and so by the previous theorem, $\bigcup_\nu C_\nu$ is connected. ∎

24.24 Theorem. *Let $\{S, \mathfrak{I}\}$ be a space such that each pair of points in S is contained in a connected subset of S. Then $\{S, \mathfrak{I}\}$ is connected.*

Proof: Let s be a given point of S and let x be any point of S. There exists a connected subset Z_x containing s and x. $S = \bigcup_x Z_x$, $\bigcap_x Z_x \neq \emptyset$ and each Z_x is connected. Hence $\{S, \mathfrak{I}\}$ is connected by the previous theorem. ∎

Product of Connected Spaces

The following lemma is needed to prove that the product $X \times Y$ of connected spaces X and Y is connected.

24.25 Lemma. *Let $X \times Y$ be the product space of the spaces X and Y. Let $x \in X$ and let $y \in Y$. Then the subspaces $\{x\} \times Y$ and $X \times \{y\}$ are homeomorphic to Y and X, respectively.*

Proof: Define the function $f: \{x\} \times Y \to Y$ by $f((x, y)) = y$. f is then the projection function p_Y restricted to $\{x\} \times Y$. By lemma 9.21 and theorem 11.8, f is continuous; by definition, f is 1:1. The collection $\mathcal{B}^* = \{U_\alpha \times V_\nu \mid U_\alpha$ and V_ν are any open sets in X and Y respectively$\}$ determines by intersection a base, $\mathcal{B}$, for the relative topology on $\{x\} \times Y$. $\mathcal{B} = \{\{x\} \times V_\nu \mid V_\nu$ is open in $Y\}$. Since $f[\{x\} \times V_\nu] = V_\nu$, f maps every open set in $\mathcal{B}$ onto an open set in Y; hence, f^{-1} is continuous. A similar argument proves that $X \times \{y\}$ is homeomorphic to X. ∎

24.26 Theorem. *The product space $X \times Y$ is connected if and only if X and Y are connected.*

Proof: A. Let $X \times Y$ be connected. Since the projection functions p_x and p_y are onto and continuous, X and Y are both connected by theorem 24.13.

B. Let X and Y both be connected spaces. Let (x, y) and (a, b) be two points of $X \times Y$. The subspaces $\{x\} \times Y$ and $X \times \{b\}$ are both connected, by lemma 24.25. Further, (x, b) is in $(\{x\} \times Y) \cap (X \times \{b\})$; hence, $(\{x\} \times Y) \cap (X \times \{b\}) \neq \emptyset$. By theorem 24.23, $(\{x\} \times Y) \cup (X \times \{b\})$ is connected. (x, y) and (a, b) are both in the connected set $(\{x\} \times Y) \cup (X \times \{b\})$. By theorem 24.24, $X \times Y$ is connected. ∎

24.27 Corollary. *Let $\prod_{i=1}^k X_i$ denote a product of k spaces, for k a natural number. $\prod_{i=1}^k X_i$ is connected if and only if each X_i, for $i = 1, 2, \ldots, k$, is connected.*

Proof: $X_1 \times X_2 \times \cdots \times X_{k-1} \times X_k$ is homeomorphic to $(X_1 \times X_2 \times \cdots \times X_{k-1}) \times X_k$. By theorem 24.26 and induction, the corollary follows. ∎

The following lemma and corollary are used to prove that the general product of connected spaces is connected.

24.28 Lemma. *If* $\prod_{\nu \in \mathfrak{A}} X_\nu$ *denotes a product space and if* $\Phi = \{\Phi_\nu\}$ *denotes a point in this product space, then the subspace* $S^{\Phi}_{\alpha_1,\ldots,\alpha_k} = \{\{x_\nu\} \mid x_\nu = \Phi_\nu$ *for* $\nu \neq \alpha_1, \ldots, \alpha_k\}$ *is homeomorphic to* $X_{\alpha_1} \times X_{\alpha_2} \times \cdots \times X_{\alpha_k}$.

Proof: Define the function f from $S^{\Phi}_{\alpha_1,\ldots,\alpha_k}$ onto $X_{\alpha_1} \times X_{\alpha_2} \times \cdots \times X_{\alpha_k}$ as follows: $f(\{x_\nu\}) = (x_{\alpha_1}, x_{\alpha_2}, \ldots, x_{\alpha_k})$. f is 1:1 and onto by definition. Now let B^* be any basic open set in $\prod_{\nu \in \mathfrak{A}} X_\nu$. $\prod_{\nu \in \mathfrak{A}} U_\nu = B^* \cap S^{\Phi}_{\alpha_1,\ldots,\alpha_k}$, where $U_\nu = \{\Phi_\nu\}$ for $\nu \neq \alpha_1, \ldots, \alpha_k$ and U_ν is open in X_ν for $\nu = \alpha_1, \ldots, \alpha_k$. $f[S^{\Phi}_{\alpha_1,\ldots,\alpha_k} \cap B^*]$ then, by definition of f, is the set $U_{\alpha_1} \times U_{\alpha_2} \times \cdots \times U_{\alpha_k}$ which is open in $X_{\alpha_1} \times \cdots \times X_{\alpha_k}$. Thus f is open. Similarly $f^{-1}[U_{\alpha_1} \times \cdots \times U_{\alpha_k}] = \prod_{\nu \in \mathfrak{A}} U_\nu$, where $U_\nu = \Phi_\nu$ for $\nu \neq \alpha_1, \ldots, \alpha_k$ and $U_\nu = U_{\alpha_i}$ for $\nu = \alpha_i$, $i = 1, 2, \ldots, k$, is open. Thus f is a homeomorphism. ▮

24.29 Corollary. *If* $\prod_{\nu \in \mathfrak{A}} X_\nu$ *is a product of connected spaces and if* $\Phi = \{\Phi_\nu\}$ *denotes a point in this product space, then the subspace* $S^{\Phi}_{\alpha_1,\ldots,\alpha_k} = \{\{x_\nu\} \mid x_\nu = \Phi_\nu$ *for* $\nu \neq \alpha_1, \ldots, \alpha_k\}$ *is connected.*

Proof: Since the product space $X\alpha_1 \times X_{\alpha_2} \times \cdots \times X_{\alpha_k}$ is connected, the corollary follows from the previous lemma and corollary 24.14. ▮

24.30 Theorem. *Let* $\{X_\nu\}$, *for* ν *in some non-empty indexing set, denote any collection of spaces. The non-empty product space* $\prod_{\nu \in \mathfrak{A}} X_\nu$ *is connected if and only if* X_ν, *for every* ν *in* $\mathfrak{A}$, *is connected.*

Proof: A. Since the projection functions are onto and continuous, if $\prod_{\nu \in \mathfrak{A}} X_\nu$ is connected, each X_ν is.

B. Let each X_ν in the collection $\{X_\nu\}$ be a connected space. Let $\Phi = \{\Phi_\nu\}$ be some given point in $\prod_{\nu \in \mathfrak{A}} X_\nu$. Each k-tuple $(\alpha_1, \alpha_2, \ldots, \alpha_k)$ in $\mathfrak{A}^k$, for k a natural number, determines a set $S^{\Phi}_{(\alpha_1,\ldots,\alpha_k)} = \{\{x_\nu\} \mid x_\nu = \Phi_\nu$ for $\nu \neq \alpha_1, \ldots, \alpha_k\}$. Φ belongs to each such set $S^{\Phi}_{(\alpha_1,\ldots,\alpha_k)}$. Let $D_k = \bigcup_{[\alpha]} S^{\Phi}_{[\alpha]}$, where $[\alpha] \in \mathfrak{A}^k$. Let $D^* = \bigcup_{k=1}^{\infty} D_k$. By corollary 24.29 and theorem 24.23, each D_k is connected. Again, by theorem 24.23, since Φ is in each D_k, D^* is connected. Now let $\xi = \{\xi_\nu\}$ denote any point in $\prod_{\nu \in \mathfrak{A}} X_\nu$ and let $G^* = \prod_{\nu \in \mathfrak{A}} U_\nu$ be any basic open set containing ξ. By definition of the product topology, $U_\nu = X_\nu$ for $\nu \neq \beta_1, \beta_2, \ldots, \beta_t$, say. Let $\Psi = \{\Psi_\nu\}$, where $\Psi_\nu = \Phi_\nu$ for $\nu \neq \beta_1, \beta_2, \ldots, \beta_t$ and $\Psi_{\beta_i} = \xi_{\beta_i}$ for $i = 1, 2, \ldots, t$. Ψ is an element in D^* and Ψ is also in G^*. Hence D^* is dense in $\prod_{\nu \in \mathfrak{A}} X_\nu$. Since D^* is connected, $\overline{D^*} = \prod_{\nu \in \mathfrak{A}} X_\nu$ is connected by theorem 24.19. ▮

Weak and Strong Topologies

Thus, the continuous image of a connected space is connected; any quotient space of a connected space is connected and the product space of connected spaces is connected. The next theorems are concerned with the weak and strong topologies and connectedness.

24.31 Theorem. *Let S be any set, $\{T, \mathfrak{I}^*\}$ a connected space and f a function from S onto T. Then $\{S, w\text{-}\mathfrak{I}\}$ is connected, where $w\text{-}\mathfrak{I}$ is the f-induced weak topology for S.*

Proof: Let G be any set in $\{S, w\text{-}\mathfrak{I}\}$ that is open and closed; $\sim G$, the complement of G in S, is open also. Since $w\text{-}\mathfrak{I}$ is the f-induced weak topology, there exist open sets G^* and G' in $\{T, \mathfrak{I}^*\}$ such that $f^{-1}[G^*] = G$ and $f^{-1}[G'] = \sim G$. Hence $f^{-1}[G^*] \cap f^{-1}[G'] = \emptyset$ and so $f^{-1}[G^* \cap G'] = \emptyset$. Therefore $G^* \cap G' = \emptyset$. Let y be any element of T. There exists x in S such that $f(x) = y$. x is in G or x is in $\sim G$. Let x be in G. Then y is in G^*. If x is in $\sim G$, y is in G'. Thus, $T = G^* \cup G'$ and since $G^* \cap G' = \emptyset$, $G^* = \sim G'$. Hence G^* is closed as well as open. Since $\{T, \mathfrak{I}^*\}$ is connected, $G^* = T$ or $G^* = \emptyset$. If $G^* = T$, $G = S$; if $G^* = \emptyset$, $G = \emptyset$. Thus the only subsets that are both open and closed in $\{S, w\text{-}\mathfrak{I}\}$ are S and $\emptyset$; hence, $\{S, w\text{-}\mathfrak{I}\}$ is connected. ▮

24.32 Corollary. *Let f be a function from $\{S, \mathfrak{I}\}$ onto the connected space $\{Y, \mathfrak{I}^*\}$ and let $\mathfrak{I} \subseteq w\text{-}\mathfrak{I}$, where $w\text{-}\mathfrak{I}$ is the f-induced weak topology for S. Then $\{S, \mathfrak{I}\}$ is connected.*

Proof: The corollary follows from lemma 24.4 and the previous theorem. ▮

24.33 Theorem. *If $\{S, \mathfrak{I}\}$ is a connected space and f is a function from $\{S, \mathfrak{I}\}$ onto a set T, then the space $\{\mathfrak{I}, s\text{-}\mathfrak{I}\}$, where $s\text{-}\mathfrak{I}$ is the f-induced strong topology, is connected.*

Proof: Since f is continuous from $\{S, \mathfrak{I}\}$ onto $\{T, s\text{-}\mathfrak{I}\}$ and $\{S, \mathfrak{I}\}$ is connected, $\{T, s\text{-}\mathfrak{I}\}$ is connected. ▮

24.34 Corollary. *If f is any function from a connected space $\{S, \mathfrak{I}\}$ onto a space $\{T, \mathfrak{I}^*\}$ and if $\mathfrak{I}^* \subseteq s\text{-}\mathfrak{I}$, where $s\text{-}\mathfrak{I}$ is the f-induced strong topology for T, then $\{T, \mathfrak{I}^*\}$ is connected.*

Proof: The corollary follows from theorem 24.33 and lemma 24.4. ▮

Weak and strong topologies that are induced by collections, $\{f_\nu\}$, of functions will now be considered.

24.35 Theorem. *If T is a set and $s\text{-}\mathfrak{I}$ is the strong topology for T induced by the functions $\{f_\nu\}$, where $f_\nu: \{S_\nu, \mathfrak{I}_\nu\} \to T$ for each ν, then $\{T, s\text{-}\mathfrak{I}\}$ is connected if any one of the spaces $\{S_\nu, \mathfrak{I}_\nu\}$ is connected.*

Proof: $f_\nu: \{S_\nu, \mathfrak{I}_\nu\} \to \{T, s\text{-}\mathfrak{I}\}$ is continuous for each ν by definition of $s\text{-}\mathfrak{I}$. Hence if one space $\{S_\nu, \mathfrak{I}_\nu\}$ *is connected*, $\{T, s\text{-}\mathfrak{I}\}$ *is connected.* ▮

24.36 Example. Let f_1 denote the identity function, $f_1(x) = x$, from the set, X, of real numbers onto the space $\{Y, \mathfrak{J}_1\}$, where Y is the set of real numbers and $\mathfrak{J}_1$ is defined by the base $\{U_y \mid U_y = \{t \mid t \leq y\}$ for t and y real$\}$. Let f_2 denote the identity function, $f_2(x) = x$, from the set X of real numbers onto the space $\{Y, \mathfrak{J}_2\}$, where $\mathfrak{J}_2$ is defined by the base $\{V_z \mid V_z = \{t \mid t \geq z\}$ for t and z real$\}$. $\{Y, \mathfrak{J}_1\}$ and $\{Y, \mathfrak{J}_2\}$ are both connected. However, the weak topology $\mathcal{S}$ induced on X by f_1 and f_2 is the discrete topology and $\{X, \mathcal{S}\}$ is not connected.

24.37 Example. Let $\{X, \mathcal{S}\}$ denote the space consisting of $\{(x, y)$ in $E^2 \mid 0 \leq x \leq 1$ and $y = 1$ or $y = 2\}$ with the relative topology. Let $\{Y, \mathfrak{J}\}$ denote the set $\{x \mid 0 \leq x \leq 1\}$ of real numbers. Let f be defined by $f(x, y) = x$ with domain X and range Y. $\{X, \mathcal{S}\}$ is not connected. Let s-$\mathfrak{J}$ denote the strong topology for Y induced by f. This strong topology s-$\mathfrak{J}$ is the relative topology for Y from E^1.

The next theorem establishes that any interval $[a, b]$ in E^1 is connected.

25. CONNECTED SETS IN E^1. THE INTERMEDIATE VALUE THEOREM.

25.1 Theorem. *The closed interval* $[a, b] = \{x \mid a \leq x \leq b$, *where* $a < b\}$ *is connected in* E^1.

Proof: Let $[a, b] = A \cup B$, where A and B are both closed in $[a, b]$. Let b be in B. Since A is a bounded set of real numbers, if A is not empty, then A has a least upper bound γ, and $a \leq \gamma \leq b$. Since A is closed, γ is in A. If $\gamma = b$, then γ is in B and $A \cap B \neq \emptyset$. If $\gamma < b$, then $\{x \mid \gamma < x \leq b\} \subseteq B$ by definition of γ, and since B is closed, γ is in B. Thus γ is in $A \cap B$ and no separation of $[a, b]$ can exist. ▮

25.2 Theorem. E^1 *is a connected space.*

Proof: Let p and q be any two distinct real numbers. Let $p < q$. The closed interval $[p, q]$ is connected and p and q are in $[p, q]$. Hence, by theorem 24.24, E^1 is connected. ▮

25.3 Theorem. *The intervals* $\{x \mid a < x\}$ *and* $\{x \mid x < b\}$, *for* a *and* b *real numbers, are connected subsets in* E^1.

Proof: Let $A = \{x \mid a < x\}$. Let p and q be any two points in A and let $p < q$. The closed interval $[p, q]$ is in A and by theorem 25.1 is connected. Hence by theorem 24.24, A is connected. Similarly, $\{x \mid x < b\}$ is connected. ▮

25.4 Corollary. *The intervals* $\{x \mid a \leq x\}$ *and* $\{x \mid x \leq b\}$, *for* a *and* b *real numbers, are connected subsets of* E^1.

Proof: $\{x \mid a \leq x\}$ and $\{x \mid x \leq b\}$ are the closures, respectively, of $\{x \mid a < x\}$ and $\{x \mid x < b\}$ in E^1. By theorem 24.19, the corollary follows. ▮

25.5 Corollary. *The open interval $\{x \mid a < x < b$, for $a < b\}$ is connected in E^1.*

Proof: Let p and q be any two distinct points in $I = \{x \mid a < x < b\}$ and let $p < q$. Then $[p, q] \subseteq I$. $[p, q]$ is connected by theorem 25.1; hence, by theorem 24.24, I is connected. ▮

25.6 Corollary. *The "half-open" intervals $\{x \mid a \leq x < b\}$ and $\{x \mid a < x \leq b\}$ are connected in E^1.*

Proof: These sets lie between the open interval $\{x \mid a < x < b\}$ and its closure $\{x \mid a \leq x \leq b\}$, and so, by theorem 24.19, are connected.

25.7 Theorem. *Let M be any connected subset of E^1. If a and b belong to M, where $a < b$, then $\{x \mid a \leq x \leq b\}$ is a subset of M.*

Proof: Let $a < \gamma < b$. Assume γ is not in M. $A = \{x \mid x < \gamma\}$ and $B = \{x \mid x > \gamma\}$ are open subsets of E^1. Hence $M \cap A$ and $M \cap B$ are open in the subspace M. Further, $M \cap A$ and $M \cap B$ are non-empty and disjoint and $M = (M \cap A) \cup (M \cap B)$ separation. This is a contradiction, since M is connected. It follows that γ belongs to M and hence $\{x \mid a \leq x \leq b\} \subseteq M$. ▮

EXERCISE 1. Prove that the plane $E^2 \sim \{(0, 0)\}$ is connected.

EXERCISE 2. Prove that the set of all points in the plane at least one of whose coordinates is rational is connected.

EXERCISE 3. Prove that the set of all points in E^2 with at least one irrational coordinate is connected.

The previous theorems and corollaries (24.1–24.7) establish that, besides singletons, the only connected subsets of E^1 are intervals—closed, open, half-open, bounded and unbounded.

25.8 Definition. A space X is called *totally disconnected* if and only if all non-empty subsets, which are not one-point sets, are disconnected.

EXERCISE 4. Prove that the Cantor ternary set is totally disconnected in E^1. See corollary 12.24 and theorem 12.26.

EXERCISE 5. Prove that the rationals (also the irrationals) constitute a totally disconnected subspace of E^1.

EXERCISE 6. Prove or disprove: Any totally disconnected space has the discrete topology.

EXERCISE 7. Prove that the Cantor ternary subspace and the subspace of irrationals in E^1 both have dimension 0 at every point.

Intermediate Value Theorem and Consequences

25.9 Theorem (Intermediate Value Theorem). *If f is a continuous function whose domain and range are subspaces of E^1, if the closed interval $\{x \mid a \leq x \leq b\}$ belongs to the domain and if $f(a) < \gamma < f(b)$ or $f(b) < \gamma < f(a)$, then γ belongs to the range of f.*

Proof: $\{x \mid a \leq x \leq b\}$ is a connected subset of E^1, by theorem 25.1. Hence the image of $\{x \mid a \leq x \leq b\}$ assigned by f must be a connected subset of E^1. Since $f(b)$ and $f(a)$ belong to this image, γ belongs to it by theorem 25.7. ∎

25.10 Corollary. *If f is a continuous function whose domain and range are subspaces of E^1, if the closed interval $[a, b]$ belongs to the domain and if $f(a)$ and $f(b)$ have opposite signs, then f has a zero in $[a, b]$.*

Proof: $f(a) < 0 < f(b)$ or $f(b) < 0 < f(a)$. ∎

25.11 Corollary. *If $P(x)$ is any polynomial with real coefficients and if $P(a)$ and $P(b)$ have opposite signs, then $P(x)$ has a zero between a and b.*

25.12 Corollary. *Let f and g be two continuous functions whose domains and ranges are subspaces of E^1. Let the closed interval $[a, b]$ belong to both domains. Further let $f(a) - g(a)$ and $f(b) - g(b)$ have opposite signs. Then there exists a real number c in the open interval (a, b) such that $f(c) = g(c)$.*

Proof: The function $f - g : x \rightarrow f(x) - g(x)$ is continuous on $[a, b]$; further, $f(a) - g(a)$ and $f(b) - g(b)$ have opposite signs. By corollary 25.10, there exists a zero of $f - g$ in (a, b). Hence there exists a real number c in (a, b) such that $f(c) - g(c) = 0$. Hence, $f(c) = g(c)$. ∎

25.13 Theorem (Fixed Point Theorem). *The closed interval $[a, b]$, as a subspace of E^1, has the fixed point property.*

Proof: Let f be any continuous function of $[a, b]$ into itself. Let i denote the identity function on $[a, b]$. If $f(a) = a$ or $f(b) = b$, then f has a fixed point. If $f(a) > a$ and $f(b) < b$, then $f(a) - i(a) > 0$ and $f(b) - i(b) < 0$. Hence, by corollary 25.12, there exists a real number c in (a, b) such that $f(c) = i(c) = c$ and so f has a fixed point. ∎

25.14 Theorem. *Euclidean n-space, E^n, is connected.*

Proof: By theorem 25.2, E^1 is connected. By corollary 24.27, E^n is connected. ∎

EXERCISE 8. Prove: The open interval $\{x \mid a < x < b\}$ does not have the fixed point property.

EXERCISE 9. Find a continuous function of $\{x \mid a < x < b\}$ into itself which does not have a fixed point. [*Hint:* Use exercise 8, above.]

INVARIANCE OF THE OPEN SET IN E^1

There is a property of functions called strongly open (sometimes interior) which depends for its definition on the fact that the range S of a "strongly open" function is a subspace (relative topology) of some space Y.

25.15 Definition. Let f be a function from a space X onto a subspace S of a space Y. f is called *strongly open* if and only if the image of every open set in X is open in Y.

25.16 Lemma. *If a function f from a space X onto a subspace S of a space Y is strongly open, then f is open.*

Proof: Exercise.

25.17 Example. Let $f:x \rightarrow |x|$ with domain all reals. The range is the set of non-negative reals with the relative topology from E^1. f is open, but f is not strongly open, since $f[\{x \mid -\epsilon < x < \epsilon\}]$, where ϵ is a positive real number, is $\{y \mid 0 \leq y < \epsilon\}$ and this is not open in E^1.

25.18 Example. Let f have as its domain $\{(x, y) \mid 0 < x < 1 \text{ and } 0 < y < 3\}$ with the relative topology from E^2; let f have as its range $\{(x, y) \mid 0 < x < 1$ and $0 < y < 2\}$ with the relative topology from E^2. Define f further, as follows: $f((x, y)) = (x, y)$ if $0 < y \leq 1$; $f((x, y)) = (x, 1)$ if $1 \leq y \leq 2$; $f((x, y)) = (x, y - 1)$ if $2 \leq y < 3$. f is continuous; the image of every interior point of the domain as a subset of E^2 is an interior point of the range as a subset of E^2. f is neither open nor strongly open since $f(\{(x, y) \mid 0 < x < 1 \text{ and } 1 < y < 2\}) = \{(x, y) \mid 0 < x < 1 \text{ and } y = 1\}$. This latter set is not open in the range and it is not open in E^2.

25.19 Theorem. *If f is a $1{:}1$ continuous function from E^1 into E^1, then f is strongly open.*

Proof: Let $G = \{x \mid a < x < b \text{ for } a < b\}$ be any open interval in E^1. $\overline{G} = \{x \mid a \leq x \leq b\}$. Since $\overline{G}$ is connected, $f[\overline{G}]$ is connected; also $f[\overline{G}]$ contains $f(a)$ and $f(b)$. By theorem 25.7, $f[\overline{G}] \supseteq \{y \mid f(a) \leq y \leq f(b) \text{ or } f(b) \leq y \leq f(a)\}$. Let $f(a) < f(b)$. Assume $\gamma < f(a)$ and γ is in $f[\overline{G}]$. Then there exists c in $\{x \mid a < x < b\}$ such that $f(c) = \gamma$. Since $\gamma < f(a) < f(b)$, there must exist, by the intermediate value theorem, x in (c, b) such that $f(x) = f(a)$. Since $c > a$, $x \neq a$. Hence, f is not $1{:}1$. This is a contradiction. If $\gamma > f(b)$, the same reasoning leads to a contradiction. If $f(b < f(a)$, the proof is analogous. Thus $f[\overline{G}]$ is the closed interval $[f(a), f(b)]$ or $[f(b), f(a)]$. Since f is $1{:}1$, $f[G]$ is $\{x \mid f(a) < x < f(b)\}$ or $\{x \mid f(b) < x < f(a)\}$. Thus the image of any bounded, open interval in E^1 is a bounded, open interval in E^1. Now let G^* be any open set in E^1. $G^* = \bigcup_\alpha G_\alpha$, where each G_α is an open, bounded interval. $f[G^*] = f[\bigcup_\alpha G_\alpha] = \bigcup_\alpha f[G_\alpha]$. Thus $f[G^*]$ is the union of bounded, open intervals of E^1 and hence is open in E^1. ▮

25.20 Corollary. *If f is a 1:1 continuous function from E^1 into E^1, then $f[E^1]$ is open in E^1.*

Proof: Exercise.

25.21 Corollary. *If f is a homeomorphism from E^1 into E^1 and if G is open in E^1, then $f[G]$ is open in E^1, i.e., f is strongly open.*

Proof: Exercise.

25.22 Corollary. *If f is a 1:1 continuous function from E^1 into E^1, then f is a homeomorphism.*

Proof: Exercise.

EXERCISE 10. Prove that a strictly monotonic function from E^1 onto E^1 is a homeomorphism.

The following theorem gives a necessary condition that a metrizable space be connected.

25.23 Theorem. *Any connected, metrizable space containing more than one point can be mapped continuously onto the unit interval space,* [0, 1].

Proof: Let S be a connected metrizable space. Let a and b be two (distinct) points in S. Define $f(x) = \rho(a, x)$ and $g(x) = \rho(x, b)$, where $x \in S$ and ρ is an admissible metric for the space S. By lemma 19.15, f and g are continuous from S into E^1. Hence, the function determined by $h(x) = (f(x))/(f(x) + g(x))$ is continuous from S into E^1. Further, $h(a) = 0$ and $h(b) = 1$ and $0 \leq h(x) \leq 1$. Now, let $0 \leq t^* \leq 1$ and assume that t^* is not in the range of h. Then if $A = \{t \mid 0 \leq t < t^* \text{ and } t \text{ is real}\}$ and if $B = \{t \mid t^* < t \leq 1 \text{ and } t \text{ is real}\}$, then $h^{-1}[A] \cup h^{-1}[B] = S$, $h^{-1}[A] \cap h^{-1}[B] = \emptyset$ and $h^{-1}[A]$ and $h^{-1}[B]$ are both open in S. Thus S is not connected. This is a contradiction. Hence $h[S] = [0, 1]$. ▮

25.24 Corollary. *Any connected metrizable space containing more than one point has cardinal number greater than or equal to c.*

Proof: Exercise (see theorem 24.8).

One topological property, in general, leads to many others. The rest of this chapter will be concerned with topological properties defined directly or indirectly in terms of connectedness.

26. COMPONENTS. QUASI-COMPONENTS. CUT POINTS.

COMPONENTS

26.1 Definition. Let Comp denote the following relation on the non-empty space X. x *Comp* y if and only if there exists in X a connected set containing x and y.

26.2 Lemma. *Comp is an equivalence relation.*

Proof: Reflexivity and symmetry are immediate. Transitivity follows from theorem 24.23. ▮

26.3 Definition. The equivalence classes determined in a non-empty space X by the relation Comp are called *components* of X. Components, then, are non-empty.

26.4 Theorem. *If any space X, components are connected and closed.*

Proof: By theorem 24.24, components are connected. Further, let C denote any component of X and let x be any point in C. By theorem 24.19, $\overline{C}$ is connected; hence, any point in $\overline{C}$ lies in the same component as x. So, $\overline{C} \subseteq C$. Therefore, $C = \overline{C}$ and C is closed. ▮

Components of a space X, being equivalence classes, are maximal connected sets, i.e., they are contained in no other connected set in X.

26.5 Theorem. *In any connected space, X, there exists exactly one component.*

Proof: Since X is connected all points are Comp-equivalent. ▮

Components are not always open, as the following examples show.

26.6 Example. Let X be the subspace of the plane consisting of $\bigcup_n A_n$, where $A_n = \{(x, y) \mid x = 1/n \text{ and } 0 \leq y \leq 1, \text{ for } n \text{ a natural number}\} \cup \{(x, y) \mid x = 0 \text{ and } 0 \leq y \leq 1\}$. The components of X are $C_0 = \{(x, y) \mid x = 0 \text{ and } 0 \leq y \leq 1\}$ and $C_n = \{(x, y) \mid x = 1/n \text{ and } 0 \leq y \leq 1\}$ for $n = 1, 2, \ldots$. It is to be observed that C_0 is not open since its complement in X is not closed; consequently, there exists no separation $A \cup B$ sep of X where either A or B is exactly C_0.

26.7 Example. Consider the subspace of rationals in E^1; this space is totally disconnected. Thus each rational constitutes a component but not an open set.

26.8 Theorem. *In a space, X, any non-empty connected subset which is both open and closed is a component.*

Proof: Let $A \subseteq X$ and let A be non-empty connected, open and closed. Further, assume $A \subseteq B$. By the definition of the relative topology, A is open and closed in B. Hence, B is not connected unless $A = B$. ∎

26.9 Theorem. *Let f be a continuous function from the space X into the space Y. The image of any component of X lies in a component of $f[X]$.*

Proof: Let C be any component of X. C is connected by theorem 26.4; hence, $f[C]$ is connected by theorem 24.13 and lemma 9.21. Hence, all points in $f[C]$ lie in the same component of $f[X]$. ∎

EXERCISE 1. Prove or disprove: the image of a component under a continuous function is a component.

26.10 Corollary. *Components are preserved by homeomorphisms.*

Proof: Exercise.

26.11 Theorem. *Let $\prod_{\nu \in \mathfrak{A}} X_\nu$ denote any non-empty product space. The components of $\prod_{\nu \in \mathfrak{A}} X_\nu$ are exactly the sets $\prod_{\nu \in \mathfrak{A}} C_\nu$, where each C_ν is a component in X_ν.*

Proof: First, each set $\prod_{\nu \in \mathfrak{A}} C_\nu$, where each C_ν is a component, is connected by definition 24.16 and theorem 24.30. Next, assume $D \supseteq \prod_{\nu \in \mathfrak{A}} C_\nu$ and that D is connected. Since any projection function p_ν is continuous, $p_\nu[D]$ is connected for each ν. Further, $p_\nu[D] \supseteq p_\nu[\prod_\nu C_\nu] = C_\nu$. Since C_ν is a component, $p_\nu[D] = C_\nu$. Hence, $D \subseteq \bigcap_\nu p^{-1}[C_\nu]$. However, $\bigcap_\nu p_\nu^{-1}[C_\nu] = \prod_{\nu \in \mathfrak{A}} C_\nu$. Thus, $D = \prod_{\nu \in \mathfrak{A}} C_\nu$ and $\prod_{\nu \in \mathfrak{A}} C_\nu$ is a component. ∎

26.12 Corollary. *The product space $\prod_\nu X_\nu$, where each X_ν is a non-empty, totally disconnected space, is a totally disconnected space.*

Proof: Exercise.

EXERCISE 2. Let $\{X, \mathfrak{J}\}$ denote the space consisting of the following subset of the plane with the relative topology: $X = \{(0, 0)\} \cup \{(0, 1)\} \cup \bigcup_{n=1}^{\infty} \{(x, y) \mid x = 1/n \text{ and } 0 \leq y \leq 1\}$. What are the components of $\{X, \mathfrak{J}\}$?

EXERCISE 3. Let $\{X, \mathfrak{J}\}$ now denote the space consisting of the set of real numbers with the topology defined by the base $\{G_{a+}^{\epsilon} \mid G_{a+}^{\epsilon} = \{x \mid a \leq x < a + \epsilon, \text{ where } \epsilon \text{ is positive}\}\}$. What are the components of $\{X, \mathfrak{J}\}$?

EXERCISE 4. Let $\{X, \mathfrak{J}\}$ be any infinite space with the smallest T_1-topology. What are the components of $\{X, \mathfrak{J}\}$?

EXERCISE 5. Let f be any continuous function from E^1 into the subspace of rationals. Prove that f is a constant function.

EXERCISE 6. Let $\{X, \mathfrak{J}\}$ denote any space and let C denote a component of $\{X, \mathfrak{J}\}$. Let $\mathfrak{J}^* \supsetneq \mathfrak{J}$. What can be said about C in $\{X, \mathfrak{J}^*\}$?

26.13 Theorem. *Let X denote any non-empty space and let $X/Comp$ denote the quotient (decomposition) space defined from X using the equivalence relation Comp. Then $X/Comp$ is totally disconnected.*

Proof: Let C^* denote a component in X/Comp. Since components are closed by theorem 26.4 and since the quotient mapping q is continuous, $q^{-1}[C^*]$ is closed in X. It must be shown that $q^{-1}[C^*]$ is connected in X and so lies in one equivalence class. Assume $q^{-1}[C^*] = A \cup B$ separation. A and B are closed in $q^{-1}[C^*]$ and since $q^{-1}[C^*]$ is closed in X, A and B are closed in X by definition of the relative topology. Further, A and B are inverse sets in $q^{-1}[C^*]$ because if a were in A and b were in B and $q(a) = q(b)$, then a and b would be in the same component, C, in $q^{-1}[C^*]$, by definition of q; and $(C \cap A) \cup (C \cap B)$ would be a separation of the connected set C. Hence, since the quotient (decomposition) topology is the strong topology induced by q, $q[A]$ and $q[B]$ are both closed in X/Comp. Since $C^* = q[A] \cup q[B]$, $q[A] \cup q[B]$ is a separation of C^*. This is a contradiction, since C^* is a component. Hence the assumption that $q^{-1}[C^*]$ is not connected is false. Since $q^{-1}[C^*]$ is connected it lies in some component, hence $q[q^{-1}[C^*]]$ is a single point in X/Comp. However, $q[q^{-1}[C^*]] = C^*$ and all non-empty connected subsets in X/Comp are singletons. ▮

QUASI-COMPONENTS

26.14 Example. Let X denote the subspace of the plane, E^2, consisting of the points $(0, 0)$, $(0, 1)$ and all points $(1/n, y)$ where n is a natural number and $0 \leq y \leq 1$. There exists no separation $A \cup B$ sep of X such that $(0, 0)$ is in A and $(0, 1)$ is in B. However $\{(0, 0), (0, 1)\}$ is not a connected set in X. Thus the set $Q(p)$ of all points in a space X which cannot be separated from p is not necessarily connected.

26.15 Definition. Let x and y be *q-Comp* in a space X if and only if $X = A \cup B$ separation implies x and y are in A or x and y are in B.

26.16 Lemma. *q-Comp is an equivalence relation.*

Proof: Exercise.

26.17 Definition. The equivalence classes determined on a space X by the equivalence relation q-Comp are called *quasi-components*.

26.18 Lemma. *Quasi-components are topological invariants.*

Proof: Exercise.

26.19 Lemma. *Quasi-components are closed.*

Proof: Let Q be a quasi-component in a space X. If $\sim Q$ is empty, Q is closed. If $\sim Q \neq \emptyset$, let y be a point in $\sim Q$. There exists a separation $A \cup B$ sep of X such that $Q \subseteq A$ and y is in B, by definition of q-component. Since B is open in X, by definition of separation, y is not a limit point of Q. Since y was any point of $\sim Q$, Q is closed. ▮

26.20 Theorem. *Every component is contained in a quasi-component.*

Proof: Exercise.

Cut Points and Sets

26.21 Definition. If X is a connected space and if p is a point of X such that $X - \{p\}$ is disconnected, then p is called a *cut point* of X. If A is a subset of a connected space X such that $X - A$ is not connected, then A is said to *separate* X.

26.22 Theorem. *Cut points are topological invariants.*

Proof: Let X be connected and let $X - \{p\} = A \cup B$ sep. Let h be a homeomorphism from X onto Y. $h[A]$ and $h[B]$ are both open and $Y - \{f(p)\} = h[A] \cup h[B]$ separation. ▮

EXERCISE 7. Prove that every point in E^1 is a cut point.

EXERCISE 8. Prove that no point of E^2 is a cut point.

EXERCISE 9. Prove that E^2 is not homeomorphic to E^1.

EXERCISE 10. Prove that $\{x \mid 0 \leq x \leq 1$ for x a real number$\}$, with the usual relative topology, has exactly two non-cut points.

EXERCISE 11. Identify a space with exactly n cut points.

EXERCISE 12. Identify a space with a countable number of cut points.

EXERCISE 13. Prove that if p is a cut point in a connected space Y and if f is a continuous function from a space X onto Y, then $f^{-1}(p)$ separates X.

26.23 Theorem. *If X is connected and if M is connected and separates X, i.e., $X - M = A \cup B$ separation, then $A \cup M$ and $B \cup M$ are both connected.*

Proof: Let $A \cup M = A_1 \cup A_2$ separation. M is connected; therefore, $M \subseteq A_1$ or $M \subseteq A_2$. Let $M \subseteq A_1$. Since $A \cup M = A_1 \cup A_2$ and $M \subseteq A_1$, A must contain A_2. Now, consider $X = (A \cup M) \cup B = A_1 \cup A_2 \cup B = A_2 \cup (A_1 \cup B)$. $\overline{A}_2 \cap A_1 = \emptyset$ and since $A_2 \subseteq A$ and $\overline{A} \cap B = \emptyset$, $\overline{A}_2 \cap B = \emptyset$. Hence $\overline{A}_2 \cap (A_1 \cup B) = \emptyset$. Further, $\overline{A}_1 \cap A_2 = \emptyset$ and since $\overline{B} \cap A = \emptyset$, $\overline{B} \cap A_2 = \emptyset$. Therefore, $X = A_2 \cup (A_1 \cup B)$ sep. This is a contradiction. The same proof is valid for $B \cup M$. ▮

26.24 Corollary. *If p is a cut point of a connected space X such that $X - \{p\} = A \cup B$ sep, then $A \cup \{p\}$ and $B \cup \{p\}$ are connected.*

26.25 Definition. If X is a connected space and M is a subset of X, then X is said to be *irreducibly connected about M* if and only if no proper connected subset of X contains M.

26.26 Example. Let X denote the unit interval with the usual relative topology and let M denote the subset $\{0, 1\}$ consisting of 0 and 1. By theorem 25.7, the only connected subset of X which contains $\{0, 1\}$ is the whole interval $[0, 1]$. Hence X is irreducibly connected about $\{0, 1\}$. On the other hand if M is any subset of X which does not contain 0 and 1, then X is not irreducibly connected about M since $X - \{0, 1\}$ is connected and contains M.

26.27 Theorem. *A space X is irreducibly connected about a subset M if and only if M contains all the non-cut points of X and for x in $X - M$ and $X - \{x\} = A \cup B$ separation, $A \cap M \neq \emptyset \neq B \cap M$.*

Proof: A. Let X be irreducibly connected about M. Let x be any point in $X - M$. $X - \{x\}$ contains M and hence, by hypothesis, cannot be connected. Let $X - \{x\} = A \cup B$ separation. By corollary 26.24, $A \cup \{x\}$ and $B \cup \{x\}$ are both connected; so, neither can contain M.

B. Let M contain all the non-cut points of the connected space X and for x in $X - M$ and $X - \{x\} = A \cup B$ separation, let $A \cap M \neq \emptyset \neq B \cap M$. Assume that $M \subseteq S \subsetneq X$ and that S is connected. Let x be in $X - S$. Then $X - \{x\} = A \cup B$ separation, such that $M \cap A \neq \emptyset \neq M \cap B$. Hence $S \cap A \neq \emptyset \neq S \cap B$. By theorem 24.17, since S is connected, $S \subseteq A$ or $S \subseteq B$. Thus a contradiction occurs and no such connected subset S can exist. Thus X is irreducibly connected about M. ∎

26.28 Definition. A subset M of a connected space X is called a *minimum set* about which X is irreducibly connected if and only if X is irreducibly connected about M, but X is not irreducibly connected about any proper subset of M.

26.29 Example. The unit interval $[0, 1]$ with the usual relative topology is irreducibly connected about the subset $\{0, 1/2, 1\}$. However, the unit interval $[0, 1]$ is irreducibly connected about the subset $\{0, 1\}$. Hence, $\{0, 1/2, 1\}$ is not a minimum set about which X is irreducibly connected.

26.30 Theorem. *If X has a minimum set M about which it is irreducibly connected, then M is exactly the set of non-cut points of X.*

Proof: Let N be the set of non-cut points of X. By theorem 26.27, $M \supseteq N$. Let x be in $M - N$. Since x is a cut point of X, $X - \{x\} = A \cup B$ separation. By corollary 26.24, $M \cap A \neq \emptyset \neq M \cap B$. Now $(M \cap A) \cup (M \cap B) = M - \{x\}$. Now X has a proper connected subset C containing $M - \{x\}$

since M is a minimum set. Since $M \cap A \neq \emptyset \neq M \cap B$ and $C \supseteq M - \{x\}$, $C \cap A \neq \emptyset \neq C \cap B$. C is connected; hence, C is not contained in $X - \{x\} = A \cup B$ separation. Therefore, x is in C and $C \supseteq M$. This means X is not irreducibly connected about M. This contradicts the hypothesis; hence, no such point x can exist. Therefore, $M - N = \emptyset$ and M is exactly the set of non-cut points of X. ▮

26.31 Corollary. *A connected space X is irreducibly connected about itself as basic set if and only if X consists entirely of non-cut points.*

Proof: A. If X is irreducibly connected about itself as minimum set, then, by the previous theorem, X consists of non-cut points.

B. If X consists entirely of non-cut points, then X is the only subset about which X is irreducibly connected by theorem 26.27. Hence, by definition 26.28, X is a minimum set about which X is irreducibly connected. ▮

EXERCISE 14. Does the space E^1 of real numbers with the usual topology have a minimum set about which it is irreducibly connected?

EXERCISE 15. Find a discrete subset of E^1 about which E^1 is irreducibly connected.

EXERCISE 16. Let X be the subspace of E^1 determined by $\{x \mid x \geq 0\}$. Does X have a minimum set about which it is irreducibly connected?

EXERCISE 17. Is there a minimum set about which $X = \{(x, y) \mid x^2 + y^2 = 1\}$ with the relative topology is irreducibly connected?

EXERCISE 18. Let $X = \{(x, y) \mid x^2 + (y - 1)^2 = 1\} \cup \{(x, y) \mid x^2 + (y + 1)^2 = 1\}$ with the relative topology from E^2. Is there a minimum set about which X is irreducibly connected?

The following five theorems are elementary theorems about subsets of the plane, E^2. The generalization of these theorems leads to the very important Jordan curve theorem which states that any homeomorphic image, C, in $E^2 \cup \{\infty\}$ (the extended plane which is topologically the surface of the 2-sphere, $\{(x, y, z) \mid (x, y, z)$ is in E^3 and $x^2 + y^2 + z^2 = 1\}$) of the unit circumference, $\{(x, y) \mid x^2 + y^2 = 1\}$, separates the plane $E^2 \cup \{\infty\}$ into two disjoint, non-empty, open connected subsets for which it is the common boundary. The proof of this Jordan curve theorem will not be included here.

26.32 Theorem. *Any straight line separates the plane into two, non-empty, disjoint, open, connected subsets.*

Proof: Let $g(x, y) = Ax + By + C$, where A, B and C are fixed real constants such that $A \neq 0$ or $B \neq 0$. g is continuous from E^2 into E^1. For, $|g(x, y) - g(a, b)| = |Ax + By + C - Aa - Bb - C| = |A(x - a) + B(y - b)|$. Hence, if $|x - a| < \epsilon/2A$ and $|y - b| < \epsilon/2B$ for $A \neq 0 \neq B$, then $|g(x, y) - g(a, b)| < \epsilon$. If $A = 0$ or $B = 0$, the proof is obvious. Next, since $P = \{s \mid s > 0\}$

is open in E^1, $g^{-1}[P]$ is open in E^2 and is not empty; similarly, $g^{-1}[N]$ is not empty and is open in E^2, where $N = \{s \mid s < 0\}$ in E^1. Since any straight line can be represented as $g^{-1}[\{0\}]$, part of the theorem is proved. Next, let $\alpha = (x_1, y_1)$ and $\beta = (x_2, y_2)$, where $g(\alpha) > 0$ and $g(\beta) > 0$. Consider the line segment $\{t\alpha + (1 - t)\beta \mid 0 \leq t \leq 1\}$ in E^2.

$$\begin{aligned} g(t\alpha + (1-t)\beta) &= A[tx_1 + (1-t)x_2] + B[ty_1 + (1-t)y_2] + C \\ &= Atx_1 + Bty_1 + tC + A(1-t)x_2 + B(1-t)y_2 + (1-t)C \\ &= t[Ax_1 + By_1 + C] + (1-t)[Ax_2 + By_2 + C] > 0. \end{aligned}$$

Hence the line segment between (x_1, y_1) and (x_2, y_2) lies in $g^{-1}[P]$ if (x_1, y_1) and (x_2, y_2) do. This implies that $g^{-1}[P]$ is connected. The proof for $g^{-1}[N]$ is similar. ▌

26.33 Theorem. *Let $M_1 = g^{-1}[P]$ and $M_2 = g^{-1}[N]$ be the two non-empty, disjoint, open, connected sets, defined in the previous theorem, into which the straight line L, $\{(x, y) \mid Ax + By + C = 0\}$, separates the plane, E^2. Let K be a connected set which contains a point of M_1 and a point of M_2. Then K contains a point of L. Further, L is the common boundary of M_1 and M_2.*

Proof: A. As in the previous theorem, let $g(x, y) = Ax + By + C$. g was proved to be continuous. Hence, $g[K]$ is a connected subset of E^1 by theorem 24.13. Since by the definition of M_1 and M_2, $g[K]$ contains a positive real number and a negative real number, $g[K]$ must contain 0, by theorem 25.7. Therefore, $g^{-1}[\{0\}] \cap K \neq \emptyset$ or $L \cap K \neq \emptyset$.

B. Let $G = \{(x, y) \mid \sqrt{(x - a)^2 + (y - b)^2} < \epsilon\}$ for (a, b) on L, $L = \{(x, y) \mid Ax + By + C = 0\}$. Assume $A \neq 0$. A can then be assumed to be positive. Consider the point $(a + \epsilon/2, b)$. $A(a + \epsilon/2) + Bb + C = A \cdot \epsilon/2 > 0$. Further, $(a + \epsilon/2, b)$ is in G. Similarly, consider the point $(a - \epsilon/2, b)$. $A(a - \epsilon/2) + Bb + C = A \cdot (-\epsilon/2) < 0$. Further, $(a - \epsilon/2, b)$ is in G. If $A = 0$, B can be considered to be positive and the points $(a, b + \epsilon/2)$ and $(a, b - \epsilon/2)$ lie in G and in M_1 and M_2, respectively. Hence $\overline{M}_1 \cap \overline{M}_2 = L$. ▌

26.34 Definition. A subset, K, of Euclidean n-space, E^n, is called *convex* if and only if α and β in K implies that the *line segment* $\{t\alpha + (1 - t)\beta \mid t$ is real and $0 \leq t \leq 1\}$ is in K.

26.35 Theorem. *Any convex subset of Euclidean n-space is connected.*

Proof: Exercise.

26.36 Theorem. *The circumference of the unit circle separates the plane into two disjoint, non-empty, open, connected subsets.*

Proof: Let $g(x, y) = x^2 + y^2$. g is a continuous function from E^2 onto the non-negative real numbers. $g^{-1}[\{1\}] = \{(x, y) \mid x^2 + y^2 = 1\}$, i.e., the circumference of the unit circle. Now if $A_1 = \{(x, y) \mid x^2 + y^2 < 1\}$ and $A_2 = \{(x, y) \mid x^2 + y^2 > 1\}$, then $A_1 = g^{-1}[(0, 1)]$ and $A_2 = g^{-1}[(1, \infty)]$ are both open in E^2 since g is continuous. Next, let $a^2 + b^2 < 1$ and $c^2 + d^2 < 1$. Consider any point P on the line segment determined by (a, b) and (c, d). P can be represented by an ordered pair $[ta + (1 - t)c,\ tb + (1 - t)d]$, where $0 \leq t \leq 1$.

$$
\begin{aligned}
&[ta + (1 - t)c]^2 + [tb + (1 - t)d]^2 \\
&\quad = t^2a^2 + (1 - t)^2c^2 + t^2b^2 + (1 - t)^2d^2 + 2t(1 - t)ac + 2t(1 - t)bd \\
&\quad = t^2a^2 + t^2b^2 + (1 - t)^2c^2 + (1 - t)^2d^2 + 2t(1 - t)(ac + bd) \\
&\quad = t^2(a^2 + b^2) + (1 - t)^2(c^2 + d^2) + 2t(1 - t)(ac + bd) \\
&\quad \leq t^2(a^2 + b^2) + (1 - t)^2(c^2 + d^2) + 2t(1 - t)\left[\frac{a^2 + c^2}{2} + \frac{b^2 + d^2}{2}\right] \\
&\quad \leq t^2(a^2 + b^2) + (1 - t)^2(c^2 + d^2) + 2t(1 - t)\left(\frac{a^2 + b^2}{2} + \frac{c^2 + d^2}{2}\right) \\
&\qquad\qquad < t^2 + (1 - t)^2 + 2t(1 - t) = [t + (1 - t)]^2 = 1.
\end{aligned}
$$

The third last inequality follows from $a^2 + c^2 \geq 2ac$, which in turn follows from $(a - c)^2 \geq 0$. Therefore, the interior of the unit circle is convex and so is connected. Next, consider $A_2 = \{(x, y) \mid x^2 + y^2 > 1\}$. The subset $B_1 = \{(x, y) \mid x > 1\}$ is connected by theorem 24.26, since it is the product of two connected sets. Similarly, $B_2 = \{(x, y) \mid y > 1\}$, $B_3 = \{(x, y) \mid x < -1\}$ and $B_4 = \{(x, y) \mid y < -1\}$ are products of connected sets and so are connected. Further, B_1, B_2, B_3 and B_4 constitute a bridge of connected sets in A_2 and hence $B^* = B_1 \cup B_2 \cup B_3 \cup B_4 = \{(x, y) \mid |x| > 1 \text{ or } |y| > 1\}$ is connected by theorem 24.22. The complement of B^* in A_2 is $\{(x, y) \mid x^2 + y^2 > 1, |x| \leq 1 \text{ and } |y| \leq 1\}$. Let (a, b) be in $A_2 - B^*$; $a^2 + b^2 > 1$, $|a| \leq 1$ and $|b| \leq 1$. Consider the set $L_{(a,b)} = \{(x, y) \mid x = ta, y = tb \text{ and } 1 \leq t \text{ for } t \text{ real}\}$. $t^2a^2 + t^2b^2 = t^2(a^2 + b^2) \geq 1$. Thus $L_{(a,b)} \subseteq A_2$. Further, $L_{(a,b)}$ is a homeomorphic image of $\{t \mid t \geq 1\}$ in E^1 and hence is connected. Now consider the collection $\bigcup_{(a,b)\in A_2 \sim B^*} \{L_{(a,b)}\} \cup B^*$. This collection constitutes a bridged system of connected sets for A_2; hence, by theorem 24.22, A_2 is connected. ▮

26.37 Corollary. *If h is a homeomorphism of E^2 into itself, then the image $h[C_1]$ of $\{(x, y) \mid x^2 + y^2 = 1\}$ separates $h[E^2]$ into two disjoint, nonempty, open, connected subsets.*

26.38 Theorem. *The circumference of the unit circle is the common boundary of the two open, connected sets A_1 and A_2, defined in the previous theorem, into which it separates E^2, and further, any connected set which contains points of both sets A_1 and A_2 contains points of the circumference.*

Proof: A. $A_1 = \{(x, y) \mid x^2 + y^2 < 1\}$ and $A_2 = \{(x, y) \mid x^2 + y^2 > 1\}$, by theorem 26.36. Let (a, b) be a point on the circumference. $a^2 + b^2 = 1$.

Let $G = \{(x, y) \mid \sqrt{(x - a)^2 + (y - b)^2} < \epsilon \text{ for } 0 < \epsilon < 1/2 \text{ and real}\}$ denote any spherical neighborhood of (a, b) in E^2. Consider the points $P_1 = ((1 - \epsilon/2)a, (1 - \epsilon/2)b)$ and $P_2 = ((1 + \epsilon/2)a, (1 + \epsilon/2)b)$. Since $a^2 + b^2 = 1$, P_1 is in A_1 and P_2 is in A_2. Further, P_1 and P_2 are both in G. Hence each point on the circumference is a limit point of A_1 and A_2, and each has the circumference as its boundary.

B. Next, let K be any connected set which contains a point of A_1 and a point of A_2. Thus $g[K]$, where $g:(x, y) \to x^2 + y^2$, contains a number greater than 1 and a number less than 1. Since K is connected and g is continuous, $g[K]$ contains 1, by theorem 25.7. ▮

The Jordan curve theorem implies theorems 26.32, 26.33, 26.36 and 26.38 as corollaries. In the Jordan curve theorem there is no homeomorphism, given by hypothesis, which is defined on all of $E^2 \cup \{\infty\}$. This makes the proof quite difficult. For a proof of the Jordan curve theorem see Alexandroff [1], Hall and Spencer [1], Whyburn [1] and [3] or Wilder [1].

27. LOCAL CONNECTEDNESS. PATHWISE CONNECTEDNESS.

LOCAL CONNECTEDNESS

27.1 Definition. A space X is *locally connected at a point* x if and only if every open set containing x contains a connected, open set containing x. A space X is called *locally connected* if and only if it is locally connected at every point.

27.2 Theorem. *Euclidean n-space, E^n, for each natural number n, is locally connected.*

Proof: By corollary 25.5, open intervals in E^1 are connected. By corollary 24.27, any product of a finite number of open intervals is connected. Hence, by definition of the product topology, E^n is locally connected. ▮

27.3 Example. The Cantor ternary space is not locally connected. See corollary 12.24.

27.4 Example. The subspace of all rational numbers in E^1 is not locally connected.

The continuous image of a locally connected space is not necessarily locally connected.

27.5 Example. Let $\{S, \mathfrak{I}_1\}$ denote the rationals with the discrete topology and let $\{S, \mathfrak{I}_2\}$ denote the rationals with the usual relative topology. The identity function maps $\{S, \mathfrak{I}_1\}$ continuously onto $\{S, \mathfrak{I}_2\}$. $\{S, \mathfrak{I}_1\}$ is locally connected; $\{S, \mathfrak{I}_2\}$ is not locally connected.

27.6 Example. The Cantor ternary space is a product space of discrete spaces and so is a product of locally connected spaces. The Cantor ternary space is not locally connected; hence, the product of locally connected spaces is not necessarily locally connected. See definition 12.14, corollary 12.24 and theorem 12.26.

27.7 Theorem. *If S is a locally connected space and if f is a continuous and open function, then $f[S]$ is locally connected.*

Proof: Exercise.

27.8 Corollary. *Local connectedness is a topological invariant.*

EXERCISE 1. Prove that the product of a finite number of locally connected spaces is locally connected.

27.9 Theorem. *A product space $\prod_{\nu \in \mathfrak{A}} X_\nu$ is locally connected if and only if each X_ν is locally connected and all but a finite number of the X_ν are connected.*

Proof: A. Let $\{X_\nu\}$ denote a collection of locally connected spaces such that at most a finite number are not connected. Let a^* be any point in $X^* = \prod_{\nu \in \mathfrak{A}} X_\nu$ and let G^* denote a base element containing a^*. $G^* = \prod_{\nu \in \mathfrak{A}} G_\nu$, where $G_\nu = X_\nu$ for $\nu \neq \beta_1, \ldots, \beta_t$, t a natural number, and G_ν is open in X_ν for all ν. Let $A = \{\nu \mid \nu \in \mathfrak{A}$ and X_ν is not connected or $G_\nu \neq X_\nu\}$. Let $A = \{\alpha_1, \alpha_2, \ldots, \alpha_k\}$. Since each X_ν is locally connected, for each α_i in A choose an open, connected set W_{α_i} which contains the α_i-th coordinate of a^* and is contained in G_{α_i}. If ν is not in A, X_ν is connected. So, for ν not in A, let $W_\nu = X_\nu$. Let $W^* = \prod_{\nu \in \mathfrak{A}} W_\nu$. $W^* \subseteq G^*$; W^* is connected by theorem 24.30 and open by definition of the product topology. a^* is in W^*. Hence $\prod_{\nu \in \mathfrak{A}} X_\nu$ is locally connected.

B. Let $X^* = \prod_{\nu \in \mathfrak{A}} X_\nu$ be locally connected. Let a^* be a point in X^*. There exists an open set G^* which contains a^* and is connected. Since each projection function p_ν, for ν in $\mathfrak{A}$, is open and continuous, $p_\nu[G^*] = W_\nu$ is open and connected. Now $W_\nu = X_\nu$ for all but a finite number of elements in $\mathfrak{A}$ by definition of the product topology, since G^* is open. Hence, all but a finite number of the spaces X_ν are connected. Since each p_ν is continuous and open and since $\prod_{\nu \in \mathfrak{A}} X_\nu$ is locally connected, by theorem 27.7, each X_ν is locally connected. ∎

27.10 Theorem. *In any locally connected space, components are open.*

Proof: Let C denote any component of the locally connected space X. Let x be any point in C. x has a connected neighborhood, W, in X. $C \cup W$ is connected. By definition of components as maximal connected sets, $W \subseteq C$. Hence every point of C is interior and so C is open. ▮

EXERCISE 2. Give an example of a space in which components are not open.

27.11 Example. Let A_n be the subset of the plane E^2 consisting of $\{(x, y) \mid x = 1/n \text{ and } -1 \leq y \leq +1\}$, where n is a natural number. Let $A_0 = \{(x, y) \mid x = 0 \text{ and } -1 \leq y \leq +1\}$; let $B^+ = \{(x, y) \mid 0 \leq x \leq 1 \text{ and } y = +1\}$ and let $B^- = \{(x, y) \mid 0 \leq x \leq 1 \text{ and } y = -1\}$. Now consider the subspace, X, of E^2 consisting of $\bigcup_{n=0}^{\infty} A_n \cup B^+ \cup B^-$. X is a connected subspace of E^2, by theorem 24.22. Hence, X has one component, X, which is, of course, open in X. However, X is not locally connected at every point. Consider, e.g., (0, 0). The details of the proof are left as an exercise.

27.12 Theorem. *A space X is locally connected if and only if every open subset has open components.*

Proof: A. Let X be locally connected and let G be an open subset of X. Let C be a component of G and let x be a point in C. Since G is open and X is locally connected, there exists in G a connected, open set W containing x. Hence $C \cup W$ is connected and so $W \subseteq C$. This means that C is open in X.

B. Let every open subset of X have open components. Let x be in X and let G be an open set which contains x. Let C be the component of G which contains x. C is connected and C is open by hypothesis. Hence, C is a connected neighborhood of x contained in G and so X is locally connected. ▮

27.13 Theorem. *A space X is locally connected at a point x if and only if every neighborhood of x contains a connected neighborhood of x.*

Proof: A. Let X be locally connected. Let N be any neighborhood of x. N contains an open set G which contains x and G contains a connected, open set W which contains x.

B. Let every neighborhood of a point x contain a connected neighborhood of the point x. Let G be an open set, such that C is a component of G and x is a point in C. There exists a neighborhood N of x such that $N \subseteq G$; there exists a connected neighborhood V of x and $V \subseteq N \subseteq G$. Since $C \cup V$ is connected and C is a component, $V \subseteq C$ and C is open. By theorem 27.12, X is locally connected. ▮

Theorem 27.7 shows that a continuous and open function on a locally connected space yields a locally connected image. Example 27.5 shows that a continuous function on a locally connected space does not always yield a locally connected space. A quasi-open function is a generalization of an open function which has special meaning for local connectedness.

27.14 Definition. A function f from a space X onto a space Y is called *quasi-open (closed)* if and only if the images of open (closed) inverse sets are open (closed).

27.15 Lemma. *A function f from a space $\{X, \mathcal{S}\}$ onto a space $\{Y, \mathfrak{J}\}$ is quasi-open if and only if $\mathfrak{J}$ contains the strong topology induced on Y by f.*

Proof: A. Let f be quasi-open. Let $B \subseteq Y$ and let $f^{-1}[B]$ be open in $\{X, \mathcal{S}\}$. Then $f[f^{-1}[B]]$ is open in $\{Y, \mathfrak{J}\}$, since f is quasi-open. Hence, B is open in $\{Y, \mathfrak{J}\}$ and $\mathfrak{J}$ contains the strong topology.

B. Let $\mathfrak{J}$ contain the strong topology. Let A be an open inverse set in $\{X, \mathcal{S}\}$. $A = f^{-1}[B]$, say. B then is contained in the strong topology by definition 10.6. Hence B is open in $\{Y, \mathfrak{J}\}$. This means $f[A]$ is open in $\{Y, \mathfrak{J}\}$ and that f is quasi-open. ▮

27.16 Example. Let $f(x) = x^3 + 3x^2$ with domain and range E^1. f is not open but f is quasi-open.

EXERCISE 3. Prove that f is a quasi-open function from a space X onto a space Y if and only if the images of closed inverse sets are closed, i.e., prove that a function is quasi-open if and only if it is quasi-closed.

27.17 Theorem. *If f is a continuous, quasi-open function on a locally connected space X, then $f[X]$ is locally connected.*

Proof: By theorem 26.9, the image of any component in the domain of a continuous function is contained in one component of the range. This can also be stated in the following manner. If K is any component of an open set G in $f[X]$, then $f^{-1}[K] = \bigcup_\nu C_\nu$, where each C_ν is a component of $f^{-1}[G]$. Since f is continuous, $f^{-1}[G]$ is open and by theorem 27.12, each C_ν is open in X. Thus, $\bigcup_\nu C_\nu = f^{-1}[K]$ is open in X. Since f is quasi-open, $f[f^{-1}[K]]$ must be open in $f[X]$. Since K, which is $f[f^{-1}[K]]$, was any component of an open set in $f[X]$, $f[X]$ is locally connected by theorem 27.12. ▮

27.18 Theorem. *If X is a locally connected space and if X/D is any quotient (decomposition) space of X, then X/D is locally connected.*

Proof: The quotient function, q, from X onto X/D sends each point onto its equivalence class. The quotient topology is, by definition, the strong topology for the range induced by q. By lemma 27.15, q is quasi-open. q, by definition of the strong topology, is continuous. Hence X/D, which is $q[X]$, is locally connected by theorem 27.17. ▮

27.19 Theorem. *If f is a function from the space $\{X, \mathcal{S}\}$ onto the locally connected space $\{Y, \mathfrak{J}\}$ and if $\mathcal{S}$ is the weak topology induced by f from $\mathfrak{J}$, then $\{X, \mathcal{S}\}$ is locally connected.*

Proof: Let G be any open set containing the point x in $\{X, \mathfrak{S}\}$, where $\mathfrak{S}$ is the weak topology induced by the function $f: \{X, \mathfrak{S}\} \to \{X, \mathfrak{J}\}$. By definition of the weak topology, G must be the inverse, $f^{-1}[H]$, of an open set H in $\{Y, \mathfrak{J}\}$. Let K be the component of H which contains $f(x)$. K is connected, by definition, and is open, by hypothesis and theorem 27.14. $f^{-1}[K]$ is then open, by definition of the weak topology, and $f^{-1}[K]$ contains x. $f^{-1}[K] \subseteq f^{-1}[H] = G$. Let $f^{-1}[K] = A \cup B$ separation. A and B are open in $f^{-1}[K]$. Hence A and B are open in $\{X, \mathfrak{S}\}$. By definition of the weak topology, A and B must be inverses of open sets in $\{Y, \mathfrak{J}\}$. Let $A = f^{-1}[H_1]$ and $B = f^{-1}[H_2]$, where H_1 and H_2 are disjoint open sets in $\{Y, \mathfrak{J}\}$ and, of course, $H_1 \subseteq K$ and $H_2 \subseteq K$. Now, $f^{-1}[H_1] \cup f^{-1}[H_2] = f^{-1}[H_1 \cup H_2] = f^{-1}[K]$. Hence, $K = H_1 \cup H_2$ separation. This is a contradiction, since K, as a component, is connected. Hence the assumption that $f^{-1}[K] = A \cup B$ separation must be false. Thus $f^{-1}[K]$ is open and connected, it contains x and is contained in G. This means that $\{X, \mathfrak{S}\}$ is locally connected. ▮

Pathwise Connectedness

Another topological property related to connectedness is pathwise connectedness.

27.20 Definition. A topological space is called a *curve* if and only if it is the continuous image of the closed unit interval, $[0, 1]$, with the usual topology. A continuous function with domain $[0, 1]$ is called a *path.* The images of 0 and 1 are called the *end points* of the curve and of the path.

27.21 Definition. A space $\{X, \mathfrak{J}\}$ is called *pathwise connected* if and only if for each two points a and b in $\{X, \mathfrak{J}\}$, there exists at least one path, i.e., one continuous function g from the unit interval $[0, 1]$ into $\{X, \mathfrak{J}\}$, such that $g(0) = a$ and $g(1) = b$. The range of g is called a curve between a and b; g is called a path from a to b.

27.22 Theorem. *Any pathwise connected space is connected.*

Proof: If a space is pathwise connected, then for each two points in the space there is a connected subset which contains the points. By theorem 24.24, the space is connected. ▮

The following example contains a space which is connected but not pathwise connected.

27.23 Example. Let X denote the following subset of the plane E^2. Let $A_n = \{(x, y) \mid -1 \leq y \leq 1 \text{ and } x = 1/n \text{ for } n \text{ some natural number}\}$; let $A_0 = \{(x, y) \mid -1 \leq y \leq 1 \text{ and } x = 0\}$; let $B_n = \{(x, y) \mid y = +1 \text{ and } 1/2^n \leq x \leq 1/2^{n-1} \text{ for } n \text{ some natural number}\}$ and let $C_n = \{(x, y) \mid y = -1 \text{ and } 1/2^{n+1} \leq x \leq 1/2^n \text{ for } n \text{ some natural number}\}$. Let $X =$

$(\bigcup_{n=0}^{\infty} A_n) \cup (\bigcup_{n=1}^{\infty} B_n) \cup (\bigcup_{n=1}^{\infty} C_n)$ (see figure 23). Assign to X the relative topology from E^2 in order to obtain a space which will also be denoted by X. Let $H_1 = \{(x, y) \text{ in } X \mid x = 0\}$ and let $H_2 = \{(x, y) \text{ in } X \mid x > 0\}$. H_2 is the union of connected subsets A_n, B_n, C_n for $n \geq 1$ and also is a bridged system of connected sets. By theorem 24.22, H_2 is connected. Every point of H_1 is a limit point of H_2; hence, $X = \overline{H}_2$. By theorem 24.19, X is connected. Assume there exists a curve K in X between $(0, 0)$

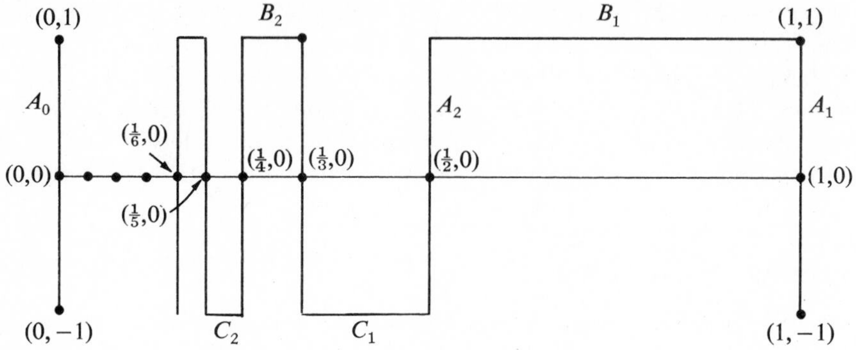

FIGURE 23

and $(1, -1)$. Let g be the continuous function whose range is K. $K \cap H_1$ is closed in K, by definition of X and of the relative topology. Hence, $g^{-1}[K \cap H_1]$ is closed in $[0, 1]$, by the continuity of g, and is not empty since it contains $g^{-1}[(0, 0)]$. Let t be any real number in $g^{-1}[K \cap H_1]$. Let $g(t) = (0, a)$ and let $V = \{(x, y) \text{ in } K \mid |x| < .1 \text{ and } |y - a| < .1\}$. There exists a connected neighborhood U of t in $[0, 1]$ such that $g[U] \subseteq V$. Since U is connected, $g[U]$ must lie in the component of V which contains $(0, a)$. This component lies in $K \cap H_1$. Hence $g[U] \subseteq K \cap H_1$ or $U \subseteq g^{-1}[K \cap H_1]$. This means that $g^{-1}[K \cap H_1]$ is open as well as closed. Since $g^{-1}[K \cap H_1]$ is non-empty and since $[0, 1]$ is connected, $g^{-1}[K \cap H_1] = [0, 1]$ or $g[[0, 1]] \subseteq H_1$. Thus there is no curve in X between $(0, 0)$ and $(1, -1)$.

EXERCISE 4. Determine the set of non-cut points for the space in the previous example.

EXERCISE 5. Is the space in example 27.23 irreducibly connected about its set of non-cut points?

EXERCISE 6. In the space X in example 27.23, omit the point $(1, -1)$. Does the resulting subspace consisting of $X \sim \{(1, -1)\}$ have a basic set about which it is irreducibly connected?

27.24 Definition. A space X is *locally pathwise connected* if and only if for each point x of X and each open neighborhood N of x, there exists a pathwise connected open neighborhood U of x such that $U \subseteq N$.

27.25 Theorem. *Any connected, locally pathwise connected space is pathwise connected.*

Proof: Let X be connected and locally pathwise connected, and let p be any point in X. Let $A = \{x \text{ in } X \mid x = p \text{ or } x \text{ can be joined to } p \text{ by a path in } X\}$. $A \neq \emptyset$. Since X is locally pathwise connected, each point a in A has an open locally pathwise connected neighborhood U_a. Thus each point in U_a can be joined to p via a by a curve in X. Hence $U_a \subseteq A$ and A is open. Now let y be a limit point of A in X. y has an open pathwise connected neighborhood U_y in X. Since y is a limit point of A, U_y contains some point a of A. Since there is a curve in X from p to a and since there is a curve in U_y from a to y, there is a curve in X from p to y and y is in A. Thus A is closed, as well as open, and $A \neq \emptyset$. This means, since X is connected, that $A = X$, and so X is pathwise connected. ▮

27.26 Corollary. *Any open connected subset of a locally pathwise connected space is pathwise connected.*

Proof: Exercise.

The following theorem is a "metrological" rather than a topological theorem; i.e., convexity depends on a metric. However, in addition to being important for the study of the Euclidean metric, it is also useful topologically.

27.27 Theorem. *The spherical neighborhoods in Euclidean n-space, E^n, are convex in the Euclidean metric, ρ_n.*

Proof: Let $U_{\rho_n}(\alpha, \epsilon) = \{x \mid \rho_n(x, \alpha) < \epsilon$ where x and α are in E^n, ϵ is positive and real and ρ_n is the Euclidean metric$\}$. Let β and γ be any two points in $U_{\rho_n}(\alpha, \epsilon)$. Let $L = \{\sigma \mid \sigma = t\beta + (1 - t)\gamma \text{ where } 0 \leq t \leq 1\}$. Consider $\rho_n\big(\alpha, t_0\beta + (1 - t_0)\gamma\big)$ for $0 \leq t_0 \leq 1$. If $\alpha = (a_1, \ldots, a_n)$, $\beta = (b_1, \ldots, b_n)$ and $\gamma = (c_1, \ldots, c_n)$, then $t_0\beta + (1 - t_0)\gamma = \big(t_0b_1 + (1 - t_0)c_1, \ldots, t_0b_n + (1 - t_0)c_n\big)$.

$$
\begin{aligned}
&\rho_n\big(\alpha, t_0\beta + (1 - t_0)\gamma\big) \\
&\quad = \sqrt{\sum_{i=1}^{n} (t_0b_i + (1 - t_0)c_i - a_i)^2} \\
&\quad = \sqrt{\sum_{i=1}^{n} [t_0(b_i - a_i) + (1 - t_0)(c_i - a_i)]^2} \\
&\quad = \sqrt{\sum_{i=1}^{n} [t_0^2(b_i - a_i)^2 + 2t_0(1 - t_0)(b_i - a_i)(c_i - a_i) + (1 - t_0)^2(c_i - a_i)^2]} \\
&\quad = \sqrt{t_0^2 \sum_{i=1}^{n} (b_i - a_i)^2 + 2t_0(1 - t_0) \sum_{i=1}^{n} (b_i - a_i)(c_i - a_i) + (1 - t_0)^2 \sum_{i=1}^{n} (c_i - a_i)^2}.
\end{aligned}
$$

Since β and γ are both in $U_{\rho_n}(\alpha, \epsilon)$,

$$\sum_{i=1}^{n} (b_i - a_i)^2 < \epsilon^2 \qquad \text{and} \qquad \sum_{i=1}^{n} (c_i - a_i)^2 < \epsilon^2.$$

Further, if A and B are any two real numbers, $(A - B)^2 \geq 0$; therefore, $A^2 - 2AB + B^2 \geq 0$ or $A^2 + B^2 \geq 2AB$. Hence

$$\sum_{i=1}^{n} 2(b_i - a_i)(c_i - a_i) \leq \sum_{i=1}^{n} [(b_i - a_i)^2 + (c_i - a_i)^2] \leq 2\epsilon^2.$$

It follows, then, that

$$\begin{aligned} \rho_n\big(\alpha, t_0\beta + (1 - t_0)\gamma\big) &\leq \sqrt{t_0^2\epsilon^2 + 2t_0(1 - t_0)\epsilon^2 + (1 - t_0)^2\epsilon^2} \\ &= \sqrt{[t_0 + (1 - t_0)]^2\epsilon^2} = \epsilon. \end{aligned}$$

Therefore, $t_0\beta + (1 - t_0)\gamma$ is in $U_{\rho_n}(\alpha, \epsilon)$, and so $U_{\rho_n}(\alpha, \epsilon)$ is convex. ▌

27.28 Corollary. *Euclidean n-space, E^n, is locally pathwise connected.*

Proof: Since any spherical neighborhood is convex, any spherical neighborhood is pathwise connected. ▌

27.29 Corollary. *Any open connected subspace of Euclidean n-space, E^n, is pathwise connected.*

27.30 Example. The following subspace of the plane, E^2, is pathwise connected but not locally pathwise connected. Let $\{S, \mathfrak{J}\}$ be the subspace of the plane consisting of $L \cup H_2$, where $L = \{(x, y) \text{ in } E^2 \mid y = 0 \text{ and } -1 \leq x \leq 0\} \cup \{(x, y) \text{ in } E^2 \mid x = -1 \text{ and } -2 \leq y \leq 0\} \cup \{(x, y) \text{ in } E^2 \mid y = -2 \text{ and } -1 \leq x \leq +1\} \cup \{(x, y) \mid x = +1 \text{ and } -2 \leq y \leq -1\}$ and H_2 is the subspace denoted by H_2 in example 27.23. See figure 23 and figure 24. $\{S, \mathfrak{J}\}$ is not locally connected at (0, 0), so it cannot be locally pathwise connected at (0, 0). Now, since any closed interval $[a, b]$ of real numbers can be mapped homeomorphically onto any interval $[c, d]$ of real numbers by the function $s = c + \big((t - a)/(b - a)\big) \cdot (d - c)$, the line segments which make up $\{S, \mathfrak{J}\}$ are each homeomorphic to closed intervals of real numbers. Hence, let $L_1 = \{(x, y) \mid y = 0 \text{ and } -1 \leq x \leq 0\}$, $L_2 = \{(x, y) \mid x = -1 \text{ and } -2 \leq y \leq 0\}$, $L_3 = \{(x, y) \mid y = -2 \text{ and } -1 \leq x \leq +1\}$ and $L_4 = \{(x, y) \mid x = +1 \text{ and } -2 \leq y \leq -1\}$. There exist homeomorphisms of [0, 1/4] onto L_1, [1/4, 1/2] onto L_2, [1/2, 3/4] onto L_3 and [3/4, 1] onto L_4 which agree on 1/4, 1/2 and 3/4 and such that the image of 0 is (0, 0) and the image of 1 is (1, −1). In addition, the closed interval $[2n - 1, 2n + 1]$ of real numbers can be mapped in a 1:1 continuous manner, by theorem 9.21, onto that part of S consisting of $\{(x, y) \text{ in } S \mid 1/(2n + 1) < x \leq 1/(2n + 1)\} \cup \{(1/(2n + 1, -1)\}$. Thus

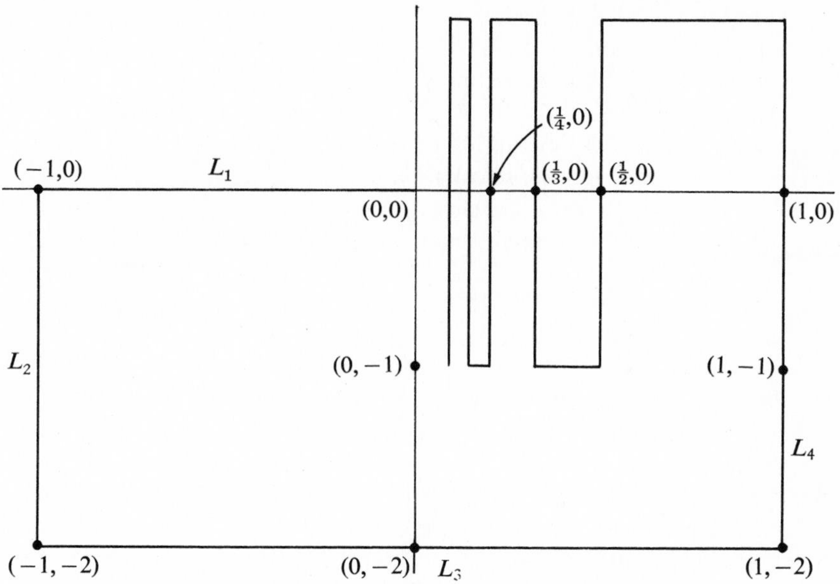

FIGURE 24

the set of non-negative real numbers has been mapped in a 1:1 piecewise homeomorphic manner onto the space $\{S, \mathfrak{I}\}$. Let this function be denoted by f. Now let (x_1, y_1) and (x_2, y_2) be two points of $\{S, \mathfrak{I}\}$. Let $(x_1, y_1) = f(t)$ and let $(x_2, y_2) = f(s)$. s and t are real numbers. The function f restricted to the interval $[s, t]$ is, by theorem 9.21, continuous. Hence, there is a curve in $\{S, \mathfrak{I}\}$ between (x_1, y_1) and (x_2, y_2).

The concepts of connectedness, local connectedness and cut point are most effective when combined with compactness. For example, a compact, connected, metrizable space with exactly two non-cut points is topologically the unit interval. A compact, connected, metrizable space S with the property that any two points separate S is topologically the circumference of the unit circle. If S is a compact, connected, locally connected, metrizable space, then S is pathwise connected. These and other similar theorems will be established, as well as the basic properties of compactness, in the next chapter.

SUMMARY FOR CHAPTER 5

Connectedness is a topological invariant which precludes the existence of non-empty proper subsets of a space which are both open and closed. Subsets which are both open and closed have empty boundaries. Thus, connectedness precludes also the existence of non-empty proper subsets with empty boundaries. No countable metric space containing more than one point is connected.

The product of connected spaces is connected.

The only connected subspaces of E^1, the usual space of real numbers, are the subspaces which contain $\{x \mid a \leq x \leq b\}$ when they contain a and b. The intermediate value theorem is a consequence of this last result.

Any closed interval, $[a, b]$, in E^1 has the fixed point property.

Any 1:1 continuous function of E^1 into E^1 is a homeomorphism.

Components are equivalence classes in a space X determined by connectedness for subsets. Components are closed, connected sets. Quasi-components are equivalence classes which contain components. Quasi-components are closed but not always connected.

A cut point is a point x in a connected space X with the property that $X - \{x\}$ is not connected. Cut points are topological invariants.

A connected space X is called irreducibly connected about a subset M if and only if no proper connected subset of X contains M. If X is irreducibly connected about a subset M, then M contains all the non-cut points of M.

A space is locally connected if and only if every neighborhood of any point contains a connected neighborhood of the point. A space is locally connected if and only if components of open sets are open. The continuous image of a locally connected space may not be locally connected. If the range carries the strong topology, then the image is locally connected. Thus, any quotient space of a locally connected space is locally connected. A product of locally connected spaces is locally connected if and only if the factor spaces are locally connected and all but a finite number are connected.

A space is called pathwise connected if and only if it contains a curve between any two points. Any open connected subspace of a locally pathwise connected space is pathwise connected. Hence, any open, connected subspace of Euclidean n-space is pathwise connected.

CHAPTER 6

Compactness

In section 18, the concept of "open covering" of a topological space was introduced. It was established (1) that second countability implied a special covering property; namely, that in a second countable space any open covering always contains a countable subcovering, and (2) that any regular space which possessed this latter covering property had to be normal. These two theorems alone establish the open covering as an important topological concept. However, it turns out that open coverings and closed coverings crop up in many other diverse situations in mathematics. Closed coverings serve to give an important definition of dimension for certain spaces. Open coverings are used to establish certain algebraic topological invariants for spaces; namely, the Čech homology and cohomology groups. In the present study, open coverings will yield two topological invariants. These invariants will serve to distinguish topologically between the circumference of the unit circle, $\{(x, y) \mid x^2 + y^2 = 1\}$, as a subspace of E^2 and the space E^1, and also between the closed interval $\{x \mid a \leq x \leq b$ for $a < b\}$ as a subspace of E^1 and the space E^1 itself. One of the first observations related to this problem was that there exist infinite sets in E^1, for example $\{1, 2, 3, \ldots\}$, which have no limit points in E^1, while it can be proved from the definition of the real space E^1 that every infinite set of real numbers in $A = \{x \mid a \leq x \leq b$ for $a < b\}$ as a subspace of E^1 has a limit point in A. This property; namely, that every infinite subset have a limit point, can be described in terms of open coverings of the space. Chapter 6 contains an introduction to the generalization of this property and its alternate definitions.

28. COMPACTNESS AND COUNTABLE COMPACTNESS.

OPEN COVERING DEFINITIONS

28.1 Definition. A topological space, S, is called *compact* if and only if every open covering of S contains a finite subcovering (definitions 18.11 and 18.13).

28.2 Definition. A topological space, S, is called *countably compact* if and only if every countable open covering of S contains a finite subcovering.

28.3 Theorem. *A space is compact if and only if it is Lindelöf and countably compact (definition 18.16).*

Proof: Exercise.

As is seen from the previous theorem, compactness is a "stronger" property than countable compactness and is actually, as the theorems which follow show, much more useful than countable compactness. However, in second countable spaces and in metrizable spaces, compactness and countable compactness are equivalent and in many instances in analysis and metric space theory the countable form of compactness is used more conveniently. For this reason, the basic properties of countable compactness will be established.

28.4 Theorem. *A space is compact (countably compact) if and only if every (countable) open covering has a finite refinement which is also an open covering.*

Proof: Exercise.

EXERCISE 1. Prove: a space S is (countably) compact if and only if every (countable) covering by elements of a base for the topology on S contains a finite subcovering.

28.5 Corollary. *If a space is second countable, countable compactness is equivalent to compactness.*

Proof: By theorem 18.15, a second countable space is Lindelöf; hence, by theorem 28.3, the corollary follows. ∎

28.6 Corollary. *For subspaces S of Euclidean n-space, E^n, countable compactness is equivalent to compactness.*

Proof: By theorems 11.21 and 5.10, E^n is second countable for all natural numbers n; hence, so are all its subspaces. ∎

28.7 Example. Let S be the space consisting of the set of all real numbers and the topology determined when each real number q is assigned $U_q = \{x \mid x \leq q\}$ as its only basic neighborhood. In example 18.20, this space was shown to be Lindelöf. If $\mathcal{G}$ is the open cover consisting of all sets U_n, for n a natural number, then no finite number of these covers S. Hence S is Lindelöf but not countably compact and hence not compact.

The set of all ordinal numbers less than the first uncountable ordinal ω_1 with the order topology yields a countably compact space which is not compact. However, before this is introduced as a formal example (28.33), some equivalent definitions of compactness are introduced.

CLOSED SET DEFINITIONS

28.8 Definition. A collection of closed sets in a topological space is said to have *the finite intersection property* if and only if the intersection of any finite number of sets in the collection is not empty.

28.9 Example. In Euclidean 1-space, E^1, consider the family $\{U_n \mid n \text{ is a natural number}\}$, where $U_n = \{x \mid x \geq n\}$. Each U_n is closed in E^1 and the intersection of any finite number of them is not empty. However, if $x \leq 0$, x is not in U_1, and if $x > 0$, by the archimedean order on the reals, there exists a natural number k such that $k \cdot 1 > x$, and x then is not in U_k. Thus $\bigcap_{n=1}^{\infty} U_n = \emptyset$.

28.10 Theorem. *A space S is compact if and only if every family of closed sets with the finite intersection property has a non-empty intersection.*

Proof: A. Let S be compact; let $\mathfrak{F} = \{F_\nu \mid \nu \in \mathfrak{A}\}$ denote a family of closed sets in S with the finite intersection property. Consider the collection $\mathfrak{G} = \{\sim F_\nu \mid \nu \in \mathfrak{A}\}$ of all complements of sets in $\mathfrak{F}$. Each $\sim F_\nu$ is open in S. Assume $\bigcap_\nu F_\nu = \emptyset$. Then $\sim \bigcap_\nu F_\nu = \sim\emptyset = S$. However, $\sim\bigcap_\nu F_\nu = \bigcup_\nu \sim F_\nu$. Hence, the collection $\{\sim F_\nu \mid \nu \in \mathfrak{A}\}$ is an open covering of S. Since S is compact, a finite number, say $\sim F_{\nu_1}, \sim F_{\nu_2}, \ldots, \sim F_{\nu_k}$, of sets in $\mathfrak{G}$ cover S. Therefore, $\bigcup_{i=1}^k \sim F_{\nu_i} = S$ and so, by De Morgan's law, $\sim\bigcap_{i=1}^k F_{\nu_i} = S$. Hence, $\bigcap_{i=1}^k F_{\nu_i} = \sim X = \emptyset$. This is a contradiction since the family $\mathfrak{F}$ was supposed to have the finite intersection property. Thus the assumption that $\bigcap_\nu F_\nu = \emptyset$ is false.

B. Let S have the property that any family $\mathfrak{F} = \{F_\nu \mid \nu \in \mathfrak{A}\}$ of closed sets with the finite intersection property has a non-empty intersection. Then let $\mathfrak{G} = \{G_\nu \mid \nu \in \mathfrak{A}\}$ be any open covering of S. Assume that no finite subset of $\mathfrak{G}$ covers S. Then if $\{G_{\nu_1}, \ldots, G_{\nu_k}\}$ is any finite subset of $\mathfrak{G}$, $\bigcup_{i=1}^k G_{\nu_i} \neq S$. Hence $\sim\bigcup_{i=1}^k G_{\nu_i} \neq \sim S = \emptyset$. Therefore, $\bigcap_{i=1}^k \sim G_{\nu_i} \neq \emptyset$. Hence, if $\mathfrak{F}$ denotes the family $\{\sim G_\nu \mid \nu \in \mathfrak{A}\}$ of the complements of sets in $\mathfrak{G}$, $\mathfrak{F}$ satisfies the finite intersection property. Hence, $\bigcap_\nu \sim G_\nu$ is not empty; therefore, $\sim\bigcup_\nu G_\nu \neq \emptyset$. Therefore, $\bigcup_\nu G_\nu$ is not equal to S. This is a contradiction since $\{G_\nu \mid \nu \in \mathfrak{A}\}$ was a covering of S. Hence, the assumption that no finite subset of $\mathfrak{G}$ covers S is false and so S is compact. ▮

28.11 Corollary. *E^1 is not compact.*

Proof: By example 28.9, there exists in E^1 a family of closed sets with the finite intersection property whose intersection is empty. Hence, by theorem 28.10, E^1 is not compact. ▮

28.12 Corollary. *E^1 is not countably compact.*

Proof: By corollaries 28.6 and 28.11, this corollary follows. ▮

EXERCISE 2. Prove, in a manner similar to that in the proof of corollary 28.11, that the space E^2 is neither compact nor countably compact.

EXERCISE 3. Let S be a set and let $\mathfrak{J}$ denote the smallest T_1-topology, i.e., $\mathfrak{J}$ consists of S, $\emptyset$ and all complements of finite subsets. Prove that $\{S, \mathfrak{J}\}$ is compact.

EXERCISE 4. Let S denote the set of real numbers and let $\mathfrak{J}$ denote the topology for S consisting of S, $\emptyset$ and all complements of countable sets. Prove or disprove: $\{S, \mathfrak{J}\}$ is (a) Lindelöf, (b) countably compact, (c) compact.

The previous theorem yields an alternate definition of compactness in terms of closed sets. The next theorem yields an alternate definition of countable compactness in terms of closed sets.

28.13 Theorem. *A space S is countably compact if and only if every countable family of closed sets with the finite intersection property has a non-empty intersection.*

Proof: The proof is left as an exercise since it is an exact analogue of the proof of theorem 28.10.

Countable Compactness and Limit Points

The axiom of choice implies that all cardinal numbers are comparable; this, among other things, implies that every infinite set contains a countably infinite set.

28.14 Lemma. *Let S be a topological space. Every infinite subset of S has a limit point in S if and only if every countably infinite subset of S has a limit point in S.*

Proof: A. Let every infinite subset of S have a limit point in S. It follows that every countably infinite subset of S has a limit point in S.

B. Let every countably infinite subset of S have a limit point in S; let A be any infinite subset of S. By the remark preceding this lemma, A contains a countably infinite subset C of S. By hypothesis, C has a limit point p in S. p is then a limit point of A. ▮

28.15 Theorem. *If a space S is countably compact, then every infinite subset of S has a limit point in S.*

Proof: Let A be any infinite subset of S and let $\{x_1, x_2, \ldots, x_n, \ldots\}$ denote any countably infinite subset of A. Let $x_i \neq x_j$ for $i \neq j$. Assume that the set $\{x_1, x_2, \ldots, x_n, \ldots\}$ has no limit point in S. Then, by corollary 2.20, no subset of $\{x_1, x_2, \ldots, x_n, \ldots\}$ has a limit point in S. In particular, the sets $F_n = \{x_n, x_{n+1}, \ldots\}$ are all closed in S. Further, the countable family $\{F_n \mid n \text{ is a natural number}\}$ has the finite intersection property, since $\{x_1, x_2, \ldots, x_n, \ldots\}$ is infinite. However, $\bigcap_{n=1}^{\infty} F_n$ is empty; for, if x_k is any point in

$\{x_1, \ldots, x_n, \ldots\}$, then x_k is not in F_{k+1}. This is a contradiction, since X is countably compact. Hence the assumption that $\{x_1, x_2, \ldots, x_n, \ldots\}$ has no limit point is false. Hence A has a limit point in S. ▌

28.16 Example. Let $\{S, \mathfrak{J}\}$ be the topological space consisting of the set of real numbers and the topology determined by the sets $V_q = \{x \mid x \geq q\}$ as base. $\{S, \mathfrak{J}\}$ is a T_0-space and has the property that every non-empty subset has a limit point; hence, every infinite subset has a limit point. $\{S, \mathfrak{J}\}$, however, is not countably compact and so is not compact. For, let $G_k = \{x \mid x \geq k, \text{ for } k \text{ an integer}\}$. The collection $\mathcal{G} = \{G_k \mid k \text{ is an integer}\}$ is a countable open covering of $\{S, \mathfrak{J}\}$. However, no finite subset of $\mathcal{G}$ covers $\{S, \mathfrak{J}\}$.

28.17 Theorem. *If S is a T_1-space, then S is countably compact if and only if every infinite subset of S has a limit point in S.*

Proof: The first half of the proof is taken care of by theorem 28.15. So, let every infinite subset of S have a limit point in S and let $\{F_1, F_2, \ldots, F_n, \ldots\}$ be any countably infinite family of closed sets with the finite intersection property. The collection $\{F_1, F_1 \cap F_2, \ldots, F_1 \cap F_2 \cap \cdots \cap F_n, \ldots\}$ is a countable collection of non-empty closed sets. Let $F_1 = F_1^*$, $F_1 \cap F_2 = F_2^*$ and $F_1 \cap F_2 \cap \cdots \cap F_n = F_n^*, \ldots$. $F_1^* \supseteq F_2^* \supseteq \cdots \supseteq F_n^* \supseteq \cdots$. If the set $\{F_1^*, F_2^*, \ldots\}$ is finite, then for some k, $F_k^* \subseteq \bigcap_{n=1}^{\infty} F_n$. Otherwise, by the axiom of choice, an infinite set $\{x_1, x_2, \ldots, x_n, \ldots\}$ of points of S is identified such that x_n is in F_n^*. By hypothesis, the infinite set $\{x_1, x_2, \ldots, x_n, \ldots\}$ has a limit point, p, in S. Let U be any neighborhood of p and let n be any natural number. There exists a neighborhood V of p which contains no point of $\{x_1, \ldots, x_{n-1}\} \sim \{p\}$ since S is a T_1-space. Hence $U \cap V$, and so U, must contain a point of the set $\{x_n, x_{n+1}, \ldots, x_{n+j}, \ldots\} \sim \{p\}$. Since U was any neighborhood of p, p is a limit point of $\{x_n, x_{n+1}, \ldots, x_{n+j}, \ldots\}$. Hence, p is also a limit point of F_n^*, since $\{x_n, x_{n+1}, \ldots, x_{n+j}, \ldots\}$ is a subset of F_n^*. Since F_n^* is closed, p is in F_n^*. Since n was any natural number, p is in $\bigcap_n F_n^*$. By definition of the F_n^*, $\bigcap_n F_n^* = \bigcap_n F_n$. Hence, $\bigcap_n F_n \neq \emptyset$, and so S is countably compact. ▌

28.18 Corollary. *A second countable, T_1-space S is compact if and only if every infinite subset of S has a limit point in S.*

Proof: By corollary 28.5, compactness and countable compactness are equivalent for S. By the previous theorem, countable compactness is equivalent to every infinite subset having a limit point in S. ▌

28.19 Definition. A subset, A, of a space $\{S, \mathfrak{J}\}$ is called *compact* (*countably compact*) if and only if the subspace $\{A, r\text{-}\mathfrak{J}\}$, where r-$\mathfrak{J}$ denotes the relative topology, is compact (countably compact).

28.20 Lemma. *A subset A of a space $\{S, \mathfrak{I}\}$ is compact (countably compact) if and only if every covering (countable covering) of A by open sets of S contains a finite subcovering.*

Proof: Exercise.

28.21 Corollary. *A subset A of a second countable metric space—in particular Euclidean n-space, E^n, for n any natural number and Hilbert space—is compact if and only if every infinite subset of A has a limit point in A.*

Proof: The corollary follows from corollary 28.18. ▮

Compactness and Convergence

28.22 Definition. A point a in a space $\{S, \mathfrak{I}\}$ is called a *cluster point of a filter* $\mathfrak{F}$ if and only if a is in $\overline{A}$ for every A in $\mathfrak{F}$.

28.23 Theorem. *A space $\{S, \mathfrak{I}\}$ is compact if and only if every filter has a cluster point.*

Proof: A. Let $\{S, \mathfrak{I}\}$ be compact. Let $\mathfrak{F}$ be a filter on $\{S, \mathfrak{I}\}$. $\mathfrak{F}$ has the finite intersection property. Hence if $\mathfrak{F}^*$ denotes the set of closures of sets in $\mathfrak{F}$, $\mathfrak{F}^*$ has the finite intersection property and hence $\bigcap \mathfrak{F}^* \neq \emptyset$ by compactness. Thus $\mathfrak{F}$ has a cluster point.

B. Let every filter on $\{S, \mathfrak{I}\}$ have a cluster point in $\{S, \mathfrak{I}\}$. Let $\mathfrak{B}$ be any collection of closed sets with the finite intersection property. Let $\mathfrak{F}$ be the filter generated by $\mathfrak{B}$ according to lemma 7.36. Let $\mathfrak{F}^*$ be the set of closures of sets in $\mathfrak{F}$. $\mathfrak{F}^* \supseteq \mathfrak{B}$. By hypothesis, $\bigcap \mathfrak{F}^* \neq \emptyset$; hence, $\bigcap \mathfrak{B} \neq \emptyset$ and $\{S, \mathfrak{I}\}$ is compact by theorem 28.10. ▮

28.24 Theorem. *A space $\{S, \mathfrak{I}\}$ is compact if and only if every filter is contained in a filter which converges to a point of $\{S, \mathfrak{I}\}$.*

Proof: A. Let S be compact and let $\mathfrak{F}$ be a filter on S. By theorem 28.23, $\mathfrak{F}$ has a cluster point. Let a be a cluster point of $\mathfrak{F}$ and let U be any neighborhood of a in $\{S, \mathfrak{I}\}$. If A is in $\mathfrak{F}$, then a is in $\overline{A}$. Hence U contains a point of A. Thus the intersection of any neighborhood of a with any set in $\mathfrak{F}$ is a non-empty set. Thus $\mathfrak{F} \cup \mathfrak{N}$, where $\mathfrak{N}$ is the set of neighborhoods of a, has the finite intersection property, and so by lemma 7.36 generates a filter, $\mathfrak{F}^*$. By definition 7.31, $\mathfrak{F}^*$ converges to a.

B. Let every filter on S be contained in a filter which converges in $\{S, \mathfrak{I}\}$. Let $\mathfrak{B}$ be any non-empty set of closed sets in $\{S, \mathfrak{I}\}$ with the finite intersection property. By lemma 7.36, $\mathfrak{B}$ generates a filter $\mathfrak{F}$ on S. By hypothesis, $\mathfrak{F}$ is contained in a filter $\mathfrak{F}^*$ which converges to a point a in S. Since $\mathfrak{F}^*$ converges to a, every neighborhood of a is in $\mathfrak{F}^*$. Hence if U is a neighborhood of a and if A is a set in $\mathfrak{F}^*$, $U \cap A \neq \emptyset$. This implies that a is in $\overline{A}$. Since each set in $\mathfrak{B}$ is closed and since each set in $\mathcal{B}$ is a set in $\mathfrak{F}^*$, a is in every set in $\mathcal{B}$. Thus $\bigcap\mathcal{B} \neq \emptyset$ and so $\{S, \mathfrak{J}\}$ is compact. ▌

The last two theorems may be translated into theorems on cluster points and convergence for nets.

28.25 Definition. A point p in a space $\{S, \mathfrak{J}\}$ is called a *cluster point of a net n* in S if and only if for each neighborhood U of p and each point δ^* in the domain of n, there is a point δ in the domain of n such that $\delta > \delta^*$ and $n(\delta)$ is in U.

28.26 Theorem. *A space $\{S, \mathfrak{J}\}$ is compact if and only if every net in S has a cluster point in $\{S, \mathfrak{J}\}$.*

Proof: A. Let $\{S, \mathfrak{J}\}$ be compact and let n be any net in S. Let $T(\delta) = \{x \mid x = n(\gamma)$, for γ in the domain of n and $\gamma \geq \delta\}$. Let $\mathcal{B}$ denote the set of all sets $T(\delta)$ for δ in the domain of n. Since the domain of any net is a directed set, $\mathcal{B}$ has the finite intersection property and hence, by lemma 7.36, generates a filter $\mathfrak{F}$ on S. By theorem 28.23, $\mathfrak{F}$ has a cluster point p in $\{S, \mathfrak{J}\}$. By definition 28.25, every neighborhood of p contains a point of each set in $\mathfrak{F}$. Hence every neighborhood of p contains a point in each set $T(\delta)$ defined above. Thus p is a cluster point of n.

B. Let every net n in $\{S, \mathfrak{J}\}$ have a cluster point and let $\mathfrak{F}$ be any filter on S. The set of sets in $\mathfrak{F}$ is directly ordered by inclusion, i.e., $A \geq B$ if and only if $A \subseteq B$. Since $\mathfrak{F}$ is a filter, the null set does not belong to $\mathfrak{F}$. Hence, the choice function on $P(S) \sim \{\emptyset\}$ restricted to $\mathfrak{F}$ determines a net, n, on S. By hypothesis, n has a cluster point p in $\{S, \mathfrak{J}\}$. Let U be any neighborhood of p and let A be any set in $\mathfrak{F}$. There is a set $B \subseteq A$ such that $n(B)$ is in U, by definition 28.25. Since $n(B)$ is a point of B and $B \subseteq A$, every neighborhood of p contains a point of A. Thus p is in $\overline{A}$ for each A in $\mathfrak{F}$. p is then a cluster point of $\mathfrak{F}$ in $\{S, \mathfrak{J}\}$ and, by theorem 28.23, $\{S, \mathfrak{J}\}$ is compact. ▌

The following definition insures that any subnet of a converging net n converges to the same limit as n.

28.27 Definition. A net $n^*: D^* \to S$ is a *subnet* of a net $n: D \to S$ if and only if (1) there exists a function σ from D^* into D such that n^* is the composite of σ and n, i.e., $n^* = n \circ \sigma$, and (2) for each α in D, there is an α^* in D^* such that if $\beta^* \geq \alpha^*$, then $\sigma(\beta^*) \geq \alpha$. n is said to contain n^*.

28.28 Lemma. *If n^* is a subnet of a net n in a space $\{S, \mathfrak{J}\}$ and if n converges to p, then n^* converges to p.*

Proof: Exercise.

28.29 Theorem. *A space $\{S, \mathfrak{J}\}$ is compact if and only if every net contains a converging subnet in $\{S, \mathfrak{J}\}$.*

Proof: A. Let $\{S, \mathfrak{J}\}$ be compact and let n be any net in $\{S, \mathfrak{J}\}$. By theorem 28.26, n has a cluster point, p, in $\{S, \mathfrak{J}\}$. What follows proves that any net with a cluster point p always has a subnet which converges to p. A subnet of n will be defined which converges to p. Let D denote the domain of n. Let D^* denote the set of all pairs $\{\alpha, V\}$ where α is an element of D, V is a neighborhood of p and $n(\alpha)$ is in V. Define the function η from D^* into D as follows: $\eta(\{\alpha, V\}) = \alpha$. Let D^* be ordered as follows: $\{\alpha, V\}\ R\ \{\beta, U\}$ if and only if $\alpha \geq \beta$ and $V \subseteq U$. R is reflexive and transitive. Next, let $\{\alpha, V\}$ and $\{\beta, U\}$ be in D^*. Since p is a cluster point of n, there exists an element γ in D such that $\gamma \geq \alpha$, $\gamma \geq \beta$ and $n(\gamma)$ is in $U \cap V$. Hence, $\{\gamma, U \cap V\}$ is in D^* and $\{\gamma, U \cap V\}\ R\ \{\alpha, V\}$ and $\{\gamma, U \cap V\}\ R\ \{\beta, U\}$. Hence D^* is directly ordered by R.

Define, next, the mapping η from D^* into D as follows: $\eta(\{\alpha, V\}) = \alpha$. Consider the composite function $n \circ \eta$ from D^* into S. Let α be any element in D and let U be any neighborhood of p. Since p is a cluster point of n, there exists a γ in D such that $\gamma \geq \alpha$ and $n(\gamma)$ is in U. Hence, $\{\gamma, U\}$ is in D^*. Now let $\{\beta, W\}$ be in D^* such that $\{\beta, W\}\ R\ \{\gamma, U\}$. Then $\eta(\{\beta, W\}) = \beta$ and, by definition of R, $\beta \geq \gamma$. Since $\gamma \geq \alpha$, $\eta(\{\beta, W\}) \geq \alpha$. Thus, $n \circ \eta$ is a subnet of n.

Finally, let V be any neighborhood of p in $\{S, \mathfrak{J}\}$. Again, since p is a cluster point of n, there exists a δ in D such that $n(\delta)$ is in V. Hence, $\{\delta, V\}$ is in D^*. Now, let $\{\alpha, W\}$ be in D^* and let $\{\alpha, W\}\ R\ \{\delta, V\}$. By definition of R, above, $\alpha \geq \delta$ and $W \subseteq V$. Now, $n \circ \eta(\{\alpha, W\}) = n(\alpha)$. Since $\{\alpha, W\}$ is in D^*, $n(\alpha)$ is in W and since $W \subseteq V$, $n(\alpha)$ is in V. Thus $n \circ \eta(\{\alpha, W\})$ is in V and so $n \circ \eta$ converges to p.

B. Conversely, let each net in $\{S, \mathfrak{J}\}$ have a subnet which converges in $\{S, \mathfrak{J}\}$. Let n be any net in $\{S, \mathfrak{J}\}$ and let n^* be a subnet of n which converges to p in $\{S, \mathfrak{J}\}$. What follows proves that if a subnet n^* of a net n converges to p, then p is a cluster point of n. Let $n^* = n \circ \eta$. Let α be any point in the domain of n and let U be any neighborhood of p. Since n^* is a subnet, there is an element d in the domain of n^* such that for $a \geq d$, $\eta(a) \geq \alpha$. Also, since n^* converges to p, there exists an element b such that $c > b$ implies that $n^*(c)$ is in U. Thus if $u \geq d$ and if $u \geq b$, then $\eta(u) \geq \alpha$ and $n^*(u)$ is in U. Thus $n(\eta(u))$ is in U and $\eta(u) \geq \alpha$. Thus p is a cluster point of n and by theorem 28.26, $\{S, \mathfrak{J}\}$ is compact. ▌

The analogue of theorem 28.26 for sequences and countable compactness now follows.

28.30 Theorem. *A space $\{S, \mathfrak{J}\}$ is countably compact if and only if every sequence contains a converging subnet.*

Proof: A. Let $\{S, \mathfrak{J}\}$ be countably compact. Let $(x_1, x_2, \ldots, x_n, \ldots)$ be a sequence in $\{S, \mathfrak{J}\}$. Let $F_n = \{x_n, x_{n+1}, \ldots\}$. $F_1 \supseteq F_2 \supseteq \cdots \supseteq F_n \supseteq \cdots$. Hence, $\overline{F}_1 \supseteq \overline{F}_2 \supseteq \cdots \supseteq \overline{F}_n \supseteq \cdots$ and $\overline{F}_n \neq \emptyset$ for $n = 1, 2, \ldots$. By hypothesis and theorem 28.13, $\bigcap_n \overline{F}_n \neq \emptyset$. By definition 28.25, $(x_1, x_2, \ldots, x_n, \ldots)$ then has at least one cluster point. By theorem 28.29, $(x_1, x_2, \ldots, x_n, \ldots)$ contains a subnet converging to p.

B. Let $\{S, \mathfrak{J}\}$ be a space with the property that every sequence contains a converging subnet. Let $\{F_1, F_2, \ldots, F_n, \ldots\}$ be any countable set of non-empty closed subsets of $\{S, \mathfrak{J}\}$ with the finite intersection property. Let $F_1^* = F_1$, $F_2^* = F_1 \cap F_2, \ldots, F_n^* = F_1 \cap F_2 \cap \cdots \cap F_n$. $F_1^* \supseteq F_2^* \supseteq \cdots \supseteq F_n^* \supseteq \cdots$. If $\{F_1^*, F_2^*, \ldots, F_n^*, \ldots\}$ is a finite set, then $\bigcap_n F_n^* = F_k^* \neq \emptyset$ for some natural number k. If $\{F_1^*, F_2^*, \ldots, F_n^*, \ldots\}$ is an infinite set, then by the axiom of choice there exists at least one sequence, $S = (x_1, x_2, \ldots, x_n, \ldots)$, such that $x_n \in F_n^*$ for $n = 1, 2, \ldots$. By hypothesis, $(x_1, x_2, \ldots, x_n, \ldots)$ contains a converging subnet, $s \circ \sigma$. Let $s \circ \sigma$ converge to p and let W be any neighborhood of p. By definition (7.20) of convergence of a net, there exists an element δ_0 in the domain of $s \circ \sigma$ such that if δ is in the domain of $s \circ \sigma$ and if $\delta \geq \delta_0$, then $s \circ \sigma(\delta) \in W$. By definition (28.27) of a subnet, for each element n in the domain of s, there exists an element δ^* in the domain of $s \circ \sigma$ such that if $\delta \geq \delta^*$, then $\sigma(\delta) \geq n$. Now by definition (7.16) of a net, there exists an element α in the domain of $s \circ \sigma$ such that $\alpha \geq \delta_0$ and $\alpha \geq \delta^*$. Hence $\sigma(\alpha) \geq n$ and $s(\sigma(\alpha)) \in W$. Thus for each natural number n, there exists a natural number $\sigma(\alpha)$ such that $\sigma(\alpha) \geq n$ and $s(\sigma(\alpha)) \in W$. This means that p is a cluster point of $s = (x_1, x_2, \ldots, x_n, \ldots)$, and that $p \in \bigcap_n F_n^* = \bigcap_n F_n$. Hence, $\bigcap_n F_n \neq \emptyset$ and $\{S, \mathfrak{J}\}$ is countably compact. ▮

28.31 Corollary. *If η is a net and if p is a limit of a subnet $\eta \circ \sigma$ of η, then p is a cluster point of η.*

Proof: The proof is contained in the proof of the previous theorem. ▮

The statement of theorem 28.30 lacks a certain symmetry in the sense that a sequence in the space ought to contain a converging subsequence. However, the subnet defined in part A of the proof of theorem 28.29 depends for its cardinality on the cardinality of the domain of the original net and of the family of neighborhoods of the point p. Hence if the original net is a sequence, then the subnet as defined will be a sequence if and only if the family of neighborhoods of p is countable. If a local base is used to define the subnet, then the resulting subnet will be a sequence if and only if the point p has a countable local base. These considerations lead to the alternate definition of countable compactness for first countable spaces which is contained in the following theorem.

28.32 Theorem. *A first countable space $\{S, \mathfrak{J}\}$ is countably compact if and only if each sequence contains a converging subsequence.*

Proof: A. Let $\{S, \mathfrak{I}\}$ be a first countable, countably compact space and let $s = (x_1, x_2, \ldots, x_n, \ldots)$ be any sequence in $\{S, \mathfrak{I}\}$. By the previous theorem (28.30) and corollary (28.31), s has a cluster point p in $\{S, \mathfrak{I}\}$. By theorem 5.5, let $\mathfrak{B} = \{B_1, B_2, \ldots, B_i, \ldots\}$ denote a countable local base at p such that $B_i \subseteq B_j$ if $i \geq j$. By definition (28.25) of a cluster point, for each B_i in the local base $\mathfrak{B}$, there is a natural number m such that $m \geq i$ and $s(m) = x_m$ is in B_i. By the axiom of choice, a function σ can be defined by $\sigma(i) = m$. Consider the sequence $s \circ \sigma$. Let n be any natural number in the domain of s. Consider n in the domain of σ and let $k \geq n$ be in the domain of σ. Since $\sigma(k) \geq k$, by definition of σ, $\sigma(k) \geq n$. Thus, $s \circ \sigma$ is a subsequence of s. Now let W be any neighborhood of p. There exists a set B_j in $\mathfrak{B}$ such that $B_j \subseteq W$. Now by above, if $k \geq j$, $\sigma(k) \geq j$, and since $s(\sigma(k)) \in B_k$, by definition of σ, $s(\sigma(k)) \in B_j$. Hence if $k \geq j$, $s \circ \sigma(k) \in W$. Thus $s \circ \sigma$ converges to p.

B. Conversely, let $\{S, \mathfrak{I}\}$ be a space such that every sequence contains a converging subsequence. By the previous theorem (28.30), $\{S, \mathfrak{I}\}$ is countably compact. ▮

If theorem 28.32 is compared with theorem 28.17, it will be observed that in general the property that every sequence contain a converging subsequence is a stronger property than the property that every infinite subset have a limit point. In the space in example 28.16, every infinite set has a limit point but the sequence $(-1, -2, -3, \ldots, -n, \ldots)$, for n a natural number, does not have a converging subsequence.

A Countably Compact but Not Compact Space

The desired space consists of the set of all countable ordinals and a natural topology defined in terms of the natural ordering on the set. A few basic facts about ordinals are listed without any axiomatic development.

An ordinal number is a set α with the special property that each of its elements is a subset of α and each of its elements is an ordinal. The collection of all ordinals cannot be called a set because a contradiction results. The first ordinal is defined to be the null set, $\emptyset$, and is denoted by 0. The next ordinal is defined to be $\{\emptyset\}$, i.e., the set whose only element is the null set. This latter ordinal is denoted by 1. The next ordinal is denoted by 2 and is defined to be $\{\emptyset, \{\emptyset\}\} = \{0, 1\}$. The next ordinal is denoted by 3 and is defined to be $\{0, 1, 2\}$. Thus the elements of 3 are subsets of 3. Any ordinal is well ordered by an order relation $<$. $\alpha < \beta$ if and only if α is in β. Each ordinal then is the set of ordinals less than itself. If α is an ordinal, then $\alpha \cup \{\alpha\}$ is the *immediate successor* of α and is denoted by $\alpha + 1$. Every ordinal, then, has an immediate successor. If β is an ordinal and if $\beta = \sigma + 1$, then σ is called the *immediate predecessor* of β. The set, ω, of ordinals which contains the first ordinal 0 and in addition contains those ordinals and only those ordinals which are immediate successors of ordinals which it contains is called the set of natural numbers or the set of finite ordinals, and is denoted by $\{0, 1, 2, \ldots\}$. If k is a natural number, then $k + 1$ is a natural number by definition and so ω has no immediate predecessor. Thus, ordinals may or may not have immediate predecessors. Those ordinals which have immediate predecessors and the ordinal 0 are called *non-limit ordinals*. Those ordinals which do not have immediate predecessors, except for 0, are called *limit ordinals*. ω is a limit ordinal. A set is *countable* if and only if it can be put into 1:1 correspondence with ω or an element of ω. Since ordinals are sets, an ordinal may be countable or uncountable. The set W of countable ordinals is an ordinal number and is the smallest uncountable ordinal. If $\alpha < W$, α is countable by definition of W. If α is a countable ordinal, then (1) α is in ω and so $\alpha + 1$ is in ω, or (2) there exists h, a 1:1 correspondence between α and ω. If (2) holds, let $h^*(\sigma) = h(\sigma) + 1$ and let $h^*(\alpha + 1) = 0$. Then $h(\sigma) + 1$ is a natural number (a finite ordinal) if $h(\sigma)$ is, and h^* is a 1:1 correspondence between $\alpha + 1$ and ω. Thus $\alpha + 1$ is countable, if α is. W, then, is a limit ordinal.

28.33 Definition. Let σ be a countable ordinal and let basic neighborhoods be defined for σ as follows: if σ is a non-limit ordinal, then $\{\sigma\}$ is the one basic neighborhood for σ. If σ is a limit ordinal, the basic neighborhoods for σ are the sets U_γ for $\gamma < \sigma$, where $U_\gamma = \{\beta \mid \gamma < \beta \leq \sigma\}$. The resulting topology, $o\text{-}\mathfrak{J}$, is called the *order topology* for W, the set of all countable ordinals. $W = \{\gamma \mid \gamma \text{ is an ordinal and } \gamma < W\}$. It is immediate that $\{W, o\text{-}\mathfrak{J}\}$ is a T_1-space. The order topology is defined in exactly the same manner for the set of all ordinals less than any ordinal α.

28.34 Lemma. *$\{W, o\text{-}\mathfrak{J}\}$ is not compact.*

Proof: Let α be any ordinal in W. Let $T(\alpha) = \{\sigma \text{ in } W \mid \sigma \geq \alpha\}$. Since $\alpha + 1$ is in W, by previous remarks above, $T(\alpha) \neq \emptyset$. Further, $T(\alpha)$ is closed in $\{W, o\text{-}\mathfrak{J}\}$ since $\sim T(\alpha) = \{\gamma \text{ in } W \mid \gamma < \alpha\}$ is open in $\{W, o\text{-}\mathfrak{J}\}$. Next, let $\{\alpha_1, \alpha_2, \ldots, \alpha_k\}$ denote a finite set of elements in W. It may be assumed that $\alpha_1 < \alpha_2 < \cdots < \alpha_k$. Then $T(\alpha_1) \supseteq T(\alpha_2) \supseteq \cdots \supseteq T(\alpha_k)$. Hence, $\bigcap_{i=1}^{k} T(\alpha_i) = T(\alpha_k) \neq \emptyset$. Thus the set of all closed subsets $T(\alpha)$, for α in W, has the finite intersection property. Next, let γ be any ordinal in W. Again, by previous remarks, $\gamma + 1$ is in W and γ is not in $T(\gamma + 1)$. Thus, $\bigcap_{\alpha \in W} T(\alpha) = \emptyset$ and, by theorem 28.10, $\{W, o\text{-}\mathfrak{J}\}$ is not compact. ▮

28.35 Lemma. *$\{W, o\text{-}\mathfrak{J}\}$ is countably compact.*

Proof: Let $A = \{\alpha_1, \alpha_2, \ldots\}$ be a countably infinite set of ordinals in W. There exists an ordinal γ in W such that $\gamma > \alpha_i$ for $i = 1, 2, \ldots$. For, if no such γ existed, then $\bigcup_{i=1}^{\infty} \alpha_i$ would be equal to W. W then would be countable and would not be the smallest uncountable ordinal. Thus, the set of ordinals in W, which are greater than all the ordinals in A, is not empty and so has a smallest element, λ. $A \subseteq \lambda$. There are two exclusive possibilities: (1) λ is a limit ordinal, and (2) λ is a non-limit ordinal. Because of the nature of W, any element λ is also a subset of W, and λ and the relative topology yield a subspace. In what follows, to make the meaning of each statement less ambiguous, $s(\lambda)$ will be used to denote the subset and subspace determined by the element λ of W, i.e., $s(\lambda) = \{\alpha \mid \alpha < \lambda\}$ for $\lambda \in W$.

Case I. Let λ be a limit ordinal and let U_σ, for $\sigma < \lambda$, be any basic neighborhood of λ. $U_\sigma = \{\beta \mid \sigma < \beta \leq \lambda\}$. Since λ is the smallest ordinal greater than every ordinal in A, there must exist α_j in U_σ. Since $\alpha_j \neq \lambda$, λ is a limit point of A in $\{W, o\text{-}\mathfrak{J}\}$.

Case II. Let λ be a non-limit ordinal. It will be shown that $s(\lambda)$, as a subset of W, is compact. Hence by definition 28.2 and theorem 28.15, A will have a limit point in $s(\lambda) \subseteq W$. Transfinite induction will be used to establish that $s(\lambda)$ is compact for all countable non-limit ordinals, λ. $\lambda \neq 0$, since $A \neq \emptyset$. The subspace $s(1)$ is $\{0\}$ and so is compact. Assume that $s(\gamma)$, as a subspace of W, is compact for every non-limit ordinal $\gamma < \lambda$. Let $\mathcal{G}$ be any covering of $s(\lambda)$ by open sets of $\{W, o\text{-}\mathfrak{J}\}$. Since λ is a non-limit ordinal and $\lambda \neq 0$, λ has an immediate predecessor which will be denoted by $\lambda - 1$. If $\lambda - 1$ is a non-limit ordinal, then $s(\lambda - 1)$, as a subspace of W, is compact by the induction assumption. Hence, a finite number of sets $G_1, G_2, \ldots, G_k$ of $\mathcal{G}$ will cover $s(\lambda - 1)$ and at most one more will cover $\lambda - 1$, as an element in λ. Thus in the case that $\lambda - 1$ is a non-limit ordinal, $s(\lambda)$, as a subspace, is compact. Lastly, let $\lambda - 1$ be a limit ordinal. There exists an open set G^* in $\mathcal{G}$ which contains $\lambda - 1$, as an element, since $\mathcal{G}$ is an open covering of the subspace $s(\lambda)$. Hence, G^* must contain a basic neighborhood U_σ of $\lambda - 1$ as an ordinal in $s(\lambda)$. Let $U_\sigma = \{\beta \mid \sigma < \beta \leq \lambda - 1\}$. $\sigma + 1$ is the immediate successor of σ and is a non-limit ordinal. Hence $s(\sigma + 1)$ is compact by the induction assumption and so a finite number, $G_1, G_2, \ldots, G_k$, of sets in $\mathcal{G}$ cover $s(\sigma + 1)$. G^* contains U_σ. Now since $s(\sigma + 1) \cup U_\sigma$ contains $s(\lambda - 1) \cup \{\lambda - 1\}$, $G_1, G_2, \ldots, G_k, G^*$ cover $s(\lambda)$. $s(\lambda)$ is then compact. Since $s(\lambda)$ contains A, A has a limit point in $s(\lambda)$, by definition 28.2 and theorem 28.15. Hence, since $\{W, o\text{-}\mathfrak{J}\}$ is a T_1-space, $\{W, o\text{-}\mathfrak{J}\}$ is countably compact by theorem 28.17. ▮

The previous lemmas and example 28.7 establish that a space can be Lindelöf and neither countably compact nor compact, and that a space can be countably compact and neither compact nor Lindelöf.

Topological Invariance

The basic equivalent definitions of compactness and those for countable compactness have now been introduced, and lemmas 28.34 and 28.35 establish compactness and countable compactness as two distinct properties. The next theorems establish that compactness and countable compactness are topological invariants.

28.36 Theorem. *If f is a continuous function from the (countably) compact space S onto the space Y, then Y is (countably) compact.*

Proof: Let $\mathcal{G} = \{G_\nu\}$ be any (countable) open covering of Y. The collection $\{f^{-1}[G_\nu]\}$ constitutes an (countable) open covering of S. Since S is (countably) compact, a finite number of these sets, say $f^{-1}[G_{\nu_1}], f^{-1}[G_{\nu_2}], \ldots, f^{-1}[G_{\nu_k}]$ covers S. $S = f^{-1}[G_{\nu_1}] \cup \cdots \cup f^{-1}[G_{\nu_k}] = f^{-1}[G_{\nu_1} \cup \cdots \cup G_{\nu_k}]$. Hence, $G_{\nu_1} \cup G_{\nu_2} \cup \cdots \cup G_{\nu_k}$ covers Y and Y is (countably) compact. ▮

28.37 Theorem. *Compactness and countable compactness are topological invariants.*

Proof: Exercise.

EXERCISE 5. Prove or disprove: If the continuous function f has a compact range, then it has a compact domain.

PRODUCTS OF COMPACT SPACES

Any product of compact spaces is compact. The proof for the general product given below is quite complicated, requiring an equivalent form of the axiom of choice. For this reason the proof that the product of two compact spaces is compact is worked out separately, first.

28.38 Theorem. *If X and Y are compact spaces, then the product space $X \times Y$ is compact.*

Proof: Let $\mathcal{G}$ denote any covering of $X \times Y$ by basic open sets. Let y be any point in Y. By lemma 24.25, $X \times \{y\}$ is homeomorphic to X and is therefore compact. Hence a finite number of the basic open sets in $\mathcal{G}$ cover $X \times \{y\}$. Let these sets be $U_1 \times V_1, U_2 \times V_2, \ldots, U_k \times V_k$. Delete those sets in this finite collection for which V_i does not contain y. Denote the remaining finite number by $\{A_1^y \times B_1^y\}, \ldots, \{A_{n_j}^y \times B_{n_j}^y\}$. y is in $\bigcap_{i=1}^m B_i^y = W_y$. These open sets W_y cover Y. Since Y is compact, a finite number, $W_{y_1}, W_{y_2}, \ldots, W_{y_n}$, cover Y. Consider, now, the finite coverings defined above for $X \times \{y_1\}$, $X \times \{y_2\}, \ldots, X \times \{y_n\}$. Let

$$\begin{aligned}
\mathcal{G}_1 &= \{A_1^{y_1} \times B_1^{y_1}\}, \ldots, \{A_{m_1}^{y_1} \times B_{m_1}^{y_1}\} \\
\mathcal{G}_2 &= \{A_1^{y_2} \times B_1^{y_2}\}, \ldots, \{A_{m_2}^{y_2} \times B_{m_2}^{y_2}\} \\
&\vdots \\
\mathcal{G}_n &= \{A_1^{y_n} \times B_1^{y_n}\}, \ldots, \{A_{m_n}^{y_n} \times B_{m_n}^{y_n}\}.
\end{aligned}$$

$\mathcal{G}_1$ covers $X \times \{y_1\}, \ldots, \mathcal{G}_n$ covers $X \times \{y_n\}$. Now let (a, b) be in $X \times Y$. b is in some set $W_{y_j} = \bigcap_{i=1}^{m_j} B_i^{y_j}$, since the sets $W_{y_1}, \ldots, W_{y_n}$ cover Y. Hence, b is in each of $B_1^{y_j}, \ldots, B_{m_j}^{y_j}$. Since $\{A_1^{y_j} \times B_1^{y_j}\}, \ldots, \{A_{m_j}^{y_j} \times B_{m_j}^{y_j}\}$ cover $X \times \{y_j\}$, a is in at least one of the sets $\{A_1^{y_j}, \ldots, A_{m_j}^{y_j}\}$. Hence, (a, b) is covered by $\mathcal{G}_1 \cup \mathcal{G}_2 \cup \cdots \cup \mathcal{G}_n$ and $X \times Y$ is compact. ▮

EXERCISE 6. Prove that any product of a finite number of compact spaces is compact.

In section 7, filters were introduced to generalize the concept of convergence of a sequence. It was established that limit points and continuity can be defined directly in terms of filters. In section 23, filters were invoked to define the most general structure on which uniform continuity can be usefully defined—the uniform space. Filters will now be used to prove that any product of compact spaces is compact.

Zorn's Lemma. *If in a non-empty partially ordered set $\mathcal{P}$, each simply ordered subset has an upper bound, then $\mathcal{P}$ has a maximal element. An element m in $\mathcal{P}$ is maximal if and only if no other element in $\mathcal{P}$ is greater than m, i.e., if R is the partial ordering on $\mathcal{P}$, then mRn is false for $m \neq n$.*

Zorn's lemma is logically equivalent to the axiom of choice.

28.39 Definition. An *ultrafilter* on a set S is a filter on S which is not contained in any other filter on S.

28.40 Lemma. *Every filter on a set S is contained in an ultrafilter on S.*

Proof: Let $\mathfrak{F}$ be any filter on the set S. Let $\mathcal{P}$ denote the set of all filters on S which contain $\mathfrak{F}$. $\mathcal{P}$ is non-empty and partially ordered by inclusion. Next let $\mathcal{L} = \{L_\nu \mid \nu \in \mathfrak{A}\}$ be any simply ordered subset of $\mathcal{P}$. Let $\mathcal{L}^* = \bigcup_\nu L_\nu$. Since each L_ν is a filter, $\mathcal{L}^*$ does not contain the empty set. If A and B are in $\mathcal{L}^*$, then A is in L_α and B is in L_β, say. Since $\mathcal{L}^*$ is linearly ordered, $L_\alpha \subseteq L_\beta$, say. Hence, A and B are in L_β, a filter, and so $A \cap B$ is in L_β. This implies that $A \cap B$ is in $\mathcal{L}^*$, if A and B are. Next, let $M \supseteq A$ for A in $\mathcal{L}^*$. A is in L_α, say. Since L_α is a filter, M is in L_α. M is then in $\mathcal{L}^*$ and $\mathcal{L}^*$ is a filter on S. $\mathcal{L}^*$ contains every filter in $\mathcal{L}$, by definition. Thus $\mathcal{L}$ has an upper bound, and so, by Zorn's lemma, $\mathcal{P}$ has a maximal element $\mathfrak{M}$. $\mathfrak{M}$ is a filter which contains $\mathfrak{F}$. Further, if $\mathfrak{H}$ is a filter such that $\mathfrak{H} \supseteq \mathfrak{M}$, then $\mathfrak{H} \supseteq \mathfrak{F}$, and so $\mathfrak{H} \in \mathcal{P}$. Hence no filter can contain $\mathfrak{M}$ properly. Thus $\mathfrak{M}$ is an ultrafilter. ▮

28.41 Corollary. *A space $\{S, \mathfrak{J}\}$ is compact if and only if every ultrafilter converges to a point of $\{S, \mathfrak{J}\}$.*

Proof: A. Let $\{S, \mathfrak{J}\}$ be compact. By theorem 28.24, any ultrafilter, $\mathfrak{M}$, must converge to a point of $\{S, \mathfrak{J}\}$.

B. Let every ultrafilter in the space $\{S, \mathfrak{J}\}$ converge to a point of $\{S, \mathfrak{J}\}$. By theorem 28.24 and lemma 28.40, $\{S, \mathfrak{J}\}$ is compact. ▮

EXERCISE 7. Give an example of a filter on the set of real numbers which is not an ultrafilter.

EXERCISE 8. Give an example of a filter on the set of real numbers which is contained in more than one ultrafilter.

The following lemmas establish important properties for ultrafilters.

28.42 Lemma. *If $\mathfrak{M}$ is an ultrafilter on a set S and if A is any subset of S with the property that A intersects every set in S on a non-empty set, then A belongs to $\mathfrak{M}$.*

Proof: Let $\mathfrak{M}^* = \mathfrak{M} \cup \{A\}$. By hypothesis, $\mathfrak{M}^*$ has the finite intersection property. Hence the collection $\mathfrak{F}^*$ of all sets in S which contain any intersection of finitely many sets in $\mathfrak{M}^*$ is a filter on S by lemma 7.36. $\mathfrak{F}^* \supseteq \mathfrak{M}$ by definition. Since $\mathfrak{M}$ is maximal, $\mathfrak{F}^* = \mathfrak{M}$ and A is in $\mathfrak{M}$. ∎

28.43 Lemma. *$\mathfrak{F}$ is an ultrafilter on a set S if and only if $A \subseteq S$ implies $A \in \mathfrak{F}$ or $\sim A \in \mathfrak{F}$.*

Proof: Exercise.

28.44 Lemma. *Let $\mathfrak{M}$ be an ultrafilter on a space $\{S, \mathfrak{I}\}$ and let p be a cluster point of $\mathfrak{M}$. Then $\mathfrak{M}$ converges to p.*

Proof: Exercise.

28.45 Lemma. *Let $\mathfrak{F}$ be an ultrafilter on a set S and let f be any function from the set S onto the set Y. Then $f^{\#}[\mathfrak{F}]$ is an ultrafilter on Y ($f^{\#}[\mathfrak{F}]$ denotes the set of images of sets in $\mathfrak{F}$ determined by f).*

Proof: Exercise.

28.46 Theorem (Tychonoff). *Any product of compact spaces is compact.*

Proof: Let $\prod_\nu X_\nu$ be a product space such that each space X_ν is compact. Let $\mathfrak{M}$ be any ultrafilter on $\prod_\nu X_\nu$. By lemma 28.45, $p_\nu^{\#}[\mathfrak{M}]$ is an ultrafilter on X_ν, and hence, by corollary 28.41, $p_\nu^{\#}[\mathfrak{M}]$ converges to some point of X_ν. By theorem 12.10, $\mathfrak{M}$ converges. Hence, by corollary 28.41, $\prod_\nu X_\nu$ is compact. ∎

The next theorem is a basic theorem about compactness but the proof uses lemma 28.40 and so it is included at this point. First a necessary lemma is also included.

28.47 Lemma. *If $\mathfrak{M}$ is an ultrafilter on a set S and if $A_1 \cup \cdots \cup A_k$ is in $\mathfrak{M}$, then A_i, for some i such that $1 \leq i \leq k$, is in $\mathfrak{M}$.*

Proof: Let $A \cup B$ be in the ultrafilter $\mathfrak{M}$ on the set S. If A is not in $\mathfrak{M}$, by lemma 28.42, there is a set M_1 in $\mathfrak{M}$ such that $A \cap M_1 = \emptyset$. Similarly, if B is not in $\mathfrak{M}$, there exists a set M_2 in $\mathfrak{M}$ such that $B \cap M_2 = \emptyset$. Now consider $M_1 \cap M_2$. $M_1 \cap M_2$ is in $\mathfrak{M}$. Further, if x is in $(A \cup B) \cap (M_1 \cap M_2)$, then x is in $A \cap M_1$ or x is in $B \cap M_2$. This contradicts that $A \cap M_1 = \emptyset = B \cap M_2$. Hence $(A \cup B) \cap (M_1 \cap M_2) = \emptyset$ and $A \cup B$ is not in $\mathfrak{M}$. This is a contradiction. Therefore A is in $\mathfrak{M}$ or B is in $\mathfrak{M}$. The lemma follows by finite induction. ∎

28.48 Theorem (Alexander's Lemma). *If every covering of a space $\{X, \mathfrak{J}\}$ by sets in a subbase for $\mathfrak{J}$ contains a finite covering, then $\{X, \mathfrak{J}\}$ is compact.*

Proof: Let $\mathfrak{F}$ be any set of closed sets in $\{X, \mathfrak{J}\}$ with the finite intersection property. By lemma 7.34, $\mathfrak{F}$ generates a filter $\mathfrak{F}^*$. By lemma 28.40, $\mathfrak{F}^*$ is contained in an ultrafilter, $\mathfrak{M}$. Let $\mathscr{C}(\mathfrak{M})$ denote the set of complements of sets in $\mathfrak{M}$. Let F be in $\mathfrak{F}$. $\sim F$ is open and is in $\mathscr{C}(\mathfrak{M})$. Hence, if x is in $\sim F$, there exist open sets $S_1, S_2, \ldots, S_k$ in any subbase $\mathcal{S}$ such that $S_1 \cap S_2 \cap \cdots \cap S_k \subseteq \sim F$ and x is in $S_1 \cap S_2 \cap \cdots \cap S_k$. Since $S_1 \cap S_2 \cap \cdots \cap S_k \subseteq \sim F$, $\sim(S_1 \cap S_2 \cap \cdots \cap S_k) \supseteq F$. Hence since $\mathfrak{M}$ is a filter, $\sim(S_1 \cap S_2 \cap \cdots \cap S_k)$ is in $\mathfrak{M}$. Since $\sim(S_1 \cap S_2 \cap \cdots \cap S_k) = \sim S_1 \cup \sim S_2 \cup \cdots \cup \sim S_k$, $\sim S_1 \cup \sim S_2 \cup \cdots \cup \sim S_k$ is in $\mathfrak{M}$. By lemma 28.47, $\sim S_j$ is in $\mathfrak{M}$ for some j such that $1 \leq j \leq k$. Therefore S_j is in $\mathscr{C}(\mathfrak{M})$ and x is in S_j. Thus $\bigcup \mathscr{C}(\mathfrak{F}) \subseteq \bigcup_{\mathscr{C}(\mathfrak{M}) \cap \mathcal{S}} S_\alpha$. Now let $S_1, S_2, \ldots, S_n$ denote any finite collection of subbase elements in $\mathscr{C}(\mathfrak{M})$. Since $\sim S_1, \sim S_2, \ldots, \sim S_n$ are in $\mathfrak{M}$ and $\mathfrak{M}$ is a filter, $\sim S_1 \cap \sim S_2 \cap \cdots \cap \sim S_n \neq \emptyset$. Therefore, $S_1 \cup S_2 \cup \cdots \cup S_k \neq X$. Since no finite subset of the set of subbase elements in $\mathscr{C}(\mathfrak{M})$ covers X, then the set of all subbase elements in $\mathscr{C}(\mathfrak{M})$ does not cover X, by hypothesis. Thus $\bigcup_{\mathscr{C}(\mathfrak{M}) \cap \mathcal{S}} S_\nu \neq X$ and so $\sim \bigcup_{\mathscr{C}(\mathfrak{M}) \cap \mathcal{S}} S_\nu \neq \emptyset$. Now by what was proved above, $\bigcup \mathscr{C}(\mathfrak{F}) \subseteq \bigcup_{\mathscr{C}(\mathfrak{M}) \cap \mathcal{S}} S_j$. Hence, $\sim \bigcup \mathscr{C}(\mathfrak{F}) \supseteq \sim \bigcup_{\mathscr{C}(\mathfrak{M}) \cap \mathcal{S}} S_j$ and so $\sim \bigcup \mathscr{C}(\mathfrak{F})$ is not empty. $\sim \bigcup \mathscr{C}(\mathfrak{F}) = \bigcap \mathfrak{F}$. Hence, $\{X, \mathfrak{J}\}$ is compact. ∎

It is not true that the product of countably compact spaces is always countably compact (see Novak [2] or Gillman and Jerison [1]). However, the next theorem establishes that the product of a compact space and a countably compact space is countably compact.

28.49 Theorem. *If X is a compact space and if Y is a countably compact space, then the product space $X \times Y$ is countably compact.*

Proof: Let $\{G_1, G_2, \ldots, G_n, \ldots\}$ be any countable open covering of $X \times Y$. Let $G_1^* = G_1$, $G_2^* = G_1 \cup G_2, \ldots, G_n^* = G_1 \cup G_2 \cup \cdots \cup G_n$. $G_1^* \subseteq G_2^* \subseteq \cdots \subseteq G_n^* \subseteq \cdots$. $\bigcup_n G_n^* = X \times Y$ and each G_n^* is open. Let $H_1 = \{y \text{ in } Y \mid \text{there exists a neighborhood } V \text{ of } y \text{ such that } X \times V \subseteq G_1^*\}$. Let $H_n = \{y \text{ in } Y \mid \text{there exists a neighborhood } V \text{ of } y \text{ such that } X \times V \subseteq G_n^*\}$. $H_1 \subseteq H_2 \subseteq \cdots \subseteq H_n \subseteq \cdots$, and each H_n is open. Now let b be any point in Y. By 28.38, $X \times \{b\}$ is compact, hence $X \times \{b\} \subseteq G_k^*$ for some natural number k. Since G_k^* is open, if (x, b) is in $X \times \{b\}$, there exists a product open set $U_x \times V_x$ such that (x, b) is in $U_x \times V_x$, U_x is open in X, V_x is open in Y and $U_x \times V_x \subseteq G_n^*$. Thus the sets $U_x \times V_x$ for $x \in X$ constitute an open covering of $X \times \{b\}$. Since $X \times \{b\}$ is compact, a finite number, say, $U_{x_1} \times V_{x_1}$, $U_{x_2} \times V_{x_2}$, . . . , $U_{x_k} \times V_{x_k}$ cover $X \times \{b\}$. Thus $V = V_{x_1} \cap V_{x_2} \cap \cdots \cap V_{x_k}$ is an open neighborhood of b in Y and $X \times V$ is in G_n^*. Hence, b is in H_n and $\{H_1, H_2, \ldots, H_n, \ldots\}$ is a countable open covering of Y. Since Y is countably compact, $Y \subseteq H_m$ for some natural number m. Thus $X \times Y \subseteq G_m^*$ and $X \times Y$ is countably compact. ▮

EXERCISE 9. Prove or find a counterexample for: if X is a countably compact space and Y is a compact space, then $X \times Y$ is countably compact.

Nets can also be used to prove that any product of compact spaces is compact with the "universal net" playing the role of the ultrafilter.

28.50 Definition. A net η in a set S is said to be *eventually in the subset A* of S if and only if there is an element δ in the domain of η such that if δ_1 is in the domain of η and if $\delta_1 \geq \delta$, then $\eta(\delta_1) \in A$. A net η in a set S is said to be *frequently in the subset A* of S if and only if for each δ in the domain of η, there exists at least one δ_1 in the domain of η such that $\delta_1 \geq \delta$ and $\eta(\delta_1) \in A$.

28.51 Definition. A net u in a set S is called a *universal net* if and only if for each subset A of S, u is eventually in A or eventually in $\sim A$.

28.52 Lemma. *A universal net, u, converges to each of its cluster points.*

Proof: Exercise.

28.53 Lemma. *Let u be a universal net in a set S. Let f be a function from S onto Y. Then $f \circ u$ is a universal net in Y.*

Proof: Exercise.

28.54 Lemma. *Every net in a set S has a universal subnet in S.*

Proof: Let η be a net in a set S. For each α in the domain of η, let $T_\alpha = \{\eta(\delta) \mid \delta \text{ is in the domain of } \eta \text{ and } \delta \geq \alpha\}$. $\mathcal{B} = \{T_\alpha \mid \alpha \text{ is in the domain of } \eta\}$ is a base for a filter $\mathcal{F}$ on S (see exercise 9 in section 7). By lemma 28.40, $\mathcal{F}$ is contained in an ultrafilter, $\mathcal{M}$. Let M be any set in the ultrafilter $\mathcal{M}$ on S. For any α in the domain of η, $M \cap T_\alpha \neq \emptyset$, by definition of filter. Hence, η is frequently in every set in $\mathcal{M}$. The procedure used in part A of the proof of theorem 28.29 is used now to define a subnet of η which is eventually in every set in $\mathcal{M}$. Let D denote the domain of η. Let D^* denote the set of all pairs $\{\alpha, M\}$, where $\alpha \in D$, $M \in \mathcal{M}$ and $\eta(\alpha) \in M$. Define the function σ from D^* into D by $\sigma(\{\alpha, M\}) = \alpha$. Order D^* as follows: $\{\alpha, M\}\ R\ \{\beta, N\}$ if and only if $\alpha \geq \beta$ and $M \subseteq N$. R is reflexive and transitive. Further, if $\{\alpha, M\}$ and $\{\beta, N\}$ are in D^*, there is a δ in D such that $\delta \geq \alpha$ and $\delta \geq \beta$ and there is a set W in $\mathcal{M}$

such that $W \subseteq M \cap N$ and $W \in \mathfrak{M}$. Hence $\{\delta, W\}\ R\ \{\alpha, M\}$ and $\{\delta, W\}\ R\ \{\beta, N\}$. Thus D^* is directly ordered by R. Now consider the composite function $\eta \circ \sigma$ from D^* into S. $\eta \circ \sigma$ is a net. Now let $\alpha \in D$. Consider $\{\alpha, T_\alpha\}$ in D^*. If $\{\beta, N\}\ R\ \{\alpha, T_\alpha\}$, then $\beta \geq \alpha$. However, if $\{\beta, N\}\ R\ \{\alpha, T_\alpha\}$, $\sigma(\{\beta, N\}) \geq \sigma(\{\alpha, T_\alpha\}) = \alpha$. Thus $\eta \circ \sigma$ is a subnet of η. Now, let M be any set in the ultrafilter $\mathfrak{M}$. By the above, η is frequently in M. Hence, there exists an element α in D such that $\eta(\alpha) \in M$. Now, let $\{\beta, N\}\ R\ \{\alpha, M\}$. By definition of R, $N \subseteq M$ and $\eta(\beta) \in N$. Hence $\eta(\beta) = \eta \circ \sigma(\{\beta, N\}) \in M$. This means that $\eta \circ \sigma$ is eventually in every set in the ultrafilter $\mathfrak{M}$. Now, let A be any subset of S. By lemma 28.43, $A \in \mathfrak{M}$ or $\sim A \in \mathfrak{M}$. Hence, for every subset A of S, $\eta \circ \sigma$ is eventually in A or eventually in $\sim A$ and so $\eta \circ \sigma$ is a universal net. ▮

28.55 Theorem. *A space $\{S, \mathfrak{J}\}$ is compact if and only if every universal net in $\{S, \mathfrak{J}\}$ converges.*

Proof: A. Let $\{S, \mathfrak{J}\}$ be compact. By theorem 28.26, every net has a cluster point in $\{S, \mathfrak{J}\}$. Hence, by lemma 28.52, every universal net converges.

B. Let each universal net in $\{S, \mathfrak{J}\}$ converge to some point of $\{S, \mathfrak{J}\}$. Let η be any net in $\{S, \mathfrak{J}\}$. By the preceding lemma (28.54), η then has a converging subnet. Hence, by theorem 28.29, $\{S, \mathfrak{J}\}$ is compact. ▮

28.56 Theorem (Tychonoff). *Any product space of compact spaces is compact.*

Proof: Let $\prod_\nu X_\nu$ be a product space such that each X_ν is compact. Let u^* be a universal net in $\prod_\nu X_\nu$. If p_ν denotes, as usual, the projection function from $\prod_\nu X_\nu$ onto X_ν, then, by lemma 28.53, the composite function $p_\nu \circ u^*$ is a universal net in X_ν. Since X_ν is compact, $p_\nu \circ u^*$ converges by the previous theorem 28.55. Thus, by theorem 12.9, the net u^* converges in $\prod_\nu X_\nu$. Hence, by the previous theorem (28.55), $\prod_\nu X_\nu$ is compact. ▮

Weak and Strong Topologies

28.57 Theorem. *Let $\{f_\nu \mid \nu \in \mathfrak{N}\}$ be a set of functions, each from a (countably) compact topological space S_ν into a set Y, i.e., $f_\nu : S_\nu \to Y$. Then $\{Y, s\text{-}\mathfrak{J}\}$, where $s\text{-}\mathfrak{J}$ is the strong topology determined by $\{f_\nu \mid \nu \in \mathfrak{N}\}$, is (countably) compact.*

Proof: Exercise.

28.58 Corollary. *If $\{S, \mathfrak{J}\}$ is a (countably) compact space, then any quotient space of $\{S, \mathfrak{J}\}$ is (countably) compact.*

28.59 Theorem. *If S is a set, $\{Y, \mathfrak{J}\}$ a (countably) compact space and if $w\text{-}\mathfrak{S}$ is the weak topology for S induced by a function f from S onto $\{Y, \mathfrak{J}\}$, then $\{S, w\text{-}\mathfrak{S}\}$ is (countably) compact.*

Proof: Exercise.

28.60 Example. If a space $\{S, \mathcal{S}\}$ has the weak topology determined by a collection of functions from S into (countably) compact spaces $\{Y_\nu, \mathfrak{J}_\nu\}$, $\{S, \mathcal{S}\}$ is not necessarily (countably) compact. Let S be the usual space E^1 of real numbers. By corollary 18.41, the topology for E^1 is the weak topology determined by the set of continuous functions from E^1 into E^1. However, if Z_f denotes the zero set of a function f from E^1 into E^1, then $Z_f = Z_g$, where $g = |f| \wedge 1$, and where $|f| \wedge 1$ is the function which assigns to x the smaller of $f(x)$ and 1. Hence the topology on E^1 is the weak topology determined by the set of continuous, bounded functions from E^1 into E^1, by lemma 18.38. E^1 is not (countably) compact by corollary 28.11, but it will be shown further on that every closed bounded set of real numbers is compact.

Compactness and Connectedness

Some of the most powerful theorems in topology result when compactness is combined with other properties. The next two theorems give significant results for compact, connected T_1-spaces, and the next several sections will continue this line of investigation.

Hausdorff's maximum principle, which is equivalent to the axiom of choice, will be used in the proof of the next theorem.

Hausdorff's Maximum Principle. Every partially ordered set $\mathcal{P}$ contains a maximal (relative to inclusion) simply ordered subset, $\mathcal{L}$ (i.e., $\mathcal{L}$ is not contained properly in any other simply ordered subset of $\mathcal{P}$).

28.61 Theorem. *A compact, connected T_1-space, S, with more than one point contains at least two non-cut points.*

Proof: A. Let N denote the set of non-cut points of S. Assume $N = \emptyset$ or $N = \{s\}$. Then, since S contains more than one point, there exists a cut point c in S. $S \sim \{c\}$ is not connected by definition (26.21) of cut point, and so $S \sim \{c\} = A \cup B$, where $A \cap B = \emptyset$, $A \neq \emptyset \neq B$, and A and B are both open in $S \sim \{c\}$. If $N = \{s\}$, then $N \subseteq A$ or $N \subseteq B$, but not both. Say $s \in B$. Then $N \subseteq B$. If $N = \emptyset$, then $N \subseteq B$. In either case, $N \subseteq B$, and so $N \cap A = \emptyset$. This means that every point of A is a cut point of S. This last conclusion will finally lead to a contradiction. For each x in A, let $A_x \cup B_x$ denote a partition of $S \sim \{x\}$. Since $c \notin A$, for x in A, $c \neq x$. Hence $c \in A_x \cup B_x$. Let $c \in B_x$ for every x in A. By corollary 26.24, for every x in A, $A_x \cup \{x\}$ is connected in S. Now, since $c \in B_x$, and $x \neq c$, $A_x \cup \{x\} \subseteq S \sim \{c\} = A \cup B$. Also, since $A_x \cup \{x\}$ is connected and $x \in A$, $A_x \cup \{x\} \subseteq A$, by theorem 24.17. Thus the set $\mathfrak{A} = \{A_x \cup \{x\} \mid x \in A\}$ is a set of subsets of A partially ordered by inclusion.

B. The Hausdorff maximum principle will be invoked on the partially ordered set $\mathfrak{A}$, but first it must be shown that if $q \in A$ and $p \in A_q$, as defined above, then $A_p \cup \{p\} \subseteq A_q$ and $q \notin A_p \cup \{p\}$. So, let $q \in A$; q is then a cut point of S and $S \sim \{q\} = A_q \cup B_q$, separation. Now let $p \in A_q$. $A_p \cup \{p\} \cap B_p \cup \{p\} = \{p\}$. Hence, $q \notin A_p \cup \{p\}$ or $q \notin B_p \cup \{p\}$. Now, $p \notin B_q$ since $p \in A_q$. Therefore, $A_p \cup \{p\} \nsubseteq B_q$ and $B_p \cup \{p\} \nsubseteq B_q$. Since $c \in B_p$ and $c \notin A_q$, $B_p \cup \{p\} \nsubseteq A_q$. Further, since $B_p \cup \{p\} \nsubseteq A_q$ and $B_p \cup \{p\} \nsubseteq B_q$, and since $B_p \cup \{p\}$ is connected, $B_p \cup \{p\} \nsubseteq A_q \cup B_q$. Therefore, $q \in B_p \cup \{p\}$. Since $p \in A_q$, $p \neq q$. Hence, $q \notin A_p \cup \{p\}$, and so $A_p \cup \{p\} \subseteq A_q$.

C. Now by the Hausdorff maximum principle, there exists a maximal simply ordered subset $\mathfrak{L}$ of the set $\mathfrak{A} = \{M \mid M = A_x \cup \{x\} \text{ for } x \in A\}$. Since S is a T_1-space, $\{x\}$ is closed in S and hence, $A_x \cup B_x$ is open in S. Since B_x is open in $A_x \cup B_x$, B_x is open in S, and so $A_x \cup \{x\}$ is closed in S for every x in A. Since $\mathfrak{L}$ is simply ordered and since $A_x \cup \{x\} \neq \emptyset$ for all x in A, $\mathfrak{L}$ satisfies the finite intersection property. Since S is compact, $\bigcap \mathfrak{L} \neq \emptyset$, by theorem 28.10. Let $\alpha \in \bigcap \mathfrak{L}$. Since $\alpha \in A_x \cup \{x\}$ for every $A_x \cup \{x\}$ in $\mathfrak{L}$ and since by part A, above, $A_x \cup \{x\} \subseteq A$, for all x in A, $\alpha \in A$. Hence by the original assumption, α is a cut point of S. This means that $S \sim \{\alpha\}$ is not connected and hence A_α and B_α are defined as in part A. $A_\alpha \cap B_\alpha = \emptyset$ and $A_\alpha \neq \emptyset \neq B_\alpha$ and $A_\alpha \cup \{\alpha\} \subseteq A$. Let $y \in A_\alpha$. By part B, above, $A_y \cup \{y\} \subseteq A_\alpha$ and $\alpha \notin A_y \cup \{y\}$. Thus $A_y \cup \{y\} \subseteq A_\alpha \cup \{\alpha\}$. Since $\alpha \in A_x \cup \{x\}$ for every $A_x \cup \{x\}$ in $\mathfrak{L}$, if $x \neq \alpha$, $\alpha \in A_x$. Therefore, by part B, above, $A_\alpha \cup \{\alpha\} \subseteq A_x$ for $x \neq \alpha$. Hence, $A_y \cup \{y\}$ is properly contained in every $A_x \cup \{x\}$ in $\mathfrak{L}$. Therefore, $\mathfrak{L} \cup \{A_y \cup \{y\}\} \supsetneq \mathfrak{L}$ and $\mathfrak{L} \cup \{A_y \cup \{y\}\}$ is linearly ordered by inclusion. This contradicts the maximality of $\mathfrak{L}$. Thus the existence of the set A_α leads to a contradiction. This means that α cannot be a cut point. However, $\alpha \in A$ and, by the original assumption that $N = \emptyset$ or $N = \{s\}$, every point of A is a cut point. Thus $N \neq \emptyset$ and $N \neq \{s\}$. ∎

In definition 26.25, a connected space S was defined to be irreducibly connected about a subset M if and only if no proper connected subset of S contained M. Theorem 26.27 established that if S was irreducibly connected about a subset M, then M contained all the non-cut points of S. However, the subspace S of E^1 determined by $\{x \mid x \geq 0\}$ is not irreducibly connected about its set of non-cut points. The next theorem establishes a sufficient condition that a space be irreducibly connected about its set of non-cut points.

28.62 Theorem. *A compact, connected T_1-space S is irreducibly connected about its set of non-cut points.*

Proof: Let N be the set of non-cut points of the compact, connected T_1-space S. Assume that S is not irreducibly connected about N. Then there exists a proper, connected subspace X of S such that $X \supseteq N$. Let $\alpha \in S \sim X$. Then α is a cut point of S and $S \sim \alpha = A \cup B$, separation. Since X is connected, $X \subseteq A$ or $X \subseteq B$, by theorem 24.17. Let $X \subseteq A$. Now, $B \cup \{\alpha\}$ is connected by corollary 26.24. Further, since S is T_1, $\{\alpha\}$ is closed. Therefore,

$A \cup B$ is open in S and since A is open in $A \cup B$, A is open in S. Thus $B \cup \{\alpha\}$ is closed in X and hence is compact. $B \cup \{\alpha\}$ is then a compact, connected T_1-space. Further, since $B \neq \emptyset$ and $\alpha \notin B$, $B \cup \{\alpha\}$ contains more than one point. Thus by the last theorem $B \cup \{\alpha\}$ contains at least two non-cut points. Let β be a non-cut point of $B \cup \{\alpha\}$ and let $\beta \neq \alpha$. Thus $\beta \in B$ and $B \cup \{\alpha\} \sim \{\beta\}$ is connected. Since $A \cup \{\alpha\}$ is connected and $(A \cup \{\alpha\}) \cap (B \cup \{\alpha\} \sim \{\beta\}) \neq \emptyset$, $(A \cup \{\alpha\}) \cup (B \cup \{\alpha\} \sim \{\beta\})$ is also connected by theorem 24.23. Now, $(A \cup \{\alpha\}) \cup (B \cup \{\alpha\} \sim \{\beta\}) = S \sim \{\beta\}$. Hence β is a non-cut point of S. However, $\beta \in B$ and $N \subseteq A$, where N is the set of non-cut points of S. Thus the existence of the proper connected subset X of S containing N leads to a contradiction. Hence, S is irreducibly connected about N. ▮

28.63 Corollary. *If S is a compact connected T_1-space and if N is the set of non-cut points of S and if $S \sim \{\alpha\} = A \cup B$ separation, then $N \cap A \neq \emptyset \neq N \cap B$.*

Proof: If $N \cap A = \emptyset$, then $N \subseteq B$. Since by corollary 26.24, $B \cup \{\alpha\}$ is connected, S would not be irreducibly connected about N. This contradicts the previous theorem. ▮

28.64 Definition. A compact, connected space is called a *continuum.*

29. COMPACTNESS IN HAUSDORFF SPACES.

Closedness and Compactness

Intuitively, because of the limit point definition (corollary 28.18) in Euclidean n-spaces, compactness and closedness for subsets appear to be related. In compact Hausdorff spaces, closedness and compactness are equivalent.

29.1 Theorem. *Every closed subset of a compact space is compact.*

Proof: Let F be a closed subset of a compact space S. Let $\mathcal{G}$ be any open covering of F. $\mathcal{G} \cup \{\sim F\}$ is an open covering of S. Hence a finite subcovering $\{\sim F, G_1, G_2, \ldots, G_k\}$ covers S and so $\{G_1, G_2, \ldots, G_k\}$ covers F. ▮

29.2 Corollary. *Every closed subset of a countably compact space is countably compact.*

Proof: Exercise.

29.3 Corollary. *Every closed subset of a Lindelöf space is Lindelöf.*

Proof: Exercise.

29.4 Example. Let S denote the set of real numbers with the smallest T_1-topology. The only closed sets are S and all finite sets. The set, P, of positive real numbers is compact since any one open set contains all but a finite number of points. However, P is not closed since it is neither a finite subset nor S itself.

29.5 Theorem. *Any compact subset of a Hausdorff space is closed.*

Proof: Let F be a compact subset of the Hausdorff space S. Let p be any point in $\sim F$. Since S is Hausdorff, for each x in F, there exist open neighborhoods U_x of x and V_x of p such that $U_x \cap V_x = \emptyset$. The collection $\{U_x \mid x \in S\}$ forms an open covering of F. F is compact; hence, a finite number of the sets, say $U_{x_1}, U_{x_2}, \ldots, U_{x_k}$, cover F. The corresponding neighborhoods of p are $V_{x_1}, V_{x_2}, \ldots, V_{x_k}$ and $U_{x_i} \cap V_{x_i} = \emptyset$ for $i = 1, 2, \ldots, k$. Hence, $\bigcap_{i=1}^{k} V_{x_i}$ is a neighborhood of p which contains no point of F. p is, then, interior to $\sim F$; $\sim F$ is open, and hence, F is closed. ▮

29.6 Example. In lemma 28.35 it was shown that if λ is a non-limit countable ordinal, then $\{\alpha \mid \alpha < \lambda\}$ is compact. The same proof establishes that if λ is any non-limit ordinal, then $\{\alpha \mid \alpha < \lambda\}$, with the order topology, is compact. Thus if W, as in definition 28.33, is the smallest uncountable ordinal, then $\{\alpha \mid \alpha \leq W\} = W + 1$ is compact and contains $\{\alpha \mid \alpha < W\} = W$. Lemma 28.35 states that $\{W, o\text{-}\mathfrak{J}\}$ is countably compact. Thus $W \subseteq W + 1$, $\{W + 1, o\text{-}\mathfrak{J}\}$ is compact and $\{W, o\text{-}\mathfrak{J}\}$ is countably compact. By definition of $o\text{-}\mathfrak{J}$ and by the remarks preceding definition 28.33, W is a limit ordinal and W in $\{\alpha \mid \alpha \leq W\} = W + 1$ is a limit point of $\{\alpha \mid \alpha < W\} = W$. Thus $\{\alpha \mid \alpha < W\} = W$ is countably compact but not closed in $\{W + 1, o\text{-}\mathfrak{J}\}$, and $\{W + 1, o\text{-}\mathfrak{J}\}$ is Hausdorff by definition 28.33.

Continuity and Compactness

Example 6.2 contains an example of a 1:1 continuous function which is not a homeomorphism; the next theorem gives an important sufficient condition for such a function to be a homeomorphism.

29.7 Theorem. *If f is a continuous function from a compact space into a Hausdorff space, then f is closed.*

Proof: Let F be any closed set in the domain of f. F is compact by theorem 29.1; hence, by theorem 28.36, $f[F]$ is compact in the range of f. Since the range of f is Hausdorff, $f[F]$ is closed in the range of f. ▮

29.8 Corollary. *Any* 1:1 *continuous function from a compact space into a Hausdorff space is a homeomorphism.*

Proof: Exercise.

EXERCISE 1. Prove that if f is a continuous function from a compact space $\{X, \mathfrak{J}\}$ onto a Hausdorff space $\{Y, \mathcal{S}\}$, then $\mathcal{S}$ is the strong topology for Y determined by f and $\mathfrak{J}$.

29.9 Theorem. *A compact, Hausdorff topology on a set X is a minimal element in the ordered (by inclusion) set of Hausdorff topologies for X.*

Proof: Exercise.

29.10 Theorem. *If $\{S, \mathfrak{J}\}$ is a compact, Hausdorff space and if $\mathfrak{J}^* \subsetneq \mathfrak{J}$, then $\{S, \mathfrak{J}^*\}$ is compact but not Hausdorff.*

Proof: Exercise.

EXERCISE 2. Let C denote the set of continuous functions from a space S into I, the unit interval space [0, 1]. Prove that the space I^C with the metric topology $\rho(f, g) = \text{l.u.b.}_{x \in S} |f(x) - g(x)|$ is not compact (assume that I is compact; see theorem 30.18).

The following theorem is the analogue of theorem 13.5 for continuous functions from compact onto Hausdorff spaces.

29.11 Theorem. *If f is a continuous function from a compact space S onto a Hausdorff space Y, then Y is homeomorphic to a quotient (decomposition) space of S and Y has the strong topology determined by f.*

Proof: As in theorem 13.5, let R denote the relation $\{(a, b) \mid f(a) = f(b)\}$. The quotient space S/R is the continuous image of S under the quotient function and hence S/R is compact. Hence, by theorem 13.5, Y is the continuous image of S/R under a 1:1 function h. Since S/R is compact, h is a homeomorphism and Y is the homeomorphic image of S/R. Further, let $f^{-1}[A]$ be open in X. $f^{-1}[A] = q^{-1}[h^{-1}[A]]$. Since q is the quotient function and S/R, as a quotient space, has the strong topology, $h^{-1}[A]$ is open in S/R. Since h is a homeomorphism, A is open in Y. Thus Y has the strong topology determined by f. ▮

SEPARATION PROPERTIES

29.12 Theorem. *Any compact, Hausdorff space, S, is normal.*

Proof: Let F_1 and F_2 be two disjoint closed sets in S. F_1 and F_2 are both, then, compact. Let p be a point in F_2. For each point x in F_1, there exist open neighborhoods U_x of x and V_x of p such that $U_x \cap V_x = \emptyset$. $\{U_x \mid x \in F_1\}$ is an open covering of F_1. Since F_1 is compact, a finite number of these sets, say, $U_{x_1}, U_{x_2}, \ldots, U_{x_k}$ cover F_1. The corresponding open neighborhoods of p are $V_{x_1}, V_{x_2}, \ldots, V_{x_k}$. $V_{x_1} \cap V_{x_2} \cap \cdots \cap V_{x_k} = V_p$ is, then, an open neighborhood of p. If $G_p = \bigcup_{i=1}^k U_{x_i}$, then $G_p \cap V_p = \emptyset$ and $F_1 \subseteq G_p$. For each q in F_2, determine such a pair G_q and V_q such that $G_q \cap V_q = \emptyset$ and $F_1 \subseteq G_q$. $\{V_q \mid q \in F_2\}$ is an open covering of F_2. Since F_2 is compact, a finite number,

$V_{q_1}, V_{q_2}, \ldots, V_{q_n}$ cover F_2. Let $G_2 = V_{q_1} \cup \cdots \cup V_{q_n}$. Each of the sets $G_{q_1}, G_{q_2}, \ldots, G_{q_n}$, corresponding to $V_{q_1}, V_{q_2}, \ldots, V_{q_n}$, covers F_1. Hence, $G_1 = \bigcap_{i=1}^{n} G_{q_i}$ contains F_1 and is open. Thus, since $G_1 \cap G_2 = \emptyset$, S is normal. ▮

29.13 Theorem. *X is completely regular if and only if it can be imbedded in a compact Hausdorff space.*

Proof: By theorem 18.46, every completely regular space can be imbedded in a product space I^A, where I is the subspace $[0, 1]$ of E^1. Since the subspace $[0, 1]$ is compact, I^A is compact and Hausdorff. ▮

29.14 Corollary. *Every completely regular space is a subspace of a normal space.*

Proof: Theorems 29.11 and 29.13 establish the corollary. ▮

In example 18.48 a space is described which is completely regular and not normal. This example along with the previous corollary, 29.14, implies that not every subspace of a normal space is normal.

29.15 Definition. A space $\{S, \mathfrak{J}\}$ is called *completely normal* if and only if every subspace of $\{S, \mathfrak{J}\}$ is normal.

The most famous example of a space which is normal but not completely normal is a compact Hausdorff space called "the Tychonoff plank."

29.16 Definition (Tychonoff Plank). Let W^* denote the space consisting of the set $W \cup \{W\} = W + 1$ and the order topology o-$\mathfrak{J}$, where W is the set of countable ordinals described in the paragraph preceding 28.33, and where the basic neighborhoods of W are defined as for a limit ordinal in 28.33. Let ω^* denote the space consisting of the set $\omega \cup \{\omega\}$ and the order topology, where ω is the subset of W consisting of all finite ordinals. The product space $W^* \times \omega^*$ is called the *Tychonoff plank*.

29.17 Lemma. *The Tychonoff plank is normal.*

Proof: It is immediate from the definition (28.33) of the order topology that W^* and ω^* are Hausdorff. By the proof of lemma 28.35, since $\omega + 1 = \omega \cup \{\omega\}$ is a non-limit countable ordinal, ω^* is compact. Similarly, it can be proved that W^* is compact. For, let $\mathcal{G}$ be any open covering of W^* and let G_W be the open set of $\mathcal{G}$ that contains W. G_W, by definition of the order topology, must contain a basic neighborhood $U_W^\gamma = \{x \mid x \text{ is an ordinal and } \gamma < x \leq W\}$. $\gamma + 1$ is then a non-limit countable ordinal and, again by the proof of lemma 28.35, $\{x \mid x \text{ is an ordinal and } x < \gamma + 1\}$ is compact. Hence W^* is compact.

Since W^* and ω^* are compact and Hausdorff, $W^* \times \omega^*$ is compact and Hausdorff, and by theorem 29.12 $W^* \times \omega^*$ is normal. ▮

29.18 Lemma. *The Tychonoff plank is not completely normal.*

Proof: Let $\mathcal{P}$ denote the Tychonoff plank and let $\mathcal{P}'$ denote the subspace of $\mathcal{P}$ consisting of $(W + 1) \times (\omega + 1) \sim \{(W, \omega)\}$ and the relative topology. Let $A = \{(x, y) \mid x = W \text{ and } y < \omega\}$; let $B = \{(x, y) \mid y = \omega \text{ and } x < W\}$. $A \cap B = \emptyset$. Further, by theorem 12.11 and the definition of the relative topology, A and B are closed in $\mathcal{P}'$. Now, let G_A be an open set in $\mathcal{P}'$ such that $A \subseteq G_A$; also, let G_B be an open set in $\mathcal{P}'$ such that $B \subseteq G_B$. Since G_A is open in $\mathcal{P}'$ and $A \subseteq G_A$, each point (W, m) in A has a product neighborhood $U \times V$ where U is open in W^* and V is open in ω^*. U then contains an interval $\{(x, y) \mid \gamma < x \leq W \text{ and } y = m$, where γ is a countable ordinal$\}$. Since $\gamma < W$, $\gamma + 1 < W$. Hence $\{x \mid \gamma < x < W\}$ is not empty. Let γ_m be an ordinal such that $\gamma < \gamma_m < W$. (γ_m, m) is then in G_A. The set $\{\gamma_1, \gamma_2, \ldots, \gamma_m, \ldots\}$ for m in ω is countable; hence, since W is not countable, there exists an ordinal γ^* such that $\gamma^* < W$ and $\gamma^* > \gamma_m$ for every m in ω. Hence for every m in ω, (γ^*, m) is in G_A. Consider, now, (γ^*, ω). (γ^*, ω) is in B and hence is an interior point of the open set G_B. Again by the definition of the relative topology on $\mathcal{P}'$, G_B contains a product set $U' \times V'$ where U' is open in W^* and V' is open in ω^*. Since ω is a limit ordinal, V must contain a point (γ^*, m^*) for some $m^* < \omega$ by definition (28.33) of the order topology. Hence (γ^*, m^*) is in $G_A \cap G_B$ and $G_A \cap G_B \neq \emptyset$. Thus, $\mathcal{P}'$ is not normal and $\mathcal{P}$ is not completely normal. ▮

29.19 Theorem. *Every metric space is completely normal.*

Proof: The proof follows immediately from theorem 19.20 and theorem 20.9. ▮

The next theorem establishes that Hausdorff spaces are, in a certain sense, quasi-regular and quasi-normal.

29.20 Theorem. *In any Hausdorff space disjoint compact sets are contained in disjoint open sets.*

Proof: Let F_1 and F_2 be disjoint compact sets in the Hausdorff space S. Since S is Hausdorff, F_1 and F_2 are closed. Let p be a given point in F_1. Let x be any point in F_2; since S is Hausdorff, there exist open neighborhoods U_x of p and V_x of x such that $U_x \cap V_x = \emptyset$. For each point x in F_2, such a pair of open neighborhoods can be chosen. Then $\{V_x \mid x \in F_2\}$ is an open cover of F_2. Since F_2 is compact, a finite number, say, $V_{x_1}, \ldots, V_{x_k}$ cover F_2. The corresponding $U_{x_i}, \ldots, U_{x_k}$ are all open neighborhoods of p in F_1. Hence $\bigcap_{i=1}^{k} U_{x_i} = W_p$ is an open neighborhood of p, $G_p = \bigcup_{i=1}^{k} V_{x_i}$ is an open set containing F_2 and $W_p \cap G_p = \emptyset$. For each p in F_1, such a pair $\{W_p, G_p\}$

of open sets can be defined. The collection $\{W_p\}$ forms an open covering of F_1 and each G_p contains F_2. Since F_1 is compact, a finite number, say, $W_{p_1}, W_{p_2}, \ldots, W_{p_n}$ cover F_1. Hence, $\bigcup_{i=1}^n W_{p_i} \supseteq F_1$ and $\bigcap_{i=1}^n G_{p_i} \supseteq F_2$. Further, since for $i = 1, \ldots, n$, $W_{p_i} \cap G_{p_i} = \emptyset$, $(\bigcup_{i=1}^n W_{p_i}) \cap (\bigcap_{i=1}^n G_{p_i}) = \emptyset$. Hence, the two open sets $\bigcup_{i=1}^n W_{p_i}$ and $\bigcap_{i=1}^n G_{p_i}$ are disjoint, $F_1 \subseteq \bigcup_{i=1}^n W_{p_i}$ and $F_2 \subseteq \bigcap_{i=1}^n G_{p_i}$. ▮

29.21 Corollary. *In a Hausdorff space S, any point p in S and any compact set $F \subseteq S$ which does not contain p are contained in disjoint open sets.*

Proof: Since S is Hausdorff, $\{p\}$ is closed; hence, by the previous theorem, the corollary follows. ▮

Closed Functions

The previous theorems and corollaries establish the combination of "compact and Hausdorff" as a powerful one. The following theorems and corollaries continue to exhibit the power of this combination.

29.22 Theorem. *If f is a continuous and closed function from a compact, Hausdorff space X onto a space Y, then Y is Hausdorff.*

Proof: Let $f(x)$ and $f(y)$ denote any two distinct points of Y. Since $\{x\}$ and $\{y\}$ are closed in S, $\{f(x)\}$ and $\{f(y)\}$ are closed in Y by hypothesis. Since f is continuous, $f^{-1}[\{f(x)\}]$ and $f^{-1}[\{f(y)\}]$ are closed. By definition of f^{-1}, $f^{-1}[\{f(x)\}] \cap f^{-1}[\{f(y)\}] = \emptyset$. By theorem 29.12, S is normal. Hence, there exist open sets G_1 and G_2 such that $G_1 \cap G_2 = \emptyset$ and $f^{-1}[\{f(x)\}] \subseteq G_1$ and $f^{-1}[\{f(y)\}] \subseteq G_2$. Since the complements $\sim G_1$ and $\sim G_2$ are both closed, $f[\sim G_1]$ and $f[\sim G_2]$ are both closed by hypothesis. Since $G_1 \cap G_2 = \emptyset$, $\sim G_1 \cup \sim G_2 = X$. Hence $f[\sim G_1] \cup f[\sim G_2] = Y$. Since $f^{-1}[\{f(x)\}] \subseteq G_1$, $\sim G_1 \subseteq \sim f^{-1}[\{f(x)\}]$. $\sim f^{-1}[\{f(x)\}] = f^{-1}[\sim \{f(x)\}]$ by definition of f^{-1}. Hence, $\sim G_1 \subseteq f^{-1}[\sim \{f(x)\}]$, and so $f[\sim G_1] \subseteq \sim \{f(x)\}$. Thus $f(x) \notin f[\sim G_1]$. Similarly, $f(y) \notin f[\sim G_2]$. By theorem 16.2, Y is then Hausdorff. ▮

29.23 Theorem. *If S is a compact, Hausdorff and second countable space and if f is a continuous, closed function from S onto Y, then Y is second countable.*

Proof: Let $\mathcal{U} = \{U_1, U_2, \ldots, U_n, \ldots\}$ be a countable base for S. The set of all finite subsets of $\mathcal{U}$ is countable, since each is identified by an n-tuple of natural numbers. Hence, let $\mathcal{B}^*$ denote the set of all unions of finite subsets of $\mathcal{U}$. $\mathcal{B}^*$ is a countable collection of open sets in X. Let $\mathcal{B}^* = \{B_1^*, B_2^*, \ldots, B_n^*, \ldots\}$. Let $V_1 = Y \sim f[S \sim B_1^*]$, $V_2 = Y \sim f[S \sim B_2^*], \ldots, V_n = Y \sim f[S \sim B_n^*], \ldots$. Let $\mathcal{V}^*$ denote the countable set $\{V_1, V_2, \ldots, V_n, \ldots\}$. It will be shown that $\mathcal{V}^*$ is a base for Y. First, the sets in $\mathcal{V}^*$ are all open in Y since by hypothesis, f is closed. Next let $f(x)$ be any point in Y and let G be any open neighborhood of $f(x)$. $f^{-1}[\{f(x)\}] \subseteq f^{-1}[G]$. Since f is continuous,

$f^{-1}[G]$ is open in S. By hypothesis and the previous theorem, $f^{-1}[\{f(x)\}]$ is compact. Hence each point in $f^{-1}[\{f(x)\}]$ is in an open set U_j from the base $\mathcal{U}$. Since $f^{-1}[\{f(x)\}]$ is compact, a finite number of the sets in $\mathcal{U}$ cover $f^{-1}[\{f(x)\}]$, say $U_{i_1}, \ldots, U_{i_k}$. $\bigcup_{j=1}^{k} U_{i_j}$ then covers $f^{-1}[\{f(x)\}]$ and is a set in $\mathcal{B}^*$, by definition of $\mathcal{B}^*$. Let $\bigcup_{j=1}^{k} U_{i_j} = B_n^*$. Then, $f^{-1}[\{f(x)\}] \subseteq B_n^* \subseteq f^{-1}[G]$. Hence, $S \sim f^{-1}[\{f(x)\}] \supseteq S \sim B_n^* \supseteq S \sim f^{-1}[G]$. Now, $S \sim f^{-1}[\{f(x)\}] = f^{-1}[Y \sim \{f(x)\}]$ and $S \sim f^{-1}[G] = f^{-1}[Y \sim G]$, by definition of f^{-1}. Hence, $f^{-1}[Y \sim \{f(x)\}] \supseteq S \sim B_n^* \supseteq f^{-1}[Y \sim G]$. Hence, $f[f^{-1}[Y \sim \{f(x)\}]] \supseteq f[S \sim B_n^*] \supseteq f[f^{-1}[Y \sim G]]$. However, $f[f^{-1}[Y \sim \{f(x)\}]] = Y \sim \{f(x)\}$ and $f[f^{-1}[Y \sim G]] = Y \sim G$. Therefore, $Y \sim \{f(x)\} \supseteq f[S \sim B_n^*] \supseteq Y \sim G$, and so $Y \sim [Y \sim \{f(x)\}] \subseteq Y \sim f[S \sim B_n^*] \subseteq Y \sim [Y \sim G]$. Hence, $\{f(x)\} \subseteq Y \sim f[S \sim B_n^*] \subseteq G$. Since f is closed, $f[S \sim B_n^*]$ is closed and $Y \sim f[S \sim B_n^*]$ is open. Thus $\mathcal{V}^*$ is a countable base for Y. ▮

29.24 Corollary. *If S is a compact, Hausdorff, second countable space and if f is a continuous function from S onto a Hausdorff space Y, then Y is second countable.*

Proof: Since Y is Hausdorff, by theorem 29.7, f is closed. Hence, the corollary follows from the previous theorem. ▮

A Baire Category Theorem

The Baire category theorem (22.28) for complete metric spaces has several generalizations. One of them follows and two others, perhaps more useful, appear in section 31.

29.25 Theorem. *A countably compact, regular space is of the second category in itself.*

Proof: Let $\{B_1, B_2, \ldots, B_n, \ldots\}$ be a countable set of nowhere dense sets of the countably compact regular space S. $\overline{B}_i$, for $i = 1, 2, \ldots$, contains, then, no non-empty open set. This means that $\sim\overline{B}_1$, the complement of $\overline{B}_1$, is a non-empty open set and hence there exists a point x_1 in $\sim\overline{B}_1$. By regularity, there exists an open neighborhood U_1 of x_1 such that $\overline{U}_1 \subseteq \sim\overline{B}_1$. Hence $\overline{U}_1 \cap \overline{B}_1 = \emptyset$ and $\overline{U}_1 \neq \emptyset$. Assume that non-empty open sets $U_1, U_2, \ldots, U_k$ have been defined such that $\overline{U}_{i+1} \subseteq U_i$, for $i = 1, 2, \ldots, k - 1$, and $\overline{U}_k \cap (\overline{B}_1 \cup \overline{B}_2 \cup \cdots \cup \overline{B}_k) = \emptyset$. Next consider $(\overline{B}_1 \cup \overline{B}_2 \cup \cdots \cup \overline{B}_k \cup \overline{B}_{k+1})$. This set is closed, and by lemma 22.27, contains no non-empty open set. Hence the open set $U_k \cap \sim(\overline{B}_1 \cup \overline{B}_2 \cup \cdots \cup \overline{B}_k \cup \overline{B}_{k+1}) \neq \emptyset$. Let x_{k+1} be a point in the open set $U_k \cap \sim(\overline{B}_1 \cup \overline{B}_2 \cup \cdots \cup \overline{B}_k \cup \overline{B}_{k+1})$. By regularity, there exists an open neighborhood U_{k+1} of x_{k+1} such that $\overline{U}_{k+1} \subseteq U_k \cap \sim(\overline{B}_1 \cup \cdots \cup \overline{B}_k \cup \overline{B}_{k+1})$. Hence U_{k+1} is a non-empty open set such that $\overline{U}_{k+1} \subseteq \overline{U}_k$ and $\overline{U}_{k+1} \cap (\overline{B}_1 \cup \cdots \cup \overline{B}_k \cup \overline{B}_{k+1}) = \emptyset$. Thus $\{\overline{U}_1, \overline{U}_2, \ldots, \overline{U}_n, \ldots\}$ is a countable set of non-empty closed sets with the finite intersection property. Since S is countably compact, by hypothesis, $\bigcap_{i=1}^{\infty} U_i \neq \emptyset$. Let q be a point in

$\bigcap_{i=1}^{\infty} \overline{U}_i$. Consider $\overline{B}_n$ for n some natural number. Since q is in $\bigcap_{i=1}^{\infty} \overline{U}_i$, q is in $\overline{U}_n$. However, by definition of U_n, $\overline{U}_n \cap (\overline{B}_1 \cup \cdots \cup \overline{B}_n) = \emptyset$. Hence q is not in $\overline{B}_n$ for $n = 1, 2, \ldots$. Thus $S \neq \bigcup_{i=1}^{\infty} B_i$ and S is of the second category in itself. ∎

29.26 Corollary. *Any compact Hausdorff space is of the second category in itself.*

Proof: By theorem 29.12, any compact Hausdorff space is normal and hence regular. Since any compact space is countably compact the corollary follows from the previous theorem. ∎

Connectedness

The next theorem exhibits a dramatic effect which the combination compact and Hausdorff has on connectedness. First a lemma is needed.

29.27 Lemma. *Let S be a compact, Hausdorff space and let $\{F_\nu \mid \nu \in \mathfrak{N}\}$ be a set of closed subspaces of S, simply ordered by inclusion. Further, let x and y be points in $\bigcap_\nu F_\nu$ such that x q-Comp y in every F_ν. (See definition 26.15.) Then x q-Comp y in $\bigcap_\nu F_\nu$.*

Proof: Let $F^* = \bigcap_\nu F_\nu$. Since F^* is the intersection of closed sets in S, F^* is closed in S. Assume x and y are not q-Comp equivalent in F^*. By definition 26.15, F^* can then be written as a union, $M \cup N$, where M and N are disjoint closed subsets of F^* such that $x \in M$ and $y \in N$. Since F^* is closed in S, and M and N are closed in F^*, M and N are then, by theorem 9.5, closed in S. Since S is compact and Hausdorff, by theorem 29.12, S is normal. Hence, there exist disjoint open sets G_1 and G_2 in S such that $M \subseteq G_1$ and $N \subseteq G_2$. Since $F^* = M \cup N$ and $F^* = \bigcap_\nu F_\nu$, for each F_ν, $F_\nu \cap G_1 \neq \emptyset \neq F_\nu \cap G_2$. Hence, since $x \in G_1$ and $y \in G_2$, $F_\nu \neq (F_\nu \cap G_1) \cup (F_\nu \cap G_2)$. Therefore $F_\nu \cap \sim(G_1 \cup G_2) \neq \emptyset$. Let $F_\nu \cap \sim(G_1 \cup G_2) = H_\nu$. The set $\{H_\nu \mid \nu \in \mathfrak{N}\}$ is simply ordered by inclusion, since $F_u \subseteq F_\nu$ implies $F_u \cap \sim(G_1 \cup G_2) \subseteq F_\nu \cap \sim(G_1 \cup G_2)$. Hence, $\{H_\nu \mid \nu \in \mathfrak{N}\}$ has the finite intersection property. Since each H_ν is the intersection of two closed sets, each H_ν is closed. Since S is compact, $\bigcap_\nu H_\nu \neq \emptyset$. Let $p \in \bigcap_\nu H_\nu$. $p \in \bigcap_\nu F_\nu$. Therefore, $\bigcap_\nu F_\nu \cap \sim(G_1 \cup G_2) \neq \emptyset$. By definition of G_1 and G_2, this is a contradiction. Hence, the original assumption is false and x q-Comp y in $\bigcap_\nu F_\nu$. ∎

29.28 Theorem. *In a compact Hausdorff space quasi-components are components.*

Proof: Let Q be any quasi-component in the compact, Hausdorff space S. Let x and y be any two points in Q. Let $\mathfrak{F} = \{F_\nu \mid \nu \in \mathfrak{N}\}$ denote the set of all closed subspaces of S in which x q-Comp y. $S \in \mathfrak{F}$. As a set of subsets of S, $\mathfrak{F}$ is partially ordered by inclusion. Therefore, by Hausdorff's maximum principle, $\mathfrak{F}$ contains a maximal simply ordered subset $\mathfrak{L} = \{L_u \mid u \in \mathfrak{M}\}$. By the previous lemma x q-Comp y in $\bigcap_u L_u$. Next, assume that $\bigcap_u L_u$ is not connected. By corollary 24.3, $\bigcap_u L_u$ is the union of two non-empty, disjoint, closed sets M and N. $\bigcup_u L_u = M \cup N$. Since x q-Comp y in $\bigcap_u L_u$, x and y are in M, say. If x and y are not q-Comp equivalent in M, then $M = M_1 \cup M_2$, where $x \in M_1$, $y \in M_2$, and M_1 and M_2 are disjoint and closed in M. Then $\bigcap_u L_u = M_1 \cup M_2 \cup N$ and x and y would not be q-Comp equivalent in $\bigcap_u L_u$. Thus M is in $\mathfrak{F}$ and $M \subseteq \bigcap_u L_u$. Hence $M \subseteq L_u$ for every L_u in $\mathfrak{L}$. Thus, $\{M\} \cup \mathfrak{L}$ is a simply ordered subset of $\mathfrak{F}$ which contains $\mathfrak{L}$ properly. This is a contradiction to the maximality of $\mathfrak{L}$. Hence, $\bigcap_u L_u$ is connected. Since x and y are in $\bigcap_u L_u$, Q is connected by theorem 24.24. Since components are maximal connected sets, $Q \subseteq C$, where C is some component. By theorem 26.20, every component is contained in a quasi-component. Since quasi-components and components are equivalence classes, $Q = C$. ∎

Inverse Limit Spaces

In theorem 16.20, an inverse limit space, $\overleftarrow{L}$, determined by an inverse limit system in which all spaces are Hausdorff is proved to be a closed subset of the corresponding product space. Example 12.50 shows that an inverse limit space can be empty. If the spaces in the inverse limit system are compact as well as Hausdorff, the inverse limit space is compact and not empty.

29.29 Theorem. *If $\{X_\nu, D, f_\alpha^\beta\}$ is an inverse limit system where each X_ν is a non-empty, compact, Hausdorff space, D is the directed set and f_α^β, for α and β in D and $\beta \geq \alpha$, is the continuous function from X_β into X_α, then the corresponding inverse limit space $\overleftarrow{L}$ is a non-empty, compact, Hausdorff space.*

Proof: By theorem 16.20, $\overleftarrow{L}$ is a closed subspace of the product space $\prod_{\nu \in D} X_\nu$. By theorem 28.46, $\prod_{\nu \in D} X_\nu$ is compact. By theorem 29.1, $\overleftarrow{L}$ is compact. Thus the theorem is proved if it can be shown that $\overleftarrow{L}$ is not-empty. Let $\alpha \in D$. Define M_α to be the set of all points x^* in $\prod_{\nu \in D} X_\nu$ whose coordinates satisfy the following condition: for $\gamma < \alpha$, $x_\gamma = f_\gamma^\alpha(x_\alpha)$, where x_γ and x_α are, respectively, the γ-th and α-th coordinates of x^*. Let y^* be any point in $\prod_{\nu \in D} X_\nu$. $\prod_{\nu \in D} X_\nu$ is not empty by the axiom of choice. Now, let $\alpha \in D$ and let y_α be the α-th coordinate of y^*. Define the point z^* in $\prod_{\nu \in D} X_\nu$ as follows: let $z_\nu = y_\nu$ for $\nu \geq \alpha$; for $\gamma < \alpha$, let $z_\gamma = f_\gamma^\alpha(y_\alpha)$. By definition of f_γ^α, z_γ exists as a unique point of the non-empty space X_γ. Further, $z^* \in M_\alpha$, by definition of M_α. Hence, M_α is not empty. Next, let $\alpha < \beta$. $M_\alpha \supseteq M_\beta$ by definition of M_α and M_β. Since D is a directed set (definition 7.15), the set $\{M_\alpha\}$ for $\alpha \in D$ has the finite intersection property. Next it will be shown that each M_α is closed in $\prod_{\nu \in D} X_\nu$. The proof is similar to the proof of theorem 16.20. Let q^* be a point in $\sim M_\alpha$, the complement of M_α in $\prod_{\nu \in D} X_\nu$. Be definition of M_α, there exists an element γ in D such that $\gamma < \alpha$ and $f_\gamma^\alpha(q_\alpha) \neq q_\gamma$, where q_α and q_γ are, respectively, the α-th and γ-th coordinate of q^* in $\prod_{\nu \in D} X_\nu$.

Since X_γ is Hausdorff, there exist disjoint open sets G_γ and H_γ in X_γ such that $f_\gamma^\alpha(q_\alpha) \in G_\gamma$ and $q_\gamma \in H_\gamma$. Since f_γ^α is continuous, $(f_\gamma^\alpha)^{-1}[G_\gamma]$ and $(f_\gamma^\alpha)^{-1}[H_\gamma]$ are open sets in X_α. Let $(f_\gamma^\alpha)^{-1}[G_\gamma] = G_\alpha$ and let $(f_\gamma^\alpha)^{-1}(H_\gamma) = H_\alpha$. Next, define the open set $V^* = \prod_{\nu \in D} V_\nu$, where $V_\nu = X_\nu$ for $\nu \neq \gamma$ and $\nu \neq \alpha$, and $V_\alpha = G_\alpha$ and $V_\gamma = H_\gamma$. Now, q^* is in V^*, since $q_\alpha \in (f_\gamma^\alpha)^{-1}[G_\gamma] = G_\alpha$ and $q_\gamma \in H_\gamma$. Next, let p^* be any point in V^*. Since p_α, the α-th coordinate of p^*, is in G_α and since $G_\alpha = (f_\gamma^\alpha)^{-1}[G_\gamma]$, $f_\gamma^\alpha(p_\alpha) \in G_\gamma$. Further, since p^* is in V^*, p_γ, the γ-th coordinate of p^*, is in H_γ. Since, by definition, $G_\gamma \cap H_\gamma = \emptyset$, $p_\gamma \neq f_\gamma^\alpha(p_\alpha)$ and so $p^* \notin M_\alpha$. Hence, $V^* \subseteq \sim M_\alpha$ and $\sim M_\alpha$ consists entirely of interior points. By theorem 3.28, $\sim M_\alpha$ is open, and so M_α is closed. Thus, the set $\{M_\alpha \mid \alpha \in D\}$ is a set of closed subsets of $\prod_{\nu \in D} X_\nu$ with the finite intersection property. Since $\prod_{\nu \in D} X_\nu$ is compact, $\bigcap_{\alpha \in D} M_\alpha \neq \emptyset$, by theorem 28.10. By definition of $\overleftarrow{L}$, $\overleftarrow{L} = \bigcap_{\alpha \in D} M_\alpha$. ∎

The Topological Group

Another structure of modern mathematics—the topological group—is now introduced.

29.30 Definition. Let S be a set, let $\mathfrak{I}$ be a topology for S and let $*$ denote an operation defined on S which satisfies the axioms for a group. The triple $\{S, \mathfrak{I}, *\}$ is called a *topological group* if and only if (1) the function $m(a, b) = a * b$ is continuous from the product space $\{S, \mathfrak{I}\} \times \{S, \mathfrak{I}\}$ into $\{S, \mathfrak{I}\}$ and (2) the function $In(a) = a^{-1}$ from $\{S, \mathfrak{I}\}$ into $\{S, \mathfrak{I}\}$ is continuous.

EXERCISE 3. Let S be the set of real numbers, let $\mathfrak{I}$ be the usual topology for S and let $+$ denote the usual addition for real numbers. Prove that $\{S, \mathfrak{I}, +\}$ is a topological group.

EXERCISE 4. Let M denote the set of non-zero real numbers; let $\mathfrak{I}$ be the usual topology and let $\times$ be the usual multiplication. Prove that $\{M, \mathfrak{I}, \times\}$ is a topological group.

EXERCISE 5. Let $\{S, \mathfrak{I}, *\}$ denote a topological group. Let r_a denote the function on S defined by $r_a(x) = x * a$. Similarly, let g_a be the function on S defined by $g_a(x) = a * x$. Prove that r_a and g_a are homeomorphisms of $\{S, \mathfrak{I}\}$ onto $\{S, \mathfrak{I}\}$.

EXERCISE 6. Prove that if $\{S, \mathfrak{I}, *\}$ is a topological group then the inverse function "In" defined by $In(a) = a^{-1}$ is a homeomorphism.

29.31 Theorem. *If $\{S, \mathfrak{I}, *\}$ is a topological group, then $\{S, \mathfrak{I}\}$ is a uniformizable space.*

Proof: First a uniform structure $\mathfrak{U}$ will be defined on S and then it will be shown that $\mathfrak{U}$ determines the topology $\mathfrak{I}$ on S, in the sense of definition 23.12.

Let $\mathfrak{N}_e$ denote the filter of neighborhoods in $\{S, \mathfrak{I}\}$ of the identity e of the group $\{S, *\}$. Let V be any neighborhood of e and define $R_V =$

$\{(x, y) \mid x * y^{-1} \in V\}$. Let $\mathcal{B}$ denote $\{R_V \mid V \text{ is in } \mathfrak{N}_e\}$. Since $x * x^{-1} = e$, $(x, x) \in R_V$ for every x in S and every V in $\mathfrak{N}_e$. Hence each relation R_V in $\mathcal{B}$ contains the diagonal, Δ, of $S \times S$ and $\emptyset$ is not in $\mathcal{B}$. Now let R_V and R_W be relations in $\mathcal{B}$. Since V and W are neighborhoods of e, $V \cap W$ is a neighborhood of e and so $R_{V \cap W}$ is in $\mathcal{B}$. Let (x, y) be in $R_{V \cap W}$. Then, $x * y^{-1} \in V \cap W$. This means that $x * y^{-1} \in V$ and $x * y^{-1} \in W$. Hence, $(x, y) \in R_V$ and $(x, y) \in R_W$, and so $R_{V \cap W} \subseteq R_V \cap R_W$. By definition (7.33) of the base of a filter and exercise 9 which follows it, $\mathcal{B}$ defines a filter $\mathcal{U}$ on $S \times S$. $\mathcal{U}$ is exactly the set of all subsets of $S \times S$ which contain at least one set in $\mathcal{B}$. Thus $\mathcal{U}$ is a filter on $S \times S$ and every set in $\mathcal{U}$ contains the diagonal Δ of $S \times S$. According to the definition (23.7) of a uniform structure, two more properties must be established. First, let M be in $\mathcal{U}$. M must then contain R_V for some V in $\mathfrak{N}_e$. $M^{-1} = \{(x, y) \mid (y, x) \in M\}$ will then contain R_V^{-1} by definition of M^{-1} and R_V^{-1}. Let V^{-1} denote $\{x \mid x^{-1} \text{ is in } V\}$, where x^{-1} denotes the inverse of x relative to the operation $*$. Since the "inverse" function, "In," defined by $In(a) = a^{-1}$, is a homeomorphism, by exercise 7 above, $V^{-1} = In[V]$ is a neighborhood of e. Hence, $R_{V^{-1}}$ is in $\mathcal{B}$. Now let (a, b) be in $R_{V^{-1}}$. This means that $a * b^{-1} \in V^{-1}$ and that $(a * b^{-1})^{-1} \in V$. $(a * b^{-1})^{-1} = b * a^{-1}$. Hence, $b * a^{-1} \in V$ and $(b, a) \in R_V$. Similarly, it can be shown that if $(b, a) \in R_V$, then $(a, b) \in R_{V^{-1}}$. This means that $R_{V^{-1}} = R_V^{-1}$. Since $M \supseteq R_V$, $M^{-1} \supseteq R_V^{-1} = R_{V^{-1}}$. Hence M^{-1} belongs to $\mathcal{U}$. The last property which must be established to show that $\mathcal{U}$ is a iniform structure is to show that for every M in $\mathcal{U}$ there is an N in $\mathcal{U}$ such that $N \circ N \subseteq M$. So, let M be in $\mathcal{U}$. By definition of $\mathcal{U}$, M must contain a subset R_V of $\mathcal{B}$, where V is a neighborhood of the identity e. Since by the definition (29.30) of a topological group, the multiplication function defined by $m\big((a, b)\big) = a * b$ is continuous and since $m\big((e, e)\big) = e * e = e$, there is a basic open set $U \times W$ in $\{S, \mathfrak{J}\} \times \{S, \mathfrak{J}\}$ which contains the point (e, e) and which is such that $m(U \times W) \subseteq V$. Now since $U \cap W \subseteq U$ and $U \cap W \subseteq W$, $(U \cap W) \times (U \cap W) \subseteq U \times W$. Hence, $m\big((U \cap W) \times (U \cap W)\big) \subseteq V$. Now let $N = U \cap W$ and consider $R_N \circ R_N$. Let $(a, b) \in R_N$ and $(b, d) \in R_N$. Then $a * b^{-1} \in N$ and $b * d^{-1} \in N$ and $(a * b^{-1}, b * d^{-1}) \in N \times N$. This means that $(a * b^{-1}) * (b * d^{-1}) \in m(N \times N) \subseteq V$. Hence, $a * d^{-1} \in V$, and $(a, d) \in R_V$. Thus if (a, d) is in $R_N \circ R_N$, then $(a, d) \in R_V$, and so $R_N \circ R_N \subseteq R_V$. $\mathcal{U}$ is then a uniform structure for S. Lastly it must be shown that $\mathcal{U}$ determines the topology $\mathfrak{J}$ on S. Let a be any point of S and let $M[a] = \{b \mid (a, b) \in M\}$ be any neighborhood assigned by $\mathcal{U}$ to a. Since M is in $\mathcal{U}$, M contains a relation R_V in the base $\mathcal{B}$ defined above, where V is a neighborhood of the identity e. V^{-1} is then, as above, a neighborhood of e. Let $V^{-1} * a = \{b^{-1} * a \mid b^{-1} \in V^{-1}\}$. $V^{-1} * a$, then, is the image of V^{-1} assigned by the function r_a defined in exercise 6, above. Since r_a is a homeomorphism, $V^{-1} * a$ is a neighborhood of a in $\{S, \mathfrak{J}\}$. Now let q be a point in $V^{-1} * a$. This means that $q = v^{-1} * a$ for v^{-1} in V^{-1}, and so $q * a^{-1} = v^{-1} \in V^{-1}$. Hence, $(q * a^{-1})^{-1} \in V$. Since $(q * a^{-1})^{-1} = a * q^{-1}$, $a * q^{-1} \in V$ and $(a, q) \in R_V$. Thus $(a, q) \in M$ and $q \in M[a]$. Since q was any point in

$V^{-1} * a$, $V^{-1} * a \subseteq M[a]$. Thus every neighborhood assigned by $\mathfrak{U}$ is a neighborhood assigned by $\mathfrak{I}$. Conversely let N be any neighborhood of a assigned by $\mathfrak{I}$. By exercise 7, above, N^{-1} is then a neighborhood of a^{-1}, and by exercise 6, above, since g_a is a homeomorphism, $g_a[N^{-1}]$ is a neighborhood of e, the identity of the group $\{S, *\}$. Denote $g_a[N^{-1}]$ by $a * N^{-1}$. By definition of $\mathfrak{U}$, there exists a relation $R_{a*N^{-1}}$ in $\mathfrak{U}$. Let $(a, q) \in R_{a*N^{-1}}$. By definition of $R_{a*N^{-1}}$ and $\mathfrak{B}$, above, this means that $a * q^{-1} \in a * N^{-1}$ or that $q \in N$. Hence $R_{a*N^{-1}}[a] \subseteq N$ and N is a neighborhood of a assigned by $\mathfrak{U}$. ▮

29.32 Corollary. *If $\{S, \mathfrak{I}, *\}$ is a topological group, then $\{S, \mathfrak{I}\}$ is either not T_0 or it is a completely regular space.*

Proof: The corollary follows from corollary 23.19. ▮

Thus the topological theory of topological groups falls under the theory of completely regular spaces.

The Compact-Open Topology

If X and Y are spaces, the set Y^X of all functions from X into Y is a product set and hence can be assigned the product topology, i.e., the topology of pointwise convergence as in definition 12.35. In the case where Y is a bounded metric space, a metric topology can be defined on Y^X—the topology of uniform convergence (lemma 21.17 and definition 21.21). Another useful topology, called the compact-open topology, can also be defined for the set Y^X.

29.33 Definition. Let X and Y be spaces. For each ordered pair (A, B) where A is a subset of X and B is a subset of Y, let $G(A, B)$ denote $\{f \mid f \in Y^X \text{ and } f[A] \subseteq B\}$. Let $\mathfrak{V}$ denote $\{G(\mathfrak{C}, \mathfrak{O}) \mid \mathfrak{C}$ is a compact subset of X and $\mathfrak{O}$ is an open subset of $Y\}$. The *compact-open topology*, $\mathfrak{I}_{c.-o.}$, for the set Y^X is defined to be the topology for Y^X determined by $\mathfrak{V}$ as a subbase.

By definition (3.52) of a subbase and by exercise 45 which follows it, a topology is determined uniquely by the set $\mathfrak{V}$ of the above definition.

29.34 Theorem. *If X and Y are spaces, the compact-open topology for Y^X contains the product topology for Y^X.*

Proof: Let B^* be a basic open set in the product topology on Y^X. $B^* = \prod_{x \in X} B_x$, where B_x is open in Y and $B_x = Y$ for $x \neq x_1, \ldots, x \neq x_k$, where k is a natural number. Hence, B^* is, by definition, a product set, the set of all functions f such that $f(x_1) \in B_{x_1}, \ldots, f(x_k) \in B_{x_k}$, i.e., $f[\{x_1\}] \subseteq B_{x_1}, \ldots, f[\{x_k\}] \subseteq B_{x_k}$. Since the singleton sets $\{x_1\}, \ldots, \{x_k\}$ are compact, $B^* = \{f \mid f \in Y^X$ and $f \in G(\{x_1\}, B_{x_1}), \ldots,$ and $f \in G(\{x_k\}, B_{x_k})\}$, where $G(A, B)$

is defined as in the previous definition (29.33). Hence, $B^* = G(\{x_1\}, B_{x_1}) \cap \cdots \cap G(\{x_k\}, B_{x_k})$ and so B^* belongs to the compact-open topology for Y^X. ▌

29.35 Corollary. *If Y is a T_0-, T_1- or T_2-space and if X is any space, then $\{Y^X, \mathfrak{I}_{c.\text{-}o.}\}$ is a T_0-, T_1- or T_2-space, respectively.*

Proof: Since, by theorem 16.18, $\{Y^X, \mathfrak{I}_P\}$, where $\mathfrak{I}_P$ is the product topology, is a T_0-, T_1- or T_2-space, respectively, if Y is such a space, then the corollary follows from exercise 2 of section 16 since by the previous theorem $\mathfrak{I}_P \subseteq \mathfrak{I}_{c.\text{-}o.}$. ▌

EXERCISE 7. Prove that if X is a space with the discrete topology, i.e., all subsets of X are open, and if Y is any space, then $\mathfrak{I}_{c.\text{-}o.} = \mathfrak{I}_P$ where, as above, $\mathfrak{I}_{c.\text{-}o.}$ is the compact-open topology for Y^X and $\mathfrak{I}_P$ is the product topology for Y^X.

The relative compact-open topology can of course be defined for any subset A of functions in Y^X, where X and Y are spaces. This topology is then called the compact-open topology for A. The next two theorems make use of the relative compact-open topology for a set of functions and, in so doing, establish a useful instance of a topological group.

29.36 Theorem. *Let X be a compact Hausdorff space and let H denote the subset of X^X consisting of the homeomorphisms of X onto X. Let $f * h$ denote the composite map $f \circ h$. Then the multiplication function $m((f, h)) = f * h$ is continuous from $\{H, \mathfrak{I}_{c.\text{-}o.}\} \times \{H, \mathfrak{I}_{c.\text{-}o.}\}$ into $\{H, \mathfrak{I}_{c.,o.}\}$.*

Proof: Let $G(\mathcal{C}, \mathcal{O})$ be a subbasic open set in the compact-open topology $\mathfrak{I}_{c.\text{-}o.}$ for H. Let (f, h) be a point in $m^{-1}[G(\mathcal{C}, \mathcal{O})]$. Then the composite function $f \circ h$ is in $G(\mathcal{C}, \mathcal{O})$. This means that $f[h[\mathcal{C}]] \subseteq \mathcal{O}$ and so $f^{-1}[\mathcal{O}] \supseteq h[\mathcal{C}]$. Since $\mathcal{C}$ is compact, $h[\mathcal{C}]$ is compact, and since X is Hausdorff, $h[\mathcal{C}]$ is closed in X by theorem 29.5. Since X is compact and Hausdorff, X is normal, by theorem 29.12. Since X is normal and $f^{-1}[\mathcal{O}]$ is open, there exists, by theorem 18.6, an open set V in X, such that $h[\mathcal{C}] \subseteq V \subseteq \overline{V} \subseteq f^{-1}[\mathcal{O}]$. Now, consider the open set $G(\overline{V}, \mathcal{O}) \times G(\mathcal{C}, V)$ in $\{H, \mathfrak{I}_{c.\text{-}o.}\} \times \{H, \mathfrak{I}_{c.\text{-}o.}\}$. First of all, (f, h) is in $G(\overline{V}, \mathcal{O}) \times G(\mathcal{C}, V)$, since $f[\overline{V}] \subseteq \mathcal{O}$ and $h[\mathcal{C}] \subseteq V$. Next, let (n, k) be any element in $G(\overline{V}, \mathcal{O}) \times G(\mathcal{C}, V)$ and consider $m((n, k))$. $m((n, k))$ is the composite function $n \circ k$ and $n \circ k[\mathcal{C}] = n[k[\mathcal{C}]]$. Since k is in $G(\mathcal{C}, V)$, $k[\mathcal{C}] \subseteq V$ and since $V \subseteq \overline{V}$ and n is in $G(\overline{V}, \mathcal{O})$, $n[k[\mathcal{C}]] \subseteq \mathcal{O}$. Thus, $n \circ k[\mathcal{C}] \subseteq \mathcal{O}$ and so $n \circ k$ is in $G(\mathcal{C}, \mathcal{O})$. This means that $m[G(\overline{V}, \mathcal{O}) \times G(\mathcal{C}, V)] \subseteq G(\mathcal{C}, \mathcal{O})$. Hence, every point in $m^{-1}[G(\mathcal{C}, \mathcal{O})]$ is interior and, by theorem 3.28, $m^{-1}[G(\mathcal{C}, \mathcal{O})]$ is open. m is then continuous by theorem 4.10. ▌

29.37 Theorem. *Let X be a compact, Hausdorff space and let H denote the set of homeomorphisms of X onto X. Let $\mathfrak{I}_{c.\text{-}o.}$ denote the compact-open topology for H. Then the "inverse" function $In: \{H, \mathfrak{I}_{c.\text{-}o.}\} \to \{H, \mathfrak{I}_{c.\text{-}o.}\}$, defined by $In(f) = f^{-1}$, is continuous.*

Proof: Let $G(\mathcal{C}, \mathcal{O})$ be any open set in the defining subbase for $\mathfrak{I}_{c.-o.}$. Let f be in $In^{-1}[G(\mathcal{C}, \mathcal{O})]$. Then f^{-1} is in $G(\mathcal{C}, \mathcal{O})$. Hence, $f^{-1}[\mathcal{C}] \subseteq \mathcal{O}$ or $\mathcal{C} \subseteq f[\mathcal{O}]$. Now consider $X \sim \mathcal{O}$ and $X \sim \mathcal{C}$. $X \sim \mathcal{O}$ is closed in X, and hence is compact. Since $\mathcal{C}$ is compact in the Hausdorff space X, it is closed by theorem 29.5. Hence $X \sim \mathcal{C}$ is open in X. Thus, $G(X \sim \mathcal{O}, X \sim \mathcal{C})$ is a subbasic open set in $\mathfrak{I}_{c.-o.}$. Now, by above, $\mathcal{C} \subseteq f[\mathcal{O}]$ and since f is a homeomorphism, $f[X \sim \mathcal{O}] \subseteq X \sim \mathcal{C}$. Thus f is in $G(X \sim \mathcal{O}, X \sim \mathcal{C})$. Now let h be any function in $G(X \sim \mathcal{O}, X \sim \mathcal{C})$. $h[X \sim \mathcal{O}] \subseteq X \sim \mathcal{C}$. Since h is a homeomorphism onto, $h[X \sim \mathcal{O}] \subseteq X \sim \mathcal{C}$ implies that $h[\mathcal{O}] \supseteq \mathcal{C}$. Hence, $\mathcal{O} \supseteq h^{-1}[\mathcal{C}]$ and h^{-1} is in $G(\mathcal{C}, \mathcal{O})$. This means that every point in $In^{-1}[G(\mathcal{C}, \mathcal{O})]$ is interior and by theorem 3.28, $In^{-1}[G(\mathcal{C}, \mathcal{O})]$ is then open. This establishes, by theorem 4.10, that In is continuous. ▮

29.38 Corollary. *If X is a compact, Hausdorff space, H is the set of homeomorphisms of X onto X, $\mathfrak{I}_{c.-o.}$ is the compact-open topology for H and $*$ is composition of functions, then $\{H, \mathfrak{I}_{c.-o.}, *\}$ is a topological group.*

Proof: The proof that $\{H, *\}$ is a group is left as an exercise. The previous two theorems then complete the proof that $\{H, \mathfrak{I}_{c.-o.}, *\}$ is a topological group. ▮

The compact-open topology yields the metrizable topology of definition 21.21 for Y^X when Y is metrizable and X is compact.

29.39 Lemma. *If F_1 and F_2 are two disjoint compact sets in a metrizable space Y, then $d_\rho(F_1, F_2) > 0$, where ρ is any admissible metric for Y.*

Proof: By theorem 19.19, ρ is continuous from the product space $Y \times Y$ into E^1. By theorem 28.38, $F_1 \times F_2$ is compact. By theorem 28.36, $\rho[F_1 \times F_2]$ is a compact subset of E^1. By theorem 29.5, $\rho[F_1 \times F_2]$ is then a closed subset of E^1. By corollary 19.18, $\rho[F_1 \times F_2]$ is a positive set of real numbers. Hence, by definition (19.3), $d_\rho(F_1, F_2) > 0$. ▮

29.40 Theorem. *If X is compact and Y is metrizable, then the compact-open topology for $C(X, Y)$, the set of all continuous functions from X into Y, is a (metrizable) topology of uniform convergence.*

Proof: Let ρ be any admissible metric for Y and let f be in $C(X, Y)$. Since f is continuous and X is compact, $f[X]$ is bounded in $\{Y, \rho\}$. Hence $\text{l.u.b.}_{x \in X} \{\rho(f(x), g(x))\}$ is a unique real number for f and g in $C(X, Y)$. Thus if $\sigma(f, g) = \text{l.u.b.}_{x \in X} \{\rho(f(x), g(x))\}$, σ is a metric on $C(X, Y)$ by lemma 21.17. $\mathfrak{I}_\sigma$, the metrizable topology determined by σ for $C(X, Y)$, is then the topology of uniform convergence for $C(X, Y)$. Now, let $G^* = G(C_1, \mathcal{O}_1) \cap \cdots \cap G(C_k, \mathcal{O}_k)$ denote any basic open set in the compact-open topology (definition 29.33) and let f be in G^*. Then, $f[C_1] \subseteq \mathcal{O}_1, \ldots, f[C_k] \subseteq \mathcal{O}_k$. Since X is compact, $(Y \sim \mathcal{O}_i) \cap f[X]$ is compact in Y and $f[C_i] \cap ((Y \sim \mathcal{O}_i) \cap f[X]) = \emptyset$. Thus, by the previous lemma, $d_\rho(f[C_i] \cap (\sim\mathcal{O}_i \cap f[X])) > 0$ for $i = 1, 2, \ldots, k$.

Let $d_\rho(f[C_i] \cap (\sim\mathcal{O}_i \cap f[X])) = \epsilon_i$, and let ϵ^* be the minimum of $\{\epsilon_1/2, \epsilon_2/2, \ldots, \epsilon_k/2\}$. Now consider the spherical neighborhood $U_\sigma(f, \epsilon^*)$ of f and let g be in $U_\sigma(f, \epsilon^*)$. It follows that $\text{l.u.b.}_{x \in X}\{\rho(f(x), g(x))\} < \epsilon^* \leq \epsilon_i/2$ for $i = 1, 2, \ldots, k$. By definition of ϵ_i, $g[C_i] \subseteq \mathcal{O}_i$ for $i = 1, 2, \ldots, k$. Thus, g is in G^* and $U_\sigma(f, \epsilon^*) \subseteq G^*$. This means that G^* is open in $\{C(X, Y), \mathfrak{J}_\sigma\}$, and hence that $\mathfrak{J}_{c.\text{-}o.} \subseteq \mathfrak{J}_\sigma$. Conversely, let $U_\sigma(f, \epsilon)$ be any spherical neighborhood of f determined by σ. For each point y in Y, $\overline{V}_\rho(y, \epsilon/4) \subseteq V_\rho(y, \epsilon)$, by lemma 19.17. Since f is continuous, there exists for each x in X a compact neighborhood $\overline{U}_x$ such that $f[\overline{U}_x] \subseteq \overline{V}_\rho(f(x), \epsilon/4)$. Since X is compact, a finite number of these cover X, say, $\overline{U}_{x_1}, \overline{U}_{x_2}, \ldots, \overline{U}_{x_m}$. This means that $f[\overline{U}_{x_1}]$, $f[\overline{U}_{x_2}], \ldots, f[\overline{U}_{x_n}]$ cover $f[X]$, and that f is in $G^* = G(\overline{U}_{x_1}, V_\rho(f(x_1), \epsilon/3)) \cap \cdots \cap G(\overline{U}_{x_n}, V_\rho(f(x_n), \epsilon/3))$, a set in $\mathfrak{J}_{c.\text{-}o.}$. Now, let g be in G^* and let x be in X. x is in some set $\overline{U}_{x_1}, \ldots, \overline{U}_{x_n}$. Say x is in $\overline{U}_{x_i}$. Then $f(x)$ is in $V_\rho(f(x_i), \epsilon/3)$. Also $g[\overline{U}_{x_i}] \subseteq V_\rho(f(x_i), \epsilon/3)$. Thus $g(x)$ is in $V_\rho(f(x_i), \epsilon/3)$. It follows that $\rho(f(x_i), g(x)) < \epsilon/3$ and that $\rho(f(x_i), f(x)) < \epsilon/3$. Hence, $\rho(f(x), g(x)) < \frac{2}{3}\epsilon$, and so $\sigma(f, g) < \epsilon$. Thus $G^* \subseteq U_\sigma(f, \epsilon)$ and $\mathfrak{J}_\sigma \subseteq \mathfrak{J}_{c.\text{-}o.}$. ∎

The compact-open topology has other properties and uses which will be introduced when appropriate.

30. COMPACTNESS IN METRIZABLE SPACES AND IN UNIFORM SPACES.

In the last section the power of the combination "compact and Hausdorff" was established. Since every metrizable space is Hausdorff, but not conversely, the combination "compact and metrizable" ought to exhibit even more power. The first set of theorems leads to the striking result that, in a metrizable space, compactness and countable compactness are equivalent—one never occurs without the other.

Equivalence of Compactness and Countable Compactness

30.1 Definition. A finite subset γ of a metric space $\{S, \rho\}$ is called an *ϵ-dense set* if and only if for every point p of S, there exists at least one point s_i of γ such that $\rho(p, s_i) < \epsilon$. A metric space $\{S, \rho\}$ is called *totally bounded* if and only if for every positive real number ϵ, $\{S, \rho\}$ has an ϵ-dense subset.

EXERCISE 1. Prove that a metric space $\{S, \rho\}$ is totally bounded if and only if for every positive real number ϵ, S is the union of sets of ρ-diameter $< \epsilon$.

30.2 Theorem. *If S is countably compact, then any metric space $\{S, \rho\}$ is totally bounded.*

Proof: Assume that there exists a positive real number ϵ^* such that $\{S, \rho\}$ has no ϵ^*-dense subset. Let p_1 be any point in $\{S, \rho\}$. If $\rho(x, p_1) < \epsilon^*$ for all

x in S, then $\{S, \rho\}$ would be totally bounded. Hence, there exists in S a point p_2 such that $\rho(p_1, p_2) \geq \epsilon^*$. Similarly, there exists a point p_3 in S such that $\rho(p_1, p_3) \geq \epsilon^*$ and $\rho(p_2, p_3) \geq \epsilon^*$; otherwise $\{S, \rho\}$ would be totally bounded. Assume that for the natural number k the subset $\{p_1, p_2, \ldots, p_k\}$ of S has been defined such that $\rho(p_i, p_j) \geq \epsilon^*$ for $i \neq j$ and $1 \leq i, j \leq k$. Since, by assumption, $\{S, \rho\}$ is not totally bounded, there exists a point p_{k+1} in S such that $\rho(p_i, p_{k+1}) \geq \epsilon^*$ for $1 \leq i \leq k$. Thus, by finite induction, a countably infinite set $\{p_1, p_2, \ldots, p_k, \ldots\}$ is defined with the property that $\rho(p_i, p_j) \geq \epsilon^*$ for $i \neq j$ and i, j natural numbers. Since S, by hypothesis, is countably compact, $\{p_1, p_2, \ldots, p_k, \ldots\}$, by theorem 28.15, has a limit point q in S. Let $U_\rho(q, \epsilon^*/2)$ denote the spherical neighborhood of q with radius $\epsilon^*/2$. Since q is a limit point of $\{p_1, p_2, \ldots, p_k, \ldots\}$, there exists $p_j \in U_\rho(q, \epsilon^*/2)$. Let $\rho(q, p_j) = \delta^*$. $\delta^* < \epsilon^*/2$. Similarly, there exists in $U_\rho(q, \delta^*)$ a point p_i. Since $\rho(q, p_j) = \delta^*$, $p_i \neq p_j$. Now, $\rho(q, p_i) < \epsilon^*/2$ and $\rho(q, p_j) < \epsilon^*/2$. Hence, $\rho(p_i, p_j) < \epsilon^*$. This is a contradiction, since $\rho(p_i, p_j) \geq \epsilon^*$. Hence, no such ϵ^* can exist and $\{S, \rho\}$ is totally bounded. ▮

30.3 Theorem. *If $\{S, \rho\}$ is totally bounded, then S is separable.*

Proof: Let n denote a positive integer. Let A_n denote a $1/n$-dense set for the totally bounded space $\{S, \rho\}$. Let $D = \bigcup_n A_n$. D, as the union of a countable set of finite sets, is countable. Now, let p be any point of $\{S, \rho\}$ and let $U_\rho(p, \epsilon)$ be any spherical neighborhood of p assigned by the metric ρ. By the archimedean order on the reals, there exists a positive integer n such that $1/n < \epsilon$. Hence, there exists a point n_i in the $1/n$-dense set A_n such that $\rho(p, n_i) < 1/n$. Hence, n_i is in $U_\rho(p, \epsilon)$ and D is dense in $\{S, \rho\}$. ▮

30.4 Theorem. *Any countably compact metrizable space is second countable.*

Proof: By theorems 30.2 and 30.3, any countably compact, metrizable space $\{S, \mathfrak{J}_\rho\}$ is separable. By theorem 20.5, $\{S, \mathfrak{J}_\rho\}$ is then second countable. ▮

EXERCISE 2. In the proof of lemma 29.17, the space W^* defined as the set $W \cup \{W\}$ and the order topology, where W is the first uncountable ordinal, was proved to be compact and Hausdorff, and hence normal. Prove that W^* is not second countable.

30.5 Theorem. *Any countably compact metrizable space is compact.*

Proof: Let $\{S, \mathfrak{J}_\rho\}$ be a countably compact metrizable space and let $\mathcal{G}$ be any open covering of $\{S, \mathfrak{J}_\rho\}$. By theorem 30.4, $\{S, \mathfrak{J}_\rho\}$ is second countable. By theorem 18.15, every open covering $\{S, \mathfrak{J}_\rho\}$ contains a countable subcovering; hence, $\mathcal{G}$ contains a countable subcovering $\{G_1, G_2, \ldots, G_n, \ldots\}$. By hypothesis, a finite number of the sets in $\{G_1, G_2, \ldots, G_n, \ldots\}$ cover $\{S, \mathfrak{J}_\rho\}$. Hence, $\mathcal{G}$ contains a finite subcovering and $\{S, \mathfrak{J}_\rho\}$ is compact. ▮

Thus, theorem 30.5 and the definition of compactness imply that countable compactness and compactness are the same property in metrizable spaces.

30.6 Theorem. *A metrizable space is compact if and only if every infinite subset has a limit point.*

Proof: By theorem 19.20, every metrizable space is T_1. By theorem 28.17, countable compactness for metrizable spaces is equivalent to every infinite set having a limit point. By theorem 30.5, then, the theorem follows. ▮

In addition to being useful in proving that countable compactness and compactness are equivalent in metrizable spaces, total boundedness yields an alternate definition of compactness for metrizable spaces.

30.7 Theorem. *A metric space $\{S, \rho\}$ is complete and totally bounded if and only if S is compact.*

Proof: A. If S is compact, then by theorem 30.2, $\{S, \rho\}$ is totally bounded. Also by theorem 28.32, every sequence in S contains a converging subsequence. Hence, let s be any Cauchy sequence in S. s contains a converging subsequence $s \circ \delta$, where δ is a function from the set of positive integers into itself (definition 28.27). Let $s \circ \delta$ converge to p. Let ϵ be any positive real number. Since s is Cauchy, there is a natural number L^* such that if $m \geq L^*$ and $n \geq L^*$, for positive integers m and n, then $\rho(s(m), s(n)) < \epsilon/2$. Similarly, since $s \circ \delta$ converges to p, there is a natural number M^* such that if $j \geq M^*$, for j a positive integer, $\rho(s \circ \delta(j), p) < \epsilon/2$.

Also by definition of a subsequence, there is a positive integer Q^* such that if $t \geq Q^*$, $\delta(t) \geq L^*$. Hence if $N^* = \max\{Q^*, L^*, M^*\}$ and if m and j are greater than N^*, $\rho(s(m), s(\delta(j))) < \epsilon/2$ and $\rho(s(\delta(j)), p) < \epsilon/2$. Hence if $m \geq N^*$, $\rho(s(m), p) < \epsilon$. Thus s converges to p and $\{S, \rho\}$ is complete.

B. Conversely, let $\{S, \rho\}$ be complete and totally bounded. S is a T_1-space by theorem 19.20. Hence, by theorems 28.17 and 30.5, it is sufficient to show that every infinite subset of S has a limit point in S. Hence, let A_0 be an infinite subset of S. Since $\{S, \rho\}$ is a totally bounded space, there exists a $\frac{1}{2}$-dense set $\{p_1, \ldots, p_t\}$, say. This means that the spherical neighborhoods $U_\rho(p_1, 1/2), \ldots, U_\rho(p_t, 1/2)$ cover S. Hence, at least one of these neighborhoods, $U_\rho(p_1, 1/2)$, say, contains an infinite subset, A_1, of A_0. Since $A_1 \subseteq U_\rho(p_1, 1/2)$, the diameter of A_1 is less than or equal to 1. Assume that infinite subsets $A_1, \ldots, A_k$ of A_0 have been defined such that $A_1 \supseteq A_2 \supseteq \cdots \supseteq A_k$ and diam $A_i \leq 1/i$ for $1 \leq i \leq k$. Since $\{S, \rho\}$ is totally bounded, there exists a $1/(2(k+1))$-dense set $\{q_1, \ldots, q_s\}$. This means that the spherical neighborhoods

$$U_\rho\left(q_1, \frac{1}{2(k+1)}\right), \ldots, U_p\left(q_s, \frac{1}{2(k+1)}\right)$$

cover S. Hence at least one of these neighborhoods, say,

$$U_\rho\left(q_1, \frac{1}{2(k+1)}\right)$$

contains an infinite subset A_{k+1} of A_k. Since

$$A_{k+1} \subseteq U\left(q_1, \frac{1}{2(k+1)}\right), \qquad \text{diam } A_{k+1} \leq \frac{1}{k+1}.$$

Hence, by induction, a sequence $(A_1, A_2, \ldots, A_n, \ldots)$ of infinite subsets of A_0 has been defined such that $A_n \supseteq A_{n+1}$ for $n = 1, 2, \ldots$ and diam $A_n \leq 1/n$. A choice function for the non-zero subsets of A_0 determines a sequence $\gamma = (a_1, a_2, \ldots, a_n, \ldots)$ such that $a_n \in A_n$ and the range of γ is infinite. Further, if ϵ is any positive real number, by the archimedean order on the reals, there exists a natural number n^* such that $1/n^* < \epsilon$. Now, if $i > n^*$ and $j > n^*$, $a_i \in A_{n^*}$ and $a_j \in A_{n^*}$. Hence, if $i > n^*$ and $j > n^*$, $\rho(a_i, a_j) \leq 1/n^* < \epsilon$. Thus $\gamma = (a_1, a_2, \ldots, a_n, \ldots)$ is a Cauchy sequence. Since $\{S, \rho\}$ is complete, γ converges to a point of S, say α. Since the range, $\{a_1, a_2, \ldots, a_n, \ldots\}$, of γ is infinite, α is a limit point of $\{a_1, a_2, \ldots, a_n, \ldots\}$ and hence of A_1. Thus α is a limit point of A_0. This means that the metrizable space S is compact. ▮

A Characterization of Compact Metrizable Spaces

Another corollary follows immediately now from theorems 30.4, 29.23 and 29.7.

30.8 Corollary. *Any continuous image of a compact metrizable space in a Hausdorff space is a compact metrizable space.*

Proof: Let f be a continuous function from the compact metrizable space $\{S, \mathfrak{I}_\rho\}$ into a Hausdorff space. Let $f[S] = Y$. By theorem 29.7, f is a closed function. By theorem 30.4, $\{S, \mathfrak{I}_\rho\}$ is second countable and by theorem 29.23, Y is second countable. By theorem 28.36, Y is compact. Since Y is Hausdorff by hypothesis, Y is normal by theorem 29.12. Thus Y is second countable and normal, and so by Urysohn's Imbedding theorem (20.16), Y is a metrizable space. ▮

EXERCISE 3. Prove that the continuous image of any compact metrizable space is either second countable and metrizable or not Hausdorff.

EXERCISE 4. Give an example of a non-Hausdorff space which is the continuous image of a compact metrizable space.

EXERCISE 5. Give an example of a totally bounded metric space $\{S, \rho\}$ such that S is not compact.

EXERCISE 6. Give an example of a metric space which is bounded but not totally bounded.

EXERCISE 7. Prove that if a metric space is totally bounded, then it is bounded.

The last corollary established a sufficient condition that a space be a compact, metrizable space—namely, that the space be the continuous image in a Hausdorff space of a compact metrizable space. The following theorem establishes a rather startling necessary condition that a space be a compact metrizable space. First a lemma is proved.

30.9 Lemma. *Any non-empty compact metrizable space is the continuous image of a closed subspace of the Cantor ternary space.*

Proof: A. First a function is defined. The Cantor ternary space (definition 12.14) is a product space 2^ω, where 2 here denotes the discrete space with two elements and ω denotes the set of natural numbers. As a product of compact spaces, 2^ω is compact by theorem 28.46. In theorem 12.26, 2^ω was imbedded topologically in the unit interval subspace, $[0, 1]$, of E^1. Thus 2^ω is itself a compact metrizable space. Let S, now, be a non-empty compact metrizable space. By theorem 30.4, S has a non-empty countable base. Let $\mathcal{B}$ denote a countable base for the metrizable topology. $\mathcal{B} = \{B_1, \ldots, B_n, \ldots\}$ or $\mathcal{B} = \{B_1, \ldots, B_n\}$, where $B_i \neq B_j$ for $i \neq j$. If $\mathcal{B} = \{B_1, \ldots, B_n\}$, i.e., if $\mathcal{B}$ is finite, define the sequence $(B_1, B_2, \ldots, B_n, B_{n+1}, \ldots, B_{n+k}, \ldots)$ in $P(S)$, where $B_{n+k} = B_n$ for $k = 1, 2, \ldots$. If $\mathcal{B}$ is infinite, the set $\{B_1, B_2, \ldots, B_n, \ldots\}$ determines the sequence $(B_1, B_2, \ldots, B_n, \ldots)$ in $P(S)$. Now let σ be any element in 2^ω. σ is a sequence in $\{0, 1\}$, i.e., $\sigma = (a_1, a_2, \ldots, a_n, \ldots)$, where, as usual, $a_n = \sigma(n)$ and where each $a_n = 0$ or $a_n = 1$ for $n \in \omega$. To σ assign the following sequence in $P(S)$: $\Psi(\sigma) = (A_1, A_2, \ldots, A_n, \ldots)$, where $A_n = \overline{B}_n$ if $\sigma(n) = 0$ and $A_n = S \sim B_n$ if $\sigma(n) = 1$. Each set A_n in the sequence $(A_1, A_2, \ldots, A_n, \ldots) = \Psi(\sigma)$ is a closed subset of the compact metrizable space S. Hence, if the range of Ψ, i.e., the set $\{A_1, A_2, \ldots, A_n, \ldots\}$, satisfies the finite intersection property, $\bigcap_{n=1}^{\infty} A_n \neq \emptyset$. Now let a and b be any two points of S. Since S is metrizable, S is regular. Hence there exists a base element B_i such that $a \in B_i$ and $b \notin \overline{B}_i$. Hence, $a \in \overline{B}_i$ and $b \in S \sim B_i$. Further, $A_i = \overline{B}_i$ or $A_i = S \sim B_i$. Hence, a and b cannot both be in $\bigcap_{n=1}^{\infty} A_n$. Thus, $\bigcap_{n=1}^{\infty} A_n = \emptyset$ or $\bigcap_{n=1}^{\infty} A_n = \{s\}$. If $\bigcap_{n=1}^{\infty} A_n = \{s\}$, where, as defined above, $\Psi(\sigma) = (A_1, A_2, \ldots, A_n, \ldots)$, then define $f(\sigma) = s$. If $\bigcap_{n=1}^{\infty} A_n = \emptyset$, $f(\sigma)$ is not defined. Let F denote the domain of f.

B. F is a closed subset of 2^ω. For, let γ be a point in $\sim F$, the complement of F in 2^ω. Let $\gamma = (c_1, c_2, \ldots, c_n, \ldots)$, where, again, $\gamma(n) = c_n$, and let $\Psi(\gamma) = (K_1, K_2, \ldots, K_n, \ldots)$ as defined in part A above. Since $f(\gamma)$ is not defined, $\bigcap_{n=1}^{\infty} K_n = \emptyset$. Further, since each K_n for $n = 1, 2, \ldots$ is a closed subset of the compact metrizable space S, $\bigcap_{n=1}^{\infty} K_n = \emptyset$ implies that for some natural number k^*, $K_1 \cap \cdots \cap K_{k^*} = \emptyset$. Now consider $G = \{(a_1, a_2, \ldots, a_n, \ldots) \mid (a_1, a_2, \ldots, a_n, \ldots) \in 2^\omega \text{ and } a_1 = c_1, a_2 = c_2, \ldots, a_{k^*} = c_{k^*}\}$. By the definition (12.5) of the product topology, the set G is open in 2^ω. Further, $\gamma \in G$. Now let σ be any point in G. $\sigma = (c_1, c_2, \ldots, c_{k^*}, a_{k^*+1}, \ldots, a_n, \ldots)$, and so $\Psi(\sigma) = (A_1, A_2, \ldots, A_n, \ldots)$, where $A_1 = K_1$, $A_2 = K_2, \ldots, A_{k^*} = K_{k^*}$. Hence $\bigcap_{n=1}^{\infty} A_n = \emptyset$ and $\sigma \in \sim F$. Thus $\sim F$ is open in 2^ω and F is closed.

C. f is onto. Let s be any point in the compact metrizable space S. Define the following sequence σ_s in 2^ω. If $s \in \overline{B}_i$, let $\sigma_s(i) = 0$; if $s \notin \overline{B}_i$ (then

$s \in S \sim B_i$) let $\sigma_s(i) = 1$. Then, if $\Psi(\sigma_s) = (A_1, A_2, \ldots, A_n, \ldots)$, $s \in A_n$ for $n = 1, 2, \ldots$. Hence, $s \in \bigcap_{n=1}^{\infty} A_n$. This means that $\bigcap_{n=1}^{\infty} A_n = \{s\}$ and $f(\sigma_s) = s$. Thus f is onto the compact metrizable space S.

D. f is continuous. Let σ be any element in the domain of f and let V be any open set which contains $f(\sigma)$. Since S is metrizable, it is regular. Hence, there exists a basic open set B_{j^*} in the base $\mathcal{B}$ such that $f(\sigma) \in B_{j^*}$ and $\overline{B}_{j^*} \subseteq V$. Now consider the basic open set $U^* = \{(a_1, a_2, \ldots, a_n, \ldots) \mid a_{j^*} = 0\}$ in the product space 2^ω. Since $f(\sigma) \in B_{j^*}$, $A_{j^*} \neq S \sim B_{j^*}$, where $\Psi(\sigma) = (A_1, A_2, \ldots, A_n, \ldots)$ as defined above. For, if $A_{j^*} = S \sim B_{j^*}$ then $f(\sigma) \notin A_{j^*}$ and so $f(\sigma) \notin \bigcap_{n=1}^{\infty} A_n$. This contradicts the definition of $f(\sigma)$. Hence, since $A_{j^*} \neq S \sim B_{j^*}$, $\sigma(j^*) \neq 1$ by definition of Ψ. Hence, $\sigma(j^*) = 0$ and $\sigma \in U^*$. Now let $\delta = (d_1, d_2, \ldots, d_n, \ldots)$ be any element in $U^* \cap F$. $d_{j^*} = 0$ by definition of U^*. Hence, if $\Psi(\delta) = (D_1, D_2, \ldots, D_n, \ldots)$, D_{j^*} must be $\overline{B}_{j^*}$ by definition of Ψ. Now $\{f(\delta)\} = \bigcap_{n=1}^{\infty} D_n$. Hence $f(\delta)$ must be in $\overline{B}_{j^*}$, and so also in V. Thus if $\delta \in U^* \cap F$, $f(\delta)$ is in V. f is then continuous at every point of F. ∎

30.10 Theorem. *Any non-empty compact metrizable space is the continuous image of the Cantor ternary space.*

Proof: Let S be a non-empty compact metrizable space. Let f be a function continuous from a closed subspace F of 2^ω onto S defined as in the previous lemma. By theorem 12.26, 2^ω can be imbedded topologically in $[0, 1]$. By theorem 12.17, the image space is closed in $[0, 1]$. Hence, since F is closed in 2^ω, its image, assigned by the imbedding, is closed in $[0, 1]$ by theorem 9.5. Thus 2^ω and F can be considered to be closed subsets of $[0, 1]$. Since $[0, 1]$ is closed in E^1, the reals with the usual topology, F is closed in E^1 by theorem 9.5. Hence $\sim F$, the complement of F in E^1 is open in E^1. E^1 is locally connected by corollary 25.5, and so components of $\sim F$, in E^1 are open, connected subsets of E^1, by theorem 27.12. By theorem 25.7, the components of $\sim F$, in E^1, are open intervals. Now, by corollary 12.24, 2^ω in E^1 contains no open sets of E^1. Hence, each component I_j of $\sim F$, in E^1, contains at least one point of $\sim 2^\omega$ in E^1. The choice axiom assigns a point ξ_j of $\sim 2^\omega$ to each component-interval, I_j, of $\sim F$ in E^1. Each component I_j, being an open interval of real numbers, has the form, $\{x \mid x > \alpha_j$, where $\alpha_j \in F\}$ or $\{x \mid x < \beta_j$, where $\beta_j \in F\}$ or $\{x \mid \alpha_j < x < \beta_j$ for $\alpha_j, \beta_j \in F\}$. If $I_j = \{x \mid x < \beta_j$ for $\beta_j \in F\}$ define $f^*(x) = f(\beta_j)$ for $x \in I_j \cap 2^\omega$. If $I_j = \{x \mid \alpha_j < x < \beta_j$ for $\alpha_j, \beta_j \in F\}$, define $f^*(x) = \alpha_j$ for $x < \xi_j$ and $x \in I_j \cap 2^\omega$, and define $f^*(x) = \beta_j$ for $x > \xi_j$ and $x \in I_j \cap 2^\omega$. If $I_j = \{x \mid \alpha_j < x$ for $\alpha_j \in F\}$, define $f^*(x) = f(\alpha_j)$ for $x \in I_j \cap 2^\omega$. Define $f^*(x) = f(x)$ for $x \in F$. Thus f^* is a function from 2^ω onto the non-empty, compact, metrizable space S. Lastly, it must be shown that f^* is continuous. $2^\omega = F \cup (\sim F \cap 2^\omega)$, where $\sim F$ here denotes the complement of F in E^1. So, first let $t_0 \in F$ and let V be any neighborhood of $f^*(t_0)$ in S. Since $f^* \mid F = f$ and since f is continuous at every point of F, there exists a closed interval $[a, b]$ such that $a < t_0 < b$ and such that for $t \in F \cap [a, b]$, $f^*(t) \in V$. If $a \in F$, then, since $f^*[[a, t_0] \cap 2^\omega] = f[[a, t_0] \cap F]$ by definition of f^*, $f^*[[a, t_0] \cap 2^\omega] \subseteq V$. If $a \notin F$, then a lies in some component-interval I_a of $\sim F$ in E^1. Let ξ_a be the point of I_a in $\sim 2^\omega$ defined above. By definition of f^*, $f^*[[\xi_a, t_0] \cap 2^\omega] \subseteq V$. A similar discussion holds for b. Hence, there exists an open interval U of real numbers such that $t_0 \in U$ and $f^*[U \cap 2^\omega] \subseteq V$, where $U = (\xi_a, \xi_b)$ or $U = (a, \xi_b)$ or $U = (\xi_a, b)$ or $U = (a, b)$. Thus for $t_0 \in F$, f^* is continuous at t_0. Now, let $t_0 \notin F$ and $t_0 \in 2^\omega$. Again let V be any neighborhood of $f^*(t_0)$ in S. Since $t_0 \in \sim F$ in E^1, t_0 lies in an interval-component I_0 of $\sim F$ in E^1, where $I_0 = \{x \mid x < b\}$ or $I_0 = \{x \mid a < x < b\}$ or $I_0 = \{x \mid a < x\}$ for a and b in F. Let ξ_0 be the point of $\sim 2^\omega$ in E^1 assigned to I_0. ξ_0 separates I_0 into two open subintervals. Let U denote the open subinterval of $I_0 \sim \{\xi_0\}$ in which t_0 lies. Then $U \cap 2^\omega$ is an open neighborhood of t_0 in 2^ω and f^* is constant on $U \cap 2^\omega$. Hence, $f^*[U \cap 2^\omega] \subseteq V$ and f^* is continuous at t_0. ∎

EXERCISE 8. Prove that any non-empty closed subset of the Cantor ternary space is a retract of the Cantor ternary space.

30.11 Corollary. *A non-empty topological space is a compact metrizable space if and only if it is the continuous image of the Cantor ternary space in a Hausdorff space.*

Proof: Theorem 30.10 establishes the "only if" part of the theorem, since any metrizable space is a Hausdorff space. Conversely, by theorem 20.12, 2^ω is a metrizable space, and, by theorem 28.46, 2^ω is a compact space. Hence, by corollary 30.8, any continuous image of 2^ω in a Hausdorff space is a compact metrizable space. ∎

30.12 Corollary. *Any compact metrizable space is finite or uncountable with cardinality $\leq c$.*

Proof: By theorem 30.10, no non-empty compact metrizable space can have cardinality greater than that of 2^ω. By corollary 29.26, no compact Hausdorff space can be of the first category in itself. Assume then that the compact metrizable space S is countable. S is immediately the union of a countable number of singletons, i.e., $S = \bigcup_{x \in S} \{x\}$. Hence, S would be of the first category if all $\{x\}$ were not open. Thus, at least one $\{x\}$ is open. However, since S is compact only a finite number of singletons can be open. Let $\{x_1, x_2, \ldots, x_k\}$ be the set of all isolated points of S. Consider the open set $S \sim \{x_1, x_2, \ldots, x_k\}$. $S \sim \{x_1, x_2, \ldots, x_k\}$ is also closed and hence is a compact metrizable space. If $S \sim \{x_1, x_2, \ldots, x_k\}$ is not empty, it is of the first category, since no singleton is open. Thus $S \sim \{x_1, x_2, \ldots, x_k\} = \emptyset$ and S is finite. ∎

Lebesgue Covering Numbers and Uniform Continuity

Compact metric spaces possess a very useful property with respect to open coverings. The next theorem establishes the existence, for any open covering on a compact metric space, of certain positive real numbers called Lebesgue numbers. The second theorem and the corollary which follows it establish a variation of this property for continuous functions defined on compact metric spaces.

30.13 Theorem. *If $\{S, \rho\}$ is a compact metric space and if $\mathcal{G}$ is any open covering of S, then there exists a positive real number $\lambda(\mathcal{G})$ such that if $A \subseteq S$ and if diam $A \leq \lambda(\mathcal{G})$, then $A \subseteq G$ for some G in $\mathcal{G}$.*

Proof: Since $\mathcal{G}$ covers S, for each x in S there exists a set G_{α_x} in $\mathcal{G}$ such that x is in G_{α_x}. Since the sets of $\mathcal{G}$ are open there also exists, for each x, a spherical neighborhood $U_\rho(x, \delta_x) \subseteq G_{\alpha_x}$. The spherical neighborhoods $U_\rho(x, \delta_x/2)$ then cover S. Since S is compact, a finite number, say, $U_\rho(x_1, \delta_{x_1}/2), \ldots, U_\rho(x_k, \delta_{x_k}/2)$ cover S. Let $\lambda(\mathcal{G}) = \text{minimum } \{\delta_{x_1}/2, \ldots, \delta_{x_k}/2\}$. Now let $A \subseteq S$, let diam $A \leq \lambda(\mathcal{G})$ and let $a_0 \in A$. Since $U_\rho(x_1, \delta_{x_1}/2), \ldots, U_\rho(x_k, \delta_{x_k}/2)$ cover S, a_0 is in $U_\rho(x_i, \delta_{x_i}/2)$, say. Hence, $\rho(a_0, x_i) < \delta_{x_i}/2$. Now, if $a \in A$, $\rho(a_0, a) \leq \lambda(\mathcal{G}) \leq \delta_{x_i}/2$. Hence, $\rho(a, x_i) < \delta_{x_i}$, and so $A \subseteq U_\rho(x_i, \delta_{x_i}) \subseteq G_{\alpha_i}$, a set in $\mathcal{G}$. ∎

30.14 Theorem. *If f is a continuous function with a compact metric space $\{S, \rho\}$ as domain and if $\mathcal{G}$ is any open covering of the range $f[S]$, then there exists a positive real number $\gamma(\mathcal{G})$ such that if $A \subseteq S$ and if diam $A \leq \gamma(\mathcal{G})$, then $f[A]$ is a subset of at least one set in $\mathcal{G}$.*

Proof: Consider the collection $\mathcal{G}^* = \{f^{-1}[G] \mid G \in \mathcal{G}\}$. Since $\mathcal{G}$ is an open covering of $f[S]$ and since f is continuous, $\mathcal{G}^*$ is an open covering of S. Since S is compact, a finite number of the sets in $\mathcal{G}^*$, say, $f^{-1}[G_1], f^{-1}[G_2], \ldots, f^{-1}[G_k]$, cover S. By the previous theorem, there exists a positive real number λ such that if $A \subseteq S$ and if diam $A \leq \lambda$, then $A \subseteq f^{-1}[G_i]$ for some i, $1 \leq i \leq k$. Hence $f[A] \subseteq G_i$. Thus let $\gamma(\mathcal{G}) = \lambda$. ∎

30.15 Corollary. *A continuous function from a compact metric space into a metric space is uniformly continuous.*

Proof: Let ϵ^* be any positive real number and let f be continuous from the compact metric space $\{S, \rho\}$ into the metric space $\{T, \xi\}$. Let $y \in T$ and let $V_\xi(y, \epsilon^*/2)$ denote the spherical neighborhood of y of radius $\epsilon^*/2$. Let $\mathcal{G} = \{V_\xi(y, \epsilon^*/2) \mid y \in T\}$. $\mathcal{G}$ is an open covering of T. Hence, by the previous theorem, there exists a positive real number $\gamma^*(\mathcal{G})$ such that if $A \subseteq S$ and if diam $A \leq \gamma^*(\mathcal{G})$, $f[A]$ is contained in some set of $\mathcal{G}$. Hence, if $\rho(\alpha, \beta) \leq \gamma^*(\mathcal{G})$, $\xi(f(\alpha), f(\beta)) < \epsilon^*$. By definition 27.3, f is uniformly continuous. ∎

EXERCISE 9. Let $\{S, \rho\}$ be the subspace of E^1 consisting of $\{x \mid x = 1/n$ for

$n = 1, 2, \ldots\}$ and the relative metric topology. Find a finite open covering of S which has no Lebesgue number.

EXERCISE 10. The topology $\mathfrak{J}_\rho$ of the previous exercise is the discrete topology for $S = \{x \mid x = 1/n, n = 1, 2, \ldots\}$. Let ζ be the discrete metric, $\zeta(1/n, 1/m) = 1$ for $m \neq n$ and $\zeta(1/n, 1/m) = 0$ for $m = n$. ζ is topologically equivalent, as a metric, to ρ (definition 19.21). Thus $\{S, \mathfrak{J}_\rho\}$ and $\{S, \mathfrak{J}_\zeta\}$ are the same topological space. Show, using the metric ζ, that every finite open covering of $\{S, \zeta\}$ has a Lebesgue number.

The last exercise shows that for non-compact metric spaces, the existence of a Lebesgue number depends on the metric.

Compact Sets and Closed Bounded Sets

The next theorem describes compact subsets of a metrizable space in terms of any admissible metric.

30.16 Theorem. *Any compact subset of a metric space $\{S, \rho\}$ is closed in S and bounded in $\{S, \rho\}$.*

Proof: Let $\{S, \rho\}$ be a metric space. By theorem 19.20, S is Hausdorff. Hence, if A is a compact subset of S, then A is closed, by theorem 29.5. Since A is compact, $\{A, \rho'\}$ where ρ' is ρ restricted to A, is totally bounded, by theorem 30.2. Hence, there exists a 1-dense set $\{s_1, \ldots, s_k\}$ such that if $s \in A$, then for some i, $1 \leq i \leq k$, $\rho(s, s_i) < 1$. Consider the set $M = \{r \mid r = \rho(s_i, s_j)$ for $1 \leq i, j \leq k\}$. M is a finite set of real numbers and so has a least upper bound, say δ. Let δ^* be the larger of δ and 1. Now, let x and y be any two points in A. For some i and j, $1 \leq i, j \leq k$, $\rho'(x, s_i) < 1$ and $\rho'(y, s_j) < 1$. By definition of a metric (19.1, part c), $\rho'(x, y) \leq \rho'(x, s_i) + \rho'(s_i, s_j) + \rho'(s_j, y)$. Hence $\rho'(x, y) < \delta^* + \delta^* + \delta^* = 3\delta^*$ and $\{A, \rho'\}$ is bounded. ∎

30.17 Example. The converse of 30.16 is false. Let S denote the reals with the discrete topology. Let $\rho(x, y) = 1$ for $x \neq y$ and $\rho(x, x) = 0$. S is closed in S and bounded in $\{S, \rho\}$, but S is not compact. Also, by theorem 19.24, the usual space E^1 of the real numbers can be described topologically by a bounded metric and, of course, E^1 is not compact. To say this yet in another way, E^1 is homeomorphic to the open interval subspace $\{x \mid 0 < x < 1\}$. However, in this metric subspace, $\{x \mid 0 < x \leq 1/2\}$ is closed and bounded but not compact.

Compactness in Euclidean n-Space

In spite of example 30.17, however, in metric Euclidean n-space, E^n, with the Euclidean metric, ρ_n, the compact subsets of E^n are exactly the closed, bounded subsets of $\{E^n, \rho_n\}$.

30.18 Theorem. *In E^1 the closed interval $[a, b] = \{x \mid a \leq x \leq b$, for a, b real and $a \leq b\}$ is compact.*

Proof: Since $\{E^1, \rho_1\}$, where $\rho_1(a, b) = |a - b|$, is complete, the metric subspace $[a, b]$ is complete by theorem 22.15. Further, by the archimedean property of the ordering on E^1, for any positive, real ϵ, there exists a natural number n such that $n \cdot \epsilon > b - a$. Now, consider the set

$$\left\{a, a + \frac{b-a}{n}, a + 2\frac{b-a}{n}, \ldots, a + i\frac{b-a}{n}, \ldots, b\right\}.$$

This set is ϵ-dense in the metric space $[a, b]$, since $((b - a)/n) < \epsilon$. Thus the metric subspace $[a, b]$ is complete and totally bounded; hence, the topological space $[a, b]$ is compact, by theorem 30.7. ▮

30.19 Theorem. *Any closed, bounded subset of $\{E^1, \rho_1\}$ is compact, where $\rho_1(a, b) = |a - b|$.*

Proof: Let M be closed and bounded in $\{E^1, \rho_1\}$. Since M is bounded, the diameter of M exists and is a non-negative real number, δ, say. If $M = \emptyset$, M is compact. If $M \neq \emptyset$, let a be a point in M. Then $|a - x| \leq \delta$ for every x in M, by definition of diameter. Hence, $M \subseteq \{x \mid a - \delta \leq x \leq a + \delta\}$. By the previous theorem, $\{x \mid a - \delta \leq x \leq a + \delta\}$ is compact. Thus M is a closed subset of a compact space and is, then, compact. ▮

The previous two theorems generalize to Euclidean n-space with the Euclidean metric.

30.20 Theorem. *In Euclidean n-space, the cube $\{(x_1, x_2, \ldots, x_n \mid |x_i| \leq \alpha_i$, for α_i real and non-negative for $i = 1, \ldots, n\}$ is compact.*

Proof: The cube is, by definition, the product space $I_{\alpha_1} \times I_{\alpha_2} \times \cdots \times I_{\alpha_n}$, where $I_{\alpha_i} = \{x \mid |x| \leq \alpha_i\}$. By theorem 30.18, I_{α_i} is compact for $i = 1, \ldots, n$, and by theorem 28.46, $I_{\alpha_1} \times \cdots \times I_{\alpha_n}$ is compact. ▮

30.21 Theorem. *Any closed, bounded subset of Euclidean n-space with the usual Euclidean metric,*

$$\rho((x_1, x_2, \ldots, x_n), (y_1, y_2, \ldots, y_n)) = \sqrt{\sum_{i=1}^{n} (x_i - y_i)^2},$$

is compact.

Proof: Let M be a closed, bounded subset of E^n. By definition 19.5, there exists a positive real number β such that if $x^* = (x_1, x_2, \ldots, x_n)$ and $y^* = (y_1, y_2, \ldots, y_n)$ are points in M, then

$$\rho(x^*, y^*) = \sqrt{\sum_{i=1}^{n} (x_i - y_i)^2} \leq \beta.$$

This means that

$$\sum_{i=1}^{n} (x_i - y_i)^2 \leq \beta^2.$$

Therefore, $(x_i - y_i)^2 \leq \beta^2$ and $|x_i - y_i| \leq \beta$ for $i = 1, \ldots, n$. From the proof of 30.19 this means that there exist positive real numbers α_i, say, such that for $x^* = (x_1, \ldots, x_n)$ in M, $|x_i| \leq \alpha_i$ for $i = 1, \ldots, n$. Thus $M \subseteq \{(x_1, x_2, \ldots, x_n) \mid |x_i| \leq \alpha_i, i = 1, 2, \ldots, n\}$. By theorem 30.20, M is then a closed subspace of a compact, metric space and hence by theorem 29.1, M is compact. ▌

Theorems 30.21 and 30.16 establish the following corollary.

30.22 Corollary. *In Euclidean n-space, E^n, the compact subsets are exactly the closed subsets which are bounded with respect to the usual Euclidean metric.*

Another immediate corollary of the preceding theorems is a generalization of a theorem in advanced calculus about maximum and minimum values of a function.

30.23 Corollary. *If f is a continuous function whose domain is a compact space, X, and whose range, Y, is a subspace of E^1, then there exist points α and β in the domain of f such that for any x in the domain, $f(\alpha) \leq f(x) \leq f(\beta)$, i.e., "$f$ assumes a maximum and a minimum value in E^1."*

Proof: Since the domain X of f is compact, the range Y of f in E^1 is a compact subspace. Hence by corollary 30.18, the range, Y, is a closed, bounded subset of E^1 with the usual metric. Since Y is bounded in E^1, Y has a least upper bound B and a greatest lower bound L. Since Y is closed, by definition of the topology on E^1 and of the least upper and greatest lower bound, L and B belong to Y. Hence, since Y is the range of f, there exist α and β in X such that $f(\alpha) = L$ and $f(\beta) = B$. Now if x is any point in X, $f(x)$ is in Y and so $f(\alpha) \leq x \leq f(\beta)$. ▌

Compactness and $C(X)$

In theorem 18.51, the set $C(X)$ of all continuous functions from a space X into the space E^1 (the usual space of real numbers) was given a ring structure. In theorem 18.52, the ring was proved to be an algebraic topological invariant in the sense of definition 18.50. The set $C(X)$ can also be given a topological structure. According to definition 12.35, the set $(E^1)^X$ of all functions from any set X into E^1 can be given the product topology—the topology of pointwise convergence. Thus, if X is any space, $C(X)$ as a subset of $(E^1)^X$ can then be assigned the relative topology of pointwise convergence. Since E^1 with the usual metric is not a bounded metric space, the metric topology of definition 21.21 cannot be assigned to all of $(E^1)^X$ via the usual metric on E^1. If, however, X is a compact space, then the range of each function in $C(X)$ is a compact subset of E^1, and hence, by theorem 30.16, it is closed and bounded relative to any admissible metric on E^1. Thus for a compact space, X, a metric topology can be defined for all of $C(X)$ by lemma 21.17 and definition 21.21. With the addition of this metric topology, $C(X)$ is converted into a complete metric space.

30.24 Definition. Let X be a compact space and let f be a continuous function from X into E^1, i.e., $f \in C(X)$. The *norm* of f, denoted by $\|f\|$, is defined to be $\text{l.u.b.}_{x \in X} \{r \mid r = |f(x)|\}$, where $|f(x)|$ denotes, as usual, the absolute value of the real number $f(x)$.

30.25 Lemma. *If X is compact and if $\nu(f, g) = \|f - g\|$, for f and g in $C(X)$, then ν is a metric for $C(X)$, and $\mathfrak{I}_\nu$, the metrizable topology determined by ν for $C(X)$, is the compact-open topology.*

Proof: The lemma follows from lemma 21.17 and theorem 29.40. ▮

30.26 Theorem. *The metric space $\{\{C(X), \mathfrak{I}_\nu\}, \nu\}$, where X is compact and ν is the metric defined in the previous lemma, is complete.*

Proof: The theorem follows from theorem 22.21. ▮

EXERCISE 11. Let X be compact and let the operation $\boxplus$ be defined as in theorem 18.51 for $C(X)$, i.e., $(f \boxplus g)(x) = f(x) + g(x)$. Prove or disprove: $\{C(X), \boxplus, \mathfrak{I}_\nu\}$ is a topological group.

EXERCISE 12. Let X be compact and let the operation $\boxtimes$ be defined as in theorem 18.51 for $C(X)$, i.e., $(f \boxtimes g)(x) = f(x) \times g(x)$. Prove or disprove: the multiplication function $m: \{C(X), \mathfrak{I}_\nu\} \times \{C(X), \mathfrak{I}_\nu\} \to \{C(X), \mathfrak{I}_\nu\}$ defined by $m((f, g)) = f \boxtimes g$ is continuous.

The Stone-Weierstrass Theorem

In theorem 18.51, a ring $\{C(X), \boxplus, \boxtimes\}$ was defined on $C(X)$, for X any topological space; and in lemma 30.25 and theorem 30.26, a complete metric space $\{C(X), \mathfrak{I}_\nu\}$ was defined on $C(X)$, for X any compact space. The Stone-Weierstrass theorem establishes that certain subrings of $\{C(X), \boxplus; \boxtimes\}$, for X a compact space, are dense subsets of $\{C(X), \mathfrak{I}_\nu\}$. Thus an algebraic condition for topological density is established. The generalizations and applications of the Stone-Weierstrass theorem are many. The theorem implies, for instance, that any real-valued continuous function on the real number interval $\{x \mid a \leq x \leq b\}$ can be approximated by ordinary polynomials "in x" or by trigonometric polynomials "in x." Similarly, the theorem implies that any real-valued continuous function on a closed bounded subset of Euclidean n-space can be approximated by polynomials "in n variables." Several lemmas precede the theorem itself.

30.27 Lemma. *Let f be defined on the real number interval $\{u \mid -1 \leq u \leq 1\}$ as follows: $f(u) = |u|$. Then there is a sequence, σ, of polynomials, each defined on $\{u \mid -1 \leq u \leq 1\}$ such that σ converges to f in $\{C(X), \mathfrak{J}_{\nu}\}$, where $X = \{u \mid -1 \leq u \leq 1\}$ and $\mathfrak{J}_{\nu}$ is the metric topology defined for $C(X)$ in lemma 30.25.*

Proof: The binomial series

$$1 + mu + \frac{m(m-1)}{2!}u^2 + \cdots + \frac{m(m-1)(m-2)\cdots(m-n+1)}{n!}u^n + \cdots$$

yields the sequence required by the theorem. When $m = 1/2$, the binomial series can be shown to converge to $(1 + u)^{1/2}$ for $-1 \leq u \leq 1$. Hence the series

$$1 + 1/2(-u) + \frac{1/2(-1/2)(-u)^2}{2!} + \cdots + \frac{1/2(-1/2)(-3/2)(-5/2)\cdots(-(2n-3)/2)}{n!}(-u)^n + \cdots$$

will certainly converge to $(1 + (-u))^{1/2}$ for $0 \leq u \leq 1$. Now for $0 \leq u \leq 1$,

$$\left|\frac{1/2(-1/2)(-3/2)\cdots(-(2n-3)/2)}{n!}(-u)^n\right| \leq \left|\frac{1/2(-1/2)(-3/2)\cdots(-(2n-3)/2)}{n!}\right|$$

and by Gauss' test for convergence of series with all positive terms, the series

$$1 + 1/2 + \left|\frac{1/2(-1/2)}{2!}\right| + \cdots + \left|\frac{1/2(-1/2)(-3/2)\cdots(-(2n-3)/2)}{n!}\right| + \cdots$$

converges. Hence, by the Weierstrass M-test, if the terms of the series $f_1(x) + f_2(x) + \cdots + f_n(x) + \cdots$ have the interval $[a, b]$ as their common domain and have their ranges in E^1 and if for all x in $[a, b]$, $|f_n(x)| \leq M_n$, where for each n, M_n is a positive real number and if the series $M_1 + M_2 + \cdots + M_n + \cdots$ converges, then the series $f_1(x) + f_2(x) + \cdots + f_n(x) + \cdots$ is uniformly convergent on $[a, b]$. Thus by the Weierstrass M-test, the series

$$1 - 1/2u + \frac{(1/2)(-1/2)(-u)^2}{2!} + \cdots + \frac{1/2(-1/2)(-3/2)\cdots(-(2n-3)/2)}{n!}(-u)^n + \cdots$$

converges uniformly to $(1 - u)^{1/2}$ in $\{u \mid 0 \leq u \leq 1\}$. Let $(s_1, s_2, \ldots, s_n, \ldots)$ denote the sequence of partial sums of the terms of the above series. The uniform convergence of this series means, then, that for any positive real number ϵ, there exists a natural number N such that if $n \geq N$, $|s_n(u) - (1 - u)^{1/2}| < \epsilon$ for all u in $[0, 1]$. Thus $\sqrt{1 - u}$ is the limit of a sequence, σ, of polynomials in $\{C(X), \mathfrak{I}_\nu\}$, where X is $[0, 1]$ with the usual topology. Now consider $|u|$. $|u| = \sqrt{1 - (1 - u^2)}$. Thus if u in the terms of the series

$$1 + 1/2(-u) + \frac{(1/2)(-1/2)(-u)^2}{2!} + \cdots + \frac{(1/2)(-3/2)\cdots(-(2n-3)/2)}{2!}(-u)^n + \cdots$$

is replaced by $(1 - u^2)$, then the resulting series will converge uniformly to $|u|$ for $-1 \leq u \leq 1$, since for $-1 \leq u \leq 1$, $1 - u^2$ will have only values between and including 0 and 1. Now each term in the resulting series will be a polynomial in u and so each partial sum in this series will be a polynomial in u. Since all polynomials are continuous, each partial sum will then respresent a function in $C(X)$. Hence in the interval $\{u \mid -1 \leq u \leq 1\}$, the function $f(u) = |u|$ is the sequential limit in $\{C(X), \mathfrak{I}_\nu\}$ of a sequence of polynomials. ▮

30.28 Definition. An *algebra over a field,* $\mathfrak{F}$, *is a quadruple* $\{S, \boxplus, \boxtimes, \mathfrak{F}\}$, where $\{S, \boxplus, \boxtimes\}$ is a ring and $\mathfrak{F}$ is a field of functions from S into S such that for r and s in $\mathfrak{F}$ and a and b in S the following hold:

(1) $r(a \boxplus b) = r(a) \boxplus r(b)$;
(2) $(r + s)(a) = r(a) \boxplus s(a)$, where $+$ is the addition in $\mathfrak{F}$;
(3) $r(a \boxtimes b) = r(a) \boxtimes b = a \boxtimes r(b)$;
(4) $1(a) = a$, where 1 is the multiplicative identity of $\mathfrak{F}$.

A subalgebra of an algebra $\{S, \boxplus, \boxtimes, \mathfrak{F}\}$ is an algebra $\{A, \boxplus, \boxtimes, \mathfrak{F}\}$ where $A \subseteq S$.

EXERCISE 13. Let $\{S, \boxplus, \boxtimes\}$ denote the usual field of complex numbers; let $\mathfrak{R}$ denote the field of real numbers. Define $r(a + bi)$ to be $ra + rbi$ for r a real number and $a + bi$ a complex number. Prove that $\{S, \boxplus, \boxtimes, \mathfrak{R}\}$ is an algebra over the field of real numbers.

30.29 Lemma. *Let X be any space and let $\{C(X), \boxplus, \boxtimes\}$ be the ring of continuous functions defined in theorem 18.51. If $r(f)$ is denoted, for convenience, by rf and is defined by $rf(x) = r \times f(x)$, for r a real number and f in $C(X)$, then $\{C(X), \boxplus, \boxtimes, \mathfrak{R}\}$ is an algebra over the field of real numbers.*

Proof: Exercise.

30.30 Lemma. *Let X be a compact space; let $\mathfrak{I}_\nu$ be the metric topology for $C(X)$ defined in lemma 30.25; let $\{A, \boxplus, \boxtimes, \mathfrak{R}\}$ be a subalgebra of $\{C(X), \boxplus, \boxtimes, \mathfrak{R}\}$ which contains the constant functions. If A is a closed subspace of $\{C(X), \mathfrak{I}_\nu\}$, then f in A implies $|f|$ is in A.*

Proof: Let f be any function in the subalgebra $\{A, \boxplus, \boxtimes, \mathcal{R}\}$. If f is the 0-function, i.e., $f(x) = 0$ for all x in X, then $|f| = f$, and so $|f|$ is in A. If for some x in $X, f(x) \neq 0$, then $\|f\| \neq 0$ by definition of $\|f\|$ (30.24). Hence, since $\{A, \boxplus, \boxtimes, \mathcal{R}\}$ is an algebra over the reals, $(1/\|f\|)f$ is in A. Let g denote $(1/\|f\|)f$. Since for every x in X,

$$|f(x)| \leq \|f\|, \qquad \left|\frac{1}{\|f\|} \cdot f(x)\right| \leq 1.$$

Thus for every x in X, $-1 \leq g(x) \leq 1$. Now let $\sigma = (s_1, s_2, \ldots, s_n, \ldots)$, where each s_n is a polynomial in u, be a sequence of polynomials which by lemma 30.27, for $-1 \leq u \leq 1$, converges to $|u|$. Now, since $\{A, \boxplus, \boxtimes, \mathcal{R}\}$ is an algebra, g^i, for i a positive integer and for g^i defined by

$$g^i(x) = \underbrace{g(x) \times \cdots \times g(x)}_{i \text{ factors}},$$

is in A. Again since $\{A, \boxplus, \boxtimes, \mathcal{R}\}$ is an algebra and contains the constant functions, any function denoted by $a_0 \boxplus a_1 g \boxplus a_2 g^2 \boxplus \cdots \boxplus a_k g^k$, for $a_0, a_1, \ldots, a_k$ real numbers, is in A. So if $s_i = c_0 + c_1 u + c_2 u^2 + \cdots + c_m u^m$ is a polynomial in the sequence $\sigma = (s_1, s_2, \ldots, s_n, \ldots)$ which converges uniformly to the function $f(u) = |u|$ for $-1 \leq u \leq 1$, then $S_i = c_0 \boxplus c_1 g \boxplus c_2 g^2 \boxplus \cdots \boxplus c_m g^m$ is a function in A. Thus a sequence $\Sigma = (S_1, S_2, \ldots, S_n, \ldots)$ of functions in A is defined. Let ϵ be any positive real number. By lemma 30.27, there exists a polynomial $s_n = b_0 + b_1 u + \cdots + b_n u^n$ such that for all u in $[-1, 1]$, $\left|b_0 + b_1 u + \cdots + b_n u^n - |u|\right| < \epsilon/2$. Since for any x in X, $g(x)$ is in $[-1, 1]$, $\left|b_0 + b_1 g(x) + \cdots + b_n g^n(x) - |g(x)|\right| < \epsilon/2$. Hence $\left\|b_0 + b_1 g + \cdots + b_n g^n - |g|\right\| < \epsilon$. Thus for any positive real number ϵ, there is a function S_n in A such that $\left\|S_n - |g|\right\| < \epsilon$. Hence, any ϵ-neighborhood V_ϵ of $|g|$ in $\{C(X), \mathfrak{I}_\nu\}$ contains a function of A, and so $|g|$ is in the closure of A. Since A is closed, $|g|$ is in A. $|g| = |f|/\|f\|$ and $\{A, \boxplus, \boxtimes, \mathcal{R}\}$ is an algebra over the reals. Hence, $\|f\|\,|g|$ is in A, and so $|f|$ is in A. ▮

30.31 Definition. Let X be any space. Let f and g be in $C(X)$. $f \vee g$ is defined by $(f \vee g)(x) = \text{maximum } \{f(x), g(x)\}$; $f \wedge g$ is defined by $(f \wedge g)(x) = \text{minimum } \{f(x), g(x)\}$.

30.32 Lemma. *Let X be any space. Let f and g be in $C(X)$. Then $f \vee g$ and $f \wedge g$ are both in $C(X)$.*

Proof:

$$(f \vee g)(x) = \frac{f(x) + g(x)}{2} + \frac{|f(x) - g(x)|}{2}$$

and

$$(f \wedge g)(x) = \frac{f(x) + g(x)}{2} - \frac{|f(x) - g(x)|}{2}.$$

If f and g are continuous, $f \boxplus g$, $f \boxplus (-g) = f \boxminus g$ and $|f \boxminus g|$ are continuous. Hence $f \vee g$ and $f \wedge g$ are in $C(X)$ whenever f and g are in $C(X)$. ▮

30.33 Corollary. *Let X be any space. Then $\{C(X), R\}$ is a lattice, where fRg if and only if $f(x) \leq g(x)$ for all x in X.*

Proof: Exercise (8.8 is the definition of a lattice).

NOTE: The R defined in the previous corollary (30.33) is usually denoted by $\leq$.

REMARK: If X is any set, the set $C(X)$ of all continuous functions from X into E^1, is the basis or foundation for many structures in modern mathematics. For instance, $\{C(X), \leq\}$ is a lattice; $\{C(X), \boxplus, \boxtimes\}$ is a ring; $\{C(X), \mathfrak{I}_P\}$, where $\mathfrak{I}_P$ is the product topology from $(E^1)^X$, is a topological space; $\{C(X), \mathfrak{I}_\nu\}$ is a metric space, whenever X is compact; $\{C(X), \boxplus, \mathfrak{I}_\nu\}$ is a topological group, whenever X is compact; $\{C(X), \boxplus, \boxtimes, \mathcal{R}\}$ is an algebra over the reals.

EXERCISE 14. Is $\{C(X), \boxplus, \mathfrak{I}_P\}$, where $\mathfrak{I}_P$ is the relative product topology from $(E^1)^X$, a topological group?

30.34 Corollary. *If X is a compact space, and if A is a subalgebra of $\{C(X), \boxplus, \boxtimes, \mathcal{R}\}$ which contains the constant functions and which is a closed subspace of $\{C(X), \mathfrak{I}_\nu\}$, then for every f and g in A, $f \vee g$ and $f \wedge g$ are in A.*

Proof:

$$(f \vee g)(x) = \frac{f(x) + g(x)}{2} + \frac{|f(x) - g(x)|}{2}$$

and

$$(f \wedge g)(x) = \frac{f(x) + g(x)}{2} - \frac{|f(x) - g(x)|}{2}.$$

By lemma 30.30, if h is in A, $|h|$ is in A. Thus, $f \vee g$ and $f \wedge g$ are in A. ▮

30.35 Definition. Let X be any space and let $M \subseteq C(X)$. M is said to separate the points of X if and only if for each pair $\{x_1, x_2\} \subseteq X$ such that $x_1 \neq x_2$, there exists a function f in M such that $f(x_1) \neq f(x_2)$.

30.36 Theorem (Stone-Weierstrass). *If X is any compact space, if $\{A, \boxplus, \boxtimes, \mathcal{R}\}$ is a subalgebra of the algebra $\{C(X), \boxplus, \boxtimes, \mathcal{R}\}$ which contains the constant functions and which separates the points of X, then A is dense in $\{C(X), \mathfrak{I}_\nu\}$, the metrizable space defined in lemma 30.25.*

Proof: Let g be any function in $C(X)$ and let N_ϵ be the spherical neighborhood of g of radius ϵ in $\{C(X), \mathfrak{I}_\nu\}$. A function h of A must be found in N_ϵ.

A. Let x_1 and x_2 be any two distinct points of X and let a and b be any two distinct real numbers. By hypothesis, there exists a function f in A such that $f(x_1) \neq f(x_2)$. Let $f(x_1) = r$ and $f(x_2) = s$. Since $\{A, \boxplus, \boxtimes, \mathfrak{R}\}$ is an algebra and since A contains the constant functions, $f \boxminus r^*$ and $f \boxminus s^*$ are in A, where r^* and s^* denote the constant functions with ranges $\{r\}$ and $\{s\}$ respectively, and $\boxminus$ denotes the inverse of $\boxplus$. Further, $(f \boxminus r^*)(x_1) = f(x_1) - r = 0$ and $(f \boxminus r^*)(x_2) = f(x_2) - r = s - r$. Therefore, if $w(x) = (f(x) - r)/(s - r)$, then $w(x_1) = 0$, $w(x_2) = 1$ and w is in A. Next, let $h = b(w) + a(1^* \boxminus w)$, where a and b are real numbers mentioned above and 1^* is the constant function with range $\{1\}$. h is in the algebra A. Further $h(x_1) = a$ and $h(x_2) = b$. Thus given any two distinct points x_1 and x_2 in X and any two distinct real numbers a and b, there is a function h in A such that $h(x_1) = a$ and $h(x_2) = b$.

B. Now let α be a given point in X. A function m_α^* will be defined such that $m_\alpha^*(\alpha) = g(\alpha)$ and $m_\alpha^*(x) > g(x) - \epsilon$ for all x in X. Further m_α^* will be in $\overline{A}$, the closure of A in $\{C(X), \mathfrak{J}_\nu\}$. First, define m_α to be g and then for each $\beta \in X$ such that $\beta \neq \alpha$, let m_β be the function in A for which $m_\beta(\alpha) = g(\alpha)$ and $m_\beta(\beta) = g(\beta)$. m_β exists by hypothesis and part (A) of this proof. Thus $\{m_\beta \mid \beta \in X\}$ is defined. Since each m_β is continuous from X into E^1, there exists for each m_β an open neighborhood N_β of β in X such that for x in N_β, $m_\beta(x) > m_\beta(\beta) - \epsilon/2$, and since g also is continuous, there exists an open neighborhood M_β of β in X such that for x in M_β, $g(\beta) > g(x) - \epsilon/2$, where ϵ is the positive real number introduced at the beginning of the proof. If x is in $M_\beta \cap N_\beta = U_\beta$, then $m_\beta(\beta) - m_\beta(x) < \epsilon/2$ and $g(x) - g(\beta) < \epsilon/2$. Hence, since $m_\beta(\beta) = g(\beta)$, $g(x) - m_\beta(x) < \epsilon$, i.e., $m_\beta(x) > g(x) - \epsilon$. Thus each point β of X has an open neighborhood U_β such that for x in U_β, $m_\beta(x) > g(x) - \epsilon$. Since X is compact, a finite number, $U_{\beta_1}, U_{\beta_2}, \ldots, U_{\beta_k}$, of these open neighborhoods cover X. Consider, now, the corresponding functions $m_{\beta_1}, m_{\beta_2}, \ldots, m_{\beta_k}$. Each m_{β_i} for $1 \leq i \leq k$ is in A. Let $m_\alpha^* = m_{\beta_1} \vee m_{\beta_2} \vee \cdots \vee m_{\beta_k}$. By corollary 30.34, m_α^* is in $\overline{A}$, the closure of A in $\{C(X), \mathfrak{J}_\nu\}$. Now let x be any point in X. Since the open neighborhoods $U_{\beta_1}, \ldots, U_{\beta_k}$ constitute a covering, x is in U_{β_j} for some j, $1 \leq j \leq k$. Hence, $m_{\beta_j}(x) > g(x) - \epsilon$. Thus for all x in X, $m_\alpha^*(x) > g(x) - \epsilon$ and $m_\alpha^*(\alpha) = g(\alpha)$. To each point α in X, then, is assigned the function m_α^* which lies in $\overline{A}$.

C. Since each function m_α^* is continuous and since the original function g is continuous, for each point α of X, there exists an open neighborhood W_α of α such that if x is in W_α, $|m_\alpha^*(x) - m_\alpha^*(\alpha)| < \epsilon/2$ and $|g(x) - g(\alpha)| < \epsilon/2$. Hence, since $m_\alpha^*(\alpha) = g(\alpha)$, $|m_\alpha^*(x) - g(x)| < \epsilon$. Thus for x in W_α, $m_\alpha^*(x) < g(x) + \epsilon$ and for all x in X, $m_\alpha^*(x) > g(x) - \epsilon$. Each point α in X has such an open neighborhood W_α. Since X is compact, a finite number of these, say, $W_{\alpha_1}, \ldots, W_{\alpha_t}$, cover X. Let $m_{\alpha_1}^*, \ldots, m_{\alpha_t}^*$ be the functions corresponding, respectively to the points $\alpha_1, \ldots, \alpha_t$. Let $\gamma = m_{\alpha_1}^* \wedge m_{\alpha_2}^* \wedge \cdots \wedge m_{\alpha_t}^*$. γ is in the closure $\overline{A}$ of A, by corollary 30.34. Now, let x be any point in X. Since the open neighborhoods $W_{\alpha_1}, \ldots, W_{\alpha_t}$ constitute a cover for X, x lies in at least one of these neighborhoods, say, W_{α_j} for some j, $1 \leq j \leq t$. By definition of W_{α_j}, $m^*_{\alpha_j}(x) < g(x) + \epsilon$ and by definition of $m^*_{\alpha_1}, \ldots, m^*_{\alpha_t}$, $m^*_{\alpha_i}(x) > g(x) - \epsilon$ for $1 \leq i \leq t$. Hence, $g(x) - \epsilon < \gamma(x) < g(x) + \epsilon$ for all x in X, and so $\|g - \gamma\| < \epsilon$ and $\nu(\gamma, g) < \epsilon$. This means that γ is in N_ϵ, the original spherical neighborhood of g in $\{C(X), \mathfrak{J}_\nu\}$. Since γ is in $\overline{A}$, N_ϵ must contain a function in A. g, then, is in $\overline{A}$. ▮

Thus the Stone-Weierstrass theorem gives an algebraic criterion for the topological property of density.

EXERCISE 15. Let X be the subspace $[a, b]$ of E^1 determined by $\{x \mid a \leq x \leq b$ and $a < b\}$. Let $\{C(X), \mathfrak{J}_\nu\}$ be the space defined in lemma 30.25. Prove that the set, A, of polynomial functions, $P(a_0, \ldots, a_n)$, defined by $P(x) = a_0 + a_1x + \cdots + a_nx^n$, for real numbers $a_0, a_1, \ldots, a_n$, is dense in $\{C(X), \mathfrak{J}_\nu\}$.

EXERCISE 16. Let X be the set of real numbers; let $\mathfrak{J}$ be the smallest T_1-topology for X. $\{X, \mathfrak{J}\}$ is compact, and hence, the space $\{C(X), \mathfrak{J}_\nu\}$ of lemma 30.25 is defined. Show that the Stone-Weierstrass theorem yields no information about dense subsets of $\{C(X), \mathfrak{J}_\nu\}$.

The Complex Stone-Weierstrass Theorem

The so-called complex version of the Stone-Weierstrass theorem contains an additional condition in its hypothesis. The complex number system, $\mathbb{C}$, like the real number system, is both an algebraic and a topological structure. The topological part of $\mathbb{C}$ is the metrizable space E^2, consisting of the set of all ordered pairs of real numbers and the topology determined by the Euclidean metric; the algebraic part of $\mathbb{C}$ is the field K consisting of the set of all ordered pairs of real numbers and the usual operations of addition, $+$, and multiplication, $\times$, for complex numbers. Thus the complex number system $\mathbb{C}$ is basically the pair $\{E^2, K\}$ and the theorems in complex analysis, like the theorems in real analysis, are sometimes algebraic, sometimes topological and sometimes, like the Stone-Weierstrass theorem, a mixture. $C(X, E^2)$ denotes, as usual, the set of all continuous functions from the space X into the space E^2 and $\{C(X, E^2), \mathfrak{J}^*_\sigma\}$ denotes the metrizable space of lemma 21.17 and theorem 29.40. $\{C(X, E^2), \boxplus, \boxtimes, K\}$ denotes the algebra over K determined by the set $C(X, E^2)$ and the operations $\boxplus$ and $\boxtimes$ defined as follows: $f \boxplus g(x) = f(x) + g(x)$ and $f \boxtimes g(x) = f(x) \times g(x)$ for x in X and $+$ and $\times$ the operations in K.

30.37 Theorem. *Let X be a compact space and let $\{A, \boxplus, \boxtimes, K\}$ be a subalgebra of the algebra $\{C(X, E^2), \boxplus, \boxtimes, K\}$ which contains all the constant functions and which contains the conjugate of each of its functions. Further, let A separate points of X. A is then dense in the space $\{C(X, E^2), \mathfrak{J}_\sigma\}$.*

Proof: First it must be recalled that $\{(x, y) \mid y = 0\}$ and the two operations $+$ and $\times$ constitute a subfield of K which is isomorphic to the field $\mathfrak{R}$

of real numbers and this same set and the relative topology constitute a subspace of E^2 which is homeomorphic to E^1. Hence, for algebraic and/or topological purposes $\mathcal{R}$ is a subfield of K and E^1 is a subspace of E^2. Now, let M denote the subset of A consisting of the real-valued functions in A. Since A contains all the constant functions, M contains all the real-valued constant functions. Now, by definition of $\boxplus$ and $\boxtimes$, $\{M, \boxplus, \boxtimes, \mathcal{R}\}$ is then an algebra. Next, let x_1 and x_2 be two (distinct) points of X. There exists, by hypothesis, a function f in A such that $f(x_1) \neq f(x_2)$. The function f can be represented by $u + iv$ where u and v are real-valued functions; i.e., $f(x)$, for x in X, is a complex number whose unique real part is $u(x)$ and whose unique imaginary part is $v(x)$. The conjugate $\bar{f}$ of f is the function, $\bar{f}(x) = u(x) - iv(x)$. Since $(f \boxplus \bar{f})/2 = u$ and $(f \boxminus \bar{f})/2i = v$, where $\boxminus$ is the inverse of $\boxplus$, u and v, by hypothesis, are both in A if f is. Hence, if f is in A, u and v are in M. Now, since $f(x_1) \neq f(x_2)$, either $u(x_1) \neq u(x_2)$ or $v(x_1) \neq v(x_2)$. Thus M separates points and so M is dense in $\{C(X), \mathfrak{J}_\nu\}$ by the previous theorem where ν is the admissible metric of lemma 30.25 for $C(X)$. Next, let $f = u + iv$ be any function in $C(X, E^2)$. Since M is dense in $\{C(X), \mathfrak{J}_\nu\}$, u and v are in $\bar{M}$. Thus for any positive real number ϵ, there are real-valued functions u^* and v^* in M such that $\nu(u, u^*) < \epsilon/2$ and $\nu(v, v^*) < \epsilon/2$. It follows then that $f^* = u^* + iv^*$ is in $C(X, E^2)$ and that $\sigma(f^*, f) < \epsilon$ where σ is the admissible metric of lemma 21.17 for $C(X, E^2)$. Now since $\{A, \boxplus, \boxtimes, K\}$ is an algebra and since $M \subseteq A$, $f^* = u^* + iv^*$ is in A. This means that $f = u + iv$ is in $\bar{A}$ and that A is dense in the metric space $\{C(X, E^2), \mathfrak{J}_\sigma\}$. ∎

The conjugacy condition in the previous theorem is necessary, as the following example shows. Let X denote the compact subspace $B^2 = \{(x, y) \mid x^2 + y^2 \leq 1\}$ of E^2. Let $\{A, \boxplus, \boxtimes, K\}$ denote the subalgebra of $\{C(X, E^2), \boxplus, \boxtimes, K\}$ consisting of those functions which are analytic on $\{(x, y) \mid x^2 + y^2 < 1\}$. A contains the constant functions, separates points and can be proved to be closed in $\{C(X, E^2), \mathfrak{J}_\sigma\}$. However, A is not dense in $\{C(X, E^2), \mathfrak{J}_\sigma\}$ since not all functions which are continuous on the closed disk, B^2, are analytic on $\{(x, y) \mid x^2 + y^2 < 1\}$, e.g., $f(z) = \bar{z}$ for z in B^2.

Compactness in Uniform Spaces

In section 23, a uniform space was defined to be a generalization of a metric space and uniform spaces were seen to have many of the properties of metric spaces. Hence, many of the theorems for compact metric spaces will have analogues for compact uniform spaces.

30.38 Theorem. *If f is a continuous function whose domain is a compact uniform space and whose range is a uniform space, then f is uniformly continuous.*

Proof: Let $\{X, \mathfrak{U}\}$, where $\mathfrak{U}$ is the given uniformity on X, be the domain of f, and let $\{Y, \mathcal{V}\}$, where $\mathcal{V}$ is the given uniformity on Y, be the range of f. Let V^* be any relation in $\mathcal{V}$. According to the definition (23.28) of uniform continuity, f will be uniformly continuous if there is a relation U^* in $\mathcal{U}$ such that (a, b) in U^* implies that $(f(a), f(b))$ is in V^*. By lemma 23.15, there exists in $\mathcal{V}$ a symmetric relation N^* such that $N^* \circ N^* \subseteq V^*$. Hence, if x is any point in X, there exists, by the continuity of f, a relation U_x^* in $\mathcal{U}$ such that $f[U_x^*[x]] \subseteq N^*[f(x)]$, where, as in section 23, $U_x^*[x]$ stands for the images of x assigned by U_x^* and $N^*[f(x)]$ stands for the images of $f(x)$ assigned by N^*. Now for each x in X a relation U_x^* in $\mathcal{U}$ is chosen such that $f[U_x^*[x]] \subseteq N^*[f(x)]$. Again, by lemma 23.15, there exists in $\mathcal{U}$ for each x in X, a symmetric relation M_x^* such that $M_x^* \circ M_x^* \subseteq U_x^*$. Now, the sets $M_x^*[x]$ cover X. Since X is compact, a finite number, say, $M_{x_1}^*[x_1], \ldots, M_{x_k}^*[x_k]$ cover X. By definition (23.7) of a uniformity, there exists a relation W^* in $\mathcal{U}$ such that $W^* \subseteq M_{x_1}^* \cap M_{x_2}^* \cap \cdots \cap M_{x_k}^*$. Let (a, b) be in W^*. Since the sets $M_{x_1}^*[x_1], M_{x_2}^*[x_2], \ldots, M_{x_k}^*[x_k]$ cover X, a is in $M_{x_i}^*[x_i]$ for some i such that $1 \leq i \leq k$. Then, $(x_i, a) \in M_{x_i}^*$. Also, since (a, b) is in W^*, $(a, b) \in M_{x_i}^*$. Hence $(x_i, b) \in M_{x_i}^* \circ M_{x_i}^*$. Thus $(x_i, a) \in M_{x_i}^* \subseteq U_{x_i}^*$ and $(x_i, b) \in M_{x_i}^* \circ M_{x_i}^* \subseteq U_{x_i}^*$. This means, by definition of $M_{x_i}^*$, that $(f(x_i), f(a)) \in N^*$ and $(f(x_i), f(b)) \in N^*$. Since N^* is symmetric, $(f(a), f(b)) \in N^* \circ N^*$. Since $N^* \circ N^* \subseteq V^*$, $(f(a), f(b)) \in V^*$. Thus, if $(a, b) \in W^*$, $(f(a), f(b)) \in V^*$ and f is uniformly continuous. ∎

In section 23, exercises 3 and 4 and theorem 23.30—which immediately follows the exercises—when applied to the usual space E^1 of real numbers, for instance, establishes that many different uniform structures for a set X can determine the same topology for X. Further, according to definition 23.28 and the paragraph immediately following it, if $\{X, \mathfrak{J}\}$ is a completely regular space and $\{Y, \mathcal{V}\}$ is a uniform space with uniformity $\mathcal{V}$, then each admissible uniformity for $\mathfrak{J}$ determines its own set of uniformly continuous functions. Hence, the last theorem seems to indicate a unique admissible uniform structure—a largest one, if it exists—for compact spaces. The next theorem establishes that for any compact topology there exists at most one uniform structure. First, however, three lemmas and a definition are needed.

30.39 Lemma. *If d is a pseudo-metric defined on a uniform space $\{X, \mathcal{U}\}$ and if for every positive real number ϵ, $\{(x, y) \mid d(x, y) < \epsilon$ for x and y in $X\}$ belongs to the uniformity $\mathcal{U}$, then d is a continuous function from the product space $X \times X$ into E^1.*

Proof: First define for each a in X the function d_a as follows: $d_a(x) = d(a, x)$. It will be shown that for each a in X, d_a is a continuous function from X into E^1. Let ϵ be any positive real number. By definition (23.41) of a pseudo-metric for a, x and y in X, $d(a, x) \leq d(a, y) + d(y, x)$ and $d(a, y) \leq d(a, x) + d(x, y)$. Hence, $|d(a, x) - d(a, y)| \leq d(x, y)$, and so $|d_a(x) - d_a(y)| \leq d(x, y)$. Thus if $d(x, y) < \epsilon$, $|d_a(x) - d_a(y)| < \epsilon$. Since $\{(x, y) \mid d(x, y) < \epsilon\}$ belongs to the uniformity $\mathcal{U}$, $V = \{y \mid d(x, y) < \epsilon\}$ is a neighborhood of x in $\{X, \mathfrak{J}_{\mathcal{U}}\}$. Thus if $y \in V$, $|d_a(x) - d_a(y)| < \epsilon$ and d_a is continuous. Now let (a, b) be any point in $X \times X$ and δ any positive real number. Since d is a pseudo-metric, if a, b, x and y are in X, $d(a, b) \leq d(a, x) + d(x, y) + d(y, b)$ and $d(x, y) \leq d(x, a) + d(a, b) + d(b, y)$. Hence, for (a, b) in $X \times X$ and (x, y) in $X \times X$, $|d(a, b) - d(x, y)| \leq d(a, x) + d(y, b) = d_a(x) + d_b(y)$. By the above, d_a and d_b are continuous functions and $d_a(a) = 0 = d_b(b)$. Hence there exists a neighborhood N_a of a and a neighborhood N_b of b such that if x is in N_a and if y is in N_b, $d_a(x) < \delta/2$ and $d_b(y) < \delta/2$. Hence if $(x, y) \in N_a \times N_b$, $|d(a, b) - d(x, y)| < \delta$ and d is continuous. ∎

30.40 Definition. Let $\{X, \mathfrak{J}\}$ be a space and let $A \subseteq X$. A subset N of X is called a *neighborhood of the subset A* if and only if there exists an open set G in $\{X, \mathfrak{J}\}$ such that $A \subseteq G \subseteq N$. This definition of neighborhood of a subset is the exact analogue, for subsets, of the definition of neighborhood of a point established by corollary 3.33.

30.41 Lemma. *Let $\mathcal{U}$ be an admissible uniformity for a topological space $\{X, \mathfrak{J}\}$. Then every element of $\mathcal{U}$ is a neighborhood of the diagonal, Δ, of $X \times X$.*

Proof: Let U^* be an element of $\mathcal{U}$. By theorem 23.47, there is a pseudo-metric, d, defined on X such that for any positive real number ϵ, the set $U_d^* = \{(x, y) \mid d(x, y) < \epsilon\}$ belongs to $\mathcal{U}$ and further, for some positive real ϵ^*, $\{(x, y) \mid d(x, y) < \epsilon^*\} \subseteq U^*$. By the previous lemma, d is continuous from $X \times X$ into E^1. Hence, if $G = \{t \mid t < \epsilon^* \text{ and } t \text{ is real}\}$, $d^{-1}[G]$ is open in $X \times X$. Since $d(x, x) = 0$, $d^{-1}[G] \supseteq \Delta$. Of course, $d^{-1}[G] = \{(x, y) \mid d(x, y) < \epsilon^*\}$. Thus, $d^{-1}[G] \subseteq U^*$ and U^* is a neighborhood of Δ. ∎

30.42 Lemma. *If $\mathcal{U}$ is a uniformity on a set X which determines the topology $\mathfrak{J}$ for X, then every set U^* in $\mathcal{U}$ contains a relation A^* in $\mathcal{U}$ with the property that A^* is closed in the product space $\{X, \mathfrak{J}\} \times \{X, \mathfrak{J}\}$. In other words, the closed relations in $\mathcal{U}$ constitute a base for $\mathcal{U}$.*

Proof: Let U^* be any relation in $\mathcal{U}$. By lemma 23.15, there exists a symmetric relation W^* of $\mathcal{U}$ such that $W^* \circ W^* \subseteq U^*$. Also, there exists a symmetric relation V^* of $\mathcal{U}$ such that $V^* \circ V^* \subseteq W^*$. Hence $V^* \circ V^* \circ V^* \circ V^* \subseteq U^*$ and $V^* \in \mathcal{U}$. Since $V^* \supseteq \Delta$, the diagonal of $X \times X$, $V^* \circ V^* \circ V^* \circ V^* \supseteq V^* \circ V^* \circ V^*$. Hence there exists a relation V^* in $\mathcal{U}$ such that $V^* \circ V^* \circ V^* \subseteq U^*$. Now, let (a, b) be a limit point in $X \times X$ of V^*. Then, $V^*[a] \times V^*[b]$ is a neighborhood of (a, b) in $X \times X$. Hence there exists a point (x, y) in V^* such that (x, y) is in $V^*[a] \times V^*[b]$. Thus $x \in V^*[a]$, $y \in V^*[b]$ and $(x, y) \in V^*$. It follows that $(a, x) \in V^*$, $(x, y) \in V^*$ and $(b, y) \in V^*$. Since V^* is symmetric, $(y, b) \in V^*$. Thus $(a, b) \in V^* \circ V^* \circ V^*$. Hence, $\bar{V}^* \subseteq V^* \circ V^* \circ V^*$. Since $\bar{V}^* \supseteq V^*$, $\bar{V}^* \in \mathcal{U}$ and since $V^* \circ V^* \circ V^* \subseteq U^*$, $\bar{V}^* \subseteq U^*$. ∎

30.43 Theorem. *If $\{X, \mathfrak{J}\}$ is a compact space, there is at most one uniform structure which determines the topology $\mathfrak{J}$ on X. It is exactly the set of all neighborhoods of the diagonal, Δ, in the product space, $X \times X$.*

Proof: Let $\mathfrak{U}$ be a uniform structure which determines a compact topology $\mathfrak{J}$ on a set X. By lemma 30.41, every element in $\mathfrak{U}$ is a neighborhood of the diagonal, Δ, in the product space $\{X, \mathfrak{J}\} \times \{X, \mathfrak{J}\}$. Conversely, let N^* be any neighborhood of the diagonal, Δ, in the product space $\{X, \mathfrak{J}\} \times \{X, \mathfrak{J}\}$. N, by definition 30.40, contains an open set G^* of $\{X, \mathfrak{J}\} \times \{X, \mathfrak{J}\}$ such that $\Delta \subseteq G^* \subseteq N^*$. By the previous lemma (30.42), the closed sets in $\mathfrak{U}$ form a base $\mathfrak{B}$ for $\mathfrak{U}$. By definition of a base for $\mathfrak{U}$, $\bigcap \mathfrak{B} = \bigcap \mathfrak{U}$. Let $(x, y) \in \bigcap \mathfrak{U}$. If $\{X, \mathfrak{J}\}$ is T_0, by lemma 23.14, $x = y$ and $\bigcap \mathfrak{B} = \bigcap \mathfrak{U} \subseteq G^*$. If $\{X, \mathfrak{J}\}$ is not T_0, then since (x, y) is in every relation in $\mathfrak{U}$, y is in every neighborhood of x in $\{X, \mathfrak{J}\}$. Since G^* is open and contains Δ in $\{X, \mathfrak{J}\} \times \{X, \mathfrak{J}\}$, there exist a neighborhood $A_x \times B_x$ of (x, x) in G^*. Since by definition of the product topology, B_x is a neighborhood of x, y is in B_x. Hence (x, y) is in $A_x \times B_x$ and so $(x, y) \in G^*$. Thus $\bigcap \mathfrak{B} \subseteq G^*$. Since G^* is open, $\sim G^*$ is closed and since $\bigcap \mathfrak{B} \subseteq G^*$, $\sim \bigcap \mathfrak{B} \supseteq \sim G^*$. Hence $\bigcup_\nu \sim B_\nu$, for B_ν in $\mathfrak{B}$, contains $\sim G^*$. Since $\{X, \mathfrak{J}\}$ is compact, the product space $\{X, \mathfrak{J}\} \times \{X, \mathfrak{J}\}$ is compact and since $\sim G^*$ is closed in $\{X, \mathfrak{J}\} \times \{X, \mathfrak{J}\}$, $\sim G^*$ is compact. Thus, a finite number of complements of sets in $\mathfrak{B}$ covers $\sim G^*$, say, $\sim B_1, \sim B_2, \ldots, \sim B_k$ for some positive integer k. Thus, $\sim B_1 \cup \sim B_2 \cup \cdots \cup \sim B_k \supseteq \sim G^*$, and so $\sim \bigcap_{i=1}^k B_i \supseteq \sim G^*$. It follows that $\bigcap_{i=1}^k B_i \subseteq G^*$. Since each B_i, for $1 \leq i \leq k$, is a relation in $\mathfrak{U}$, by definition (23.6) of a uniform structure, $\bigcap_{i=1}^k B_i$ is in $\mathfrak{U}$, and so G^* is in $\mathfrak{U}$. This means, since $N^* \supseteq G^*$, that N^* is in $\mathfrak{U}$. Thus every neighborhood of Δ in the product space must belong to $\mathfrak{U}$. $\mathfrak{U}$ must then be exactly the set of all neighborhoods of the diagonal Δ in the product space $\{X, \mathfrak{J}\} \times \{X, \mathfrak{J}\}$. ▮

30.44 Example. By lemma 23.8, the uniformity $\mathfrak{U}$ with base $\mathfrak{B} = \{R_\epsilon \mid \epsilon$ is a positive real number and $R_\epsilon = \{(x, y) \mid |x - y| < \epsilon\}\}$ is admissible for the usual space E^1 of real numbers. In addition, $\mathfrak{N} = \{(x, y) \mid x$ and y are real and $xy - x^2 < 1\}$ is a neighborhood of the diagonal, Δ, in the product space, $E^1 \times E^1$. This can be proved as follows. Let $f(x, y) = xy - x^2$. By definition of the product topology on $E^1 \times E^1$, f can be considered to be the difference of two continuous functions $g(x, y) = xy$ and $h(x, y) = x^2$. Thus $f = g - h$ and f is continuous. Let $G = \{t \mid t$ is real and $t < 1\}$. G is open in E^1. Hence, $f^{-1}[G]$ is open in $E^1 \times E^1$. Further, if $x = y$, $xy - x^2 = 0 < 1$. Hence $\Delta \subseteq f^{-1}[G]$. By definition, $\mathfrak{N} = f^{-1}[G]$. Now, let ϵ^* be any positive real number and consider $R_{\epsilon^*} = \{(x, y) \mid x$ and y are real and $|x - y| < \epsilon^*\}$. By the archimedean order on E^1, there exists a positive real number a such that $1/a < \epsilon^*/2$. Hence, the point $(a, a + \epsilon^*/2)$ is not in $\mathfrak{N}$, i.e., $xy - x^2$ becomes $a(a + \epsilon^*/2) - a^2$, which is $a \cdot \epsilon^*/2$ and since, by choice of a, $1/a < \epsilon^*/2$, it follows that $a \cdot \epsilon^*/2 > 1$. However, $|x - y|$ becomes $|a + \epsilon^*/2 - a| = \epsilon^*/2 < \epsilon^*$. Hence $(a, a + \epsilon^*/2)$ is in R_{ϵ^*}. Thus there is no relation R_ϵ in the base $\mathcal{B}$ which is a subset of $\mathfrak{N}$. Thus $\mathfrak{N}$ is a neighborhood of Δ in $E^1 \times E^1$, but $\mathfrak{N}$ is not in $\mathfrak{U}$.

Theorem 30.7 establishes an alternate definition for compactness for metric spaces in terms of completeness and total boundedness. An analogous definition can also be established for compact uniform spaces.

30.45 Definition. A uniform space $\{X, \mathfrak{U}\}$ is *totally bounded* if and only if for every relation U^* in $\mathfrak{U}$ there exists a finite set $\{p_1, \ldots, p_k\}$ of points in X such that the neighborhoods $U^*[p_1], \ldots, U^*[p_k]$ cover X.

30.46 Theorem. *Let $\{X, \mathfrak{U}\}$ be a uniform space. X is compact if and only if $\{X, \mathfrak{U}\}$ is complete and totally bounded.*

Proof: A. Let X be compact. Let U^* be any relation in $\mathfrak{U}$. For each point x in X, let $U^*[x]$, as usual, denote the neighborhood of x determined by U^*. The collection of these neighborhoods, for all x in X, constitutes a cover of X. By corollary 3.33, each neighborhood $U^*[x]$ contains an open set G_x which also contains x. The set of all G_x for x in X is an open covering of X. Since X is compact, a finite number, say, $G_{x_1}, G_{x_2}, \ldots, G_{x_k}$ cover X. Hence $U^*[x_1], U^*[x_2], \ldots, U^*[x_k]$ cover X and $\{X, \mathfrak{U}\}$ is totally bounded. Now, it must be shown that $\{X, \mathfrak{U}\}$ is complete. The proof of completeness is similar to the part of the proof of theorem 30.7 in which it is proved that if a subsequence of a Cauchy sequence converges to α, the original sequence converges to α. So, let η be any Cauchy net in $\{X, \mathfrak{U}\}$ (definitions 23.31 and 23.33). Since X is compact, by theorem 28.29, η has a subnet (definition 28.27) $\eta^* = \eta \circ \delta$, such that $\eta \circ \delta$ converges to p, say, in X. Now, let W be any relation in $\mathfrak{U}$. By lemma 23.15, there exists in $\mathfrak{U}$ a symmetric relation V such that $V \circ V \subseteq W$. Further, since η is a Cauchy net, there exists an element $\bar{n}$ in the domain $\overline{D}$ of η such that if $n_1 \geq \bar{n}$ and $n_2 \geq \bar{n}$, both in $\overline{D}$, then $(\eta(n_1), \eta(n_2)) \in V$. Since $\eta^* = \eta \circ \delta$ converges to p, say, in X, there is an element n^* in the domain, D^*, of η^* such that if ν is in D^* and if $\nu \geq n^*$, then $\eta^*(\nu) = \eta(\delta(\nu))$ is in $V[p]$, i.e., $(p, \eta(\delta(\nu))) \in V$. By definition of subnet (28.27), there is an element Q^* in the domain D^* of $\eta^* = \eta \circ \delta$ such that if q is in D^* and if $q \geq Q^*$, then $\delta(q) \geq n^*$. Now, by definition (7.16) of a net, there exists in the domain D^* of $\eta^* = \eta \circ \delta$ a point P^* such that $P^* \geq n^*$ and $P^* \geq Q^*$. Thus if M is in D^* and if $M \geq P^*$, then $(p, \eta \circ \delta(M)) \in V$. Now, let m be any element in the domain of η such that $m \geq \bar{n}$. Choose M in D^* such that $M \geq P^*$. Then, $\delta(M) \geq \bar{n}$, $(p, \eta \circ \delta(M)) \in V$ and $(\eta(\delta(M)), \eta(m)) \in V$. Thus $(p, \eta(m)) \in V \circ V \subseteq W$. η converges then to p and $\{X, \mathfrak{U}\}$ is complete.

B. Conversely, let $\{X, \mathfrak{U}\}$ be complete and totally bounded. By theorem 28.41, the theorem will be proved if it can be shown that every ultrafilter converges. So, let $\mathfrak{F}$ be an ultrafilter on X and let U^* be any relation in $\mathfrak{U}$. By lemma 23.15, there exists a symmetric relation W^* in $\mathfrak{U}$ such that $W^* \circ W^* \subseteq U^*$. Since $\{X, \mathfrak{U}\}$ is totally bounded, there exists a finite set of points, say, $\{p_1, \ldots, p_k\}$ such that $W^*[p_1], \ldots, W^*[p_k]$ cover X. Hence $\bigcup_{i=1}^k W^*[p_i] = X$. Since $X \in \mathfrak{F}$, it follows, by lemma 28.47, that for some j, $1 \leq j \leq k$, $W^*[p_j] \in \mathfrak{F}$. Now consider $W^*[p_j] \times W^*[p_j]$ and let $(r, s) \in W^*[p_j] \times W^*[p_j]$. It follows that $r \in W^*[p_j]$ and $s \in W^*[p_j]$, and so that $(p_j, r) \in W^*$ and $(p_j, s) \in W^*$. Thus $(r, s) \in W^* \circ W^* \subseteq U^*$. Hence $W^*[p_j] \times W^*[p_j] \subseteq U^*$, and so $\mathfrak{F}$ is Cauchy. Since $\{X, \mathfrak{U}\}$ is complete, $\mathfrak{F}$ converges by theorem 23.37. X is then compact. ▌

Thus many of the theorems for compact metric spaces have exact analogues for compact uniform spaces. There are however some differences. The most striking one relates to theorem 30.5.

30.47 Example. Let $\{W, o\text{-}\mathfrak{J}\}$ denote the space of countable ordinals, W, with the order topology $o\text{-}\mathfrak{J}$ as described in definition 28.33 and lemmas 28.34 and 28.35. $\{W, o\text{-}\mathfrak{J}\}$ is countably compact but not compact. Also, the proof of lemma 29.17 establishes that $\{W, o\text{-}\mathfrak{J}\}$ is the subspace of a normal space and hence is completely regular, by theorems 18.34, 18.42 and 16.17. By theorem 23.25, $\{W, o\text{-}\mathfrak{J}\}$ is a uniformizable space. Thus $\{W, o\text{-}\mathfrak{J}\}$ is a countably compact uniformizable space which is not compact and theorem 30.5 has no analogue for uniform spaces.

30.48 Example. Let $T = 2^c$, i.e., the set of all functions from the set of real numbers into $\{0, 1\}$, the set with two elements. Let I, as usual, denote the closed unit interval, $[0, 1]$, with the usual topology. Let I^T denote the product space consisting of the set of all functions from T into I with the product topology. Since I is compact and Hausdorff, I^T is compact and Hausdorff. Hence I^T is normal, and so completely regular. Thus I^T is a compact uniformizable space and so, by theorem 30.46, any uniform space $\{I^T, \mathfrak{U}\}$ is complete and totally bounded. Since $2^c > c$, I^T is not separable by theorem 12.42. I^T is also then not second countable. Thus, theorems 30.3 and 30.4 have no analogues in the theory of uniform spaces; i.e., a compact uniform space need not be second countable and a totally bounded uniform space need not be separable.

31. LOCAL COMPACTNESS AND COMPACTIFICATIONS.

$T_{1+1/3}$-SPACES AND $T_{1+2/3}$-SPACES

There exist two classes of spaces less useful but slightly more general than Hausdorff spaces. Some of the important properties of Hausdorff spaces hold for these spaces. Further, one of these classes has some significance for local compactness.

31.1 Definition. A space S is called a $T_{1+2/3}$-space if and only if its compact subsets are closed.

31.2 Lemma. *If a space S has the property that compact subsets are closed, then S is T_1.*

Proof: Exercise.

The previous lemma and theorem 29.5 establish that $T_{1+2/3}$-spaces lie between T_1-spaces and T_2-spaces. The following lemma is the analogue of theorem 29.7.

31.3 Lemma. *If S is a compact space and f is a continuous function from S into a space T in which compact subsets are closed, then f is closed.*

Proof: Exercise.

31.4 Example. Let S denote the set of all real numbers. Let $\mathfrak{I}_1$ denote the smallest T_1-topology for S, i.e., S and the finite sets are the only closed sets, and let $\mathfrak{I}_2$ denote the topology for which S and the countable sets are the only closed sets. $\{S, \mathfrak{I}_1\}$ is a T_1-space but not all compact subsets are closed. $\{S, \mathfrak{I}_2\}$ has the property that all compact subsets are closed but $\{S, \mathfrak{I}_2\}$ is not Hausdorff.

31.5 Lemma. *If S is a space in which compact subsets are closed, then in S sequential limits, if they exist, are unique.*

Proof: Let $\sigma = (x_1, x_2, \ldots, x_n, \ldots)$ denote a sequence in the space S. Let σ converge to α in S. Let β be any point of S other than α. By lemma 31.2, S is T_1. Hence α has an open neighborhood U which does not contain β. Since σ converges to α, all but a finite number, say, $x_1, \ldots, x_N$ of points in the range of σ lie in U. Now the set $\{x_{N+1}, x_{N+2}, \ldots\} \cup \{\alpha\}$ is compact, i.e., any open set containing α must contain all but a finite number of the points of the set $\{x_{N+1}, x_{N+2}, \ldots\} \cup \{\alpha\}$. Hence, $\{x_{N+1}, x_{N+2}, \ldots\} \cup \{\alpha\}$ is closed by hypothesis. Since $\beta \notin \{x_{N+1}, x_{N+2}, \ldots\} \cup \{\alpha\}$ by definition of U, there must exist a neighborhood W of β such that W contains no point of $\{x_{N+1}, x_{N+2}, \ldots\} \cup \{\alpha\}$. σ cannot, then, converge to β. ▌

31.6 Corollary. *A first countable space is Hausdorff if and only if its compact subsets are closed.*

Proof: The previous lemma, corollary 16.10 and theorem 16.13, together, imply the corollary. ▌

31.7 Definition. A space S is called a $T_{1+1/3}$-space if and only if in S each sequence has at most one limit.

31.8 Lemma. *If S is any space then $T_2 \Rightarrow T_{1+2/3} \Rightarrow T_{1+1/3} \Rightarrow T_1$.*

Proof: Theorem 29.5, lemma 31.5 and theorem 16.12 imply the lemma. ▮

31.9 Example. If S is the set of all real numbers and $\mathfrak{J}_1$ is the smallest T_1-topology on S, i.e., X and the finite sets are the only closed sets, then $\{S, \mathfrak{J}_1\}$ is T_1 but sequential limits are not unique. Further, let X denote the set $R \cup \{\alpha\}$, where R is the set of real numbers and α is any element which is not a real number, and let $\mathfrak{J}$ denote the topology consisting of the usual open sets of real numbers plus $\{G \mid \alpha \in G, \sim G$ is compact in the usual topology on R and $\sim G$ is countable$\}$. Now, $\{x \mid 0 \leq x \leq 1\}$ is compact in $\{R \cup \{\alpha\}, \mathfrak{J}\}$ but this set is not closed. Hence, in $\{R \cup \{\alpha\}, \mathfrak{J}\}$ compact subsets are not closed. However, in $\{R \cup \{\alpha\}, \mathfrak{J}\}$ sequential limits are unique; for, the range of a converging sequence is compact and, of course, countable. Hence, any sequence which converges to a real number in $\{R \cup \{\alpha\}, \mathfrak{J}\}$ cannot converge to α. Thus $T_{1+1/3} \not\Rightarrow T_{1+2/3}$. Further, example 31.4 shows that $T_{1+2/3} \not\Rightarrow T_2$ and $T_1 \not\Rightarrow T_{1+1/3}$.

Local Compactness and the One-Point Compactification

The localization of the property of compactness is called local compactness. There are at least three living definitions of local compactness which can be found in the literature. Two of these are equivalent.

31.10 Definition. A space $\{S, \mathfrak{J}\}$ is called *locally compact* if and only if each point of S has at least one compact neighborhood.

31.11 Definition. A space $\{S, \mathfrak{J}\}$ is called *strongly locally compact* if and only if for each point x of S and each open neighborhood U of x there exists an open neighborhood V of x such that $V \subseteq U$ and $\overline{V}$ is compact, i.e., if and only if the topology $\mathfrak{J}$ has a base consisting of open sets whose closures are compact.

31.12 Definition. A space S is called *strongly locally compact-(A)* if and only if for each point x in S there is at least one open neighborhood U of p such that $\overline{U}$ is compact.

31.13 Lemma. *A space S is strongly locally compact if and only if S is strongly locally compact-(A).*

Proof: Exercise.

31.14 Lemma. *If a space S is strongly locally compact, then S is locally compact.*

Proof: Exercise.

31.15 Example. Let S denote the set of real numbers and let $\mathfrak{I}$ be the topology determined by $\{U_p \mid p \text{ is real and } U_p = \{x \mid x \geq p\}\}$ as base. Each point p has a compact neighborhood; namely, U_p which, by the way, is not closed; further no point p has a neighborhood whose closure is compact. Thus $\{S, \mathfrak{I}\}$ is locally compact but not strongly locally compact. Hence, local compactness is not equivalent to strong local compactness.

31.16 Lemma. *If S is a space in which compact subsets are closed (i.e., S is $T_{1+2/3}$), then strong local compactness is equivalent to local compactness.*

Proof: Exercise.

31.17 Theorem. *In any Hausdorff space strong local compactness and local compactness are equivalent.*

Proof: The theorem follows from the previous lemma (31.16) and theorem 29.5. ▮

EXERCISE 1. Prove that E^n, Euclidean n-space, is strongly locally compact and hence, locally compact.

EXERCISE 2. Find a subspace of E^2, Euclidean 2-space, which is not locally compact.

31.18 Lemma. *If S is locally compact, then any closed subspace of S is locally compact.*

Proof: Let $F \subseteq S$ and let F be closed in S. Let $x \in F$. Let K be a compact neighborhood of x in S. Consider $K \cap F$. $K \cap F$ is a neighborhood of x in F by definition of the relative topology. Let $\mathcal{G}$ be any open covering of $K \cap F$ in F. If $G_\nu \in \mathcal{G}$, then there is identified by the choice axiom a set G_ν^* open in S such that $G_\nu = G_\nu^* \cap F$, again, by definition of the relative topology. Let $\mathcal{G}^*$ denote the collection $\{G_\nu^* \mid G_\nu^* \cap F \in \mathcal{G}\}$. $\mathcal{G}^* \cup \{\sim F\}$ is an open covering of K in S. Since K is compact, a finite number of the sets in $\mathcal{G}^* \cup \{\sim F\}$ cover K, say, $G_{\nu_1}^*, \ldots, G_{\nu_k}^*, \sim F$. This means that $G_{\nu_1}, \ldots, G_{\nu_k}$, as defined above, cover $K \cap F$. ▮

EXERCISE 3. Prove that if a space S is strongly locally compact and if F is a closed subset of S, then S is strongly locally compact.

31.19 Lemma. *If a space S is compact, then it is strongly locally compact and hence, locally compact.*

Proof: Exercise.

A continuous image of a locally compact space need not be locally compact, and a quotient space of a locally compact space need not be locally compact.

31.20 Example. Let E^2 denote, as usual, Euclidean 2-space. E^2 is strongly locally compact as well as locally compact. Let X denote the quotient space of E^2 determined by the relation $\{(a, b), (c, d) \mid (a = c \text{ and } b = d) \text{ or } (a = c = 0)\}$. By definition (13.3) of the quotient topology, the quotient function, $q: E^2 \to X$ is continuous. X, however, is not locally compact.

31.21 Theorem. *If f is a continuous, open function from a locally compact space S onto a space T, then T is locally compact.*

Proof: Let y be any point of T and let $f(x) = y$. Since S is locally compact, there exists in S a compact neighborhood K of x. Since f is continuous and open, $f[K]$ is a compact neighborhood of $f(x) = y$. ∎

The previous theorem, of course, establishes that local compactness is a topological invariant.

A continuous image of a strongly locally compact space under a function which is also open need not be strongly locally compact.

31.22 Example. Let S denote the set of all ordered pairs of real numbers and let $\mathfrak{J}_1$ denote the topology determined by the base $\mathcal{B}_1 = \{B \mid B = \{(x, y) \mid x = c \text{ for } c \text{ real}\} \text{ or } B = \{(x, y) \mid x = c \text{ and } |y| \geq \alpha \text{ for } c \text{ and } \alpha \text{ real}\}\}$. Let X denote the set of all real numbers and let $\mathfrak{J}_2$ denote the topology determined by the base $\mathcal{B}_2 = \{U_p \mid U_p = \{x \mid x \geq p \text{ for } p \text{ real}\}\}$. Define the function f from $\{S, \mathfrak{J}_1\}$ onto $\{X, \mathfrak{J}_2\}$ as follows: $f((x, y)) = x + |y|$. f is continuous and open. $\{S, \mathfrak{J}_1\}$ is strongly locally compact. $\{X, \mathfrak{J}_2\}$, however, is not strongly locally compact.

EXERCISE 4. Prove that strong local compactness is a topological invariant.

31.23 Theorem. *If X and Y are locally compact then the product space $X \times Y$ is locally compact.*

Proof: Let (a, b) be any point in $X \times Y$. a has a compact neighborhood K in X and b has a compact neighborhood L in Y. By definition (11.2) of the product topology, $K \times L$ is a neighborhood of (a, b). By theorem 28.38, $K \times L$ is compact. ∎

31.24 Corollary. *The product space of any finite number of locally compact spaces is locally compact.*

Proof: The proof follows, by induction, from the previous theorem 31.23.

EXERCISE 5. Prove that the product space of any finite number of strongly locally compact spaces is strongly locally compact.

31.25 Theorem. *Any non-empty product space $\prod_{\nu \in \mathfrak{A}} X_\nu$ is locally compact if and only if all but at most a finite number of the spaces X_ν for $\nu \in \mathfrak{A}$ are compact and all the spaces X_ν for $\nu \in \mathfrak{A}$ are locally compact.*

Proof: A. First assume that the product space $\prod_{\nu \in \mathfrak{A}} X_\nu$ is locally compact. Let ϕ be any point in $\prod_{\nu \in \mathfrak{A}} X_\nu$. ϕ has a compact neighborhood K^* which must contain a basic neighborhood $\prod_{\nu \in \mathfrak{A}} U_\nu$, where $U_\nu = X_\nu$ except for at most a finite set $\{U_{\nu_1}, \ldots, U_{\nu_k}\}$. Hence, if $\alpha \in \mathfrak{A}$, if $\alpha \neq \nu_1$, $\alpha \neq \nu_2$, $\ldots$, $\alpha \neq \nu_k$ and if p_α is the projection function from $\prod_{\nu \in \mathfrak{A}} X_\nu$ onto X_α, then $p_\alpha[K^*] \supseteq X_\alpha$. Since p_α is continuous and K^* is compact, X_α is compact. Thus all but at most a finite number of the spaces X_ν are compact. Further, consider X_{ν_i}. Let x_{ν_i} be any point in X_{ν_i}. There is a point Ψ in $\prod_{\nu \in \mathfrak{A}} X_\nu$ such that $p_{\nu_i}(\Psi) = x_{\nu_i}$. Ψ has a compact neighborhood L^*. Since p_{ν_i} is continuous and open, $p_{\nu_i}[L^*]$ is a compact neighborhood of x_{ν_i} in X_{ν_i} and X_{ν_i} is locally compact.

B. Next, assume that all X_ν for $\nu \in \mathfrak{A}$ are locally compact and that all but a finite number are compact. Let ϕ be any point in $\prod_{\nu \in \mathfrak{A}} X_\nu$. Let X_ν be compact for $\nu \neq \nu_1$, $\nu \neq \nu_2$, $\ldots$, $\nu \neq \nu_k$ and k a positive integer. $\phi(\nu_i)$ has a compact neighborhood, K_i, in X_{ν_i}, for $i = 1, 2, \ldots, k$, by hypothesis. Hence, $\prod_{\nu \in \mathfrak{A}} W_\nu$, where $W_\nu = X_\nu$ for $\nu \neq \nu_1$, $\nu \neq \nu_2$, $\ldots$, $\nu \neq \nu_k$ and $W_{\nu_i} = K_i$ for $i = 1, \ldots, k$, is a compact neighborhood for ϕ in $\prod_{\nu \in \mathfrak{A}} X_\nu$ by theorem 28.46 and the definition (12.5) of the product topology. ▮

31.26 Theorem. *A non-empty product space, $\prod_{\nu \in \mathfrak{A}} X_\nu$, is strongly locally compact if and only if all but at most a finite number of the spaces X_ν are compact, and all the spaces X_ν are strongly compact.*

Proof: Exercise.

Local compactness yields two Baire category theorems. One follows and the other is a corollary after theorem 31.35.

31.27 Theorem (Baire Category). *Any locally compact, regular space is of the second category in itself.*

Proof: Let $\{A_1, A_2, \ldots, A_n, \ldots\}$ denote a countable set of nowhere dense subsets of the locally compact, regular space S. For each positive integer n, then, $\overline{A}_n$ contains no non-empty open sets. Thus if G is a non-empty open set in S, $G \cap \sim\overline{A}_1 \neq \emptyset$. By regularity and local compactness there exists a non-empty open subset U_1 such that $\overline{U}_1 \subseteq G \cap \sim\overline{A}_1$ and $\overline{U}_1$ is compact. Assume then that $\overline{U}_1 \supseteq \overline{U}_2 \supseteq \cdots \supseteq \overline{U}_n$ have been defined so that U_i is open and non-empty, $\overline{U}_i$ is compact and $\overline{U}_i \subseteq U_{i-1} \cap \sim\overline{A}_i$ for $i = 1, 2, \ldots, n$. Then there exists a non-empty open set U_{n+1} such that $\overline{U}_{n+1}$ is compact and $\overline{U}_{n+1} \subseteq U_n \cap \sim\overline{A}_{n+1}$. Since $\overline{U}_i$ is non-empty and compact and $\overline{U}_{i+1} \subseteq \overline{U}_i$ for $i = 1, 2, \ldots$, $\bigcap_{i=1}^{\infty} \overline{U}_i \neq \emptyset$. Let p be in $\bigcap_{i=1}^{\infty} \overline{U}_i$. Then p is in $\bigcap_{i=1}^{\infty} (\sim\overline{A}_i)$. Therefore p is in $\sim\bigcup_{i=1}^{\infty} \overline{A}_i$ and so p is not in $\bigcup_{i=1}^{\infty} A_i$. Thus $S \neq \bigcup_{i=1}^{\infty} A_i$. ▮

31.28 Definition. Let S be any space. A *compactification* of S is a pair, $\{S^*, \kappa\}$, where κ is a homeomorphism from S onto a dense subspace of S^* and S^* is a compact space.

31.29 Definition. Two compactifications $\{S_1^*, \kappa_1\}$ and $\{S_2^*, \kappa_2\}$ of a space S are called *equivalent* if and only if there exists a homeomorphism h from S_1^* onto S_2^* such that $h \circ \kappa_1 = \kappa_2$.

31.30 Example. The following example illustrates the need for including the imbedding homeomorphism in the definition. Let $S = \{x \mid x \text{ is real and } (-1 < x < 0 \text{ or } 0 < x < +1)\}$. Let $\kappa_1(x) = 1 - x$ for $0 < x < 1$ and let $\kappa_1(x) = -1 - x$ for $-1 < x < 0$. Then $\{[-1, +1], \kappa_1\}$ is a compactification of S. So is $\{[-1, +1], \kappa_2\}$, where $\kappa_2(x) = x$. The only difference in the two compactifications is in imbedding homeomorphisms, i.e., in the way S is "placed" in the compact space $[-1, 1]$. Consider now the two sequences $\sigma = (1/2, 2/3, \ldots, 1 - 1/n, \ldots)$ and $\eta = (-1/2, -2/3, \ldots, -1 + 1/n, \ldots)$. The two image sequences assigned by κ_1 are respectively $\kappa_1(\sigma) = (1/2, 1/3, \ldots, 1/n, \ldots)$ and $\kappa_1(\eta) = (-1/2, -1/3, \ldots, -1/n, \ldots)$. Now if κ_1 is to be followed by any homeomorphism h from $[-1, 1]$ onto $[-1, 1]$, then $h \circ \kappa_1(\sigma)$ must converge to the same limit as $h \circ \kappa_1(\eta)$. However, $\kappa_2(\sigma)$ converges to $+1$ and $\kappa_2(\eta)$ converges to -1. Thus $\kappa_2 \neq h \circ \kappa_1$ and the compactifications are essentially different.

31.31 Lemma. *Let $\{S, \mathfrak{I}\}$ be a non-compact space. Let $S^+ = S \cup \{\alpha\}$, where $\alpha \notin S$. Let $\mathfrak{I}^+$ have as base $\mathfrak{I} \cup \{G \mid G \subseteq S^+, \sim G \subseteq S$ and $\sim G$ is closed and compact in $S\}$. $\{\{S^+, \mathfrak{I}^+\}, i\}$ is a compactification of $\{S, \mathfrak{I}\}$, where $i(s) = s$ for all s in S.*

Proof: Exercise.

31.32 Definition. If $\{S, \mathfrak{I}\}$ is any non-compact space, then the pair $\{\{S^+, \mathfrak{I}^+\}, i\}$ of the previous lemma is called the *one-point compactification* of $\{S, \mathfrak{I}\}$.

31.33 Example. The space $\{S, \mathfrak{I}\}$, where S is the set of real numbers and $\mathfrak{I}$ is the topology determined by each real number p having a local base consisting of one set $U_p = \{x \mid x \geq p\}$, has a one-point compactification which is T_0.

31.34 Theorem. *If $\{S, \mathfrak{I}\}$ is a space, then a one-point compactification exists as a Hausdorff space if and only if $\{S, \mathfrak{I}\}$ is locally compact and Hausdorff.*

Proof: A. Let $\{\{S^+, \mathfrak{I}^+\}, i\}$ be a one-point compactification of $\{S, \mathfrak{I}\}$. If $\{S^+, \mathfrak{I}^+\}$ is Hausdorff, then since, by definition, $\{S, \mathfrak{I}\}$ is a subspace of $\{S^+, \mathfrak{I}^+\}$, $\{S, \mathfrak{I}\}$ is Hausdorff by theorem 16.17. Next let x be any point of the space $\{S, \mathfrak{I}\}$. There exists an open neighborhood V of α, where $S^+ = S \cup \{\alpha\}$, and an open neighborhood U of x such that $U \cap V = \emptyset$. This implies that $\sim V \supseteq U$. By definition of $\mathfrak{J}^+$, $\sim V$ is closed and compact. Hence, x has a neighborhood, $\sim V$, which is compact, and so $\{S, \mathfrak{J}\}$ is locally compact.

B. Let $\{S, \mathfrak{J}\}$ be locally compact and Hausdorff, and let $S^+ = S \cup \{\alpha\}$. Let x be any point in S. Since $\{S, \mathfrak{J}\}$ is Hausdorff, $\{S, \mathfrak{J}\}$ is strongly locally compact. Hence, x has a closed, compact neighborhood K. $S^+ \sim K$ is then a neighborhood of α in the standard model $\{S^+, \mathfrak{J}^+\}$ and, of course, $(S^+ \sim K) \cap K = \emptyset$. Thus, $\{S^+, \mathfrak{J}^+\}$ is Hausdorff. ▮

The previous theorem has many useful consequences. The first is an analogue of theorem 29.12, which states that every compact Hausdorff space is normal.

31.35 Theorem. *Any locally compact, Hausdorff space is completely regular.*

Proof: Let $\{S, \mathfrak{J}\}$ be locally compact and Hausdorff. A one-point compactification exists by theorem 31.34. Let $\{\{S^+, \mathfrak{J}^+\}, i\}$ again denote the one-point compactification of $\{S, \mathfrak{J}\}$. $\{S^+, \mathfrak{J}^+\}$ is compact and Hausdorff by the previous theorem. Hence, by theorem 29.12, $\{S^+, \mathfrak{J}^+\}$ is normal. By theorem 18.34, $\{S^+, \mathfrak{J}^+\}$ is completely regular and by theorem 18.42, $\{S, \mathfrak{J}\}$, as a subspace of $\{S^+, \mathfrak{J}^+\}$, is completely regular. ▮

Next comes a Baire theorem.

31.36 Corollary (A Baire Theorem). *Any locally compact, Hausdorff space is of the second category in itself.*

Proof: By the previous theorem, the space is regular, and so, by theorem 31.27, the space is of the second category in itself. ▮

The compact-open topology has a special property for locally compact Hausdorff spaces, which the following theorem establishes. First, an often-used lemma is needed.

31.37 Lemma. *Let S be any space and let K be a compact space. Further, let A be a subset of S and let G^* be open in $S \times K$ such that $A \times K \subseteq G^*$. Then there is an open set U in S such that $A \subseteq U$ and $U \times K \subseteq G^*$.*

Proof: Let a be any point in A. $\{a\} \times K$ is a compact subset of the open set G^*. Hence, since each point (a, k) of $\{a\} \times K$ is interior to G^* in $S \times K$, there exists a finite set $\{U_1 \times V_1, \ldots, U_n \times V_n\}$ of basic open sets of $S \times K$ which are subsets of G^* and which cover $\{a\} \times K$. Now, $p_s[U_i \times V_i] = U_i$, where p_s is the projection function from $S \times K$ onto S. Now let $U_1 \cap U_2 \cap \cdots \cap U_n = U_a$. $a \in U_a$. U_a is open in S and $U_a \times K \subseteq G^*$. For each a in A, define such a set U_a and let $U = \bigcup_{a \in A} U_a$. Then if (a, k) is in $U \times K$, (a, k) is in $U_a \times K$ and $U_a \times K \subseteq G^*$. Hence, $U \times K \subseteq G^*$. ▮

31.38 Theorem. *Let X be a locally compact, Hausdorff space and let $\mathcal{E}:C(X, Y) \times X \to Y$ be defined by $\mathcal{E}((f, x)) = f(x)$ for a space Y. Then the compact-open topology for $C(X, Y)$ is the smallest topology such that $\mathcal{E}$ is continuous from the product space $\{C(X, Y), \mathfrak{J}_{c.-o.}\} \times X$ into Y.*

Proof: Since X is locally compact and Hausdorff, X is completely regular, and hence regular. Now let (f_0, x_0) be in the domain of $\mathcal{E}$, let $f_0(x_0) = y_0$ and let V be a neighborhood of y_0 in Y. Since f_0 is continuous from X into Y, there exists a neighborhood U of x_0 in X such that $f_0[U] \subseteq V$. Also, since X is regular and locally compact, there exists a compact neighborhood $\overline{N}$ of x_0 such that $\overline{N} \subseteq U$. Hence, $f_0[\overline{N}] \subseteq V$. Now, consider the neighborhood $G(\overline{N}, V) \times \overline{N}$ of (f_0, x_0) in $\{C(X, Y), \mathfrak{J}_{c.-o.}\} \times X$ and let (g, x) be any element in $G(\overline{N}, V) \times \overline{N}$. Since g is in $G(\overline{N}, V)$ and x is in $\overline{N}$, $g(x)$ is in V. Hence, $\mathcal{E}[G(\overline{N}, V) \times \overline{N}] \subseteq V$. Thus $\mathcal{E}$ is continuous from $\{C(X, Y), \mathfrak{J}_{c.-o.}\} \times X$ into Y. Now let $\mathfrak{J}^*$ be a topology for $C(X, Y)$ such that $\mathcal{E}$, again, is continuous from $\{C(X, Y), \mathfrak{J}^*\} \times X$ into Y. Then let $G(K, V)$ be any subbasic open set in $\{C(X, Y), \mathfrak{J}_{c.-o.}\}$ and let f be in $G(K, V)$. Since $\mathcal{E}$ is continuous, $\mathcal{E}^{-1}[V]$ is open in $\{C(X, Y), \mathfrak{J}^*\} \times X$. Since f is in $G(K, V)$, $\{f\} \times K$ is in $\mathcal{E}^{-1}[V]$. Then by the previous lemma, there is an open set U in $\{C(X, Y), \mathfrak{J}^*\}$ such that $\{f\} \subseteq U$ and $U \times K \subseteq \mathcal{E}^{-1}[V]$. Hence, if g is in U, $g[K] \subseteq V$, and so g is in $G(K, V)$. Thus, $U \subseteq G(K, V)$ and every point of $G(K, V)$ is interior relative to $\mathfrak{J}^*$. Thus $\mathfrak{J}^* \supseteq \mathfrak{J}_{c.-o.}$. ▮

The function $\mathcal{E}$ of the previous theorem is often called "the evaluation map."

The next theorem is an analogue of Urysohn's metrization theorem (20.16), which says that any second countable, normal space is metrizable.

31.39 Theorem. *Any locally compact, second countable, Hausdorff space is metrizable.*

Proof: Let $\{S, \mathfrak{J}\}$ be locally compact, second countable and Hausdorff. $\{S, \mathfrak{J}\}$ is completely regular by the previous theorem, and hence regular by theorem 18.34. Since $\{S, \mathfrak{J}\}$, then, is regular and second countable, $\{S, \mathfrak{J}\}$ is normal, by theorem 18.22. Since $\{S, \mathfrak{J}\}$ is second countable and normal, $\{S, \mathfrak{J}\}$ is metric, by theorem 20.16. ▮

The following theorem states an important property of Hausdorff compactifications in general.

31.40 Theorem. *Let $\{S^*, \kappa\}$ be a Hausdorff compactification of a space S. Then $\kappa[S]$ is open in S^* if and only if S is locally compact.*

Proof: Let $\kappa[S]$ be denoted more simply by X. X is then a dense subspace of S^* homeomorphic to S. First assume that X is open in S^* and let $x \in X$. x, then, has a neighborhood $U \subseteq X$. Since S^* is compact and Hausdorff, it is normal and hence regular (theorems 29.12 and 18.8). This means that there exists a neighborhood V of x in S^* such that $\overline{V} \subseteq U$ (theorem 17.6). Since $U \subseteq X$, $\overline{V} \subseteq X$, and since S^* is compact, $\overline{V}$ is compact (theorem 29.1). Hence, x has a compact neighborhood in X and X is locally compact. Since X is homeomorphic to S, S is then, locally compact. Conversely, let S be locally compact. Then, $X = \kappa[S]$ is a locally compact subspace of S^*. Since S^* is Hausdorff, X is Hausdorff. By theorem 31.17, X is then strongly locally compact and x, then, has a neighborhood U such that $U \subseteq X$, U is open in X and $Cl_X U$ is compact, where $Cl_X U$ denotes the closure of U in X. $Cl_X U$ is then a compact subset of the Hausdorff space S^*. By theorem 29.5, $Cl_X U$ is then closed in S^*. Now let V be open in S^* and let $V \cap X = U$. Since X is dense in S^*, if p is a limit point of V in S^*, every neighborhood of p must contain a point of $V \cap X$. Since $V \cap X = U$, $Cl_{S^*}V = Cl_{S^*}U$. However, by the above, $Cl_{S^*}U = Cl_X U$. Hence, $Cl_{S^*}V \subseteq X$ and $V \subseteq X$. Thus $V \cap X = V = U$, and U is open in S^* as well as in X. This makes X open in S^*. ▮

31.41 Theorem. *If a space S has a Hausdorff compactification, then it is completely regular.*

Proof: Let $\{S^*, \kappa\}$ be a Hausdorff compactification of a space S. S^* is, then, a compact Hausdorff space and, by theorem 29.12, is normal. By theorem 18.34, S^* is completely regular and, by theorem 18.42, any subspace of S^* is completely regular. Since S is homeomorphic to a subspace of S^*, S is, then, completely regular. ▮

The Stone-Čech Compactification

One of the most studied compactifications is the Stone-Čech compactification. The Stone-Čech compactification is characterized by an extension property for certain functions.

31.42 Definition. Let $\{S^*, \kappa\}$ be a compactification of a space S. $\{S^*, \kappa\}$ is said to have *the extension property for compactifications* of S if and only if for every continuous function m from S into a compact Hausdorff space Y, the composite function $m \circ \kappa^{-1}$ has a continuous extension which maps S^* into Y.

31.43 Theorem. *Let* $\{S_1^*, \kappa_1\}$ and $\{S_2^*, \kappa_2\}$ *be Hausdorff compactifications of a space S and let both have the extension property for compactifications of S. Then $\{S_1^*, \kappa_1\}$ is equivalent to $\{S_2^*, \kappa_2\}$; i.e., there is essentially one such compactification.*

Proof: Since S_2^* is a compact Hausdorff space, the composite function $\kappa_2 \circ \kappa_1^{-1}$ has a continuous extension f^* from S_1^* into S_2^* by the extension property. Similarly, the composite $\kappa_1 \circ \kappa_2^{-1}$ has a continuous extension g^* from

S_2^* into S_1^*. Now consider the composite $g^* \circ f^* : S_1^* \to S_1^*$. Let $s \in S$ and consider $g^* \circ f^*(\kappa_1(s))$. $g^* \circ f^*(\kappa_1(s)) = \kappa_1 \circ \kappa_2^{-1} \circ \kappa_2 \circ \kappa_1^{-1}(\kappa_1(s)) = \kappa_1(s)$. Thus $g^* \circ f^*$ is an extension of the inclusion function $j(x) = x$ from $\kappa_1[S]$ into S_1^*. Since S_1^* is Hausdorff and $\kappa_1[S]$ is dense in S_1^*, j can have at most one continuous extension, by theorem 16.24. Since the identity function $i_1 : S_1^* \to S_1^*$ is a continuous extension of j, $g^* \circ f^* = i_1$. Similarly, $f^* \circ g^* = i_2$, where i_2 is the identity function on S_2^*. This means that f^* and g^* are homeomorphisms onto, and that $f^{*-1} = g^*$ and $g^{*-1} = f^*$. ▮

31.44 Lemma. *Let S be any completely regular space. Let κ denote the homeomorphism, in theorem 18.46, which imbeds S topologically into the product space $[0, 1]^{C_s}$, where C_s denotes the set of continuous functions from S into the unit interval space, $[0, 1]$. Then $\overline{\kappa[S]}$, the closure of $\kappa[S]$ in $[0, 1]^{C_s}$, is a Hausdorff compactification of S.*

Proof: The unit interval space, [0, 1], is compact (theorem 30.18). The unit interval space, [0, 1], is also Hausdorff (theorem 16.17). Hence any product space $[0, 1]^{C_s}$ is compact and Hausdorff (theorems 28.46 and 16.18). Thus $\overline{\kappa[S]}$, as a closed subset of a compact space, is compact (theorem 29.1), and as a subspace of a Hausdorff space is Hausdorff (theorem 16.17). Further, $\kappa[S]$ is, of course, dense in $\overline{\kappa[S]}$. Thus $\overline{\kappa[S]}$ is a Hausdorff compactification of the completely regular space S. ▮

31.45 Corollary. *A space S is completely regular if and only if it has a Hausdorff compactification.*

Proof: Theorem 31.41 and the previous lemma 31.44 imply the corollary. ▮

31.46 Definition. The Hausdorff compactification $\{\overline{\kappa[S]}, \kappa\}$ of the previous lemma (31.44) is called the *Stone-Čech compactification* of the completely regular space S. It is also customary to denote $\overline{\kappa[S]}$ by βS and to call it the Stone-Čech compactification of S, with the homeomorphism κ understood.

31.47 Corollary. *A space S is completely regular if and only if it has a Stone-Čech compactification.*

Proof: Lemma 31.44 and corollary 31.45 imply the corollary. ▮

31.48 Theorem. *The Stone-Čech compactification for a completely regular space S has the extension property for compactifications.*

Proof: Let m be a continuous function from S into a compact Hausdorff space Y. To establish, then, that βS has the extension property for compactifications of S, it must be shown (definition 31.42) that $m \circ \kappa^{-1}$ has a continuous extension $\hat{M}$ from βS into Y.

A. A function M is defined from $[0, 1]^{C_s}$ into $[0, 1]^{C_Y}$, where C_Y is the set of continuous functions from Y into $[0, 1]$. κ_Y will denote the homeomorphism which imbeds Y into $[0, 1]^{C_Y}$ and which is defined in theorem 18.46. The points in $[0, 1]^{C_s}$ and $[0, 1]^{C_Y}$ are functions from C_s into $[0, 1]$, and C_Y into $[0, 1]$, respectively. Hence, the points can be considered to be like nets and sequences except that no orderings on the indexing sets (domains) C_s and C_Y are used. Nevertheless, if convenient, the same symbol can be used for these elements as is used for nets or sequences. The symbol (a_n) denotes a sequence; n denotes an element in the domain, and a_n denotes the image of n assigned by the sequence. Thus (t_f) will denote a point in $[0, 1]^{C_s}$, where f is in the domain, C_s, and t_f is the image of f. t_f is then a real number in $[0, 1]$. Similarly, (u_g) denotes a point in $[0, 1]^{C_Y}$; u_g is the real number in $[0, 1]$ assigned to g by the point (function) (u_g). t_f and u_g are also referred to, in the language of product spaces, as the f-th coordinate of the point (t_f) and the g-th coordinate of the point (u_g), respectively. Now, by definition of κ, if $s \in S$, $\kappa(s)$ is the point whose f-th coordinate is $f(s)$, i.e., $\kappa(s) = \big(f(s)\big)$. Similarly, if $y \in Y$, $\kappa_Y(y)$ is the point whose g-th coordinate is $g(y)$. Thus, $\kappa_Y(y) = \big(g(y)\big)$. Next consider the function M from $[0, 1]^{C_s}$ into $[0, 1]^{C_Y}$ defined in what follows. Each function g in C_Y determines uniquely a composite function $g \circ m$ in C_s. Thus if (t_f) is any point in $[0, 1]^{C_s}$, it assigns an image $t_{g \circ m}$ to $g \circ m$. $t_{g \circ m}$ is a real number in $[0, 1]$; hence, if to each function g in C_Y is assigned the $g \circ m$-th coordinate of the point (t_f), a unique point of $[0, 1]^{C_Y}$ is determined. Denote this function from $[0, 1]^{C_s}$ into $[0, 1]^{C_Y}$ by M. $M\big((t_f)\big) = (u_g)$, where $u_g = t_{g \circ m}$.

B. M is now proved to be continuous. Let p_g denote the g-th projection function from $[0, 1]^{C_Y}$ onto $[0, 1]$, i.e., as usual, each point in $[0, 1]^{C_Y}$ is mapped onto its g-th coordinate, a real number in $[0, 1]$. Consider the composite function $p_g \circ M$. $p_g \circ M : [0, 1]^{C_s} \to [0, 1]$. $p_g \circ M\big((t_f)\big) = u_g = t_{g \circ m}$, by definition of M. Hence, $p_g \circ M = p_{g \circ m}$, which is the $g \circ m$-th projection function from $[0, 1]^{C_s}$ onto $[0, 1]$. Since $p_{g \circ m}$ is continuous, by definition of the product topology, $p_g \circ M$ is continuous. This means that M is continuous by theorem 12.13.

C. M is now proved to be an extension of $\kappa_Y \circ m \circ \kappa^{-1}$. First, for convenience's sake, denote the imbedded image, $\kappa[S]$, of S in $[0, 1]^{C_s}$ by X. If $x \in X$, then $x = \kappa(s)$ and $x = \big(f(s)\big)$, where $f(s)$ is the f-th coordinate of x. M, by definition, assigns to such a point x the point (u_g) in $[0, 1]^{C_Y}$ determined by $u_g = g \circ m(s)$ for every g in C_Y. Consider next $\kappa_Y \circ m \circ \kappa^{-1}(x)$. Since $x = \kappa(s)$, $\kappa_Y \circ m \circ \kappa^{-1}(x) = \kappa_Y \circ m(s)$. Now, $\kappa_Y \circ m(s)$, by definition of κ_Y, is the point in $[0, 1]^{C_Y}$ whose g-th coordinate is $g\big(m(s)\big)$. $g\big(m(s)\big) = g \circ m(s)$. Thus for every g in C_Y, the g-th coordinate of $\kappa_Y \circ m \circ \kappa^{-1}(x)$ is equal to the g-th coordinate of $M(x)$. Hence M is a continuous extension of $\kappa_Y \circ m \circ \kappa^{-1}$.

D. Let $\hat{M}$ denote the restriction of M to $\beta S = \overline{\kappa[S]}$. It will now be shown that $\hat{M}\,[\beta S] \subseteq \kappa_Y[Y]$ in $[0, 1]^{C_Y}$. First, $\kappa_Y \circ m \circ \kappa^{-1}\big[\kappa[S]\big] = \kappa_Y \circ m[S] \subseteq \kappa_Y[Y]$. By part C, above, M is a continuous extension of $\kappa_Y \circ m \circ \kappa^{-1}$. Hence, $M\big[\kappa[S]\big] \subseteq \kappa_Y[Y]$. Since M is continuous, $M\big[\overline{\kappa[S]}\big] \subseteq \overline{\kappa_Y[Y]}$ (theorem 4.3). Since Y is compact and κ_Y is a homeomorphism, $\kappa_Y[Y]$ is compact in $[0, 1]^{C_Y}$.

Since $[0, 1]^{C_Y}$ is Hausdorff, $\kappa_Y[Y]$ is then closed in $[0, 1]^{C_Y}$ (theorem 29.5). Thus $\overline{\kappa_Y[Y]} = \kappa_Y[Y]$ and $M[\overline{\kappa[S]}] \subseteq \kappa_Y[Y]$. Since $\beta S = \overline{\kappa[S]}$, $M[\beta S] \subseteq \kappa_Y[Y]$. Hence the restriction $\hat{M}$ of M to βS has its range in $\kappa_Y[Y]$.

E. Consider, now, the composite function $\kappa_Y^{-1} \circ \hat{M}$. $\kappa_Y^{-1} \circ \hat{M}:\beta S \to Y$. $\kappa_Y^{-1} \circ \hat{M}$ is continuous, since it is the composite of two continuous functions. Further, let $x \in X = \kappa[S]$. $x = \kappa(s)$ for some s in S. Then $m \circ \kappa^{-1}(x) = m(s)$. Now consider $\kappa_Y^{-1} \circ \hat{M}(x)$. In part C above M was proved to be an extension of $\kappa_Y \circ m \circ \kappa^{-1}$. Hence, by definition, $\hat{M}$ is an extension of $\kappa_Y \circ m \circ \kappa^{-1}$. This means that $\kappa_Y^{-1} \circ \hat{M}(x) = \kappa_Y^{-1} \circ \kappa_Y \circ m \circ \kappa^{-1}(x)$. $\kappa_Y^{-1} \circ \kappa_Y \circ m \circ \kappa^{-1}(x) = m \circ \kappa^{-1}(x)$. Thus $\kappa_Y^{-1} \circ \hat{M}$ is a continuous extension of $m \circ \kappa^{-1}$ and βS has the extension property for compactifications. ▮

EXERCISE 6. Let N denote the discrete space defined on the set $\{1, 2, \ldots, n, \ldots\}$ of natural numbers. Let $\{N^+, i\}$ denote the one-point compactification of N (definition 31.32). Prove that $\{N^+, i\}$ is not a Stone-Čech compactification of N.

EXERCISE 7. Let S be the subspace of the usual space E^1 of real numbers determined by the subset $\{x \mid 0 < x < 1\}$. Prove that the compactification $\{S^*, i\}$, where S^* is the subspace of E^1 determined by $\{x \mid 0 \leq x \leq 1\}$ and $i(x) = x$, is neither a one-point compactification nor a Stone-Čech compactification.

EXERCISE 8. Let S be any completely regular space and let m be a continuous function from S into the completely regular space T. Prove that the function $m \circ \kappa^{-1}$, where κ is the standard imbedding homeomorphism of S into βS, has a continuous extension $\hat{m}:\beta S \to \beta T$.

EXERCISE 9. Let S be any completely regular space. Let $C^*(S)$ denote the subring of $C(S)$ consisting of bounded continuous functions from S into E^1, the usual space of reals ($C(S)$) is the ring of continuous functions from S into E^1 defined in theorem 18.51). Prove that $C^*(S)$ is isomorphic to $C(\beta S)$.

Compactifications of the Space of Countable Ordinals

The next three lemmas and two theorems close this section by establishing some additional properties of the space W of countable ordinals with the natural order topology (definition 28.33).

31.49 Lemma. *If A is a countable set of countable ordinals, then there exists a countable ordinal γ^* such that if $\alpha \in A$, then $\alpha < \gamma^*$.*

Proof: Assume that there exists no countable ordinal such that if $\alpha \in A$, $\alpha < \gamma^*$. Then if W denotes the space consisting of all countable ordinals with the order topology, there exists for each $\gamma \in W$ an ordinal $\alpha \in A$ such that $\gamma < \alpha$ (W will be used ambiguously for both the set and the space). This means from the definition of $<$ that $\gamma \in \alpha$ (see discussion preceding definition 28.33). Hence, $W = \bigcup_{\alpha \in A} \alpha$. Now each ordinal α in A is defined as the countable set of all ordinals less than itself. Thus $\bigcup_{\alpha \in A} \alpha$ is countable and W would not be an uncountable ordinal. Thus there must exist an ordinal γ^* in W such that if $\alpha \in A$, $\alpha < \gamma^*$. ▮

31.50 Lemma. *If A and B are non-empty, disjoint closed sets in the space W, then at least one of A or B has an upper bound in W.*

Proof: Let A have the property that if $\gamma \in W$, there exists an ordinal α in A such that $\alpha > \gamma$. Now, assume that B has this property also. A sequence (γ_n) is defined as follows. Let Ψ_A denote a choice function on $P(A) \sim \{\emptyset\}$ and let Ψ_B denote a choice function on $P(B) \sim \{\emptyset\}$. Define $\gamma_1 = \Psi_A(A)$. By the assumption about B, $M = \{\gamma \mid \gamma \in B \text{ and } \gamma > \alpha_1\} \neq \emptyset$. Hence define $\gamma_2 = \Psi_B(M)$. Assume next that $\gamma_1, \gamma_2, \ldots, \gamma_{2k}, \gamma_{2k+1}$ have been defined so that $\gamma_{2j} \in A$, $\gamma_{2j+1} \in B$, for $1 \leq j \leq k$, and $\gamma_m < \gamma_n$, if $m < n$. Now, by definition of A, $N = \{\alpha \mid \alpha \in A \text{ and } \alpha > \gamma_{2k+1}\} \neq \emptyset$. Hence, define $\gamma_{2k+2} = \Psi_A(N)$. Further, by the assumption on B, $Q = \{\beta \mid \beta \in B \text{ and } \beta > \gamma_{2k+2}\} \neq \emptyset$. Define $\gamma_{2k+3} = \Psi_B(Q)$. Thus, by induction, a strictly increasing sequence, $s = (\gamma_1, \gamma_2, \ldots, \gamma_n, \gamma_{n+1}, \ldots)$, has been defined such that $\gamma_{2k} \in A$ and $\gamma_{2k+1} \in B$ for all $k = 1, 2, \ldots$. Now the range of s is countable, and hence, by lemma 31.49, the set $\{\gamma_1, \gamma_2, \ldots, \gamma_n, \ldots\}$ has an upper bound. By the well-ordering property for $<$ in W, the set $\{\gamma_1, \gamma_2, \ldots, \gamma_n, \ldots\}$ has, then, a least upper bound γ^* in W. If $\gamma^* = \gamma_n$, then $\gamma_{n+1} > \gamma^*$. This is a contradiction. Hence, $\gamma^* \notin \{\gamma_1, \gamma_2, \ldots, \gamma_n, \ldots\}$. If γ^* were a non-limit ordinal, i.e., had an immediate predecessor, $\gamma^* - 1$, then $\gamma^* - 1$ would be an upper bound of $\{\gamma_1, \gamma_2, \ldots, \gamma_n, \ldots\}$ and γ^* would not be the least upper bound of $\{\gamma_1, \gamma_2, \ldots, \gamma_n, \ldots\}$. Hence, γ^* is a limit ordinal. By definition 28.33, a basic neighborhood of γ^* has the form $\{\alpha \mid \sigma < \alpha \leq \gamma^*\}$. Let $U\sigma$ be such a neighborhood. Since γ^* is the least upper bound of $\{\gamma_1, \gamma_2, \ldots, \gamma_n, \ldots\}$, there exists a natural number k such that $\sigma < \gamma_k < \gamma^*$. Hence if $n > k$, $\gamma_n \in U_\sigma$. Thus γ^* is a limit point of A and B. Hence $\overline{A} \cap \overline{B} \neq \emptyset$ and this is a contradiction. Thus if A has no upper bound in W, B has an upper bound in W. ▌

31.51 Theorem. *If m is a continuous function from the space W of all countable ordinals into the space E^1 of real numbers, then there exists an ordinal γ_m in W with the property that m is constant on $\{\alpha \in W \mid \gamma_m < \alpha\}$.*

Proof: Let γ be any ordinal in W and let $T(\gamma) = \{\alpha \in W \mid \alpha \geq \gamma\}$. By definition of the order topology on W, $T(\gamma)$ is closed for every γ in W. Since, by lemma 28.35, W is countably compact, $T(\gamma)$ is, by corollary 29.2, countably compact. Thus it follows, by theorem 28.36, that the image $m[T(\gamma)]$ is countably compact in E^1. By theorem 30.5, $m[T(\gamma)]$ is compact. By theorem 29.5, $m[T(\gamma)]$ is closed, since E^1 is Hausdorff. Now since $T(\gamma_1) \subsetneq T(\gamma_2)$, for $\gamma_1 > \gamma_2$, $\{m[T(\gamma)] \mid \gamma \in W\}$ has the finite intersection property. Hence, since $m[T(0)]$ is compact, $\bigcap_{\gamma \in W} m[T(\gamma)] \neq \emptyset$. Let t^* be a real number in $\bigcap_{\gamma \in W} m[T(\gamma)]$. By definition of t^*, for any $\gamma \in W$, there exists an $\alpha \in W$ such that $\alpha > \gamma$ and $m(\alpha) = t^*$. Thus the set $m^{-1}[\{t^*\}]$ has no upper bound in W. Now let k be a natural number and let $F_k = \{\alpha \in W \mid |m(\alpha) - t^*| \geq 1/k\}$. Now, $A_k = \{t \in E^1 \mid |t - t^*| \geq 1/k\}$ is closed in E^1; m is continuous and $F_k = m^{-1}[A_k \cap m[W]]$. Hence, F_k is closed in W. Further, since $m^{-1}[\{t^*\}]$ is also closed in W and since, by definition of F_k, $m^{-1}[\{t^*\}] \cap F_k = \emptyset$, by lemma

31.50 and the above definition of t^*, F_k has an upper bound α_k in W. $P = \{\alpha \in W \mid \alpha = \alpha_k$ for some natural number $k\}$ is countable, and hence, by lemma 31.49, P has an upper bound α^*. Now if $\gamma > \alpha^*$, there exists no natural number k such that $|m(\gamma) - t^*| \geq 1/k$. Hence, for all natural numbers k, $|m(\gamma) - t^*| < 1/k$. Thus, by the archimedean order property of $<$ on the positive reals, $|m(\gamma) - t^*| = 0$. Therefore, for $\gamma > \alpha^*$, $m(\gamma) = t^*$. ▮

REMARK: The real number t^* of the previous theorem is called the *tail value* or the *end value* of the function $m: W \rightarrow E^1$.

31.52 Lemma. *The space $W \cup \{W\}$ with the inclusion function is a one-point compactification of the space W.*

Proof: Let $U_\sigma = \{\alpha \mid \alpha$ is an ordinal and $\sigma < \alpha \leq W\}$. U_σ is a basic neighborhood of W from the defining system (definition 28.33). $\sim U_\sigma = \{\alpha \in W \mid \alpha \leq \sigma\}$. $\sim U_\sigma = S(\sigma + 1)$, where $\sigma + 1$ is the immediate successor of σ and $S(\sigma + 1) = \{\alpha \in W \mid \alpha < \sigma + 1\}$. In the proof of lemma 28.35, case II, $S(\sigma + 1)$ was proved to be compact. Since W is Hausdorff, $S(\sigma + 1)$ is closed. Thus the neighborhoods for W are as required for the one-point compactification of W. ▮

31.53 Theorem. *The one-point compactification of the space W of all countable ordinals with the order topology is the Stone-Čech compactification of W.*

Proof: By the previous lemma (31.52), $W \cup \{W\}$ with the order topology and the inclusion function, $i(\alpha) = \alpha$, is the one-point compactification of the subspace W. Let C_W again denote the set of continuous functions from W into $[0, 1]$ and let κ_W denote the imbedding homeomorphism from W into $[0, 1]^{C_W}$, which is defined in theorem 18.46 and used in theorem 31.48. $\kappa_W(\alpha) = (t_f)$, where $t_f = f(\alpha)$ for every f in C_W. Next define a function $\overset{+}{\kappa}_W$ from $W \cup \{W\}$ into $[0, 1]^{C_W}$ as follows. For each f in C_W, by theorem 31.51, there exists an ordinal γ_f in W such that f is constant on $\{\alpha \in W \mid \alpha \geq \gamma_f\}$. Denote this tail-value of f by c_f and consider the point Γ in $[0, 1]^{C_W}$ whose f-th coordinate is c_f for every f in C_W, $\Gamma = (c_f)$. Define $\overset{+}{\kappa}_W(W) = \Gamma$ and define $\overset{+}{\kappa}_W(\alpha) = \kappa_W(\alpha)$ for $\alpha \in W$. Thus $\overset{+}{\kappa}_W$ is an extension of κ_W. $\overset{+}{\kappa}_W: W \cup \{W\} \rightarrow [0, 1]^{C_W}$. First, $\overset{+}{\kappa}_W$ is 1:1. For, let α be any ordinal in W. Then if β is any ordinal in W such that $\alpha < \beta$, there is, by the complete regularity of W, a function g in C_W such that $g(\alpha) \neq g(\beta)$. This means that $g(\alpha)$ cannot be the tail value of g. Hence, the g-th coordinate of $\overset{+}{\kappa}_W(\alpha) \neq g$-th coordinate of $\overset{+}{\kappa}_W(W)$ and $\overset{+}{\kappa}_W(\alpha) \neq \overset{+}{\kappa}_W(W)$, for all $\alpha \in W$. Since, by theorem 18.46, κ_W is 1:1, $\overset{+}{\kappa}_W$ is 1:1. Lastly, it will be shown that $\overset{+}{\kappa}_W$ is continuous. Let U^* be any neighborhood of $\overset{+}{\kappa}_W(W)$ in $[0, 1]^{C_W}$, from the defining base. $U^* = \prod_f U_f$, where $U_f = [0, 1]$ except for at most a finite number, say, $f_1, f_2, \ldots, f_k$ of functions in the indexing set C_W. By theorem 31.51, there exist ordinals $\gamma_1, \gamma_2, \ldots, \gamma_k$ in W such that f_i is constant on $\{\alpha \in W \mid \alpha \geq \gamma_i\}$ for $1 \leq i \leq k$. By lemma 31.49, the set $\{\gamma_1, \gamma_2, \ldots,$

$\gamma_{k}\}$ has an upper bound, γ^*, in W. Now consider the neighborhood $M = \{\alpha \in W \cup \{W\} \mid \alpha > \gamma^*\}$ of the element W in $W \cup \{W\}$. If $\alpha \in M$, then $f_i(\alpha) = c_{f_i}$ for $i = 1, 2, \ldots, k$. Thus, for $\alpha \in M$, $\kappa_W^+(\alpha) = (t_f)$, where $t_{f_i} = c_{f_i}$, the tail value of f_i. Thus $\kappa_W^+(\alpha)$ has the same f_i-th coordinate as $\kappa_W^+(W)$ for $i = 1, 2, \ldots, k$. Hence, $\kappa_W^+(\alpha) \in U^*$, and so $\kappa_W^+[M] \subseteq U^*$. κ_W^+ is, then, 1:1 and continuous from the compact space $W \cup \{W\}$ into the Hausdorff space $[0, 1]^{C_W}$, and so is a homeomorphism, by corollary 29.8. Now, $W \subseteq W \cup \{W\}$ and $\overline{W} = W \cup \{W\}$. Since κ_W^+ is a homeomorphism, $\kappa_W^+[\overline{W}] = \overline{\kappa_W^+[W]}$. By definition, $\kappa_W^+[W] = \kappa_W[W]$. Hence, $\kappa_W^+[\overline{W}] = \overline{\kappa_W[W]}$. Since $\overline{\kappa_W[W]} = \beta W$, $\overline{W} = W \cup \{W\}$ is homeomorphic to βW. In addition, $\kappa_W(\alpha) = \kappa_W^+(\alpha)$ for α in W; hence, $\kappa_W^+ \circ i(\alpha) = \kappa_W(\alpha)$. Thus $\{W \cup \{W\}, i\}$ is equivalent to $\{\beta W, \kappa_W\}$ and so, as compactifications of W, they are essentially the same. ▮

32. CURVES.

In definition 27.20, a curve was defined to be any continuous image of the unit interval space, [0, 1]. The most useful curves are the curves which lie in Hausdorff spaces; these will be shown to be exactly the non-empty, compact, connected, locally connected, metrizable spaces. First, however, two very special types of curves; namely, the "arc" and the "simple closed curve" will be characterized. These two characterization theorems, along with the characterization of the curve in a Hausdorff space, are among the highwater marks of non-algebraic methods in topology. With just compactness, connectedness and metrizability considerations these ubiquitous spaces of modern mathematics can be completely characterized.

The Arc

32.1 Definition. A topological space is called an *arc* if and only if it is homeomorphic to the unit interval subspace, [0, 1], of E^1.

32.2 Theorem. *If A is an arc, then A is a compact, connected, metrizable space with exactly two non-cut points.*

Proof: By theorem 25.1, [0, 1] is a connected subspace of E^1; by theorem 20.9, [0, 1] is a metrizable space, and by theorem 30.18, [0, 1] is a compact space. Thus since connectedness, compactness and metrizability are topological invariants, any arc is connected, compact and metrizable. By corollary 25.5, the open interval $\{x \mid 0 < x < 1\}$ is connected. By theorem 24.19, any set "between" a connected set and its closure is connected. Hence, $\{x \mid 0 \leq x < 1\}$ and $\{x \mid 0 < x \leq 1\}$ are connected. This means that 0 and 1 are non-cut points of [0, 1]. Now let $0 < p < 1$. If $M = \{x \mid 0 \leq x < p\}$ and $N = \{x \mid p < x \leq 1\}$, then $[0, 1] \sim \{p\} = M \cup N$ separation and p is a cut point of [0, 1]. Since cut points and non-cut points are topological invariants, any arc has exactly two non-cut points. ▮

The next several definitions and lemmas will lead to the converse of the previous theorem; namely, that any compact, connected metrizable space S with exactly two non-cut points is an arc. The main step will be to establish a linear (simple) ordering on S which is associated with the topology on S in exactly the same way that the linear ordering on $[0, 1]$ is associated with the usual topology for $[0, 1]$. Then the final homeomorphism will be established as an order isomorphism. It is to be recalled that a linearly ordered set is a pair $\{L, <*\}$, where L is a set, and $<*$ is an order relation on L which is (1) irreflexive: $x <* x$ for no x in L, (2) asymmetric: $x <* y$ implies $y \not<* x$, and (3) transitive: $x <* y$ and $y <* z$ implies $x <* z$.

32.3 Definition. Let p and q be points of a connected space S. A point x is said to *separate p and q in S* if and only if there exists a separation $P_x \cup Q_x$ of $S \sim \{x\}$ such that $p \in P_x$ and $q \in Q_x$. Thus if x separates p and q in S, x must be a cut point of S. Further, $E(p, q)$ is defined to be $\{x \mid x = p$, or $x = q$, or x separates p and q in $S\}$.

32.4 Lemma. *Let S be a connected space; let p and q be two distinct points of S; let a and b be two distinct points of $E(p, q) \sim \{p, q\}$. Let $P_a \cup Q_a$ be any separation of $S \sim \{a\}$ such that $p \in P_a$ and $q \in Q_a$, and let $P_b \cup Q_b$ be any separation of $S \sim \{b\}$ such that $p \in P_b$ and $q \in Q_b$. Then $P_a \subsetneq P_b$ or $P_b \subsetneq P_a$.*

Proof: Since $S \sim \{a\} = P_a \cup Q_a$ and $P_a \cap Q_a = \emptyset$, and since $b \neq a$, $b \in P_a$ or $b \in Q_a$, but not both. (a) Let $b \in P_a$. By corollary 26.26, $Q_a \cup \{a\}$ is a connected subset of S. Further, since $b \neq a$ and $b \in P_a$, $b \notin Q_a \cup \{a\}$. Hence $Q_a \cup \{a\} \subseteq P_b \cup Q_b$. Since $q \in Q_a \cup \{a\}$ and $q \in Q_b$, the connected set $Q_a \cup \{a\} \subseteq Q_b$, by theorem 24.17. Hence $Q_a \cup \{a\} \cap P_b \cup \{b\} = \emptyset$. Since $Q_a \cup \{c\} \cup P_a = S$, $P_b \cup \{b\} \subseteq P_a$. This means, since $b \notin P_b$, that $P_b \subsetneq P_a$. (b) Let $b \in Q_a$. Since $Q_a \cap P_a = \emptyset$ and $b \neq a$, $b \notin P_a \cup \{a\}$. Hence, since $S \sim \{b\} = P_b \cup Q_b$, $P_a \cup \{a\} \subseteq P_b \cup Q_b$. As above, since $P_a \cup \{a\}$ is connected and $p \in P_b \cap (P_a \cup \{a\})$, $P_a \cup \{a\} \subseteq P_b$. Since $a \notin P_a$, $P_a \subsetneq P_b$. ∎

32.5 Corollary. *If a and b are any two distinct points of $E(p, q) \sim \{p, q\}$, then $P_a \subsetneq P_b$ is equivalent to $a \in P_b$, where P_a and P_b are as defined in the previous theorem.*

Proof: In the proof of the previous theorem, it was established that $b \in P_a$ implied that $a \in Q_b$. It follows from this then that if $a \notin Q_b$, then $b \notin P_a$. Hence, if $a \notin Q_b$, $b \in Q_a$. It was also shown that $b \in Q_a$ implied that $P_a \subsetneq P_b$. Thus it follows that if $a \in P_b$, then $a \notin Q_b$, and so $P_a \subsetneq P_b$. Conversely, let $P_a \subsetneq P_b$. Then $P_b \not\subseteq P_a$. From the proof of the previous theorem, this means that $b \notin P_a$. Thus $b \in Q_a$. This was proved to imply that $a \in P_b$. ∎

32.6 Definition. Let S be a connected space. Let p and q be distinct points of S. A relation $<*$ on $E(p, q)$ (definition 32.3) is defined as follows.

$<* = \{(x, y) \mid (x = p$ and $y \neq p)$ or $(y = q$ and $x \neq q)$ or $(P_x \subsetneq P_y$, for $p \neq x \neq q$ and $p \neq y \neq q)\}$, where of course $P_x \cup Q_x$ is any separation of $S \sim \{x\}$ such that $p \in P_x$ and $q \in Q_x$ and $P_y \cup Q_y$ is any separation of $S \sim \{y\}$ such that $p \in P_y$ and $q \in Q_y$.

32.7 Lemma. *$<*$ is a linear (simple) order relation on $E(p, q)$ in the connected space S.*

Proof: (a) Let $(x, y) \in <*$. By definition of $<*$, $x \neq q$ and $y \neq p$. Hence if $x = p$, $y \neq p$ and if $y = q$, then $x \neq q$. So let $x \neq p$ and $y \neq q$. Then $(x, y) \in <*$ implies $P_x \subsetneq P_y$. This is a contradiction if $x = y$. Hence $<*$ is irreflexive. (b) Let $(x, y) \in <*$. Then $x \neq q$ and $y \neq p$ from the definition of $<*$. If $x = p$, then $(y, x) \notin <*$. If $y = q$, then $(y, x) \notin <*$. So, let $x \neq p$ and $y \neq q$. $(x, y) \in <*$ implies, then, that $P_x \subsetneq P_y$. If (y, x) were also in $<*$ then also $P_y \subsetneq P_x$. This is a contradiction. Hence $<*$ is asymmetric. (c) Let (x, y) and (y, z) be in $<*$. Again $x \neq q \neq y$ and $y \neq p \neq z$. So let $x = p$, then $(x, z) \in <*$. Also, let $z = q$; then $(x, z) \in <*$. Now let $x \neq p$ and $z \neq q$. Then x, y and z are in $E(p, q) \sim \{p, q\}$. Since $(x, y) \in <*$ and $(y, z) \in <*$, $P_x \subsetneq P_y$ and $P_y \subsetneq P_z$. Therefore, $P_x \subsetneq P_z$ and $x <* z$. Thus $<*$ is transitive. (d) Let x and y be any two distinct points of $E(p, q)$. If $x = p$, $(x, y) \in <*$; if $y = q$, $(x, y) \in <*$. Let $q \neq x \neq p$ and $p \neq y \neq q$. By lemma 32.4, $P_x \subsetneq P_y$ or $P_y \subsetneq P_x$. Hence, $x <* y$ or $y <* x$. ∎

Thus in any connected space S, each two-point set $\{p, q\}$ determines a linearly ordered subset $\{E(p, q), <*\}$.

32.8 Lemma. *Let S be a compact, connected T_1-space with exactly two non-cut points, p and q. Then, $S = E(p, q)$.*

Proof: Let $x \in S$ and $x \notin E(p, q)$. Then $p \neq x \neq q$. Hence x is a cut point of S. So $S \sim \{x\}$ is not connected. Since x does not separate p and q in S, there exists a separation $A \cup B$ of $S \sim \{x\}$ such that p and q are both in A. Since S has no non-cut points but p and q, this is a contradiction by corollary 28.63. Thus every point of $S \sim \{p, q\}$ separates p and q in S, and so $S = E(p, q)$. ∎

The last lemma established then that any compact, connected T_1-space with exactly two non-cut points is linearly ordered by $<*$.

32.9 Definition. Let S be a set and $<$ any linear order relation on S. The topology for S determined by the subbase $\{A \mid (A \subseteq S)$ and $(A = \{x \mid x < b\}$ or $A = \{x \mid x > a\}$ for a and b in $S)\}$ is called the *order topology* for S determined by $<$.

32.10 Lemma. *Let S be any set and $<$ any linear order relation on S. The order topology for S determined by $<$ is Hausdorff.*

Proof: Exercise.

32.11 Theorem. *Let $\{S, \mathfrak{I}\}$ be a compact, connected, Hausdorff space with exactly two non-cut points. Then the original topology $\mathfrak{I}$ on S is an order topology for S.*

Proof: By lemmas 32.7 and 32.8, S can be linearly ordered by the relation $<*$ of definition 32.6. $S = E(p, q)$, for p and q the two non-cut points of S. Let $o\text{-}\mathfrak{I}$ denote the order topology for $E(p, q)$ determined by $<*$. Let B be a base element determined by the defining subbase for the order topology. $B \subseteq S = E(p, q)$, $B = \{x \mid x <* b \text{ for } b \in S\}$, $B = \{x \mid a <* x \text{ for } a \in S\}$ or $B = \{x \mid a <* x <* b \text{ for } a \in S \text{ and } b \in S\}$. Now $S \in \mathfrak{I}$. If $p \neq a \neq q$ and $p \neq b \neq q$, then by definition of $<*$ and by corollary 32.5, $\{x \mid x <* b\} = P_b$, $\{x \mid a <* x <* b\} = P_b \cap Q_a$ and $\{x \mid a <* x\} = Q_a$. Since $\{S, \mathfrak{I}\}$ is a T_1-space, for $s \in S$, $\{s\}$ is closed. Hence if $p \neq s \neq q$, $S \sim \{s\} = P_s \cup Q_s$ separation. Now, P_s and Q_s are open in the subspace determined by $S \sim \{s\}$, but $S \sim \{s\}$ is open in $\{S, \mathfrak{I}\}$. Hence, by definition of the relative topology, P_s and Q_s are open in $\{S, \mathfrak{I}\}$. It follows now that if $a = p$ or $a = q$ or $b = p$ or $b = q$, $B \in \mathfrak{I}$. Thus each B in the base for the order topology, determined by the defining subbase, is open in $\{S, \mathfrak{I}\}$. Thus $o\text{-}\mathfrak{I} \subseteq \mathfrak{I}$. Since $\{S, \mathfrak{I}\}$ is a compact, Hausdorff space, by hypothesis, and since, by lemma 32.10, $o\text{-}\mathfrak{I}$ is Hausdorff, $o\text{-}\mathfrak{I} = \mathfrak{I}$ by theorem 29.10. ▌

Thus the topology on any compact, connected Hausdorff space, S, which has exactly two non-cut points has been proved to be an order topology. This means that any order-preserving isomorphism from S onto a subset of the reals will be a homeomorphism. In this manner a homeomorphism between S and the unit interval will be established. The next two theorems will give characterizations of the natural order relations on the rational numbers and on the real numbers.

32.12 Theorem. *If $\{D, <*\}$ is a countable, linearly ordered set and if $<*$ has the following two properties: (1) $<*$ determines no first and no last element in D, and (2) for any two (distinct) elements a and b in D, such that $a <* b$, there is at least one other element c such that $a <* c <* b$; then there exists a 1:1 order-preserving function from D onto the rational numbers in the open interval* (0, 1).

Proof: Since both D and the set Q of rationals in (0, 1) are countable, D can be represented as $\{d_1, d_2, \ldots, d_n, \ldots\}$, where $d_i \neq d_j$ for $i \neq j$, and Q can be represented as $\{r_1, r_2, \ldots, r_n, \ldots\}$, where $r_i \neq r_j$ for $i \neq j$. The given linear ordering on D will be denoted, as in the hypothesis, by $<*$. The natural ordering on the set of all natural numbers and the natural ordering on the set Q of rational numbers in (0, 1) will both be denoted by $<$.

A. A 1:1 function f from D into Q is defined. Let $f(d_1) = r_1$. Let $f(d_2) = r_{i_2}$, where i_2 is the smallest natural number in the following set $\{n \mid r_n < r_1$, if $d_2 <* d_1$; and $r_1 < r_n$, if $d_1 <* d_2\}$. This set is not empty since the natural ordering on Q does not determine a first or a last element. Thus if $d_1 <* d_2, f(d_1) < f(d_2)$; and if $d_2 <* d_1, f(d_2) < f(d_1)$. Assume, now, that $f(d_1), f(d_2), \ldots, f(d_{k-1})$ have all been defined in Q so that $f(d_i) < f(d_j)$, if $d_i <* d_j$ for $1 \leq i, j \leq k - 1$. Consider d_k. Since D is linearly ordered by $<*$, the subset $\{d_1, \ldots, d_{k-1}\}$ is also linearly ordered by $<*$. Let $d_{j_1} <* d_{j_2} <* \cdots <* d_{j_{k-1}}$ be the linear ordering on $\{d_1, d_2, \ldots, d_{k-1}\}$ induced by $<*$ on D. If $d_k <* d_{j_1}$, then $d_k <* d_{j_i}$ for all $i = 1, 2, \ldots, k - 1$. Since Q has no first element, there is a rational number r in (0, 1) such that $r < f(d_{j_1}) < f(d_{j_2}) < \cdots < f(d_{j_{k-1}})$. Hence if $A = \{t \mid r_t < f(d_{j_1})\}$, then $A \neq \emptyset$. Let q be the smallest natural number in A. Define $f(d_k) = r_q$. Similarly, if $d_{j_{k-1}} <* d_k$, then $d_{j_i} <* d_k$ for $i = 1, \ldots, k - 1$. Since Q has no last number, $\{s \mid f(d_{j_{k-1}}) < r_s\} \neq \emptyset$. Let m be the smallest natural number in this set. Define $f(d_k) = r_m$. Then $f(d_{j_1}) < \cdots < f(d_k)$. Lastly, for some one $i = 1, 2, \ldots, k - 2$, let $d_{j_i} <* d_k <* d_{j_{i+1}}$. Since between any two rationals lies a third rational, $\{n \mid f(d_{j_i}) < r_n < f(d_{j_{i+1}})\} \neq \emptyset$. Let p be the smallest natural number in this set. Define $f(d_k) = r_p$. Thus f has been defined by induction on all of D in such a way that (1) if $d_s <* d_t$, then $f(d_s) < f(d_t)$; and (2) for every natural number s, i_s, where $f(d_s) = r_{i_s}$, is the smallest subscript in the given listing $\{r_1, r_2, \ldots, r_n, \ldots\}$ such that f preserves order.

B. Next it is shown that f is onto. r_1 is in the range of f since $f(d_1) = r_1$. Let $r_1, r_2, \ldots, r_{k-1}$ be in the range of f for some natural number $k \geq 2$. Then $\{m \mid \{r_1, r_2, \ldots, r_{k-1}\} \subseteq \{f(d_1), \ldots, f(d_m)\}\} \neq \emptyset$. Let q be the smallest natural number in this set. $\{r_1, \ldots, r_{k-1}\} \subseteq \{f(d_1), \ldots, f(d_q)\}$. If $r_k \in \{f(d_1), \ldots, f(d_q)\}$ then, of course, r_k is in the range of f. Assume, then, that $r_k \notin \{f(d_1), \ldots, f(d_q)\}$. There are now three cases to consider: (1) $r_k < f(d_j)$ for all $j = 1, \ldots, q$, (2) $r_k > f(d_j)$ for all $j = 1, \ldots, q$, and (3) $f(d_i) < r_k < f(d_j)$ for some i, j such that $1 \leq i, j \leq q$. The proofs for (1) and (2) are exactly analogous; hence, the details for the proof of (2) will not be given. Also, only the parts of the proof of (3) which differ from the corresponding steps in the proof of (1) will be given. Let, then, $r_k < f(d_j)$ for all $j = 1, \ldots, q$. Since D has no first element $\{m \mid d_{q+m} <* d_j$ for all $j = 1, \ldots, q\} \neq \emptyset$. Let m^* be the smallest natural number in this set. Then $d_{q+m^*} <* d_j$ for all $j = 1, \ldots, q$. Also, for each natural number t such that $1 \leq t < m^*$, there is at least one natural number, j, such that $d_j < d_{q+t}$ and $1 \leq j \leq q$. By assumption, $f(d_j) \neq r_k$ for all $j = 1, \ldots, q$. Further, $f(d_{q+t}) \neq r_k$ for $1 \leq t < m^*$, since f preserves order. Now, the domain of f is D; hence, $f(d_{q+m^*})$ is defined as a rational number. Let $f(d_{q+m^*}) = r_p$. Since f is order-preserving, f is 1:1. Further, by definition of q, $\{r_1, \ldots, r_{k-1}\} \subseteq \{f(d_1), \ldots, f(d_q)\}$. Hence, $k - 1 < p$. If $k < p$, then the definition of f is contradicted. Hence, $f(d_{q+m^*}) = r_k$, and so r_k is in the range of f. The proof of (2) is exactly analogous but depends on the fact that D has no last element instead of the fact that D has no first element. The proof of (3) is also similar. Let $\{d_1, d_2, \ldots, d_q\}$ and k be as defined in the proof of (1). Let $f(d_i) < r_k < f(d_j)$ for some natural numbers i and j such that $1 \leq i, j \leq q$. The set $\{f(d_1), f(d_2), \ldots, f(d_q)\}$ is linearly ordered by the natural ordering on the rationals. Let $\{\rho_1, \rho_2, \ldots, \rho_q\}$ denote the set $\{f(d_1), f(d_2), \ldots, f(d_q)\}$, where $\rho_1 < \rho_2 < \cdots < \rho_q$. There is then a smallest natural number $t^* \neq 1$ such that $r_k < \rho_{t^*}$. Hence $\rho_{t^*-1} < r_k < \rho_{t^*}$. By hypothesis, $\{n \mid f^{-1}(\rho_{t^*-1}) <_* d_n <_* f^{-1}(\rho_{t^*})\} \neq \emptyset$. Let n^* be the smallest natural number in this set. Since $r_k \notin \{f(d_1), f(d_2), \ldots, f(d_q)\}$, if $j \leq q$, then $f(d_j) \neq r_k$. Further, by definition of n^*, if $q < j < n^*$, $f(d_j) \neq r_k$ since f preserves order. Now $f(d_{n^*})$ is defined, since the domain of f is D. Let $f(d_{n^*}) = r_p$. Since $\{r_1, \ldots, r_{k-1}\} \subseteq \{f(d_1), \ldots, f(d_q)\}$, $p \geq k$. If $p > k$, the definition of f is again contradicted as it was in the proof of (1). Thus if $r_1, r_2, \ldots, r_{k-1}$ are in the range of f, r_k is also. Hence the range of f is Q. Thus a 1:1 order-preserving function from D onto Q has been established. ∎

Theorem 32.12 gives a characterization of the usual ordering on the rationals. The next step in the characterization of the arc is to characterize the ordering on the real numbers.

32.13 Definition. In any linearly ordered set, $\{L, <\}$, cuts are defined. A *cut* is an ordered pair (A, B) of subsets of L such that (1) $L = A \cup B$, (2) $A \neq \emptyset \neq B$, and (3) $x \in A$ and $y \in B$ implies that $x < y$. There are three types of cuts. A cut (A, B) is a *jump* if and only if A has a last element and B has a first element. A cut (A, B) is called a *lacuna* or *gap* if and only if A has no last element and B has no first element. A cut is called a *filled cut* if and only if A has a last element and B has no first element, or A has no last element and B has a first element.

EXERCISE 1. Give examples of cuts in the integers, rationals or reals which are (1) jumps, (2) gaps, and (3) filled cuts.

32.14 Definition. A linearly ordered set $\{L, <\}$ with no jumps is called *order-dense in itself*, and a linearly ordered set with neither jumps nor gaps is called *order-connected*.

32.15 Lemma. *A linearly ordered set $\{L, <\}$ is order-dense in itself if and only if for each two elements α and β in L, there exists at least one element γ in L such that $\alpha < \gamma < \beta$.*

Proof: Exercise.

32.16 Definition. Let $\{L, <\}$ be a linearly ordered set and let D be a subset of L. D is called *order-dense in* $\{L, <\}$ if and only if for each two elements α and β in L, there exists at least one element δ of D such that $\alpha < \delta < \beta$.

EXERCISE 2. Let $\{L, <\}$ be a linearly ordered set and o-$\mathfrak{J}$ the order topology. Prove or disprove: a subset D of L is dense in the space $\{L, o\text{-}\mathfrak{J}\}$ if and only if D is order-dense in $\{L, <\}$.

32.17 Theorem. *Let $\{L, <\}$ be a linearly ordered set and let o-$\mathfrak{J}$ be the order topology for L. $\{L, o\text{-}\mathfrak{J}\}$ is a connected space if and only if $\{L, <\}$ is order-connected.*

Proof: A. Let $\{L, o\text{-}\mathfrak{J}\}$ be connected and let (A, B) be a cut in $\{L, <\}$. Assume first that (A, B) is a lacuna or gap. By definition of the order topology, $\{x \mid x < z \text{ for } x, z \in L\}$ is open in $\{L, o\text{-}\mathfrak{J}\}$. Let $\alpha \in A$. Since A has no last element, then there exists z such that $z \in A$ and $\alpha < z$. Hence every point of A is interior and A is open. A similar procedure establishes that B is open. Hence $\{L, o\text{-}\mathfrak{J}\}$ is not connected. This is a contradiction, so L has no gaps. Assume next that (A, B) is a jump. Let α be the last point in A and β the first point in B. By definition of the order topology, $\{x \mid x < \beta\}$ and $\{x \mid x > \alpha\}$ are both open in $\{L, o\text{-}\mathfrak{J}\}$. Since $A = \{x \mid x < \beta\}$ and $B = \{x \mid x > \alpha\}$, $\{L, o\text{-}\mathfrak{J}\}$ is not connected. This is a contradiction; hence, $\{L, <\}$ has no jumps.

B. Let $\{L, <\}$ be order-connected. Assume that $\{L, o\text{-}\mathfrak{J}\}$ is not connected and $A \cup B$ is a separation of $\{L, o\text{-}\mathfrak{J}\}$. Let G be an non-empty open interval in A. Since $B \neq \emptyset$, G has an upper bound in B or a lower bound in B. Let G have an upper bound in B. Let $M = \{y \mid (\exists b)\,(b \in B \text{ and } b \text{ is an upper bound of } G \text{ and } y > b)\}$. Let H be the complement of M in L. Thus $G \subseteq H$ and $H \cup M = L$. Further, $H = \{y \mid \textit{not}\ (\exists b)\,(b \in B \text{ and } b \text{ is an upper bound of } G \text{ and } y > b)\} = \{y \mid (\forall b)\,(b \in B \text{ and } b \text{ an upper bound of } G \text{ imply } y \not> b)\} = \{y \mid (\forall b)\,(b \in B \text{ and } b \text{ an upper bound of } G \text{ imply } y \leq b)\}$. Now let $x \in H$ and $y \in M$. By definition of M, $(\exists b^*)\,(b^* \in B, b^* \text{ is an upper bound of } G \text{ and } y > b^*)$. By definition of H, $x \leq b^*$. Hence $x < y$ and (H, M) is a cut in $\{L, <\}$. Since $\{L, <\}$ is order-connected, H has a last element and M has no first element, or M has a first element and H has no last element. M, however, can have no first element; for, let m be any element in M. Then, by definition of M, there exists b in B such that b is an upper bound of G and $b < m$. Since $\{L, <\}$ is order-connected, it has no jumps. Hence, there exists y, $b < y < m$. This means that $y \in M$ and m is not the first element in M. H, then, must have a last element, λ. Since (H, M) is a cut, $M \neq \emptyset$. Hence there exists an element y in M such that $\lambda < y$. Now, by definition of M, $(\exists b)\,(b \in B, b \text{ is an upper bound of } G \text{ and } b < y)$. Since $\lambda \in H$, $\lambda \leq b$, by definition of H. Hence, every interval neighborhood of λ in the space $\{L, o\text{-}\mathfrak{J}\}$ contains a point of B, and so $\lambda \in \overline{B} = B$. Now since $\lambda \in H$ and $\lambda \in B$, and since $G \subseteq A$ and $A \cap B = \emptyset$, $\lambda \notin G$. Further, since $G \neq \emptyset$, there exists a point $z \in G$. $z \neq \lambda$. Since $G \subseteq H$, $z \in H$. Hence, $z < \lambda$, by definition of λ. Assume now that $\{x \mid z < x < \lambda\} \subseteq B$. Then z is an upper bound of G and $\lambda \in M$. This is a contradiction, since $\lambda \in H$ and $H \cap M = \emptyset$. Therefore $(\exists x)\,(z < x < \lambda \text{ and } x \in A)$. Hence $\lambda \in \overline{A} = A$. $\lambda \in A \cap B \neq \emptyset$. This also is a contradiction. Hence, $\{L, o\text{-}\mathfrak{J}\}$ is a connected space. If G has no upper bound in B, then it must have a lower bound in B and the proof is exactly analogous. ∎

32.18 Theorem. *Any compact connected metrizable space* $\{S, \mathfrak{J}\}$ *with exactly two non-cut points is an order-connected set relative to the ordering which determines the topology. Further, there exists a denumerable subset D which is order-dense in L.*

Proof: By lemma 32.8, $\{S, \mathfrak{J}\}$ is an $E(p, q)$, where p and q are the two non-cut points. Hence $\mathfrak{J}$ is the order-topology defined from the linear order relation $<*$ of definition 32.6. By the previous theorem, 32.17, $\{S, <*\}$ is order-connected. Further, by theorems 30.2 and 30.3, $\{S, \mathfrak{J}\}$ is separable. Hence, $\{S, \mathfrak{J}\}$ has a countable subset D which is dense in the space $\{S, \mathfrak{J}\}$. Since $\{S, <*\}$ is order-connected, there are no jumps. Hence, by definition of the order topology, between any two points of S lies a point of D. D is then order-dense in $\{S, <*\}$. ▮

The next theorem will use order-connectedness and the order-denseness of a countable subset to help characterize the ordered set of real numbers in the usual open interval (0, 1).

32.19 Theorem. *If* $\{L, <*\}$ *is a non-empty linearly ordered set with the following properties: (1)* $<*$ *determines no first and no last element on L, (2)* $<*$ *is order-connected, and (3) there exists a countable subset D which is order-dense in* $\{L, <*\}$*; then* $\{L, <*\}$ *is order-isomorphic to* $\{x \mid x \text{ is real and } 0 < x < 1\}$, *i.e., to* (0, 1), *with the usual ordering.*

Proof: A. First a function f^* from $\{L, <*\}$ into (0, 1) is defined. By theorem 32.12, there is a 1:1 order-preserving function, f, from the order-dense subset $\{D, <*\}$ of $\{L, <*\}$ onto the set Q of rational numbers in (0, 1), with the usual ordering. (*Note:* $<*$ will be used ambiguously to denote the given order relation on L and also its restriction to D.) Thus for every element d in D, $f(d)$ is a unique rational number in (0, 1). Now, let $\alpha \in L \sim D$, let $B'_\alpha = \{y \text{ in } L \mid \alpha \leq^* y\}$ and let $A'_\alpha = \{y \text{ in } L \mid y <* \alpha\}$. Let $H^\alpha = \{t \text{ in } (0, 1) \mid r \in f[B'_\alpha \cap D] \Rightarrow t < r\}$ and let $M^\alpha = (0, 1) \sim H^\alpha$. Since f is order-preserving and D is order-dense, $H^\alpha \neq \emptyset \neq M^\alpha$. Now let $t_1 \in H^\alpha$ and $t_2 \in M^\alpha$. Since $t_2 \notin H^\alpha$, $(\exists r^*)$ $(r^* \in f[B'_\alpha \cap D]$ and $r^* \leq t_2)$. Since $t_1 \in H^\alpha$, $t_1 < r^*$. Hence $t_1 < t_2$. Also for any t in (0, 1), $(\exists r)\,(r \in f[B'_\alpha \cap D]$ and $r \leq t)$ or *not* $(\exists r)\,(r \in f[B'_\alpha \cap D]$ and $r \leq t)$. This last disjunction is equivalent to $(\exists r)\,(r \in f[B'_\alpha \cap D]$ and $r \leq t)$ or $(\forall r)\,(r \in f[B'_\alpha \cap D] \Rightarrow r < t)$. Thus $t \in H^\alpha$ or $t \in M^\alpha$. Hence (H^α, M^α) is a cut in (0, 1). Since (0, 1) is order-connected, H^α has a last element or M^α has a first element. Let, now, m be any element in M^α. By definition of M^α, $(\exists r)\,(r \in f[B'_\alpha \cap D]$ and $r \leq m)$. Consider $f^{-1}(r)$ in $B'_\alpha \cap D$. By definition of B'_α, $\alpha <* f^{-1}(r)$. Since D is dense in $\{L, <*\}$, $(\exists d)\,(d \in D \text{ and } \alpha <* d <* f^{-1}(r))$. $d \in B'_\alpha \cap D$, by definition of B'_α. Hence, $f(d) \in f[B'_\alpha \cap D]$ and $f(d) < r$, by definition of f. This means that $f(d) < m$. Since $f(d) \in f[B'_\alpha \cap D]$, $f(d) \notin H^\alpha$. Hence, $f(d) \in M^\alpha$ and m is not the first element of M^α. Thus H^α has a last element β and $H^\alpha = \{t \text{ in } (0, 1) \mid t \leq \beta\}$. Define $f^*(\alpha) = \beta$ and for d in D let $f^*(d) = f(d)$.

B. Secondly, it is shown that f^* is order-preserving, and hence 1:1. First let $d \in D$, let $\alpha \in L \sim D$ and let $\alpha <_* d$. $d \in B'_\alpha \cap D$ by definition, above, of B'_α. Hence $f(d) \in f[B'_\alpha \cap D]$, and so $f(d) \in M^\alpha$, as defined above in part A. Now by definition of f^*, $f^*(\alpha)$ is the last element of H^α. Hence, $f^*(\alpha) < f(d) = f^*(d)$. Similarly, if $d \in D$, $\alpha \in L \sim D$ and $d <_* \alpha$, then $f(d) < r$ for all r in $f[B'_\alpha \cap D]$, by definition of B'_α and f. Hence, $f(d) \in H^\alpha$, by definition of H^α. Since $f^*(\alpha)$ is the last element in H^α, $f^*(d) = f(d) < f^*(\alpha)$. Lastly, let α_1 and α_2 both be in $L \sim D$ and let $\alpha_1 <_* \alpha_2$. Since D is order-dense in $\{L, <_*\}$, $(\exists d)$ $(d \in D$ and $\alpha_1 <_* d <_* \alpha_2)$. Thus, by what was just proved above, $f^*(\alpha_1) < f^*(d) < f^*(\alpha_2)$. Therefore, $f^*(\alpha_1) < f^*(\alpha_2)$ and f^* is order-preserving and 1:1.

C. Lastly, it is shown that f^* is onto. Let t^* be any real number in (0, 1). If t^* is rational, then t^* is in the range of f and hence in the range of f^*. If t^* is irrational, let $A_{t^*} = \{x \text{ in } (0, 1) \mid x \leq t^*\}$ and let $B_{t^*} = \{x \text{ in } (0, 1) \mid t^* < x\}$. $Q = (A_{t^*} \cap Q) \cup (B_{t^*} \cap Q)$, where Q is the set of rationals in (0, 1). Hence $D = f^{-1}[A_{t^*} \cap Q] \cup f^{-1}[B_{t^*} \cap Q]$ in L. Let $G_\gamma = \{y \mid d \in f^{-1}[A_{t^*} \cap Q]$ implies $d <_* y\}$ and let $F_\gamma = L \sim G_\gamma$. Since D is order-dense and f is order-preserving, $F_\gamma \neq \emptyset \neq G_\gamma$. If $y_1 \in F_\gamma$, then $y_1 \notin G_\gamma$. Hence, $(\exists \tilde{d})$ $(\tilde{d} \in f^{-1}[A_{t^*} \cap Q]$ and $\tilde{d} \not<_* y_1)$. Hence $y_1 \leq_* \tilde{d}$. Now let $y_2 \in G_\gamma$. By definition of G_γ, $\tilde{d} <_* y_2$. Hence $y_1 <_* y_2$, and (F_γ, G_γ) is a cut in $\{L, <_*\}$. Since $\{L, <_*\}$ is order-connected, F_γ has a last element, or G_γ has a first element. Denote this element by γ. Assume first that $f^*(\gamma) < t^*$. Since Q is order-dense in (0, 1), $(\exists r)$ $(f^*(\gamma) < r < t^*)$. Hence $r \in A_{t^*} \cap Q$ and $f^{-1}(r) \in f^{-1}[A_{t^*} \cap Q]$ and $\gamma <_* f^{-1}(r)$. Therefore, $\gamma \notin G_\gamma$, and so $\gamma \in F_\gamma$. Further, since $f^{-1}(r) \in f^{-1}[A_{t^*} \cap Q]$, $f^{-1}(r) \notin G_\gamma$ and so $f^{-1}(r) \in F_\gamma$. Thus γ is not the last element of F_γ. This contradicts the definition of γ. Hence, $t^* \leq f^*(\gamma)$. Assume, next, that $t^* < f^*(\gamma)$. Again, since Q is order-dense in (0, 1), $(\exists \tilde{r})$ $\big(\tilde{r} \in Q$ and $t^* < \tilde{r} < f^*(\gamma)\big)$. This means that if $d \in f^{-1}[A_{t^*} \cap D]$, $f(d) \in A_{t^*}$, and hence $f(d) \leq t^*$. Thus $f(d) < \tilde{r} < f^*(\gamma)$, and so $d <_* f^{-1}(\tilde{r}) <_* \gamma$. This means that $f^{-1}(\tilde{r})$ and γ are both in G_γ. Thus γ is in G_γ but is not the first element of G_γ. This is a contradiction. Hence, $f^*(\gamma) = t^*$ and f^* is onto. ▌

The converse of theorem 32.2 now follows.

32.20 Theorem. *Any compact, connected metrizable space,* $\{S, \mathfrak{I}\}$, *with exactly two non-cut points is an arc.*

Proof: By lemmas 32.7 and 32.8, S is $E(p, q)$ (definition 32.3), where p and q are the two non-cut points. The natural linear ordering, $<_*$, on $E(p, q)$, defined in 32.6, determines the topology $\mathfrak{I}$ for S by theorem 32.11, and determines p as the first element and q as the last element. Further, by theorem 32.18, $\{S, <_*\}$ is order-connected and there exists a countable order-dense subset D in $\{S, <_*\}$. Now let $x \in S$ and $x \neq p$. Since D is order-dense in $\{S, <_*\}$, there exists $d \in D$ such that $p <_* d <_* x$. Hence $S \sim \{p\} = E(p, q) \sim \{p\}$ has no first element. Similarly $S \sim \{q\} = E(p, q) \sim \{q\}$ has no last element.

Hence, $S \sim \{p, q\}$ is linearly ordered by the restriction of $<_*$ to $S \sim \{p, q\}$. This restriction will also be denoted by $<_*$. $<_*$ determines no first element and no last element on $S \sim \{p, q\}$. Let $L = S \sim \{p, q\}$. Then $\{L, <_*\}$ is a linearly ordered set with no first and no last element. Further, $D \cap L$ is denumerable and order-dense in $\{L, <_*\}$, since D is order-dense in $\{S, <_*\}$. Also, $\{L, <_*\}$ is order-connected because any jump or gap in $\{L, <_*\}$ would yield a jump or gap in $\{S, <_*\}$. Since $\{S, <_*\}$ is order-connected, this is a contradiction. Thus, $\{L, <_*\}$ is a linearly ordered, order-connected set with no first element, no last element and with a denumerable order-dense subset, D. Hence, by theorem 32.19, $\{L, <_*\}$ is order-isomorphic to the open interval (0, 1) with the usual ordering, $<$. Let h be the 1:1 function from $\{L, <_*\}$ onto (0, 1) which preserves order. Define $h^*: \{S, <_*\} \xrightarrow{\text{onto}} [0, 1]$ as follows: $h^*(p) = 0$, $h^*(q) = 1$ and $h^*(x) = h(x)$ for $p \neq x \neq q$. By definition of the ordering on $\{S, <_*\}$ and [0, 1], h^* is an order-isomorphism from $\{S, <_*\}$ onto [0, 1]. By definition (33.9) of the order topology, h^* is a homeomorphism from $\{S, \mathfrak{I}\}$ onto [0, 1], and $\{S, \mathfrak{I}\}$ is, then, an arc. ∎

The Simple Closed Curve

Thus the arc has been completely characterized topologically as a compact, connected metrizable space with exactly two non-cut points. The same concepts which characterize the arc, namely, compactness, connectedness, metrizability and cut set, also serve to characterize the circumference of the unit circle. The following four lemmas and one theorem will characterize topologically the circumference.

NOTATION: S^1 will denote, throughout, the subspace of E^2, Euclidean 2-space, determined by $\{(x, y) \mid x^2 + y^2 = 1\}$.

32.21 Lemma. *Let (a, b) and (c, d) be two (distinct) points of S^1. $S^1 \sim (\{(a, b)\} \cup \{(c, d)\})$ is not connected.*

Proof: If $a = c$, then $-1 \neq a \neq +1$ and the projection function p_x maps $S \sim (\{(a, b)\} \cup \{(c, d)\})$ continuously onto $\{x \mid -1 \leq x \leq 1\} \sim \{a\}$. By theorem 25.7, $\{x \mid -1 \leq x \leq 1\} \sim \{a\}$ is not connected in E^1, the usual space of reals. Hence, by theorem 24.13, $S^1 \sim (\{(a, b)\} \cup \{(c, d)\})$ is not connected. If $a \neq c$, $S^1 \sim (\{(a, b)\} \cup \{(c, d)\})$ is homeomorphic via a rotation of the plane to $S^1 - (\{(x, y)\} \cup \{(x, z)\})$, where (x, y) and (x, z) are points of S^1. Hence $S^1 \sim (\{(a, b)\} \cup \{(c, d)\})$ is not connected, for (a, b) and (c, d) any two (distinct) points of S^1. ∎

32.22 Lemma. *S^1 is the union of two arcs with only their end points in common and hence is connected.*

Proof: Let A_1 denote the subspace of S^1 determined by $\{(x, y) \text{ in } S^1 \mid x \geq 0\}$. By theorem 30.21, A_1 is compact. Let p_x denote the projection function restricted to A_1. p_x is 1:1 and continuous from A_1 onto $\{x \mid -1 \leq x \leq 1\}$. Hence, by corollary 29.8, A_1 is an arc. Similarly, if A_2 denotes the subspace of S^1 determined by $\{(x, y) \mid x \leq 0\}$, A_2 is an arc. By theorems 32.2 and 24.23, S^1 is then connected. Thus every two-(distinct) point subset of S^1 is a cut set. ∎

32.23 Lemma. *If a space X is the union of two arcs with exactly their end points in common, then X is Hausdorff.*

Proof: Exercise.

32.24 Lemma. *If a space X is the union of two arcs with exactly their end points in common, then X is homeomorphic to* S^1.

Proof: Let $X = B_1 \cup B_2$, where B_1 and B_2 are arcs. Let γ_1 and γ_2 be two homeomorphisms from $[0, 1]$ onto B_1 and B_2 respectively. Then $B_1 \cap B_2 = \{\gamma_1(0), \gamma_1(1)\} = \{\gamma_2(0), \gamma_2(1)\}$. Let h be a homeomorphism from $[0, 1]$ onto the subspace of E^1 determined by $\{x \mid -1 \leq x \leq 1\}$, say, for instance $h(t) = 2t - 1 = x$ for $0 \leq t \leq 1$. Then $h(0) = -1$ and $h(1) = 1$. Again let A_1 be the subspace of S^1 determined by $\{(x, y) \mid x \geq 0\}$, and A_2 that determined by $\{(x, y) \mid x \leq 0\}$. As established in the proof of lemma 32.22, the projection function p_x restricted to A_1 and A_2 yields homeomorphisms g_1 and g_2 from A_1 and A_2 respectively onto $[-1, 1]$. Thus if $f_1 = \gamma_1 \circ h^{-1} \circ g_1$, then f_1 is a homeomorphism from A_1 onto B_1 with $f_1((-1, 0)) = \gamma_1(0)$ and $f_1((1, 0)) = \gamma_1(1)$. Similarly, if $f_2 = \gamma_2 \circ h^{-1} \circ g_2$, then f_2 is a homeomorphism from A_2 onto B_2 such that $f_2((-1, 0)) = \gamma_2(0)$ and $f_2((1, 0)) = \gamma_2(1)$. Now g_1 and g_2 are defined on closed subspaces A_1 and A_2, respectively, of S^1 and they agree on $A_1 \cap A_2 = \{(-1, 0), (1, 0)\}$. Hence, by theorem 9.23, $g_1 \cup g_2$ is continuous from S^1 onto X. By definition, $g_1 \cup g_2$ is 1:1. Since X is Hausdorff, by the previous lemma and since S^1 is compact, $g_1 \cup g_2$ is a homeomorphism by corollary 29.8. ∎

32.25 Definition. A topological space X is called a *simple closed curve* if and only if it is the homeomorphic image of S^1.

32.26 Theorem. *A topological space X is a simple closed curve if and only if it is a compact connected metrizable space with at least two points and with the property that any two-(distinct) point subset is a cut set of X.*

Proof: A. If X is homeomorphic to S^1, then any two (distinct) points disconnect X by lemma 32.21 and corollary 24.14.

B. Let, now, X be a compact connected metrizable space with the property that any two-(distinct) point subset separates X. Let x be any point in X and assume that x is a cut point in X. $X \sim \{x\} = A \cup B$ with $A \cap B = \emptyset$, $A \neq \emptyset \neq B$ and A and B both open in $X \sim \{x\}$. Since $\{x\}$ is closed, A and B are open in X as well as in $X \sim \{x\}$, by definition (9.2) of the relative topology. This means that the respective complements of A and B in X are closed. Thus $A \cup \{x\}$ and $B \cup \{x\}$ are closed, and hence compact subsets of X. By corollary

26.24, $A \cup \{x\}$ and $B \cup \{x\}$ are connected. Thus $A \cup \{x\}$ and $B \cup \{x\}$ are both compact, connected metrizable spaces with more than one point. By theorem 28.61, there exists a non-cut point y in $A \cup \{x\}$ such that $y \neq x$, and a non-cut point z in $B \cup \{x\}$ such that $y \neq z \neq x$. Thus $A \cup \{x\} \sim \{y\}$ and $B \cup \{x\} \sim \{z\}$ are connected subsets of X and both contain $\{x\}$. By theorem 24.23, then, $A \cup \{x\} \sim \{y\} \cup B \cup \{x\} \sim \{z\}$ is connected. Thus $X \sim (\{y\} \cup \{z\})$ is connected, and this is a contradiction. X then has no cut points. Now let x and y again denote any two (distinct) points of X. By hypothesis $X \sim (\{x\} \cup \{y\})$ is not connected. Let $X \sim (\{x\} \cup \{y\}) = C \cup D$, where $C \cap D = \emptyset$ and C and D are both non-empty and open in $X \sim (\{x\} \cup \{y\})$. Again since $\{x\} \cup \{y\}$ is closed in X, $C \cup D$ is open in X. Now, since C and D are open in $C \cup D$, C and D are open in X. Hence, the respective complements $C \cup \{x\} \cup \{y\}$ and $D \cup \{x\} \cup \{y\}$ are closed in X. $C \cup \{x\} \cup \{y\}$ and $D \cup \{x\} \cup \{y\}$ are then compact metrizable spaces. It must now be shown that they are also connected. Consider $C \cup \{x\} \cup \{y\}$. $C \cup D \subseteq C \cup D \cup \{x\}$, and $C \cup D \cup \{x\}$ is connected, by above. Hence, since C and D are non-empty and open in X and disjoint, x is a cut point of $C \cup D \cup \{x\}$. Thus $C \cup D$ is a separation of $(C \cup D \cup \{x\}) \sim \{x\}$. Hence, by corollary 26.24, $C \cup \{x\}$ and $D \cup \{x\}$ are connected in $C \cup D \cup \{x\}$. By theorem 9.27, the relative topologies on $C \cup \{x\}$ and $D \cup \{x\}$ from $C \cup D \cup \{x\}$ are the same as the relative topologies from X. Hence, $C \cup \{x\}$ and $D \cup \{x\}$ are connected in X. Similarly, $C \cup \{y\}$ and $D \cup \{y\}$ are connected in X. This means, again by theorem 24.23, that $C \cup \{x\} \cup \{y\}$ and $D \cup \{x\} \cup \{y\}$ are both connected. Thus $C \cup \{x\} \cup \{y\}$ and $D \cup \{x\} \cup \{y\}$ are both compact, connected metrizable spaces. By theorem 28.61, then, $C \cup \{x\} \cup \{y\}$ and $D \cup \{x\} \cup \{y\}$ both have at least two non-cut points. Assume that there exists a point c in C such that $x \neq c \neq y$ and c is a non-cut point of $C \cup \{x\} \cup \{y\}$; also assume that there exists a point d in D such that $x \neq d \neq y$ and that d is a non-cut point of $D \cup \{x\} \cup \{y\}$. Then $C \cup \{x\} \cup \{y\} \sim \{c\}$ and $D \cup \{x\} \cup \{y\} \sim \{d\}$ are both connected. Since $(C \cup \{x\} \cup \{y\} \sim \{c\}) \cap (D \cup \{x\} \cup \{y\} \sim \{d\}) \neq \emptyset$, then $(C \cup \{x\} \cup \{y\} \sim \{c\}) \cup (D \cup \{x\} \cup \{y\} \sim \{d\})$ is, by theorem 24.23, connected. This is a contradiction, since $(C \cup \{x\} \cup \{y\} \sim \{c\}) \cup (D \cup \{x\} \cup \{y\} \sim \{d\}) = X \sim (\{c\} \cup \{d\})$ which by hypothesis is not connected. Thus c and d as defined above cannot both exist. Hence $C \cup \{x\} \cup \{y\}$ or $D \cup \{x\} \cup \{y\}$ is an arc, by theorem 32.20. Let $C \cup \{x\} \cup \{y\}$ be an arc. x and y must then, by the above, be the two non-cut points of $C \cup \{x\} \cup \{y\}$. Assume now that $D \cup \{x\} \cup \{y\}$ is not an arc. This means that the point d as defined above exists. $x \neq d \neq y$ and d is a non-cut point of $D \cup \{x\} \cup \{y\}$. Let p now be any point of C. p is a cut point, since $C \cup \{x\} \cup \{y\}$ is an arc, and x and y are the end points. $C \cup \{x\} \cup \{y\} \sim \{p\}$ is then the union of two connected subsets M and N one of which contains x and the other of which contains y. Hence, $X \sim (\{p\} \cup \{d\}) = (D \cup \{x\} \cup \{y\} \sim \{d\}) \cup (M \cup N)$ is connected, by theorem 24.23. This is a contradiction. $D \cup \{x\} \cup \{y\}$ must then also be an arc with x and y as the two end points. Thus X is the union of two arcs with exactly their end points in common. By lemma 32.24, X is a simple closed curve. ▮

Arcwise Connectedness

In definition 27.21, a space X was defined to be pathwise connected if and only if for each two points a and b of the space there exists at least one continuous function g with domain the unit interval space, $[0, 1]$, and with range in X, such that $g(0) = a$ and $g(1) = b$. g was called a path between a and b, and the range of g was called a curve between a and b. Related to pathwise connectedness is a property called arcwise connectedness. In general, arcwise connectedness is a stronger property; however, in Hausdorff spaces the two properties are equivalent. Further, the property of arcwise connectedness will be used in the characterization of curves in Hausdorff spaces.

32.27 Definition. A space X is said to be *arcwise connected* if and only if for each two points a and b in X there exists at least one homeomorphism h from the unit interval space, $[0, 1]$, into X such that $h(0) = a$ and $h(1) = b$. The range of h is called an *arc from a to b*.

32.28 Lemma. *If a space X is arcwise connected, then it is pathwise connected.*

Proof: By definition, any arc is a path.

32.29 Example. Let $\{X, \mathfrak{I}\}$ denote the space consisting of the set of real numbers with the smallest T_1-topology, i.e., X and the finite sets are the only closed sets. $\{X, \mathfrak{I}\}$ is pathwise connected but not arcwise connected.

32.30 Theorem. *Arcwise connectedness is a topological invariant.*

Proof: Exercise.

The next theorem contains a sufficient condition that a space be arcwise connected. However, two definitions and two lemmas must first be established.

32.31 Definition. Let X be a space and let a and b be points of X. A bridge (definition 24.21) $(M_1, M_2, \ldots, M_n)$ of subsets of X is called an *irreducible bridge from a to b* if and only if (1) $a \in M_i$ if and only if $i = 1$, and (2) $b \in M_j$ if and only if $j = n$.

The above irreducibility condition is simply a convenient device to locate exactly the two points a and b relative to the sets in the bridge. This is sometimes useful.

32.32 Lemma. *If a and b are points of a connected space X and if $\mathcal{G}$ is an open covering of X, then there is an irreducible bridge of sets of $\mathcal{G}$ from a to b.*

Proof: Let $A = \{x \mid$ there exists at least one irreducible bridge of sets of $\mathcal{G}$ from a to $x\}$. $a \in A$; hence, $A \neq \emptyset$. Next, it will be shown that A is open. Let $y \in A$. By definition of A, there must exist an irreducible bridge $(G_1, \ldots, G_k)$

of sets of $\mathcal{G}$ from a to y. $a \in G_1$; $y \in G_k$. Let $z \in G_k$. If $z \in G_{k-1} \cap G_k$, then $(G_1, G_2, \ldots, G_{k-1})$ is an irreducible bridge from a to z and $z \in A$. If $z \notin G_{k-1}$, then $(G_1, G_2, \ldots, G_k)$ is an irreducible bridge from a to z and $z \in A$. Thus $G_k \subseteq A$ and A is open. Lastly, it will be proved that A is closed. Let p be a limit point of A. Since $\mathcal{G}$ is an open covering of X, p lies in some set, say G_α, of $\mathcal{G}$. Since G_α is open and p is a limit point of A, there exists a point q such that $q \in G_\alpha \cap A$. Since q is in A, there exists an irreducible bridge $(V_1, V_2, \ldots, V_t)$ of sets of $\mathcal{G}$ from a to q, by definition of A. Since $q \in G_\alpha \cap V_t$, $G_\alpha \cap V_t \neq \emptyset$. Hence, $Q = \{m \mid G_\alpha \cap V_m \neq \emptyset\} \neq \emptyset$. Therefore, there exists a smallest natural number m^* in Q. This means that $(V_1, V_2, \ldots, V_{m^*})$ or $(V_1, V_2, \ldots, V_{m^*}, G_\alpha)$ is an irreducible bridge of sets of $\mathcal{G}$ from a to p. Hence $p \in A$ and A is closed. Since X is connected and the non-empty set A is both open and closed, $X = A$. ▌

32.33 Definition. Let X be a space and let $(G_1, G_2, \ldots, G_n)$ be a bridge of subsets of X. The bridge $(V_1, V_2, \ldots, V_k)$ is called a *refinement* of the bridge $(G_1, G_2, \ldots, G_n)$ if and only if for each i, $1 \leq i \leq k$, there exists at least one j, $1 \leq j \leq n$, such that $V_i \subseteq G_j$. The bridge $(V_1, V_2, \ldots, V_t)$ is called a *monotonic refinement* of the bridge $(G_1, G_2, \ldots, G_n)$ if and only if (1) $(V_1, V_2, \ldots, V_t)$ is a refinement of the bridge $(G_1, G_2, \ldots, G_n)$, and (2) if $r < s$ and $V_r \subseteq G_{m^*}$, where m^* is the smallest natural number in $\{m \mid V_r \subseteq G_m\}$, then $V_s \subseteq G_n$ for some natural number n such that $n \geq m^*$.

In the following sketch (figure 25), the bridge $(V_1, V_2, \ldots, V_{23})$ is a refinement of the bridge $(G_1, G_2, G_3, G_4, G_5)$ but it is not a monotonic refinement of the bridge $(G_1, G_2, G_3, G_4, G_5)$. $V_{12} \subseteq G_4$ and $V_{12} \not\subseteq G_j$ for $j < 4$, while $V_{16} \not\subseteq G_j$ for $j \geq 4$.

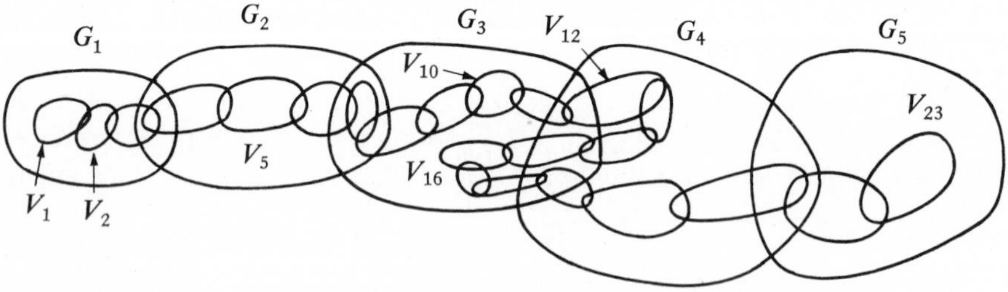

FIGURE 25

32.34 Lemma. *Let X be a space. Let a and b be points of X. Let $\mathcal{B}$ be an irreducible bridge of open connected sets from a to b. Let $\mathcal{G}$ be a set of open subsets of X such that each set in the bridge $\mathcal{B}$ is a union of sets of $\mathcal{G}$. Then there exists a monotonic refinement $\mathcal{M}$ of the bridge $\mathcal{B}$ such that the sets of $\mathcal{M}$ are sets of $\mathcal{G}$ and $\mathcal{M}$ is an irreducible bridge from a to b.*

Proof: Let $\mathcal{B} = (U_1, U_2, \ldots, U_n)$. U_i is open and connected for $1 \leq i \leq n$; $a \in U_1 \sim U_2$; $b \in U_n \sim U_{n-1}$. Let $x_1 \in U_1 \cap U_2$, $x_2 \in U_2 \cap U_3, \ldots, x_i \in U_i \cap U_{i+1}, \ldots, x_n = b \in U_n \sim U_{n-1}$. Let $Q = \{q \mid q$ is a natural number and $q > n$ or there exists a monotonic refinement of $(U_1, U_2, \ldots, U_q)$ which is irreducible from a to x_q and which consists of sets of $\mathcal{G}\}$. First, it will be shown that $1 \in Q$. U_1 is the union of sets in $\mathcal{G}$. Hence, by the previous lemma (32.32), applied to U_1, there is a bridge, $\mathcal{D}_1$, of sets of $\mathcal{G}$ which is irreducible from a to x_1 and such that each set of $\mathcal{D}_1$ is a subset of U_1. Thus $\mathcal{D}_1$ is a monotonic refinement of the bridge (U_1) from a to x_1. Assume now that there is a monotonic refinement $\mathcal{D}_q = (V_1, V_2, \ldots, V_t)$ of the bridge $(U_1, U_2, \ldots, U_q)$ which is irreducible from a to x_q for $q \leq n - 1$ and which consists of sets of $\mathcal{G}$. Consider now x_{q+1} in $U_{q+1} \cap U_{q+2}$ or in U_n. $x_q \in U_{q+1}$ and $x_{q+1} \in U_{q+1}$. U_{q+1} is open and connected and is a union of sets of $\mathcal{G}$. Hence, again by the previous lemma (32.32) applied to U_{q+1}, there is an irreducible bridge $\alpha = (W_1, W_2, \ldots, W_s)$ of sets of $\mathcal{G}$ from x_q to x_{q+1} such that each set in this bridge is a subset of U_{q+1}. Since $x_q \in V_t \cap W_1$, $\{j \mid$ there exists an i such that $V_j \cap W_i \neq \emptyset\}$ is not empty. Let j^* be the smallest natural number in this set. Then $V_j \cap W_i = \emptyset$ for $1 \leq j < j^*$ and $1 \leq i \leq s$. If $V_{j^*} \cap W_s \neq \emptyset$, then $(V_1, V_2, \ldots, V_{j^*}, W_s)$ is a monotonic refinement of $(U_1, \ldots, U_{q+1})$ irreducible from a to x_{q+1}. If $V_{j^*} \cap W_s = \emptyset$, then $\{i \mid V_{j^*} \cap W_j = \emptyset$ for $j \geq i\}$ is not empty. Hence, there is a smallest natural number i^* in this set. $i^* > 1$ by definition of j^*. Hence, $V_{j^*} \cap W_{i^*-1} \neq \emptyset$ and $V_{j^*} \cap W_i = \emptyset$ for $i^* \leq i$. Now consider the finite sequence $(V_1, V_2, \ldots, V_{j^*}, W_{i^*-1}, W_{i^*}, \ldots, W_s)$. By definition of $(V_1, \ldots, V_t)$, $(W_1, \ldots, W_s)$, i^* and j^*, $(V_1, \ldots, V_{j^*}, W_{i^*-1}, W_{i^*}, W_{i^*+1}, \ldots, W_s)$ is a bridge of sets of $\mathcal{G}$. Further, since $(V_1, V_2, \ldots, V_t)$ is irreducible from a to x_q, $a \notin V_j$ for $1 < j \leq t$. Also since $(U_1, \ldots, U_n)$ is a bridge, irreducible from a to b, with $a \in U_1$ and since $W_i \subseteq U_{q+1}$ for $1 \leq i \leq s$, it follows that $a \notin W_i$ for $i \geq i^* - 1$. In addition, since $x_{q+1} \in U_{q+1} \cap U_{q+2}$ or $x_{q+1} \in U_n$ and $(W_1, \ldots, W_s)$ is irreducible from x_q to x_{q+1}, it follows that $x_{q+1} \notin V_j$ for $1 < j \leq j^*$ and $x_{q+1} \notin W_i$ for $i < s$. Hence $(V_1, \ldots, V_{j^*}, W_{i^*-1}, W_{i^*}, W_{i^*+1}, \ldots, W_s)$ is an irreducible bridge from a to x_{q+1}. Lastly, since the sets $V_1, V_2, \ldots, V_{j^*}$ satisfy conditions (1) and (2) of definition 32.33 for a monotonic refinement with respect to $(U_1, U_2, \ldots, U_q)$ and since $W_i \subseteq U_{q+1}$ for $1 \leq i \leq s$, $(V_1, V_2, \ldots, V_{j^*}, W_{i^*-1}, W_{i^*}, W_{i^*+1}, \ldots, W_s)$ is a monotonic refinement of $(U_1, U_2, \ldots, U_{q+1})$. By the induction property for the set of natural numbers, Q is the set of all natural numbers. Hence, $n \in Q$, and so there exists a monotonic refinement $(G_1, G_2, \ldots, G_k)$ of the bridge $(U_1, U_2, \ldots, U_n)$ such that $G_i \in \mathcal{G}$ for $1 \leq i \leq k$, and $(G_1, G_2, \ldots, G_k)$ is irreducible from a to $b = x_n$. ∎

32.35 Theorem. *If X is a locally compact, connected, locally connected, metrizable space, then X is arcwise connected.*

Proof: Let a and b be two (distinct) points of X. A. First a special sequence $(\mathcal{B}^1, \mathcal{B}^2, \ldots, \mathcal{B}^k, \ldots)$ of bridges is defined such that $\mathcal{B}^k$ is irreducible from a to b and $\mathcal{B}^{k+1}$ is a monotonic refinement of $\mathcal{B}^k$ for $k = 1, 2, \ldots$. By definition

(19.10) of a metrizable space, each point x of X has a spherical neighborhood $U_\rho(x, 1/4)$ of radius $1/4$ and diameter $1/2$, where ρ is an admissible metric. By lemma 19.17, the closure $\overline{U}_\rho(x, 1/4)$ has diameter $1/2$. Further, since X is locally compact, $U_\rho(x, 1/4)$ contains an open neighborhood V_x such that $\overline{V}_x$ is compact. Since $\overline{V}_x \subseteq \overline{U}_\rho(x, 1/4)$, the diameter of $\overline{V}_x$ is less than or equal to $1/2$. Also, since X is locally connected, V_x contains a connected open neighborhood, W_x. By theorem 24.19, the closure $\overline{W}_x$ of W_x is also connected. Since $\overline{W}_x \subseteq \overline{V}_x$, $\overline{W}_x$ is thus compact and connected and has diameter less than or equal to $1/2$. Thus each point, x, in X is an element of an open, connected set W_x whose closure $\overline{W}_x$ is compact with diameter < 1. The axiom of choice determines for each x in X one such set W_x. Let $\mathcal{G}_1 = \{W_x \mid x \in X\}$. $\mathcal{G}_1$ is a covering of X and, by lemma 32.32, there is an irreducible bridge $\mathcal{B}^1 = (B_1^1, \ldots, B_{n_1}^1)$ of sets of $\mathcal{G}_1$ from a to b. Thus each set of $\mathcal{B}^1$ is open and connected with compact closure of diameter < 1. Now, assume that $\mathcal{B}^1, \mathcal{B}^2, \ldots, \mathcal{B}^k$, for k a natural number, have all been defined as irreducible bridges from a to b consisting of open, connected sets such that each set in $\mathcal{B}^i$ has compact closure with diameter $< 1/i$. Further, let $\mathcal{B}^i$ be a monotonic refinement of $\mathcal{B}^{i-1}$ for $1 < i \leq k$. Let $\mathcal{B}^k = (B_1^k, B_1^k, \ldots, B_{n_k}^k)$. By the same reasoning which was used above on X, each set B_j^k in $\mathcal{B}^k$ is the union of open connected sets whose closures have diameters $< 1/i + 1$. There is, then, by lemma 32.34, an irreducible bridge, $\mathcal{B}^{k+1}$, from a to b which is a monotonic refinement of $\mathcal{B}^k$ and whose sets are open connected subsets of X with compact closures of diameters $< 1/i + 1$. Thus, by induction, a sequence $(\mathcal{B}^1, \mathcal{B}^2, \ldots, \mathcal{B}^k, \ldots)$ of irreducible bridges from a to b has been defined such that $\mathcal{B}^{k+1}$ is a monotonic refinement of $\mathcal{B}^k$ and the sets in $\mathcal{B}^k$ are open and connected with compact closures of diameter $< 1/k$ for $k = 1, 2, \ldots$.

B. A special compact connected subspace containing a and b is now defined from the bridges $\mathcal{B}^1, \mathcal{B}^2, \ldots, \mathcal{B}^k, \ldots$. Let

$$\begin{aligned} K_1 &= \overline{B_1^1} \cup \overline{B_2^1} \cup \cdots \cup \overline{B_{n_1}^1} \\ &\vdots \qquad\qquad\quad \vdots \\ K_k &= \overline{B_1^k} \cup \overline{B_2^k} \cup \cdots \cup \overline{B_{n_k}^k} \\ &\vdots \qquad\qquad\quad \vdots \end{aligned}$$

Each K_k is, then, for $k = 1, 2, \ldots$, the union of the closures of the sets in the bridge $\mathcal{B}^k$. Thus, each K_k is the union of a finite number of compact sets, and hence is compact. Further, as the union of a bridge of connected sets, each K_k is connected, by theorem 24.22. Since $\mathcal{B}^{k+1}$ is a refinement of $\mathcal{B}^k$ for $k = 1, 2, \ldots$ it follows that $K_1 \supseteq K_2 \supseteq \cdots \supseteq K_k \supseteq \cdots$. Since each K_k is closed, $\bigcap_{k=1}^{\infty} K_k$ is closed. K_1 is compact. Hence, $\bigcap_{k=1}^{\infty} K_k$ is a closed subset of a compact space, and so by theorem 29.1, is compact. Since X is a metrizable space, each subspace K_k for $k = 1, 2, \ldots$ is then a compact, connected, metrizable space by theorem 20.9. Since by theorem 19.20, each metrizable space is a Hausdorff space, $\bigcap_{k=1}^{\infty} K_k$ is also Hausdorff. By lemma 29.27 and theorem 29.28,

$\bigcap_{k=1}^{\infty} K_k$ is, then, a compact, connected, metrizable space. Since $\{a\} \cup \{b\} \subseteq \bigcap_{k=1}^{\infty} K_k$, $\bigcap_{k=1}^{\infty} K_k$ contains more than one point, and hence has at least two non-cut points, by theorem 28.61.

C. It will be shown that $\bigcap_{k=1}^{\infty} K_k$ has exactly two non-cut points; namely, a and b, and hence is an arc from a to b. Let $c \in \bigcap_{k=1}^{\infty} K_k$ such that $a \neq c \neq b$. Since $c \in \bigcap_{k=1}^{\infty} K_k$, $c \in K_k$ for all $k = 1, 2, \ldots$. Consider, then, K_k defined from the bridge $\mathcal{B}^k = (B_1^k, B_2^k, \ldots, B_{n_k}^k)$. Let i^* be the minimum natural number and let $\tilde{i}$ be the maximum natural number in the one- or two-element set $\{i \mid c \in B_i^k\}$. Define $H_k = \bigcup\{B_i^k \mid i < i^*\}$, and define $M_k = \bigcup\{B_i^k \mid i > \tilde{i}\}$. Thus the sets of the bridge $\mathcal{B}^k$ are separated into three subsets: the set (or sets) which contain c as an element, the sets which precede this set (these sets), and the sets which follow this set (these sets) in $\mathcal{B}^k$. $H_k \subseteq K_k$ and $M_k \subseteq K_k$. Further, by definition (24.21) of a bridge, $H_k \cap M_k = \emptyset$ for all natural numbers k. Define $H^* = \bigcup_{k=1}^{\infty} H_k$ and $M^* = \bigcup_{k=1}^{\infty} M_k$. Since the sets in each bridge $\mathcal{B}^k$ are open, the sets H_k and M_k are open for $k = 1, 2, \ldots$. Hence H^* and M^* are both open subsets of the space X. Further, let $\rho(a, c) = \delta$, where ρ is an admissible metric on X. There is, by the archimedean ordering on the positive real numbers, a natural number k such that $1/k < \delta/2$. Hence, the diameters of the sets in the corresponding bridge $\mathcal{B}^k$ are all $< \delta/2$. Further, since $\mathcal{B}^k$ is irreducible from a to b, $a \in B_1^k$, the first set in $\mathcal{B}^k$. This means that $c \notin B_1^k$, $B_1^k \subseteq H_k$, and so $a \in H_k$. Hence, $H_k \neq \emptyset \neq H^*$. A similar argument proves that $b \in M^*$ and $M^* \neq \emptyset$. Thus H^* and M^* are non-empty open subsets of the space X. Now let y be any point of $(\bigcap_{k=1}^{\infty} K_k) \sim \{c\}$ and let $\rho(c, y) = \alpha$. There is, as above, a natural number n such that $1/n < \alpha/2$. Hence, since the diameters of the sets in the bridge $\mathcal{B}^n$ are less than $1/n$, c and y cannot be in the same set of $\mathcal{B}^n$. Thus $y \in H_n$ or $y \in M_n$ and $H^* \cup M^* \supseteq \bigcap_{k=1}^{\infty} K_k \sim \{c\}$. Let $\tilde{H} = H^* \cap ((\bigcap_{k=1}^{\infty} K_k) \sim \{c\})$ and let $\tilde{M} = M^* \cap ((\bigcap_{k=1}^{\infty} K_k) \sim \{c\})$. $\tilde{H}$ and $\tilde{M}$ are then open subsets in the relative topology on $(\bigcap_{k=1}^{\infty} K_k) \sim \{c\}$. Also, since $a \in \tilde{H}$ and $b \in \tilde{M}$, $\tilde{H} \neq \emptyset \neq \tilde{M}$. Further, by the above, $\tilde{H} \cup \tilde{M} = (\bigcap_{k=1}^{\infty} K_k) \sim \{c\}$. Lastly, it must be shown that $\tilde{H} \cap \tilde{M} = \emptyset$. First it will be established that $M_1 \subseteq M_2 \subseteq \cdots \subseteq M_k \subseteq \cdots$ and $H_1 \subseteq H_2 \subseteq \cdots \subseteq H_k \subseteq \cdots$. Let k be any natural number and let $z \in M_k$. M_k is defined from the bridge $\mathcal{B}^k$. Let $\mathcal{B}^k = (B_1^k, B_2^k, \ldots, B_{n_k}^k)$. Again let $\tilde{i}$ be the maximum natural number in $\{i \mid c \in B_i^k\}$ and let j^* be the minimum natural number in $\{j \mid z \in B_j^k\}$. By definition of M_k, $\tilde{i} < j^*$. Consider now the bridge $\mathcal{B}^{k+1} = (B_1^{k+1}, B_2^{k+1}, \ldots, B_{n_{k+1}}^{k+1})$. Let $\tilde{r}$ denote the maximum number in $\{r \mid c \in B_r^{k+1}\}$ and let s^* denote the minimum number in $\{s \mid z \in B_s^{k+1}\}$. If $\tilde{r} = s^*$, then z and c lie in a common set in $\mathcal{B}^{k+1}$ and since $\mathcal{B}^{k+1}$ is a refinement of $\mathcal{B}^k$, z and c would then lie in a common set in $\mathcal{B}^k$. This contradicts the fact that $z \in M_k$. Hence $\tilde{r} \neq s^*$. Let $s^* < \tilde{r}$. Since $z \in B_{s^*}^{k+1} \cap B_{j^*}^k$, then $B_{s^*}^{k+1} \subseteq B_{j^*}^k$ or $B_{s^*}^{k+1} \subseteq B_{j^*+1}^k$, by definition of j^*. Since $\mathcal{B}^{k+1}$ is a monotonic refinement of $\mathcal{B}^k$, $B_{\tilde{r}}^{k+1} \subseteq B_{j^*}^k$ or $B_{\tilde{r}}^{k+1} \subseteq B_t^k$ for some $t > j^*$. In either case then, since $c \in B_{\tilde{r}}^{k+1}$, $z \notin M_k$, by definition of M_k. Again, this is a contradiction. Hence $\tilde{r} < s^*$ and $z \in M_{k+1}$. Thus $M_k \subseteq M_{k+1}$. It now follows by the well-ordering property of the natural numbers that $M_1 \subseteq M_2 \subseteq \cdots \subseteq M_k \subseteq \cdots$. By an exactly analogous argument, it follows that $H_1 \subseteq H_2 \subseteq \cdots \subseteq H_k \subseteq \cdots$. Now, let $\alpha \in \tilde{H} \cap \tilde{M}$. By definition of $\tilde{H}$ and $\tilde{M}$, there exists a natural number m such that $\alpha \in H_m$ and there exists a natural number n such that $\alpha \in M_n$. Let q be the maximum in $\{m, n\}$. Then, by the above, $H_m \subseteq H_q$ and $M_n \subseteq M_q$. Hence $\alpha \in H_q \cap M_q$. This contradicts the definition of H_q and M_q. Thus $\tilde{H} \cap \tilde{M} = \emptyset$ and $\tilde{H} \cup \tilde{M}$ is a separation of $(\bigcap_{k=1}^{\infty} K_k) \sim \{c\}$ into two non-empty, disjoint, open subsets such that $\tilde{H} \cup \tilde{M} = (\bigcap_{k=1}^{\infty} K_k) \sim \{c\}$. Thus c is a cut point of $\bigcap_{k=1}^{\infty} K_k$, and so $\bigcap_{k=1}^{\infty} K_k$, by theorem 32.20, is an arc from a to b. ▮

The role of the property of monotonicity for refinements relative to the inclusions $H_1 \subseteq H_2 \subseteq \cdots \subseteq H_k \subseteq \cdots \subseteq \cdots$ and $M_1 \subseteq M_2 \subseteq \cdots \subseteq M_k \subseteq \cdots$ is illustrated in the next sketch (figure 26). $z \in M_1$ and $z \in H_2$, and so $z \in \tilde{H} \cap \tilde{M}$.

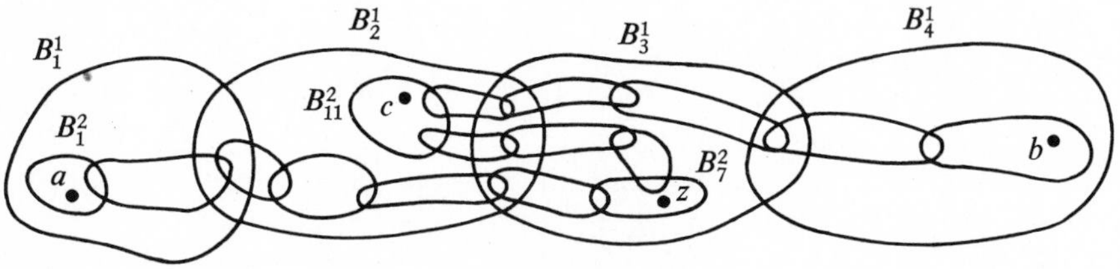

FIGURE 26

The previous theorem now permits a generalization of corollary 27.29, which states that every open connected subset of Euclidean n-space is pathwise connected.

32.36 Corollary. *Any open, connected subset of a locally compact, connected, locally connected, metrizable space X is also arcwise connected.*

Proof: Let G be an open, connected subset in the space X. Let c be any point in G. Since X is metrizable, X is regular. Hence, since G is open, there exists an open set U such that $x \in U$ and $\bar{U} \subseteq G$. Since X is compact, $\bar{U}$ is compact by theorem 29.1. Further, since X is locally connected, U can be considered to be connected. Hence G is a locally compact connected, locally connected metrizable space, and hence is arcwise connected by the previous theorem. ▮

In example 27.23, a connected but non-open subset of the locally compact, connected, locally connected, metrizable space E^2 was given which is not arcwise connected.

Another main result of this section states that for Hausdorff spaces arcwise connectedness is equivalent to pathwise connectedness. Two theorems related to this result follow.

32.37 Theorem. *If a space L is a curve in a Hausdorff space, then L is a compact, connected, locally connected, metrizable space.*

Proof: Since L is a curve, there exists a continuous function f from the unit interval space, [0, 1], onto L. [0, 1] is a compact, connected metrizable space by theorems 30.18, 25.1, 20.9. By corollary 30.8, L is a compact metrizable space, and by theorem 24.13, L is connected. By theorem 29.7, f is a closed function. By the definition (27.14) of a quasi-closed function, f is quasi-closed. Hence, by theorem 27.17 and exercise 3 preceding it, L is locally connected. ▮

32.38 Theorem. *In Hausdorff spaces, arcwise connectedness and pathwise connectedness are equivalent properties.*

Proof: Let X be any Hausdorff space. If X is arcwise connected, then, by lemma 32.28, X is pathwise connected. Conversely, let X be Hausdorff and pathwise connected and let a and b be two (distinct) points of X. Since X is pathwise connected, there is a curve L between a and b. By the previous theorem (32.37), L is a compact, connected, locally connected, metrizable space. By theorem 32.35, L is arcwise connected and hence contains an arc A from a to b. A is then an arc in X from a to b and X is arcwise connected. ▮

32.39 Definition. Let X be a space. Let *arc comp* denote the relation $\{(a, b) \mid a \in X \text{ and } b \in X, \text{ and } a = b \text{ or there is an arc in } X \text{ from } a \text{ to } b\}$ and let *path comp* denote the relation $\{(a, b) \mid a \in X, b \in X \text{ and there is a path in } X \text{ from } a \text{ to } b\}$.

32.40 Lemma. *In any space X, path comp is an equivalence relation.*

Proof: Exercise.

32.41 Definition. Let X be a space. The equivalence classes determined by the equivalence relation *path comp* are called *path components.*

The following example establishes that in general arc comp is not an equivalence relation.

32.42 Example. Let X be a set consisting of $\{O'\} \cup \{O''\} \cup \{x \mid 0 < x \leq 1, x \text{ real}\}$. Let $\mathfrak{J}$ be defined as follows. $\mathfrak{J}$ contains all the usual open sets in $\{x \mid 0 < x \leq 1, x \text{ real}\}$. Further, let a local base at O' be $\{V'_\epsilon \mid \epsilon \text{ is real and positive and } V'_\epsilon = \{x \mid 0 < x < \epsilon\}\} \cup \{O'\}$ and let a local base at O'' be $\{V''_\epsilon \mid \epsilon \text{ is real and positive and } V''_\epsilon = \{x \mid 0 < x < \epsilon\}\} \cup \{O''\}$. The space $\{X, \mathfrak{J}\}$ is a compact T_1-space. In $\{X, \mathfrak{J}\}$, there is an arc from O' to 1 and an arc from 1 to O''. However, there is no arc from O' to O''. This space $\{X, \mathfrak{J}\}$ also gives an example of an intersection of two compact sets which is not compact, i.e., $A = \{O'\} \cup \{x \mid 0 < x \leq 1\}$ and $B = \{O''\} \cup \{x \mid 0 < x \leq 1\}$.

32.43 Lemma. *In a Hausdorff space arc comp is an equivalence relation.*

Proof: Exercise.

32.44 Definition. Let X be a Hausdorff space. The equivalence classes determined by the equivalence relation *arc comp* are called the *arc components* of X.

32.45 Theorem. *In a Hausdorff space the arc components are identical with the path components.*

Proof: Exercise.

EXERCISE 3. If X is the set of real numbers and if $\mathfrak{J}$ is the smallest T_1-topology, i.e., X and the finite sets are the only closed sets; determine the path components and arc components, if defined, in $\{X, \mathfrak{J}\}$.

EXERCISE 4. Prove or disprove: if X is a space, P is a path component of X and f is continuous from X onto Y, then $f[P]$ is always a path component in Y.

EXERCISE 5. Prove or disprove: if X is a space, f is a continuous function from X onto Y and Q is a path component in Y, then $f^{-1}[Q]$ is always a path component in X.

32.46 Theorem. *Path components and arc components are topological invariants.*

Proof: Exercise.

32.47 Definition. A space X is called *locally pathwise connected* if and only if for each point x in X and each open neighborhood U of x there exists an open neighborhood V of x such that $V \subseteq U$ and V is pathwise connected.

The subspace of the plane, E^2, determined by the following sketch (figure 27) is pathwise connected but not locally pathwise connected at (0, 0).

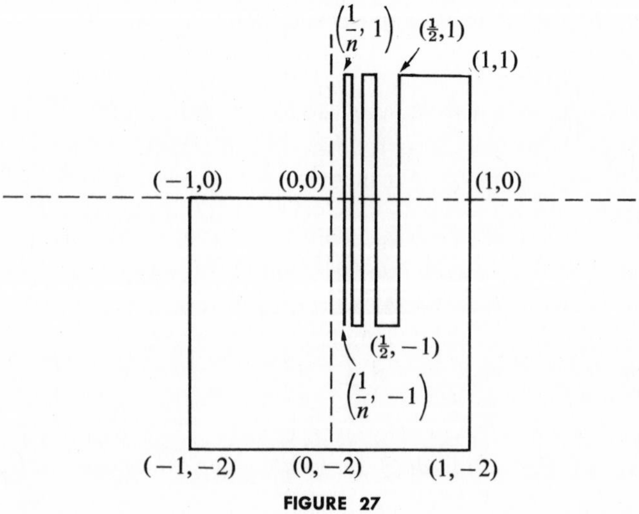

FIGURE 27

The Hahn-Mazurkiewicz Theorem

In theorem 32.37, a curve in a Hausdorff space was proved to be a compact, connected, locally connected, metrizable space. The converse of this theorem, which, together with theorem 32.37, completely characterizes the topological space which is a curve in a Hausdorff space, is next established. First, however, two lemmas are needed.

The following two definitions introduce concepts related to the next two lemmas.

32.48 Definition. A metric space $\{X, \rho\}$ is called *uniformly locally connected* if and only if for each positive real number ϵ, there is a positive real number δ such that if $\rho(a, b) < \delta$, there is a connected set C of diameter $< \epsilon$ and $a \in C$ and $b \in C$.

32.49 Lemma. *If a compact metric space $\{X, \rho\}$ is locally connected, then it is uniformly locally connected.*

Proof: Let ϵ be a positive real number. Since $\{X, \rho\}$ is locally connected, each point x has an open connected neighborhood U_x of diameter $< \epsilon$. Since X is compact, a finite number of these open neighborhoods cover it, say, $U_{x_1}, U_{x_2}, \ldots, U_{x_k}$. By theorem 30.13 (the Lebesgue number theorem), there exists a positive number δ such that if $\rho(a, b) < \delta$, then $a \in U_{x_i}$ and $b \in U_{x_i}$ for some i, $1 \leq i \leq k$. Thus, $\{X, \rho\}$ is uniformly locally connected. ▌

32.50 Example. The subspace X of Euclidean 2-space, E^2, determined by $\{(x, y) \mid y \neq 0\} \cup \{(x, y) \mid y = 0 \text{ and } x < 0\}$ is locally connected. However, if $\epsilon = 1$, then for any positive real number δ, let $a = (2, \delta/4)$ and $b = (2, -\delta/4)$. $\rho(a, b) = \delta/2 < \delta$. However, there is no connected set which has diameter $< \epsilon$ and which contains both a and b.

32.51 Definition. A metric space $\{X, \rho\}$ is called *uniformly locally arcwise connected* if and only if for each positive real number ϵ there exists a positive real number δ such that if $\rho(a, b) < \delta$, then there exists an arc, A, from a to b such that the diameter of $A < \epsilon$.

The space in example 32.50, above, is locally arcwise connected but not uniformly locally arcwise connected.

32.52 Lemma. *Any compact, connected, locally connected, metric space $\{X, \rho\}$ is uniformly locally arcwise connected.*

Proof: Let ϵ be any positive real number. By lemma 32.49, $\{X, \rho\}$ is uniformly locally connected. Hence, there exists a positive real number δ such that if $\rho(a, b) < \delta$, then there exists a connected set C which contains both a

and b and which has diameter $< \epsilon/2$. Now for $c \in C$, define U_c to be the spherical neighborhood with center c and radius $\epsilon/9$. U_c has diameter $< \epsilon/4$. Since X is locally connected, there exists for each c in C, a connected, open neighborhood V_c such that $V_c \subseteq U_c$. Thus the diameter of $V_c < \epsilon/4$. Consider $G = \bigcup_{c \in C} V_c$. G is open and has diameter $< \epsilon$. Further, G is connected. For, if $G = M \cup N$ separation, then since each V_c is connected, $V_c \subseteq M$ or $V_c \subseteq N$ by theorem 24.17. This means, since $V_c \cap C \neq \emptyset$ for every c in C, that $C \cap M \neq \emptyset \neq C \cap N$. This is a contradiction, since C is connected. Hence, G is connected, as well as open and, by corollary 32.36, G is arcwise connected. Thus G contains an arc from a to b which must, then, have diameter $< \epsilon$. This makes $\{X, \rho\}$ uniformly locally arcwise connected. ▌

32.53 Theorem (The Hahn-Mazurkiewicz Theorem). *Any non-empty, compact, connected, locally connected, metrizable space X is the image assigned by a continuous function to the unit interval space* [0, 1] *as domain.*

Proof: A. First a function is defined from [0, 1] onto X. By theorem 30.10, there exists a continuous function f from the Cantor ternary space, CTS, onto the non-empty, compact, metrizable space X. By theorems 12.17 and 12.26, the Cantor ternary space can be considered to be a closed subset of the closed unit interval space, [0, 1]. This means that $\sim CTS$, the complement of CTS, is open in the space [0, 1]. Since, by corollaries 25.5 and 26.5, [0, 1] is locally connected, the components of $\sim CTS$ are open, as well as connected subsets of [0, 1], by theorem 27.12. Since 0 and 1 are in CTS, the components of $\sim CTS$ in [0, 1] must, then, by theorem 25.7, be open intervals of real numbers with end points in CTS. By theorem 24.23, components are, of course, disjoint. Since the rationals are dense in the reals and since the rationals are countable, there can be at most a countable number of such disjoint components. Thus $\sim CTS = \bigcup_{k=1}^{\infty} (a_k, b_k)$, where (a_k, b_k) denotes the open interval $\{x \mid a_k < x < b_k\}$ and where $a_k \in CTS$ and $b_k \in CTS$. In what follows, this countable set $\{(a_1, b_1), (a_2, b_2), \ldots, (a_k, b_k), \ldots\}$ of open intervals of real numbers, whose union is $\sim CTS$, will be split into disjoint finite sets $C_1, C_2, \ldots, C_n, \ldots$. The function f, mentioned above, will then be extended first to $CTS \cup (\overline{\bigcup C_1})$, and then to $CTS \cup (\overline{\bigcup C_1}) \cup (\overline{\bigcup C_2})$, etc. By lemma 32.52, $\{X, \rho\}$, for ρ an admissible metric, is uniformly locally arcwise connected. Hence, there exists a positive real number δ_1, such that if $\rho(f(a_k), f(b_k)) < \delta_1$, then there is an arc in X from $f(a_k)$ to $f(b_k)$ whose ρ-diameter is less than 1. Since CTS is a closed subset of [0, 1], it is compact by theorems 29.1 and 30.18. By corollary 30.15, f, then, is uniformly continuous on CTS with the usual metric, and so there exists a positive real number α_1 such that if $|a_k - b_k| < \alpha_1$, $\rho(f(a_k), f(b_k)) < \delta_1$. Hence, if $|a_k - b_k| < \alpha_1$, an arc A_k from $f(a_k)$ to $f(b_k)$ can be chosen with diameter less than 1. By the archimedean order on the positive reals, there is a natural number k, such that $k \cdot \alpha_1 > 1$. Hence since [0, 1] has diameter 1, only a finite number (i.e., $< k$) of the interval components of $\sim CTS$, say, (a_1^1, b_1^1), (a_2^1, b_2^1), $\ldots$, $(a_{n_1}^1, b_{n_1}^1)$ can have diameter greater than or equal to α_1. Let C_1 denote this set of intervals, i.e., $C_1 = \{(a_1^1, b_1^1), (a_2^1, b_2^1), \ldots, (a_{n_1}^1, b_{n_1}^1)\}$. Since X is arcwise connected, for each (a_i^1, b_i^1) in C_1, by a choice function, an arc A_i^1 can be chosen in X from $f(a_i^1)$ to $f(b_i^1)$. Each such arc, A_i^1 determines, again by a choice function, a homeomorphism h_i^1 from the closed interval $[a_i^1, b_i^1]$ into X. Let g_1 be defined from $\overline{\bigcup C_1}$ into X as follows: $g_1(x) = h_i^1(x)$ if $x \in [a_i^1, b_i^1]$. Since CTS and $\overline{\bigcup C_1}$ are both closed in [0, 1], $f \cup g_1$, by theorem 9.23, is continuous from $CTS \cup (\overline{\bigcup C_1})$ onto X. Now, again, since $\{X, \rho\}$ is uniformly locally arcwise connected, there is a positive real number δ_2, such that if $\rho(f(a_k), f(b_k)) < \delta_2$, then an arc can be defined from $f(a_k)$ to $f(b_k)$ whose diameter is less than 1/2. Since f is uniformly continuous on CTS, there is a real number $\alpha_2 \leq \alpha_1/2$ such that if $|a_k - b_k| < \alpha_2$, then $\rho(f(a_k), f(b_k)) < \delta_2$. Again, as above, by the archimedean property of the order on the positive reals, there exists a finite number of interval components of $\sim CTS$ whose diameter is greater than or equal to α_2. Let C_2 denote $\{(a_k, b_k) \mid (a_k, b_k)$ is a component of $\sim CTS$ in [0, 1] and $\alpha_2 \leq |a_k - b_k| < \alpha_1\}$. C_2 can then be denoted by $\{(a_1^2, b_1^2), (a_2^2, b_2^2), \ldots, (a_{n_2}^2, b_{n_2}^2)\}$, where $\alpha_2 \leq |a_i^2 - b_i^2| < \alpha_1$ for $1 \leq i \leq n_2$. By the definition of α_1, above, for each (a_i^2, b_i^2) in C_2, an arc A_i^2 can be chosen in X, from $f(a_i^2)$ to $f(b_i^2)$ with diameter < 1. These arcs can be used, as above, to define for each (a_i^2, b_i^2) in C_2 a homeomorphism, h_i^2, from the closed interval $[a_i^2, b_i^2]$ into X. Let g_2, from $\overline{\bigcup C_2}$ into X, be defined as follows: $g_2(x) = h_i^2(x)$ if $x \in [a_i^2, b_i^2]$. The diameter of $g_2[[a_i^2, b_i^2]] < 1$ for $(a_i^2, b_i^2) \in C_2$. Again, since $CTS \cup (\overline{\bigcup C_1})$ and $\overline{\bigcup C_2}$ are both closed in [0, 1], $f \cup g_1 \cup g_2$ is continuous by theorem 9.23. Assume next that positive real numbers $\alpha_1, \alpha_2, \ldots, \alpha_k$ have been defined such that $\alpha_j \leq \alpha_1/j$ for $1 \leq j \leq k$ and such that if $|a_i - b_i| < \alpha_j$ for $(a_i, b_i) \in \sim CTS$, then there exists an arc A_i in X from $f(a_i)$ to $f(b_i)$ whose diameter is less than $1/j$. Assume also that the finite, disjoint sets $C_1, C_2, \ldots, C_k$ have been defined as follows; $C_j = \{(a_i, b_i) \mid (a_i, b_i)$ is a component of $\sim CTS$ in [0, 1] and $\alpha_j \leq |a_i - b_i| < \alpha_{j-1}\}$ for $1 < j \leq k$ and $C_1 = \{(a_i, b_i) \mid (a_i, b_i)$ is a component of $\sim CTS$ in [0, 1] and $\alpha_1 \leq |a_i - b_i|\}$. Further, assume that a continuous function F_k has been defined from $CTS \cup (\overline{\bigcup C_1}) \cup \cdots \cup (\overline{\bigcup C_k})$ into X such that F_k is an extension of f and the diameter of the image $F_k[[a_i^j, b_i^j]]$ is less than $1/(j-1)$ for $(a_i^j, b_i^j) \in C_j$ and $1 < j \leq k$. Now, consider that $\{X, \rho\}$ is still uniformly locally arcwise connected, and hence that there exists a positive real number δ_{k+1} such that if $\rho(f(a_i), f(b_i)) < \delta_{k+1}$ for a_i and b_i in CTS, then there is an arc in X from $f(a_i)$ to $f(b_i)$ whose diameter $< 1/(k+1)$. Since f is uniformly continuous from CTS onto $\{X, \rho\}$, there exists a positive real number $\alpha_{k+1} \leq \alpha_1/(k+1)$ such that if $|a_i - b_i| < \alpha_{k+1}$ for a_i and b_i in CTS, then $\rho(f(a_i), f(b_i)) < \delta_{k+1}$. As above, there can exist only a finite number of open interval components (a_i^{k+1}, b_i^{k+1}) of $\sim CTS$ such that $\alpha_{k+1} \leq |a_i^{k+1} - b_i^{k+1}| < \alpha_k$. Denote this finite set of intervals by C_{k+1}. Then by definition of α_k, above, there exists an arc from $f(a_i^{k+1})$ to $f(b_i^{k+1})$ whose diameter is less than $1/k$. These arcs can be used, as above, to define a continuous function g_{k+1} from $[a_1^{k+1}, b_1^{k+1}] \cup [a_2^{k+1}, b_2^{k+1}] \cup \cdots \cup [a_{n_{k+1}}^{k+1}, b_{n_{k+1}}^{k+1}] = \overline{\bigcup C_{k+1}}$ into $\{X, \mathfrak{I}_\rho\}$. Since $\overline{\bigcup C_{k+1}}$ and $CTS \cup (\overline{\bigcup C_1}) \cup \cdots \cup (\overline{\bigcup C_k})$ are both closed,

$F_k \cup g_{k+1}$ is continuous by theorem 9.23. Let $F_k \cup g_{k+1} = F_{k+1}$. Thus, by induction, for every natural number $k = 1, 2, \ldots,$ a finite set C_k of open interval components of $\sim CTS$ and a continuous function F_k from $CTS \cup (\overline{\bigcup C_1}) \cup \cdots \cup (\overline{\bigcup C_k})$ onto X have been defined such that if the open interval (a_i^j, b_i^j) is in C_j, then the diameter of $F_k[[a_i^j, b_i^j]]$ is less than $1/(j-1)$ for $1 < j \leq k$. Further, by definition, $F_1 \subseteq F_2 \subseteq \cdots \subseteq F_k \subseteq \cdots$. Let $F^* = \bigcup_{k=1}^{\infty} F_k$. Since $F_i \subseteq F_j$ for $i < j$, F^* is a function. Since $f \subseteq F^*$, F^* is an extension of f. Now let x be any point in $[0, 1]$. If $x \in CTS$, then x is in the domain of F^*, since $f \subseteq F^*$. If $x \in \sim CTS$, then $x \in (a_i, b_i)$ for some open interval component (a_i, b_i) of $\sim CTS$ in $[0, 1]$. Let $|a_i - b_i| = \xi$. By the archimedean property of the order on the positive reals, there is a natural number k such that $\alpha_1/k < \xi$. Now, since $\alpha_k \leq \alpha_1/k$, $\alpha_k \leq \xi$. Hence, $\alpha_k \leq |a_i - b_i|$, and so $(a_i, b_i) \in C_1 \cup C_2 \cup \cdots \cup C_k$, by definition of $C_1, C_2, \ldots, C_k$. Thus x is in the domain of F_k and since $F_k \subseteq F^*$, $F^*(x)$ is defined. The domain of F^* is, then, $[0, 1]$ and the range, since $f \subseteq F^*$ and f is onto, is X.

B. F^* is next proved to be continuous at every point of $\sim CTS = [0, 1] \sim CTS$. Let p denote any point of $\sim CTS$. p, then, lies in some open interval component, (a_i, b_i), of $\sim CTS$. Further, F^* restricted to (a_i, b_i) is F_k for some natural number k as defined above. Since F_k is continuous on (a_i, b_i), for any neighborhood V of $F_k(p)$ in X, there exists an open interval $(p - \delta, p + \delta)$, for δ real and positive, such that $(p - \delta, p + \delta) \subseteq (a_i, b_i)$ and $F_k[(p - \delta, p + \delta)] \subseteq V$. Hence, $F^*[(p - \delta, p + \delta)] \subseteq V$ and F^* is continuous at $p \in \sim CTS$.

C. F^* will, lastly, be shown to be continuous at every point q in CTS. Let q be any point in CTS and let $V(\epsilon)$ denote any spherical neighborhood of $F^*(q)$ in $\{X, \rho\}$, where as usual ϵ denotes the positive, real radius of the neighborhood. By the archimedean property of the order on the positive reals, there exists a natural number n^* such that $1/n^* < \epsilon$. Since $F^* = f$ is continuous on CTS, there exists an open interval $(q - \delta, q + \delta)$ for δ positive and real, such that if $t \in (q - \delta, q + \delta) \cap CTS$, then $\rho(F^*(t), F^*(q)) < 1/2n^*$. Let α_{2n^*} be the positive real number, defined above, such that if (a_i, b_i) is an open-interval component of $\sim CTS$ and if $|a_i - b_i| < \alpha_{2n^*}$, then the diameter of the image $F^*[[a_i, b_i]]$ is less than $1/2n^*$. Let, now, δ^* be any positive lower bound for the set $\{\delta, \alpha_{2n^*}\}$. Consider the open interval $(q - \delta^*, q + \delta^*)$. Since, by theorem 12.28, every point of CTS is a limit point of CTS, at least one of the intervals $(q - \delta^*, q)$, $(q, q + \delta^*)$ must contain a point of CTS. Thus exactly three cases can occur: (1) $(q - \delta^*, q) \cap CTS \neq \emptyset \neq (q, q + \delta^*)$, (2) $(q - \delta^*, q) \cap CTS = \emptyset$, or (3) $(q, q + \delta^*) \cap CTS = \emptyset$. Assume that $(q - \delta^*, q) \cap CTS \neq \emptyset \neq (q, q + \delta^*) \cap CTS$. Let $q - \gamma' \in (q - \delta^*, q) \cap CTS$ and let $q + \gamma'' \in (q, q + \delta^*) \cap CTS$. By definition, the open interval $(q - \gamma', q + \gamma'') \subsetneq (q - \delta^*, q + \delta^*) \subseteq (q - \delta, q + \delta)$. Hence, by definition of δ, if $t \in (q - \gamma', q + \gamma'') \cap CTS$, $\rho(F^*(t), F^*(q)) < 1/2n^* < \epsilon$ and $F^*(t) \in V(\epsilon)$. On the other hand, if $t \in (\sim CTS) \cap (q - \gamma', q + \gamma'')$ then $t \in (a_i, b_i)$, where (a_i, b_i) is the component of $\sim CTS$ which contains t. Since the points $q - \gamma'$ and $q + \gamma''$ are in CTS and since components are connected, $(a_i, b_i) \subseteq$

$(q - \gamma', q + \gamma'') \subsetneq (q - \delta^*, q + \delta^*)$. By definition of δ^*, the diameter of the image $F^*[[a_i, b_i]] < 1/2n^*$. Hence, $\rho(F^*(a_i), F^*(t)) < 1/2n^*$. Further, since $a_i \in CTS \cap (q - \delta, q + \delta)$, $\rho(F^*(q), F^*(a_i)) < 1/2n^*$. It follows, then, from the triangle property for any metric that $\rho(F^*(q), F^*(t)) < 1/n^* < \epsilon$ and that $F^*(t) \in V(\epsilon)$. Hence, $F^*[[q - \gamma', q + \gamma'']] \subseteq V(\epsilon)$ and F^* is continuous at q. Assume, next, case (2); namely, that $(q - \delta^*, q) \cap CTS = \emptyset$. Let, again, $q + \gamma'' \in (q, q + \delta^*) \cap CTS$. The proof for case (1) establishes that $F^*[[q, q + \gamma'')] \subseteq V(\epsilon)$. Now consider $(q - \delta^*, q]$. Since $(q - \delta^*, q) \cap CTS = \emptyset$ and since q is assumed to be in CTS, $(q - \delta^*, q)$ is a subset of a component (a_i, q) of $\sim CTS$. F^* restricted to this component is F_k for some natural number k. Since F_k is continuous on $[a_i, q]$, there is a real number α' such that $F_k[(q - \alpha', q]] \subseteq V(\epsilon)$. Thus $F^*[(q - \alpha', q + \gamma'')] \subseteq V(\epsilon)$ and F^* is, again, continuous at q. The argument for case (3), i.e., $(q, q + \delta^*) \cap CTS = \emptyset$, is exactly analogous to the argument for case (2). Thus F^* is continuous at every point of $[0, 1]$ and X is a curve. ▮

32.54 Corollary. *A topological space is a curve in a Hausdorff space if and only if it is a non-empty, compact, connected, locally connected, metrizable space.*

Proof: The corollary follows from the previous theorem (32.53) and theorem 32.37.

32.55 Definition. A curve in a Hausdorff space is called a Peano space.

Thus the Peano spaces are exactly the non-empty, compact, connected, locally connected, metrizable spaces.

33. PARACOMPACTNESS.

The topological property of compactness has been localized in yet another significant way by Dieudonné to obtain what is called paracompactness. Compactness can be defined in terms of refinements of open coverings (see theorem 28.4). A space S is compact if and only if every open covering of S has a refinement which is a finite open covering of S. Paracompactness demands only that the refinement be locally finite in a certain sense.

Locally Finite Systems and Paracompactness

33.1 Definition. Let S be a space and let $\mathfrak{M}$ be a set of subsets of S. The set $\mathfrak{M}$ is called *a locally finite system on S* if and only if each point $s \in S$ has at least one neighborhood which intersects at most a finite number of sets in $\mathfrak{M}$ on a non-empty set.

Of course, any finite set of subsets of a space S is locally finite.

33.2 Example. Let S denote the subspace of E^1, the usual space of reals, determined by the non-negative real numbers. Let $\mathfrak{M} = \{F_n \mid n$ is a non-negative integer and $F_n = \{x \mid x \geq n\}\}$. $\mathfrak{M}$ is a locally finite system with respect to S.

33.3 Example. Let $\mathfrak{M} = \{G_n \mid n$ is an integer and $G_n = \{x \mid x$ is real and $x > n\}\}$. Let E^1 be the usual space of reals. $\mathfrak{M}$ is not a locally finite system with respect to E^1.

One of the useful topological properties of finite sets (systems) of sets is that the union of the closures is the closure of the union (corollary 3.5). The following theorem establishes this useful property for locally finite systems of sets.

33.4 Theorem. *If $\mathfrak{M}$ is a locally finite system in a space S, then $\overline{\bigcup \mathfrak{M}}$ is equal to the union of the closures of the sets in $\mathfrak{M}$.*

Proof: Let $\mathfrak{M}$ be indexed by the set $\mathfrak{A}$. $\mathfrak{M} = \{A_\alpha \mid \alpha \in \mathfrak{A}\}$. $\bigcup \mathfrak{M} = \bigcup_{\alpha \in \mathfrak{A}} A_\alpha$. Since, by definition of $\bigcup$, $A_\alpha \subseteq \bigcup \mathfrak{M}$, $\overline{A}_\alpha \subseteq \overline{\bigcup \mathfrak{M}}$, by corollary 3.6, for each $\alpha \in \mathfrak{A}$. Hence $\bigcup_{\alpha \in \mathfrak{A}} \overline{A}_\alpha \subseteq \overline{\bigcup \mathfrak{M}}$. Conversely, let $x \in \overline{\bigcup \mathfrak{M}}$. x has at least one neighborhood, U_x, which intersects at most a finite number of sets of $\mathfrak{M}$ on a non-empty set. Assume that $U_x \cap A_{\alpha_i} \neq \emptyset$ for $i = 1, 2, \ldots k$ and k a natural number, and that $U_x \cap A_\alpha = \emptyset$ for $\alpha \neq \alpha_1, \ldots, \alpha \neq \alpha_k$. Let N_x be any neighborhood of x and let $N_x \cap U_x = V_x$. $V_x \cap A_\alpha = \emptyset$ for $\alpha \neq \alpha_1, \ldots, \alpha \neq \alpha_k$. Since $x \in \overline{\bigcup \mathfrak{M}}$, V_x, then, must contain a point of $A_{\alpha_1} \cup \cdots \cup A_{\alpha_k}$. Hence, N_x must contain a point of $A_{\alpha_1} \cup \cdots \cup A_{\alpha_k}$ and $x \in \overline{A_{\alpha_1} \cup \cdots \cup A_{\alpha_k}}$. By corollary 3.5, $\overline{A_{\alpha_1} \cup A_{\alpha_2} \cup \cdots \cup A_{\alpha_k}} = \overline{A}_{\alpha_1} \cup \cdots \cup \overline{A}_{\alpha_k}$. Consequently, $x \in \overline{A}_{\alpha_i}$ for some $i = 1, 2, \ldots, k$ and $\overline{\bigcup \mathfrak{M}} \subseteq \bigcup_{\alpha \in \mathfrak{A}} \overline{A}_\alpha$. Thus $\overline{\bigcup \mathfrak{M}} = \bigcup_{\alpha \in \mathfrak{A}} \overline{A}_\alpha$. ∎

33.5 Definition (Dieudonné). A space is called *paracompact* if and only if every open covering of S has a locally finite refinement which is also an open covering of S.

EXERCISE 1. For the space E^1 and the system $\mathfrak{M}$ of example 33.3, find a locally finite refinement of $\mathfrak{M}$ which is also an open cover of E^1.

33.6 Theorem. *If a space S is compact, then it is paracompact.*

Proof: Exercise.

EXERCISE 2. Prove that the space $\{S, \mathfrak{J}\}$, where S is the set of real numbers and $\mathfrak{J}$ is the topology determined when each point, p, is assigned a local base consisting of the one set $V_p = \{x \mid x \geq p\}$, is not paracompact.

EXERCISE 3. Prove that every discrete space is paracompact.

EXERCISE 4. Prove or disprove: if S is a paracompact space and if f is a continuous function from S onto T, then T is paracompact.

EXERCISE 5. Prove that the smallest T_1-topology on the set S of real numbers, i.e., S and the finite subsets are the only closed sets, yields a non-Hausdorff, paracompact space.

33.7 Lemma. *Every closed subset of a paracompact space is paracompact.*

Proof: Exercise (see the proof of theorem 29.1).

The following lemma and theorem, proved by J. Dieudonné, locate paracompactness in the separation-axiom spectrum.

33.8 Lemma (Dieudonné). *Every paracompact, Hausdorff space, S, is regular.*

Proof: Let $p \in S$ and let F be a closed subset of S such that $p \notin F$. Let $x \in S$ and let $x \neq p$. Since S is Hausdorff, there exist open neighborhoods U_x of x and $N_p(x)$ of p such that $U_x \cap N_p(x) = \emptyset$. Further, since $\sim F$ is open and $p \in \sim F$, $V_p(x) = N_p(x) \cap \sim F$ is an open neighborhood of p which is also disjoint from U_x. $\{U_x \mid x \in S \sim \{p\}\} \cup \{V_p(x) \mid x \in S \sim \{p\}\}$ is an open covering, $\mathcal{G}^*$, of S. Since S is paracompact, $\mathcal{G}^*$ has a locally finite refinement, $\mathcal{G}$, which is an open covering of S. Let $\mathcal{G}$ be denoted by $\{G_\alpha \mid \alpha \in \mathfrak{A}\}$. Assume that $G_\alpha \cap F \neq \emptyset$. Since $V_p(x) \cap F = \emptyset$ for all $x \in S \sim \{p\}$, $G_\alpha \not\subseteq V_p(x)$ for any x. Since $\mathcal{G}$ is a refinement of $\mathcal{G}^*$, $G_\alpha \subseteq U_x$ for some $x \in S \sim \{p\}$. Since $U_x \cap V_p(x) = \emptyset$, then p is not in G_α. Further, since $V_p(x) \cap G_\alpha = \emptyset$, $p \notin \overline{G}_\alpha$. Thus $G_\alpha \cap F \neq \emptyset$ implies that $p \notin \overline{G}_\alpha$. Let C denote $\{\alpha \in \mathfrak{A} \mid G_\alpha \cap F \neq \emptyset\}$. By definition of C, then, $p \notin \bigcup_{\alpha \in C} \overline{G}_\alpha$. Since $\mathcal{G}$ is locally finite, $\bigcup_{\alpha \in C} \overline{G}_\alpha = \overline{\bigcup_{\alpha \in C} G_\alpha}$ by lemma 33.4. Hence, $p \notin \overline{\bigcup_{\alpha \in C} G_\alpha}$. Now, since $\mathcal{G}$ covers S, $\mathcal{G}$ covers F. Thus $F \subseteq \bigcup_{\alpha \in C} G_\alpha$, by definition of C. Since $p \notin \overline{\bigcup_{\alpha \in C} G_\alpha}$, $p \in \sim\overline{\bigcup_{\alpha \in C} G_\alpha}$. Now, $\sim\overline{\bigcup_{\alpha \in C} G_\alpha} \cap \bigcup_{\alpha \in C} G_\alpha = \emptyset$. Further, $\sim\overline{\bigcup_{\alpha \in C} G_\alpha}$ and $\bigcup_{\alpha \in C} G_\alpha$ are both open. Hence, S is regular. ∎

33.9 Theorem (Dieudonné). *Any paracompact Hausdorff space is normal.*

Proof: Let F_1 and F_2 be disjoint closed sets in S. Since S is regular by the previous lemma (33.8), for each point x_1 in F_1, by the axiom of choice, an open neighborhood U_{x_1} can be chosen such that $\overline{U}_{x_1} \subseteq \sim F_2$ (alternate definition of regularity, corollary 17.7). Similarly for each point $y \in \sim F_1$, an open neighborhood V_y can be chosen such that $\overline{V}_y \subseteq \sim F_1$. Let $\mathcal{G}' = \{U_{x_1} \mid x_1 \in F_1\} \cup \{V_y \mid y \in \sim F_1\}$. $\mathcal{G}'$ is an open covering of S and S is paracompact. Hence, $\mathcal{G}'$ has a locally finite refinement $\mathcal{G}$ which is also an open covering of S. Let $\mathcal{G}$ be denoted by $\{G_\alpha \mid \alpha \in \mathfrak{A}\}$. Assume that $G_\alpha \cap F_1 \neq \emptyset$. Since for $y \in \sim F_1$, $\overline{V}_y \subseteq \sim F_1$ or, equivalently, $\overline{V}_y \cap F_1 = \emptyset$, $G_\alpha \not\subseteq V_y$ for any $y \in \sim F_1$. Hence, since $\mathcal{G}$ is a refinement of $\mathcal{G}'$, for some $x_1 \in F_1$, $G_\alpha \subseteq U_{x_1}$. Further, since $\overline{U}_{x_1} \subseteq \sim F_2$, $\overline{G}_\alpha \subseteq \sim F_2$. Thus, if $G_\alpha \cap F_1 \neq \emptyset$, $\overline{G}_\alpha \subseteq \sim F_2$. Now, let $C = \{\alpha \in \mathfrak{A} \mid G_\alpha \cap F_1 \neq \emptyset\}$. Since $\mathcal{G}$ is a covering of S, $\mathcal{G}$ covers F_1. By definition of C, then, $\bigcup_{\alpha \in C} G_\alpha \supseteq F_1$. By what was just proved above, $\bigcup_{\alpha \in C} \overline{G}_\alpha \subseteq \sim F_2$. By lemma 34.4, $\bigcup_{\alpha \in C} \overline{G}_\alpha = \overline{\bigcup_{\alpha \in C} G_\alpha}$, and consequently $\sim\bigcup_{\alpha \in C} \overline{G}_\alpha$ is open. Since $\bigcup_{\alpha \in C} \overline{G}_\alpha \subseteq \sim F_2$, $\sim\bigcup_{\alpha \in C} \overline{G}_\alpha \supseteq F_2$. Thus, $\bigcup_{\alpha \in C} G_\alpha$ and $\sim\bigcup_{\alpha \in C} \overline{G}_\alpha$ are the required disjoint open sets and so S is normal. ▌

The converse of the previous theorem is false, as lemmas 33.37 and 33.38 below show. However, for Lindelöf spaces regularity (or normality) does imply paracompactness. This will be shown below as a result of some alternate definitions of paracompactness.

33.10 Lemma. *If a Hausdorff space S is paracompact, then every open covering of S has a closed, locally finite refinement which covers S.*

Proof: Let S be Hausdorff and paracompact and let $\mathcal{G}$ be any open covering of S. By lemma 33.8, S is regular. Hence, each point s in S, has an open neighborhood U_s with the property that its closure $\overline{U}_s$ is contained in some set G_s in $\mathcal{G}$. If one such neighborhood, U_s, is chosen for each s in S, then $\mathcal{M} = \{U_s \mid s \in S\}$ is an open refinement of $\mathcal{G}$. Since S is paracompact, $\mathcal{M}$ has an open, locally finite refinement, $\mathcal{H}$, which covers S. Thus, if H is in $\mathcal{H}$, $H \subseteq U_s$ for some U_s in $\mathcal{M}$. Then, $\overline{H} \subseteq \overline{U}_s \subseteq G_s$ for some G_s in $\mathcal{G}$. So, if $\mathcal{H}^*$ denotes the set of closures of all sets in $\mathcal{H}$, then $\mathcal{H}^*$ is a closed, locally finite refinement of $\mathcal{G}$ which covers S. ▌

33.11 Lemma. *If S has the property that every open covering of S has a closed, locally finite refinement which covers S, then S is paracompact.*

Proof: Let $\mathcal{G}$ be any open covering of S. Let $\mathcal{M}$ be any locally finite refinement of $\mathcal{G}$ which covers S. Since $\mathcal{M}$ is locally finite, each point s in S has an open neighborhood U_s which intersects on a non-empty set at most a finite number of sets in $\mathcal{M}$. Choose from $\{U_s \mid s \in S\}$ a covering $\mathcal{H}$ of S. $\mathcal{H}$ is an open covering of S, and hence by hypothesis, has a closed, locally finite refinement $\mathcal{K}$ which covers S. Now for each M in $\mathcal{M}$, define $M^* = S \sim \bigcup\{L \text{ in } \mathcal{K} \mid M \cap L = \emptyset\}$. Since $\mathcal{K}$ is a closed, locally finite covering, $\bigcup\{L \text{ in } \mathcal{K} \mid M \cap L = \emptyset\}$ is, by theorem 34.4, closed in S. Hence, for each M in $\mathcal{M}$, M^* is open in S and $M \subseteq M^*$. Further, by definition, if L is in $\mathcal{K}$, $L \cap M^* \neq \emptyset$ if and only if $L \cap M \neq \emptyset$. Now since $\mathcal{M}$ is a refinement of the original open covering $\mathcal{G}$, for each M in $\mathcal{M}$, a set G_M in $\mathcal{G}$ can be chosen so that $M \subseteq G_M$. Define $\mathcal{W} = \{M^* \cap G_M \mid M \in \mathcal{M}\}$. Since M^* and G_M are both open and since $M \subseteq M^* \cap G_M$, $\mathcal{W}$ is an open covering of S. Further, since $M^* \cap G_M \subseteq G_M$, $\mathcal{W}$ is a refinement of $\mathcal{G}$. Lastly, for each s in S there exists a neighborhood N_s which intersects on a non-empty set at most a finite number of the sets in $\mathcal{K}$. Now since each set L in $\mathcal{K}$ intersects at most a finite number of sets in $\mathcal{M}$ on a non-empty set and since $M \subseteq M^* \cap G_M \subseteq M^*$, each such L intersects at most a finite number of sets in $\mathcal{W}$ on a non-empty set. Since $\mathcal{K}$ covers S, N_s intersects at most a finite number of sets in $\mathcal{W}$ on a non-empty set. $\mathcal{W}$, then, is an open, locally finite refinement of $\mathcal{G}$ which covers S, and so S is paracompact. ▌

33.12 Corollary. *A regular space S is paracompact if and only if every open covering of S has a closed, locally finite refinement which covers S.*

33.13 Lemma. *A regular space S is paracompact if and only if every open covering of S has a locally finite refinement which also covers S.*

Proof: If S is paracompact, then every open covering has a locally finite refinement which covers S. So, let every open covering of S have a locally finite refinement which covers S and let $\mathcal{G}$ be any open covering of S. Since S is regular and $\mathcal{G}$ is an open covering, each point s in S has an open neighborhood U_s with the property that its closure $\overline{U}_s$ is a subset of some set G_s in $\mathcal{G}$. Thus if $\mathcal{H} = \{\overline{U}_s \mid s \in S\}$, $\mathcal{H}$ is a closed refinement of $\mathcal{G}$ which covers S. By hypothesis, there exists a locally finite refinement $\mathfrak{M}$ of $\mathcal{H}$ which covers S. Now if M is in $\mathfrak{M}$, there exists a $\overline{U}_s$ in $\mathcal{H}$ such that $M \subseteq \overline{U}_s$. Thus $\overline{M} \subseteq \overline{U}_s \subseteq G_s$, for some G_s in $\mathcal{G}$. Thus if $\mathfrak{M}^* = \{\overline{M} \mid M \text{ is in } \mathfrak{M}\}$, $\mathfrak{M}^*$ is a closed refinement of $\mathcal{G}$ which covers S. Now if V is open and if $V \cap \overline{M}_s \neq \emptyset$, then $V \cap M_s \neq \emptyset$. Thus since $\mathfrak{M}$ is locally finite, $\mathfrak{M}^*$ is locally finite. S, then, by the previous corollary (33.12), is paracompact. ▌

33.14 Lemma. *Every countable, open covering of a topological space, S, has a countable, locally finite refinement which covers S. Further, if* $\{G_1, G_2, \ldots, G_n, \ldots\}$ *is the original, countable, open covering, then the locally finite refinement* $\{A_1, A_2, \ldots, A_n, \ldots\}$ *can be chosen so that* $A_n \subseteq G_n$.

Proof: Let $V_1 = G_1, V_2 = G_1 \cup G_2, \ldots, V_n = G_1 \cup G_2 \cup \cdots \cup G_n, \ldots$. Then, let $A_1 = V_1, A_2 = V_2 \sim V_1, \ldots, A_n = V_n \sim V_{n-1}, \ldots$. $\{A_1, A_2, \ldots, A_n, \ldots\}$ is countable. Now, since $\{G_1, \ldots, G_n, \ldots\}$ covers S, for each s in S, there is a smallest positive integer i such that s is in G_i. s is then in A_i and $\{A_1, A_2, \ldots, A_n, \ldots\}$ covers S. Now let s be any point in S. Since $\{A_1, A_2, \ldots, A_n, \ldots\}$ covers S, s is in A_n, say. s, then, is in G_n. Since G_n is open, s has a neighborhood N_s which is a subset of G_n. By definition, $A_k \cap G_n = \emptyset$ for $k > n$. Hence, $N_s \cap A_k = \emptyset$ for $k > n$ and $\{A_1, A_2, \ldots, A_n, \ldots\}$ is locally finite. ▌

33.15 Corollary. *Every regular, Lindelöf space, S, is paracompact.*

Proof: Let $\mathcal{G}$ be any open covering of S. Since S is Lindelöf, $\mathcal{G}$ has a countable subcovering $\{G_1, G_2, \ldots, G_n, \ldots\}$. By the previous lemma, $\{G_1, G_2, \ldots, G_n, \ldots\}$, and hence $\mathcal{G}$, has a locally finite refinement which covers S. By lemma 33.13, S then is paracompact. ▌

33.16 Example. Let S denote the set of real numbers and let $\mathfrak{I}$ denote the topology determined when each real number q is assigned the local base $\mathcal{B}_q = \{U_q^\epsilon \mid U_q^\epsilon = \{x \mid q \leq x < q + \epsilon\}\}$. $\{S, \mathfrak{I}\}$ was proved in example 18.48 to be regular and Lindelöf. By the previous theorem, then, $\{S, \mathfrak{I}\}$ is paracompact. However, the product space $\{S, \mathfrak{I}\} \times \{S, \mathfrak{I}\}$ was shown in example 18.48 not to be normal. Thus $\{S, \mathfrak{I}\} \times \{S, \mathfrak{I}\}$, by theorem 33.9, cannot be paracompact, and so a product of paracompact spaces is not necessarily paracompact.

33.17 Corollary. *If S is the union of a countable number of compact sets and if S is locally compact and Hausdorff, then S is paracompact.*

Proof: Since S is locally compact and Hausdorff, S is completely regular by theorem 31.35. Now let $\mathcal{G}$ be any open covering of S and let $S = \bigcup_{n=1}^{\infty} K_n$, where each K_n is compact. A finite subset $\mathcal{H}_1$ of $\mathcal{G}$ covers K_1. Similarly, a finite subset $\mathcal{H}_i$ of $\mathcal{G}$ covers K_i. Hence, $\mathcal{H} = \bigcup_{i=1}^{\infty} \mathcal{H}_i$ is a countable, open covering of S and $\mathcal{H}$ is a subcovering of $\mathcal{G}$. Thus S is Lindelöf and, by the previous lemma (33.15), S is, then, paracompact. ∎

Another useful alternate definition of paracompactness for regular spaces follows.

33.18 Definition. A family $\mathcal{M}$ of subsets of a space S is called σ-locally finite if and only if $\mathcal{M}$ is the union of a countable number of locally finite systems.

33.19 Lemma. *A regular space, S, is paracompact if and only if each open covering $\mathcal{G}$ of S has a σ-locally finite open refinement which covers S.*

Proof: If S is paracompact, then by definition, every open covering $\mathcal{G}$ has a σ-locally finite open refinement which covers S. So, let $\mathcal{G}$ be any open covering of S, and assume that $\mathcal{G}$ has a σ-locally finite open refinement $\mathcal{M}^*$ which covers S. Let $\mathcal{M}^* = \bigcup_{i=1}^{\infty} \mathcal{M}_i$, where each $\mathcal{M}_i$ is a locally finite family of open sets. Define G_i to be $\bigcup \mathcal{M}_i$. Since $\mathcal{M}^*$ covers S, $\{G_1, G_2, \ldots, G_n, \ldots\}$ is an open covering of S. By lemma 33.14, there exists a locally finite refinement $\{A_1, A_2, \ldots, A_n, \ldots\}$ which covers S and has the property that $A_n \subseteq G_n$ for all n. Now let $\mathcal{H}_i = \{A_i \cap M_\alpha^i \mid M_\alpha^i \text{ is in } \mathcal{M}_i\}$. Let $\mathcal{H}^* = \bigcup_{i=1}^{\infty} \mathcal{H}_i$. Since $M_\alpha^i \in \mathcal{M}^*$ and since $\mathcal{M}^*$ is a refinement of $\mathcal{G}$, $\mathcal{H}^*$ is a refinement of $\mathcal{G}$. Now if s is any point in S, s is in A_n, say. s is then in $G_n = \bigcup \mathcal{M}_n$. Hence for some M_α^n in $\mathcal{M}_n$, s is in M_α^n. Thus s is in $A_n \cap M_\alpha^n$ and $\mathcal{H}^*$ covers S. Since $\{A_1, A_2, \ldots, A_n, \ldots\}$ is a locally finite covering and since each $\mathcal{M}_n$ is locally finite, $\mathcal{H}^*$ is a locally finite refinement of $\mathcal{G}$. S, then, by lemma 33.13, is paracompact. ∎

Thus three alternate definitions for paracompactness in regular spaces have been established. A regular space is paracompact if and only if (1) every open covering has a closed, locally finite refinement which is also a cover, or (2) every open covering has a locally finite refinement which is also a cover, or (3) every open covering has a σ-locally finite, open refinement which is also a cover.

The next theorem with its ingenious proof by A. H. Stone, establishes metrizable spaces as a special type of paracompact spaces.

33.20 Theorem (A. H. Stone). *Every metrizable space, S, is paracompact.*

Proof: Let $\mathcal{G}$ be any open covering of the metrizable space S. Let ρ be an admissible metric for S. An open locally finite refinement of $\mathcal{G}$ which covers S

must be defined. The desired refinement is obtained by first defining a closed refinement, $\mathfrak{F}$, of $\mathcal{G}$ which covers S, and then, in terms the closed sets in $\mathfrak{F}$, defining the sets in the desired open covering $\mathcal{G}^*$.

A. First a family of closed subsets of sets in $\mathcal{G}$ is defined. By the axiom of choice, $\mathcal{G}$ can be well-ordered by some linear order relation $<$. Let $\{\mathcal{G}, <\}$ be isomorphic to γ^*-an ordinal number. $\{\mathcal{G}, <\}$ can then be represented by $\{G_1, G_2, \ldots, G_\omega, \ldots, G_\alpha, \ldots\}$, where $\alpha < \gamma^*$. Let $\{\epsilon_1, \epsilon_2, \ldots, \epsilon_n, \ldots\}$ denote a sequence of positive real numbers which converges to 0 and which has the additional property that $\epsilon_{j+1} < \epsilon_j/2$ for $j = 1, 2, \ldots$. Now if $A \subseteq S$, let $N_n(A)$ denote $\{x \in S \mid d_\rho(\{x\}, A) < \epsilon_n\}$, where d_ρ is the distance between subsets of S determined by ρ, as defined in 19.3 and 19.4. For each natural number n, then, $N_n(A)$ is an open neighborhood of the set A in the sense of definition 30.40. Now, in terms of $N_n(A)$, there is defined, for each subset A of S, a set $F_n(A) = \sim N_n(\sim A)$. As the complement of an open set, $F_n(A)$ is closed; further, by definition, $F_n(A) \subseteq A$. $F_n(A)$ is actually the set of all interior points of A which are at least a distance ϵ_n from the boundary of A. Now for each G_γ in the given open covering $\mathcal{G}$, define a subset $\Phi_n(G_\gamma)$ as follows: $\Phi_n(G_1) = F_n(G_1), \ldots,$ $\Phi_n(G_\gamma) = F_n\big(G_\gamma \sim \bigcup_{\alpha<\gamma} \Phi_n(G_\alpha)\big)$. $\Phi_n(G_\gamma)$ is, then, $\sim N_n\big(\sim(G_\gamma \sim \bigcup_{\alpha<\gamma} \Phi_n(G_\alpha))\big)$, which is equal to $\sim N_n\big(\sim G_\gamma \cup (\bigcup_{\alpha<\gamma} \Phi_n(G_\alpha))\big)$. Thus for each n and each γ, $\Phi_n(G_\gamma)$ is a closed subset of $F_n(G_\gamma)$, and hence, of G_γ. Each $\Phi_n(G_\gamma)$ is actually a closed subset of the interior of G_γ consisting of all those points of G_γ whose distance from $\bigcup_{\alpha<\gamma} \Phi_n(G_\alpha)$, as well as from $\sim G_\gamma$, is at least ϵ_n. Let $\mathfrak{F} = \{\Phi_n(G_\alpha) \mid n = 1, 2, \ldots \text{ and } \alpha < \gamma^*\}$.

B. Next, it will be shown that $\mathfrak{F} = \{\Phi_n(G_\alpha) \mid n = 1, 2, \ldots \text{ and } \alpha < \gamma^*\}$ is a covering of S. Let x be any point in S. The sets in the covering $\mathcal{G}$ have been well-ordered; hence, there is a smallest ordinal β such that $x \in G_\beta$. Since G_β is open for some ϵ_n in the given sequence, there is a spherical neighborhood $N_n(x)$, i.e., $\{y \mid \rho(x, y) < \epsilon_n\}$, such that $N_n(x) \subseteq G_\beta$. Assume that $x \notin \Phi_n(G_\beta)$. Since by definition $\Phi_n(G_\beta) = \sim N_n\big(\sim G_\beta \cup (\bigcup_{\alpha<\beta} \Phi_n(G_\alpha))\big)$, x must lie in $N_n\big(\sim G_\beta \cup (\bigcup_{\alpha<\gamma} \Phi_n(G_\alpha))\big)$. However, $N_n\big(\sim G_\beta \cup (\bigcup_{\alpha<\beta} \Phi_n(G_\alpha))\big) = \{y \mid d_\rho(\{y\}, \sim G_\beta \cup (\bigcup_{\alpha<\beta} \Phi_n(G_\alpha))) < \epsilon_n\} = \{y \mid d_\rho(\{y\}, \sim G_\beta) < \epsilon_n\} \cup \{y \mid d_\rho(\{y\}, \bigcup_{\alpha<\beta} \Phi_n(G_\alpha)) < \epsilon_n\} = N_n(\sim G_\beta) \cup N_n\big(\bigcup_{\alpha<\beta} \Phi_n(G_\alpha)\big)$. Thus $x \in N_n(\sim G_\beta)$ or $x \in N_n\big(\bigcup_{\alpha<\beta} \Phi_n(G_\alpha)\big)$. Since, by definition of G_β and ϵ_n, $N_n(x) \subseteq G_\beta$, $d_\rho(\{x\}, \sim G_\beta) \geq \epsilon_n$. Hence, $x \notin N_n(\sim G_\beta)$. Thus $x \in N_n\big(\bigcup_{\alpha<\beta} \Phi_n(G_\alpha)\big)$. This means that $d_\rho\big(\{x\}, \bigcup_{\alpha<\beta} \Phi_n(G_\alpha)\big) < \epsilon_n$. Thus there must exist a point z in $\bigcup_{\alpha<\beta} \Phi_n(G_\alpha)$ such that $\rho(x, z) < \epsilon_n$. Let $z \in \Phi_n(G_\xi)$ for some $\xi < \beta$. Then $N_n(x) \cap \Phi_n(G_\xi) \neq \emptyset$, and so $d_\rho\big(\{x\}, \Phi_n(G_\xi)\big) < \epsilon_n$. Consequently $x \in N_n\big(\Phi_n(G_\xi)\big)$. Now, by definition $N_n\big(\Phi_n(G_\xi)\big) = N_n\big(F_n(G_\xi \sim \bigcup_{\alpha<\xi} \Phi_n(G_\alpha))\big)$. Further, for any subset A of S, $N_n\big(F_n(A)\big) \subseteq A$. Hence, $N_n\big(F_n(G_\xi \sim \bigcup_{\alpha<\xi} \Phi_n(G_\alpha))\big) \subseteq G_\xi \sim \bigcup_{\alpha<\xi} \Phi_n(G_\alpha) \subseteq G_\xi$. Consequently, $N_n\big(\Phi_n(G_\xi)\big) \subseteq G_\xi$ and $x \in G_\xi$. Since $\xi < \beta$, this contradicts the definition of β. Thus, the assumption that $x \notin \Phi_n(G_\beta)$ is false. So, $x \in \Phi_n(G_\beta)$ and $\mathfrak{F} = \{\Phi_n(G_\alpha) \mid n = 1, 2, \ldots \text{ and } \beta < \gamma^*\}$ is a closed refinement of $\mathcal{G}$ which also covers S.

C. Now, a family of open subsets of sets in $\mathcal{G}$ is defined in terms of the sets in $\mathfrak{F}$. For each integer n and each $\gamma < \gamma^*$, two open neighborhoods of $\Phi_n(G_\gamma)$ are defined. Consider $N_{n+3}(\Phi_n(G_\gamma)) = \{y \mid d_\rho(\{y\}, \Phi_n(G_\gamma)) < \epsilon_{n+3}\}$ and $N_{n+2}(\Phi_n(G_\gamma)) = \{y \mid d_\rho(\{y\}, \Phi_n(G_\gamma)) < \epsilon_{n+2}\}$. $\Phi_n(G_\gamma) \subseteq N_{n+3}(\Phi_n(G_\gamma)) \subseteq N_{n+2}(\Phi_n(G_\gamma))$, since $\epsilon_{n+3} < \epsilon_{n+2}$. Further, by lemma 19.17, $\overline{N_{n+3}(\Phi_n(G_\gamma))} \subseteq N_{n+2}(\Phi_n(G_\gamma))$. Also, by definition of $\Phi_n(G_\gamma)$, $N_{n+2}(\Phi_n(G_\gamma)) \subseteq G_\gamma$. Hence, $\Phi_n(G_\gamma) \subseteq \overline{N_{n+3}(\Phi_n(G_\gamma))} \subseteq N_{n+2}(\Phi_n(G_\gamma)) \subseteq G_\gamma$, for each $n = 1, 2, \ldots$ and each ordinal $\gamma < \gamma^*$. For brevity's sake, let $\overline{N_{n+3}(\Phi_n(G_\gamma))}$ be denoted by $K_{(n,\gamma)}$, and let $N_{n+2}(\Phi_n(G_\gamma))$ be denoted by $L_{(n,\gamma)}$. Thus, $K_{(n,\gamma)}$ is closed, $L_{(n,\gamma)}$ is open and $\Phi_n(G_\gamma) \subseteq K_{(n,\gamma)} \subseteq L_{(n,\gamma)} \subseteq G_\gamma$. The desired open sets will be subsets of these open sets $L_{(n,\gamma)}$. However, in order to define these subsets it will be important to know that for any given integer n, $\bigcup_{\gamma<\gamma^*} K_{(n,\gamma)}$ is a closed set. The proof of this now follows. Let G_ξ and G_γ be any two sets in $\mathcal{G}$, the original open covering. $\xi \neq \gamma$. Let $\xi < \gamma$. Consider $N_n(\Phi_n(G_\gamma)) \cap \Phi_n(G_\xi)$. $N_n(\Phi_n(G_\gamma))$ is, by definition, $N_n(F_n(G_\gamma \sim \bigcup_{\alpha<\gamma} \Phi_n(G_\alpha)))$. As was shown in part B above, $N_n(F_n(G_\gamma \sim \bigcup_{\alpha<\gamma} \Phi_n(G_\alpha))) \subseteq G_\gamma \sim \bigcup_{\alpha<\gamma} \Phi_n(G_\alpha)$. Thus, $N_n(\Phi_n(G_\gamma)) \subseteq G_\gamma \sim \bigcup_{\alpha<\gamma} \Phi_n(G_\alpha)$. Also, since $\xi < \gamma$, $G_\gamma \sim \bigcup_{\alpha<\gamma} \Phi_n(G_\alpha) \subseteq G_\gamma \sim \Phi_n(G_\xi)$. Hence, $N_n(\Phi_n(G_\gamma)) \subseteq G_\gamma \sim \Phi_n(G_\xi)$, and so $N_n(\Phi_n(G_\gamma)) \cap \Phi_n(G_\xi) = \emptyset$. This means, by definition of $N_n(\Phi_n(G_\gamma))$, that for $x \in \Phi_n(G_\gamma)$, $y \in \Phi_n(G_\xi)$, $\rho(x, y) \geq \epsilon_n$. Thus, $d_\rho(\Phi_n(G_\gamma), \Phi_n(G_\xi)) \geq \epsilon_n$. Now, consider $L_{(n,\xi)}$ and $L_{(n,\gamma)}$. By definition, $L_{(n,\xi)} = N_{n+2}(\Phi_n(G_\xi))$ and $L_{(n,\gamma)} = N_{n+2}(\Phi_n(G_\gamma))$. Hence, if $p \in L_{(n,\gamma)}$ and $q \in L_{(n,\xi)}$, there exist x in $\Phi_n(G_\gamma)$ and y in $\Phi_n(G_\xi)$ such that $\rho(p, x) < \epsilon_{n+2}$ and $\rho(q, y) < \epsilon_{n+2}$. Now, by the preceding considerations, $\rho(x, y) \geq \epsilon_n$. Hence, $\epsilon_n \leq \rho(x, y) \leq \rho(x, p) + \rho(p, q) + \rho(q, y) \leq \epsilon_{n+2} + \rho(p, q) + \epsilon_{n+2}$. It follows that $\epsilon_n - 2\epsilon_{n+2} \leq \rho(p, q)$. Since $\epsilon_{n+2} < \epsilon_{n+1}/2$, and $\epsilon_{n+1} < \epsilon_n/2$, $\epsilon_{n+2} < \epsilon_n/4$. Thus, $2\epsilon_{n+2} < \epsilon_n/2$. Therefore, $-2\epsilon_{n+2} > -\epsilon_n/2$, and so $\epsilon_n - 2\epsilon_{n+2} > \epsilon_n - \epsilon_n/2 = \epsilon_n/2$. Thus $\rho(p, q) > \epsilon_n/2$. This means that $d_\rho(L_{(n,\gamma)}, L_{(n,\xi)}) \geq \epsilon_n/2 > \epsilon_{n+1}$. Since $K_{(n,\gamma)} \subseteq L_{(n,\gamma)}$ and $K_{(n,\xi)} \subseteq L_{(n,\xi)}$, it also follows that $d_\rho(K_{(n,\gamma)}, K_{(n,\xi)}) > \epsilon_{n+1}$ for $\xi \neq \gamma$. This last inequality is the main item needed to prove that for each integer n, $\bigcup_{\gamma<\gamma^*} K_{(n,\gamma)}$ is closed. Let z, now, be a limit point of $\bigcup_{\gamma<\gamma^*} K_{(n,\gamma)}$ and consider $N_{n+2}(z)$, the open spherical neighborhood of z of radius ϵ_{n+2}. $N_{n+2}(z)$ must contain a point s of $\bigcup_{\gamma<\gamma^*} K_{(n,\gamma)}$; let $s \in K_{(n,\alpha)}$, where $\alpha < \gamma^*$. Now, let $G_\xi \in \mathcal{G}$ such that $\xi \neq \alpha$ and let $t \in K_{(n,\xi)}$. By what was just proved above, $\rho(s, t) > \epsilon_{n+1}$. Since $\rho(s, t) \leq \rho(s, z) + \rho(z, t)$, $\epsilon_{n+1} < \rho(s, z) + \rho(z, t) < \epsilon_{n+2} + \rho(z, t)$. It then follows that $\epsilon_{n+1} - \epsilon_{n+2} < \rho(z, t)$. Since $\epsilon_{n+2} < \epsilon_{n+1}/2$, $\epsilon_{n+1}/2 < \rho(z, t)$, and so $\epsilon_{n+2} < \rho(z, t)$. Thus t cannot lie in $N_{n+2}(z)$, and so for $\xi \neq \alpha$, $N_{n+2}(z) \cap K_{(n,\xi)} = \emptyset$. This implies that $N_{n+2}(z) \cap \bigcup_{\gamma\neq\alpha} K_{(n,\gamma)} = \emptyset$. Now, since z is a limit point of $\bigcup_{\gamma<\gamma^*} K_{(n,\gamma)}$, every neighborhood of z must contain a point of $K_{(n,\alpha)}$ and z is a limit point of $K_{(n,\alpha)}$. Since, however, $K_{(n,\alpha)}$ is closed, $z \in K_{(n,\alpha)}$, and hence $z \in \bigcup_{\gamma<\gamma^*} K_{(n,\gamma)}$. Thus, for each natural number n, $\bigcup_{\gamma<\gamma^*} K_{(n,\gamma)}$ is closed. Let $\bigcup_{\gamma<\gamma^*} K_{(n,\gamma)}$ be denoted more briefly by K_n. These closed sets, K_n, will now be used to define the open subsets of each $L_{(n,\gamma)}$ which will yield the final open covering. Consider, now, that $\Phi_n(G_\gamma) \subseteq K_{(n,\gamma)} \subseteq L_{(n,\gamma)}$. Hence, $\bigcup_{\gamma<\gamma^*} \Phi_n(G_\gamma) \subseteq K_n \subseteq \bigcup_{\gamma<\gamma^*} L_{(n,\gamma)}$.

Define, next, for each $\gamma < \gamma^*$, the following sequence of sets: $G^*_{(1,\gamma)} = L_{(1,\gamma)}$ and $G^*_{(n,\gamma)} = L_{(n,\gamma)} \sim \bigcup_{k<n} K_k$, for $n = 2, 3, 4, \ldots$. Each $L_{(n,\gamma)}$ is open, by definition; further, since for each natural number k, K_k is closed, $\bigcup_{k<n} K_k$, as the union of a finite number of closed sets, is closed. Thus for each n and γ, $G^*_{(n,\gamma)}$ is open. Further since $G^*_{(n,\gamma)} \subseteq L_{(n,\gamma)}$ and since $L_{(n,\gamma)} \subseteq G_\gamma$, $\mathcal{G}^* = \{G_{(n,\gamma)} \mid n = 1, 2, \ldots \text{ and } \gamma < \gamma^*\}$ is an open refinement of the original covering $\mathcal{G}$.

D. Lastly it will be proved that $\mathcal{G}^* = \{G^*_{(n,\gamma)} \mid n = 1, 2, \ldots \text{ and } \gamma < \gamma^*\}$ is a locally finite covering of S. First let $x \in S$. By part B, above, $\{\Phi_n(G_\gamma) \mid n = 1, 2, \ldots \text{ and } \gamma < \gamma^*\}$ is a covering of S. Hence, let $x \in \Phi_n(G_\gamma)$. $\Phi_n(G_\gamma) \subseteq K_{(n,\gamma)}$, by definition of $K_{(n,\gamma)}$. Thus $\{n \mid \text{for some } \gamma < \gamma^*, x \in K_{(n,\gamma)}\} \neq \emptyset$. Let n^* be the smallest natural number in this set. Then for some $\xi < \gamma^*$, $x \in K_{(n^*,\xi)}$ and for $n < n^*$, $x \notin K_{(n,\gamma)}$ for all $\gamma < \gamma^*$. Thus $x \in K_{(n^*,\xi)} \sim \bigcup_{k<n^*} K_k$. Now, $K_{(n^*,\xi)} \sim \bigcup_{k<n^*} K_k \subseteq L_{(n^*,\xi)} \sim \bigcup_{k<n^*} K_k = G^*_{(n^*,\xi)}$. Hence, $x \in G^*_{(n^*,\xi)}$ and $\mathcal{G}^* = \{G^*_{(n,\gamma)} \mid n = 1, 2, \ldots \text{ and } \gamma < \gamma^*\}$ is an open covering of S as well as a refinement of $\mathcal{G}$. Now it must be shown that $\mathcal{G}^*$ is locally finite. Again, let x be any point of S. Since $\{\Phi_n(G_\gamma) \mid n = 1, 2, \ldots \text{ and } \gamma < \gamma^*\}$ covers S, there exists a natural number m and an ordinal ξ such that $x \in \Phi_m(G_\xi)$. Then $N_{m+3}(x) \subseteq \overline{N_{m+3}(\Phi_m(G_\xi))} = K_{(m,\xi)} \subseteq K_m = \bigcup_{\gamma<\gamma^*} K_{(m,\gamma)}$, where it is to be recalled, $N_{m+3}(A) = \{y \mid d_\rho(\{y\}, A) < \epsilon_{m+3}\}$. By definition, if $n > 1$, $G^*_{(n,\gamma)} = L_{(n,\gamma)} \sim \bigcup_{k<n} K_k$. Hence if $n > m$, $K_m \subseteq \bigcup_{k<n} K_k$, and so for $n > m$ and any $\gamma < \gamma^*$, $G^*_{(n,\gamma)} \cap K_m = \emptyset$. By definition of $N_{m+3}(x)$, its diameter is $\leq 2 \cdot \epsilon_{m+3}$ and $2 \cdot \epsilon_{m+3} < 2 \cdot \epsilon_{m+2}/2 < \epsilon_{m+1}/2$. Further, it was shown in part C that $d_\rho(L_{(m,\xi)}, L_{(m,\gamma)}) > \epsilon_{m+1}$ for $\xi \neq \gamma$. Hence if $N_{m+3}(x) \cap L_{(m,\xi)} \neq \emptyset$, $N_{m+3}(x) \cap L_{(m,\gamma)} = \emptyset$ for $\gamma \neq \xi$. Thus $N_{m+3}(x)$ can intersect, on a non-empty set, at most one set in $\{L_{(m,\gamma)} \mid \gamma < \gamma^*\}$. Further, since for any $n = 1, 2, \ldots$ and any $\gamma < \gamma^*$, $G^*_{(n,\gamma)} \subseteq L_{(n,\gamma)}$, $N_{m+3}(x)$ can intersect, on a non-empty set, at most one set in $\{G^*_{(m,\gamma)} \mid \gamma < \gamma^*\}$. Now, as was shown above, $N_{m+3}(x) \cap L_{(n,\alpha)} = \emptyset$ for any α and for all $n > m$. Thus $N_{m+3}(x) \cap G^*_{(n,\alpha)} = \emptyset$ for any α and all $n > m$. This means that the only sets in $\mathcal{G}^*$ which can intersect $N_{m+3}(x)$ on a non-empty set are possibly the sets $G^*_{(k,\gamma)}$, for $k \leq m$. Now if $k \leq m$, $\epsilon_k \geq \epsilon_m$. Hence $d_\rho(L_{(k,\gamma)}, L_{(k,\alpha)}) > \epsilon_{k+1} \geq \epsilon_{m+1}$. Now, $\epsilon_{m+1} > 2 \cdot \epsilon_{m+2} > 2 \cdot 2 \cdot \epsilon_{m+3} > 2 \cdot \epsilon_{m+3}$; the diameter of $N_{m+3}(x)$ is $\leq 2 \cdot \epsilon_{m+3}$. Hence, if $N_{m+3}(x) \cap L_{(k,\gamma)} \neq \emptyset$, $N_{m+3}(x) \cap L_{(k,\alpha)} = \emptyset$ for $\alpha \neq \gamma$. Consequently, for any integer $k \leq m$, $N_{m+3}(x)$ can intersect, on a non-empty set, at most one set in $\{L_{(k,\gamma)} \mid \gamma < \gamma^*\}$. It follows, since $G^*_{(k\cdot\gamma)} \subseteq L_{(k,\gamma)}$, that $N_{m+3}(x)$ can intersect, on a non-empty set, at most m sets in $\mathcal{G}^*$. Consequently, $\mathcal{G}^*$ is locally finite. ∎

In example 17.5 a space X is described which is Hausdorff but not regular. In the remarks following corollary 18.41, this space is described as a quotient space of a subspace, S, of Euclidean 2-space, E^2. S, as a subspace of E^2, is by theorem 20.9, metrizable, and hence, by the previous theorem, paracompact. Since, however, X is not regular, it is not paracompact by lemma 33.8. Thus not every quotient space of a paracompact space is paracompact.

Smirnov's Metrization Theorem

The classical metrization theorem of Urysohn (theorem 20.16) states, in an equivalent form (corollary 20.18) that any second countable, regular space is metrizable. Since every metrizable space is regular (theorem 19.20), regularity is a necessary condition for metrizability. However, not every metrizable space is second countable (see example 20.4 and exercise 1 following it). This means, of course, that although second countability and regularity yield together a sufficient condition for metrizability, this condition is not necessary. Yu. M. Smirnov succeeded in replacing the second countability property with a weaker one to obtain a necessary and sufficient condition for metrizability. The new property depends on the concept of a locally finite system (definition 33.1).

33.21 Definition. A topological space $\{S, \mathfrak{J}\}$ will be called *Smirnov countable* if and only if there exists a base for the topology, $\mathfrak{J}$, which is the union of a countable number of locally finite systems. Further, any base for a topology $\mathfrak{J}$ which is the union of a countable number of locally finite systems will be called a *Smirnov base.*

33.22 Theorem. *If $\{S, \mathfrak{J}\}$ is second countable, then $\{S, \mathfrak{J}\}$ is Smirnov countable.*

Proof: Any finite set of subsets of S is locally finite in $\{S, \mathfrak{J}\}$. Consequently, if $\mathcal{B} = \{G_1, G_2, \ldots, G_n, \ldots\}$ is a countable base for the topology $\mathfrak{J}$, each singleton set $\{G_n\}$ is a locally finite system, and so $\mathcal{B}$ is the union of a countable number of locally finite systems. ∎

33.23 Theorem. *If $\{S, \mathfrak{J}\}$ is Smirnov countable, then $\{S, \mathfrak{J}\}$ is first countable.*

Proof: Let $\mathcal{B}$ denote a base for $\mathfrak{J}$ which is the union of a countable number of locally finite systems. Let $\mathcal{B} = \bigcup_i \mathfrak{M}_i$, where $\mathfrak{M}_i$, for $i = 1, 2, \ldots$, is a locally finite system of open sets in $\mathfrak{J}$. Let p be any point of $\{S, \mathfrak{J}\}$. For each natural number i, p has an open neighborhood U_i such that U_i intersects, on a non-empty set, at most a finite number of sets in $\mathfrak{M}_i$. Let $V_1 = U_1$, $V_2 = U_1 \cap U_2, \ldots, V_n = U_1 \cap \cdots \cap U_n, \ldots$. $p \in \bigcap_i V_i$. Thus p lies in at most a finite number of sets in $\mathfrak{M}_i$, for $i = 1, 2, \ldots$. Since $\bigcup_i \mathfrak{M}_i$ is a base for $\mathfrak{J}$, p, then, lies in at most a countable number of sets in $\mathcal{B}$. Hence, $\{S, \mathfrak{J}\}$ is first countable. ∎

33.24 Theorem (Stone-Smirnov). *If a topological space S is metrizable, then S is regular and Smirnov countable.*

Proof: If S is metrizable, it is regular (theorem 19.20) and paracompact (theorem 33.20). So for n a positive integer, let $\mathcal{G}_n = \{G_p^n \mid p \in S \text{ and } G_p^n = \{x \mid \rho(p, x) < 1/n, \text{ for } \rho \text{ an admissible metric on } S\}\}$. $\mathcal{G}_n$ has a locally finite refinement $\mathfrak{M}_n$ which is an open covering of S. Thus the set $\{\mathfrak{M}_1, \mathfrak{M}_2, \ldots, \mathfrak{M}_n, \ldots\}$ is a countable set of locally finite systems, each of which covers S. It must be shown that $\bigcup_n \mathfrak{M}_n$ is a base for the topology on S. Let $p \in S$ and let N be any neighborhood of p in S. By definition of a metrizable space, there exists a spherical neighborhood G_p^k such that $G_p^k \subseteq N$. $G_p^k = \{x \mid \rho(p, x) < 1/k\}$. Now consider $\mathcal{G}_{2k}$, the open covering of S consisting of all spherical neighborhoods of radius $1/2k$, and its locally finite refinement $\mathfrak{M}_{2k}$ mentioned above. Since $\mathfrak{M}_{2k}$ covers S, there exists a set M_{2k} of $\mathfrak{M}_{2k}$ such that $p \in M_{2k}$. Since $\mathfrak{M}_{2k}$ is a refinement of $\mathcal{G}_{2k}$, there exists a spherical neighborhood G_q^{2k}, such that $M_{2k} \subseteq G_q^{2k}$. Now let $y \in M_{2k}$. Then $\rho(q, y) < 1/2k$ and $\rho(q, p) < 1/2k$. Consequently, $\rho(p, y) < 1/k$ and $y \in G_p^k$. This means that $M_{2k} \subseteq G_p^k \subseteq N$. Since $M_{2k} \in \bigcup_n \mathfrak{M}_n$, $\bigcup_n \mathfrak{M}_n$ is a base for the topology on S. Thus S is Smirnov countable. ▮

Smirnov's metrization theorem (the converse of the previous theorem), proved below, will establish examples of spaces which are first countable and not Smirnov countable, and of spaces which are Smirnov countable but not second countable.

First, a special case of the metrization theorem is proved.

33.25 Theorem. *If a T_1-space $\{S, \mathfrak{I}\}$ has a Smirnov base which is the union of a finite number of locally finite systems, then $\{S, \mathfrak{I}\}$ is discrete, and hence metrizable.*

Proof: Let $\{\mathfrak{M}_1, \mathfrak{M}_2, \ldots, \mathfrak{M}_n\}$ be a finite set of locally finite systems such that $\mathcal{B} = \bigcup_{i=1}^n \mathfrak{M}_i$ is a base for the topology $\mathfrak{I}$. Let $x \in S$. Since each $\mathfrak{M}_i$ is locally finite, x has open neighborhoods $U_1, U_2, \ldots, U_i, \ldots, U_n$, such that U_i, for $i = 1, \ldots, n$, intersects on a non-empty set at most a finite number of the sets in $\mathfrak{M}_i$. Let $V = \bigcap_{i=1}^n U_i$. V is a neighborhood of x which intersects on a non-empty set at most a finite number of the sets in the base $\mathcal{B}$. Thus x is in at most a finite number of the sets in $\mathcal{B}$ and x, then, has a finite local base, $N_1, N_2, \ldots, N_k$, say. By corollary 15.11, $\bigcap_{i=1}^k N_i = \{x\}$. Hence, $\{x\}$ is a neighborhood of x and is in the discrete topology for S. The metric defined by $\rho(x, x) = 0$, and $\rho(x, y) = 1$ for $x \neq y$, determines $\mathfrak{I}$. ▮

To prove his, now classical, metrization theorem, Urysohn established for each regular, second countable space, a topological imbedding into a metrizable space which can be taken to be Hilbert space (theorems 18.22, 20.16 and corollary 21.14). Smirnov first defines a generalized Hilbert space and then defines, for any regular, Smirnov countable space, S, a homeomorphism from S into a particular model of a generalized Hilbert space.

33.26 Definition. Let $\mathfrak{A}$ be any set. Let $R^{\mathfrak{A}}$ denote the product set consisting of all functions f from $\mathfrak{A}$ into R, the set of real numbers. Let $H_{\mathfrak{A}}$ be defined as follows: $H_{\mathfrak{A}} = \{f \in R^{\mathfrak{A}} \mid f(a) = 0$ except for at most a countable number of elements in $\mathfrak{A}$, and $\sum_{a \in \mathfrak{A}} (f(a))^2$ converges$\}$. $H_{\mathfrak{A}}$ will be called a *generalized Hilbert set*.

33.27 Lemma. *Let f and g be points of $H_{\mathfrak{A}}$. If $\rho_{H_{\mathfrak{A}}}(f, g)$ is defined as $\sqrt{\sum_{a \in \mathfrak{A}} (f(a) - g(a))^2}$, then $\rho_{H_{\mathfrak{A}}}$ is a metric on $H_{\mathfrak{A}}$ and is called the Hilbert metric.*

Proof: The proofs of lemmas 21.6 and 21.7 apply here line by line, since the set of coordinates on which either f or g is non-zero is countable, and hence can be considered to be a sequence. ∎

33.28 Definition. If $\mathfrak{A}$ is any set, then the space $\{H_{\mathfrak{A}}, \mathfrak{J}_{\rho_{H_{\mathfrak{A}}}}\}$, where $\mathfrak{J}_{\rho_{H_{\mathfrak{A}}}}$ denotes the metrizable topology determined on $H_{\mathfrak{A}}$ by the Hilbert metric $\rho_{H_{\mathfrak{A}}}$, is called a *generalized Hilbert space.*

The following definition and lemma will be used in Smirnov's metrization theorem.

33.29 Definition. A set A in a space S is called a *G_δ-set* if and only if A is the intersection of a countable number of open sets. A set B in a space S is called an *F_σ-set* if and only if B is the union of a countable number of closed sets.

33.30 Lemma. *If S is a normal space and U is an open F_σ-subset of S, then there exists a continuous function g from S into the unit interval space,* [0, 1], *such that $g^{-1}(0) = S \sim U$.*

Proof: Let $U = \bigcup_{n=1}^{\infty} A_n$, where A_n is closed for $n = 1, 2, \ldots$. $\sim U$, the complement of U in S, is closed. $\sim U = \sim \bigcup_{n=1}^{\infty} A_n = \bigcap_{n=1}^{\infty} \sim A_n$. S is normal; hence, since $\sim U \cap A_1 = \emptyset$, there exists, by theorem 18.23, a continuous function f_1 from S into [0, 1] such that $f_1[\sim U] = 0$ and $f_1[A_1] = 1$. Similarly, for each natural number n define a continuous function f_n from S into [0, 1] such that $f_n[\sim U] = 0$ and $f_n[A_n] = 1$. Next, for $x \in S$, define $g_n(x) = 1/2$ minimum $\{|f_n(x)|, 1/2^n\}$ and define $g(x) = \sum_n g_n(x)$. $\sum_n g_n(x)$ converges uniformly, by the comparison test with $(1/2)(1 + 1/2 + \cdots + 1/2^n + \cdots)$. Hence, $g(x)$ is defined for every x in S and is continuous by corollary 21.23. Now, if $x \in \sim U$, $g(x) = 0$, by definition. Hence, $\sim U \subseteq g^{-1}(0)$. Further, if $x \in g^{-1}(0)$, then $g(x) = 0$, i.e., $\sum_n g_n(x) = 0$. Thus $g_n(x) = 0$ for all n. This means that $f_n(x) = 0$ for every n, and so that $x \in \sim A_n$ for every n. Thus $x \in (\bigcap_{n=1}^{\infty} \sim A_n) = \sim U$ and $g^{-1}(0) \subseteq \sim U$. Thus $g^{-1}(0) = \sim U$. ∎

33.31 Theorem. (Smirnov) *If a topological space S is regular and Smirnov countable, then it is metrizable.*

Proof: Let $\{\mathfrak{M}_1, \mathfrak{M}_2, \ldots, \mathfrak{M}_n, \ldots\}$ be a countable set of locally finite systems of open sets such that $\bigcup_n \mathfrak{M}_n$ is a base, $\mathfrak{B}$, for the topology on S. The sets in $\mathfrak{M}_n$ can be denoted by symbols $M_{(n,\alpha)}$, where $n = 1, 2, \ldots$ and α denotes an element in some indexing set for $\mathfrak{M}_n$.

A. First it will be shown that S is normal. Let F_1 and F_2 be two disjoint closed sets in S. Since S is regular, for each x in F_1 a set $M_{(n(x),\alpha(x))}$ in $\mathcal{B}$ can be chosen such that $\overline{M}_{(n(x),\alpha(x))} \cap F_2 = \emptyset$. Thus an open covering $\mathcal{G}_1$ of F_1 is defined. Similarly for each y in F_2 a set $M_{(m(y),\gamma(y))}$ in $\mathcal{B}$ can be chosen such that $\overline{M}_{(m(y),\gamma(y))} \cap F_1 = \emptyset$ and an open covering $\mathcal{G}_2$ of F_2 is defined. Now for each natural number k, let $G_k = \bigcup_{x \in F_1} M_{(k,\alpha(x))}$, i.e., G_k is the union of all the sets of $\mathcal{G}_1$ which lie in $\mathfrak{M}_k$, and let $H_k = \bigcup_{y \in F_2} M_{(k,\gamma(y))}$, i.e., H_k is the union of all the sets of $\mathcal{G}_2$ which lie in $\mathfrak{M}_k$. $\mathfrak{M}_k$ is locally finite. Hence, by lemma 33.4, $\overline{G}_k = \bigcup_{x \in F_1} \overline{M}_{(k,\alpha(x))}$ and $\overline{H}_k = \bigcup_{y \in F_2} \overline{M}_{(k,\gamma(y))}$. By definition of $M_{(k,\alpha(x))}$ and $M_{(k,\gamma(y))}$, $\overline{G}_k \cap F_2 = \emptyset$ and $\overline{H}_k \cap F_1 = \emptyset$, for each natural number k. Now let $U_k = G_k \sim \bigcup_{j \leq k} \overline{H}_j$ and let $V_k = H_k \sim \bigcup_{j \leq k} \overline{G}_j$. For each natural number k, U_k and V_k are open subsets of S. Hence, $U^* = \bigcup_k U_k$ and $V^* = \bigcup_k V_k$ are also open subsets of S. Further, by definition of $\overline{H}_j$ and $\overline{G}_j$, $U^* \cap F_2 = \emptyset$, $V^* \cap F_1 = \emptyset$, $F_1 \subseteq U^*$ and $F_2 \subseteq V^*$. Lastly, let $z \in U^* \cap V^*$. Let $z \in U_n$ and let $z \in V_m$ and let $n \leq m$. This implies that $z \in V_m = H_m \sim \bigcup_{j \leq m} \overline{G}_j$. However, since $U_n = G_n \sim \bigcup_{j \leq n} \overline{H}_j$, $z \in G_n$. This is a contradiction. Hence, $U^* \cap V^* = \emptyset$ and S is normal. Thus every regular, Smirnov countable space is normal.

B. Now, it will be shown that every open set in S is an F_σ-set. Let G be any open set in S and let $p \in G$. Since $\bigcup_n \mathfrak{M}_n$ is a base for the topology on S and since S is regular, there exists a set $M_{(n(p),\alpha(p))}$ in $\bigcup_n \mathfrak{M}_n$ such that $p \in M_{(n(p),\alpha(p))}$ and $\overline{M}_{(n(p),\alpha(p))} \subseteq G$. Hence, an open covering $\mathcal{G}$ of G is defined. Let G_1 denote the union of all sets of $\mathcal{G}$ which lie in $\mathfrak{M}_1$, and similarly, for each natural number n let G_n be $\bigcup_{p \in G} M_{(n,\alpha(p))}$, i.e., G_n is the union of all sets in the covering $\mathcal{G}$ which lie in $\mathfrak{M}_n$. Now, certainly, $\bigcup_n G_n = G$ and, since $\mathfrak{M}_n$ is locally finite, $\overline{G}_n = \bigcup_{p \in G} \overline{M}_{(n,\alpha(p))}$, by lemma 33.4. Hence, since $\overline{M}_{(n,\alpha(p))} \subseteq G$, $G = \bigcup_n \overline{G}_n$ and G is an F_σ-subset of S.

C. Next a function from S into a generalized Hilbert space is defined. As above, $\mathcal{B} = \bigcup_{i=1}^{\infty} \mathfrak{M}_i$, where each $\mathfrak{M}_i$ is a locally finite system of open sets and $\mathcal{B}$ is a base for the topology on S. Hence, the sets in $\mathcal{B}$ can again be indexed by ordered pairs in the set $(\{1\} \times \mathfrak{M}_1) \cup (\{2\} \times \mathfrak{M}_2) \cup \cdots \cup (\{n\} \times \mathfrak{M}_n) \cup \cdots$. Let $M_{(i,\alpha)}$ be, then, a set in $\mathfrak{M}_i$. $M_{(i,\alpha)}$ is open in S, and hence by what was proved above, $M_{(i,\alpha)}$ is an F_σ-subset of S. By lemma 33.30, a continuous function $g_{(i,\alpha)}$ can be defined from S into $[0, 1]$ such that $g_{(i,\alpha)}^{-1}(0) = S \sim M_{(i,\alpha)}$. Now, $\mathfrak{M}_i$ is locally finite. Hence, if $s \in S$, s has a neighborhood U_s which intersects, on a non-empty set, at most a finite number of the sets in $\mathfrak{M}_i$. Hence, for a fixed natural number i and any point s in S, there exists at most a finite number of the functions $g_{(i,\alpha)}$ which are not 0 at s. Thus

$$1 + \sum_{\alpha} (g_{(i,\alpha)}(s))^2$$

is defined for any s in S. Let

$$h_{(i,\alpha)}(s) = \frac{g_{(i,\alpha)}(s)}{\sqrt{1 + \sum_\alpha (g_{(i,\alpha)}(s))^2}}.$$

$h_{(i,\alpha)}$ is continuous and $0 \leq h_{(i,\alpha)}(s) < 1$ for all s in S. Now for each s in S define the function ξ_s from $\mathcal{B}$ into [0, 1] as follows:

$$\xi_s(M_{(i,\alpha)}) = \frac{h_{(i,\alpha)}(s)}{2^i}.$$

For each $M_{(i,\alpha)}$ in $\mathcal{B}$, $0 \leq \xi_s(M_{(i,\alpha)}) < 1/2^i$. Further, ξ_s is non-zero on at most a finite number of sets in each $\mathfrak{M}_i$, by definition. Since there are only a countable number of $\mathfrak{M}_i$, ξ_s is non-zero on at most a countable number of sets in $\mathcal{B}$. Also,

$$\sum_{i,\alpha} (\xi_s(M_{(i,\alpha)}))^2 = \sum_{i,\alpha} \left(\frac{h_{(i,\alpha)}(s)}{2^i}\right)^2$$

by definition of ξ_s. Thus, by the comparison test with $\sum_{i=1}^{\infty} 1/2^i$,

$$\sum_{(i,\alpha)} (\xi_s(M_{(i,\alpha)}))^2$$

is defined, as a unique real number, and, by definitions 33.26, 33.28 and lemma 33.27, ξ_s is a point in the generalized Hilbert space, $H_{\mathcal{B}}$. Next, define $h^*(s) = \xi_s$ for each s in S. h^* is, then, a function from S into the metrizable space $H_{\mathcal{B}}$.

D. h^* is, now, proved to be 1:1 and continuous. Let s and t be distinct elements in S. Since S is regular and $\bigcup_{i=1}^{\infty} \mathfrak{M}_i$ is a base for the topology on S, there exists an open neighborhood $M_{(i,\alpha)}$ of s in $\bigcup_{i=1}^{\infty} \mathfrak{M}_i$ such that $t \notin M_{(i,\alpha)}$. Hence, $\xi_s(M_{(i,\alpha)}) \neq 0$ and $\xi_t(M_{(i,\alpha)}) = 0$, by definition. Thus $h^*(s) \neq h^*(t)$ and h^* is 1:1. To prove that h^* is continuous let $s \in S$ and let V_ϵ be a spherical neighborhood of $h^*(s)$ in the metrizable space $H_{\mathcal{B}}$ using the Hilbert metric. Let $V^* = V_\epsilon \cap h^*[S]$.

$$V^* = \left\{\xi_t \,\middle|\, \sqrt{\sum_{i,\alpha} (\xi_t(M_{(i,\alpha)}) - \xi_s(M_{(i,\alpha)}))^2} < \epsilon\right\}.$$

Now, by definition,

$$\sum_{i,\alpha} (\xi_t(M_{(i,\alpha)}) - \xi_s(M_{(i,\alpha)}))^2 = \sum_{i,\alpha} \left(\frac{h_{(i,\alpha)}(s)}{2^i} - \frac{h_{(i,\alpha)}(t)}{2^i}\right)^2.$$

By the archimedean property of the order on the real numbers, there exists a natural number q such that $1/2^q < \epsilon^2/4$. Since each $\mathfrak{M}_i$ is locally finite, for each $i \leq q$, s has a neighborhood U_s^i which intersects, on a non-empty set, at most a finite number of sets in $\mathfrak{M}_i$. Let $U_s^* = U_s^1 \cap \cdots \cap U_s^q$. U_s^* is then a neighborhood of s which intersects, on a non-empty set, at most a finite number of sets in $\mathfrak{M}_1 \cup \cdots \cup \mathfrak{M}_q$. Let these sets be k in number and be denoted by $M_{(i_1,\alpha_1)}, M_{(i_2,\alpha_2)}, \ldots, M_{(i_k,\alpha_k)}$, where, of course, $i_1 \leq q, \ldots, i_k \leq q$. Now consider the corresponding continuous functions $h_{(i_1,\alpha_1)}, \ldots, h_{(i_k,\alpha_k)}$. For each j, such that $1 \leq j \leq k$, there exists a neighborhood N_s^j of s such that $N_s^j \subseteq U_s^*$ and such that for $x \in N_s^j$,

$$\left| \frac{h_{(i_j,\alpha_j)}(x)}{2^{i_j}} - \frac{h_{(i_j,\alpha_j)}(s)}{2^{i_j}} \right| < \frac{\epsilon}{\sqrt{2k}}.$$

Let $N_s^* = N_s^1 \cap \cdots \cap N_s^k$. Now N_s^* is a neighborhood of s which has the property that if $x \in N_s^*$,

$$\left| \frac{h_{(i_j,\alpha_j)}(x)}{2^{i_j}} - \frac{h_{(i_j,\alpha_j)}(s)}{2^{i_j}} \right| < \frac{\epsilon}{\sqrt{2k}}$$

for $1 \leq j \leq k$. Further, if $i \leq q$ and if $\alpha \neq \alpha_1, \ldots, \alpha \neq \alpha_k$, then $M_{(i,\alpha)} \cap N_s^* = \emptyset$. Also, for such pairs (i, α), $h_{(i,\alpha)}(s) = 0 = h_{(i,\alpha)}(x)$. Thus, for x in N_s^*,

$$\sum_{i \leq q, \alpha} \left(\frac{h_{(i,\alpha)}(x)}{2^i} - \frac{h_{(i,\alpha)}(s)}{2^i} \right)^2$$

has at most a finite number of non-zero terms and, by definition of N_s^*,

$$\sum_{i \leq q, \alpha} \left(\frac{h_{(i,\alpha)}(x)}{2^i} - \frac{h_{(i,\alpha)}(s)}{2^i} \right)^2 \leq k \cdot \left(\frac{\epsilon}{\sqrt{2k}} \right)^2 = \frac{\epsilon^2}{2}.$$

The rest of the summation that enters the definition of $\rho(\xi_s, \xi_x)$ in $H_{\mathfrak{B}}$ is

$$\sum_{i > q, \alpha} \left(\frac{h_{(i,\alpha)}(x)}{2^i} - \frac{h_{(i,\alpha)}(s)}{2^i} \right)^2.$$

Now

$$\sum_{i > q, \alpha} \left(\frac{h_{(i,\alpha)}(x)}{2^i} - \frac{h_{(i,\alpha)}(s)}{2^i} \right)^2 \leq \sum_{i > q, \alpha} \left(\frac{h_{(i,\alpha)}(x)}{2^i} \right)^2 + \left(\frac{h_{(i,\alpha)}(s)}{2^i} \right)^2.$$

This latter follows from the basic inequality $(A - B)^2 \leq A^2 + B^2$ for $A \geq 0$ and $B \geq 0$. Now by definition,

$$\sum_\alpha (h_{(i,\alpha)}(x))^2 < 1 \quad \text{and} \quad \sum_\alpha (h_{(i,\alpha)}(s))^2 < 1.$$

Hence,

$$\sum_\alpha \left(\frac{h_{(i,\alpha)}(x)}{2^i} \right)^2 + \left(\frac{h_{(i,\alpha)}(s)}{2^i} \right)^2$$

$$= \frac{1}{(2^i)^2} \left(\sum_\alpha (h_{(i,\alpha)}(x))^2 + (h_{(i,\alpha)}(s))^2 \right) < \frac{1}{(2^i)^2} \cdot 2.$$

Thus

$$\sum_{i > q, \alpha} \left(\left(\frac{h_{(i,\alpha)}(x)}{2^i} \right)^2 + \left(\frac{h_{(i,\alpha)}(s)}{2^i} \right)^2 \right) < \sum_{i > q} \frac{2}{(2^i)^2} < \sum_{i > q} \frac{2}{2^i} = \sum_{i > q} \frac{1}{2^{i-1}}.$$

Since, by definition of q, $1/2^q < \epsilon^2/4$,

$$\sum_{i>q} \frac{1}{2^{i-1}} = \frac{1}{2^q} \cdot 2 < 2 \cdot \frac{\epsilon^2}{4} = \frac{\epsilon^2}{2}.$$

Hence, if $x \in N_s^*$,

$$\rho(\xi_x, \xi_s) = \sqrt{\sum_{i,\alpha} \left(\frac{h_{(i,\alpha)}(x)}{2^i} - \frac{h_{(i,\alpha)}(s)}{2^i}\right)^2} < \sqrt{\frac{\epsilon^2}{2} + \frac{\epsilon^2}{2}} = \epsilon.$$

Consequently, $h^*[N_s^*] \subseteq V^*$ and h^* is continuous.

E. Lastly, it is proved that $(h^*)^{-1}$ is continuous. Let ξ_s, as defined in part C, be any point in $h^*[S]$ in $H_{\mathcal{B}}$ and let s be its pre-image in S. Let U_s be any neighborhood of s in S. Since $\mathcal{B} = \bigcup_{i=1}^{\infty} \mathfrak{M}_i$ is a base for the topology on S, there exists a set $M_{(j,\gamma)}$ in $\mathcal{B}$ such that $M_{(j,\gamma)} \subseteq U_s$ and such that $s \in M_{(j,\gamma)}$. Now, by definition of $h_{(j,\gamma)}$, $h_{(j,\gamma)}(s) > 0$. Hence, $\xi_s(M_{(j,\gamma)}) > 0$. Now consider ξ_x in $h^*[S]$ such that $\rho(\xi_x, \xi_s) < \xi_s(M_{(j,\gamma)})$, where ρ denotes the Hilbert metric on $H_{\mathcal{B}}$. If $\xi_x(M_{(j,\gamma)}) = 0$, then $\xi_x(M_{(j,\gamma)}) - \xi_s(M_{(j,\gamma)}) = -\xi_s(M_{(j,\gamma)})$, and hence

$$\rho(\xi_x, \xi_s) = \sqrt{\sum_{i,\alpha} (\xi_x(M_{(i,\alpha)}) - \xi_s(M_{(i,\alpha)}))^2} \geq \xi_s(M_{(j,\gamma)}).$$

This contradicts the definition of ξ_x, and so $\xi_x(M_{(j,\gamma)}) > 0$. Thus, by definition of $\xi_x(M_{(j,\gamma)})$, $(h_{(j,\gamma)}(x))/2^j > 0$ and, by definition of $h_{(j,\gamma)}$, $x \in M_{(j,\gamma)} \subseteq U_s$. Consequently, if $\rho(\xi_x, \xi_s) < \xi_s(M_{(j,\gamma)})$, $(h^*)^{-1}(\xi_x) \in U_s$ and h^{*-1} is continuous. Thus h^* is a homeomorphism from S into the metrizable space $H_{\mathcal{B}}$. By theorem 20.9 and lemma 20.15, S is then metrizable. ∎

Thus theorems 33.24 and 33.31 together state that a space S is metrizable if and only if S is regular and Smirnov countable. As a result of theorem 33.22, Urysohn's metrization theorem (corollary 20.18) is then an immediate corollary of Smirnov's metrization theorem.

33.32 Example. Consider the space $\{S, \mathfrak{I}\}$ of example 18.48 where S is the set of real numbers and $\mathfrak{I}$ is the topology determined by the local bases $\mathcal{B}_q = \{U^\epsilon \mid U^\epsilon = \{x \mid q \leq x < q + \epsilon\}\}$. Let $\mathcal{G} = \{G_p^n \mid p \in S, n$ is a natural number and $G_p^n = \{x \mid p \leq x < p + 1/n\}\}$. $\mathcal{G}$ is a base for $\mathfrak{I}$ and, as a result, $\{S, \mathfrak{I}\}$ is first countable. In example 18.48, $\{S, \mathfrak{I}\}$ was proved to be regular. Thus $\{S, \mathfrak{I}\}$ is regular and first countable. However in example 18.48, $\{S, \mathfrak{I}\} \times \{S, \mathfrak{I}\}$ was proved to be non-normal. By theorem 19.20, $\{S, \mathfrak{I}\} \times \{S, \mathfrak{I}\}$ is then not metrizable. By theorem 20.12, this means that $\{S, \mathfrak{I}\}$ is not metrizable. It then follows, from theorem 33.31, that $\{S, \mathfrak{I}\}$ is not Smirnov countable. Thus $\{S, \mathfrak{I}\}$ is regular and first countable but not Smirnov countable, and the converse of theorem 33.23 is false. Further, example 20.4 and exercise 1 following it, show that not every metrizable space is second countable. Thus the converse of theorem 33.22 is false.

EXERCISE 6. Consider the space $\{S, \mathfrak{I}\}$ of the previous example and the base $\mathcal{G} = \{G_p^n \mid p \in S, n$ is a natural number$\}$, where $G_p^n = \{x \mid p \leq x < p + 1/n\}$. For each natural number k, let $\Gamma_k = \{G_p^n \mid n = k\}$. Γ_k is, then, an open covering of $\{S, \mathfrak{I}\}$, and $\mathcal{G} = \bigcup_k \Gamma_k$. In example 33.16, $\{S, \mathfrak{I}\}$ was shown to be paracompact. Hence, for each natural number k, Γ_k has an open locally finite refinement, $\mathcal{V}_k$, which also covers S. Let $\mathcal{V}^* = \bigcup_k \mathcal{V}_k$. $\mathcal{V}^*$ is, then, the union of a countable number of locally finite open systems. Why, then, in the light of theorem 33.31, is $\{S, \mathfrak{I}\}$ not a metric space?

LOCAL METRIZABILITY AND COMPACTNESS

Smirnov proved another metrization theorem which states that Dieudonné's paracompactness is a necessary and sufficient condition for locally metrizable, Hausdorff spaces to be metrizable.

33.33 Lemma. *Let S be a normal space and let $\mathcal{G}$ be a locally finite open covering of S. Then there is an open covering $\mathcal{H}$ of S such that for each G_α in $\mathcal{G}$ there is an H_α in $\mathcal{H}$ such that $\overline{H}_\alpha \subseteq G_\alpha$.*

Proof: Let $\mathcal{G}$ be well ordered. $\mathcal{G} = \{G_1, G_2, \ldots; G_\omega, G_{\omega+1}, \ldots; \ldots G_\alpha \ldots\}$. Let α^* be the ordinal number of this ordering of $\mathcal{G}$. Let $F_1 = S \sim \bigcup_{\alpha>1} G_\alpha$. $F_1 \subseteq G_1$ and, since S is normal, there exists an open set U, such that $F_1 \subseteq H_1 \subseteq \overline{H}_1 \subseteq G_1$. Let $\mathcal{H}_1$ denote $\{M \mid M = H_1$ or $M = G_\alpha$ for $\alpha > 1\}$. $\mathcal{G}_1$ is an open covering of S. Assume next that for some ordinal γ in α^*, H_α has been defined for every $\alpha < \gamma$ such that $\overline{H}_\alpha \subseteq G_\alpha$ and $\mathcal{H}_\alpha = \{M \mid M = H_\lambda$ for $\lambda \leq \alpha$ or $M = G_\lambda$ for $\alpha < \lambda < \alpha^*\}$ is an open covering for S. Consider, now, $\mathcal{H}_\gamma^* = \{M \mid M = H_\lambda$ for $\lambda < \gamma$ or $M = G_\lambda$ for $\gamma \leq \lambda < \alpha^*\}$. If γ is a non-limit ordinal (definition 28.33 and the preceding discussion), then $\gamma = \alpha + 1$ for some ordinal α. This means that $\mathcal{H}_\gamma^* = \mathcal{H}_\alpha$. Hence, $\mathcal{H}_\gamma^*$ is a covering of S. If γ is a limit ordinal, then γ is not finite. Let $s \in S$. If $s \in \bigcup_{\gamma\leq\lambda<\alpha^*} G_\lambda$, then $\mathcal{H}_\gamma^*$ covers $\{s\}$. Let $s \notin \bigcup_{\gamma\leq\lambda<\alpha^*} G_\lambda$. Since the original covering $\mathcal{G}$ is locally finite, there exists a neighborhood N_s of s which intersects, on a non-empty set, at most a finite number of the sets in $\mathcal{G}$. Since γ is not finite, this means that for some $\tilde{\alpha} < \gamma$, $s \notin \bigcup_{\alpha^*>\lambda>\tilde{\alpha}} G_\lambda$. However, since $\mathcal{H}_{\tilde{\alpha}}$, which is $\{M \mid M = H_\lambda$ for $\lambda \leq \tilde{\alpha}$, or $M = G_\lambda$ for $\tilde{\alpha} < \lambda < \alpha^*\}$, is, by definition of γ, a covering of S, $s \in H_\lambda$ for some λ such that $\lambda \leq \tilde{\alpha} < \gamma$. Consequently, $\mathcal{H}_\gamma^*$ is a covering of S. Thus whether γ is a limit ordinal or a non-limit ordinal, $\mathcal{H}_\gamma^*$ is a covering of S. Now, let $F_\gamma = S \sim (\bigcup_{\gamma<\lambda<\alpha^*} G_\lambda \cup \bigcup_{\lambda<\gamma} H_\lambda)$. F_γ is closed in S. Further, since $\mathcal{H}_\gamma^*$ is a covering of S, $F_\gamma \subseteq G_\gamma$. Also, since S is normal, there exists an open set H_γ such that $F_\gamma \subseteq H_\gamma \subseteq \overline{H}_\gamma \subseteq G_\gamma$. Now let $\mathcal{H}_\gamma = \{M \mid M = H_\lambda$ for $\lambda \leq \gamma$ or $M = G_\lambda$ for $\gamma < \lambda < \alpha^*\}$. If $s \in S$ and if $s \notin G_\lambda$ for all λ such that $\gamma < \lambda < \alpha^*$ and $s \notin H_\lambda$ for all λ such that $\lambda < \gamma$, then $s \in S \sim (\bigcup_{\gamma<\lambda<\alpha^*} G_\lambda \cup \bigcup_{\lambda<\gamma} H_\lambda)$. Consequently, $s \in F_\gamma$ and $F_\gamma \subseteq H_\gamma$. Thus $\mathcal{H}_\gamma$ is a covering of S. It follows then by transfinite induction, which is a result of the well-ordering property of the natural ordering on any set of ordinals, that for each $\gamma < \alpha^*$ an open set H_γ has been defined such that $\overline{H}_\gamma \subseteq G_\gamma$ for G_γ in $\mathcal{G}$ and an open covering $\mathcal{H}_\gamma$ has been defined such that $\mathcal{H}_\gamma = \{M \mid M = H_\lambda$ for $\lambda \leq \gamma$, or $M = G_\lambda$ for $\gamma < \lambda < \alpha^*\}$. Now let $\mathcal{H} = \{M \mid M = H_\gamma$ for some $\gamma < \alpha^*\}$. If α^* is a non-limit ordinal, then $\alpha^* = \alpha + 1$ and $\alpha < \alpha^*$. Hence, $\mathcal{H}_\alpha$ is defined as $\{M \mid M = H_\lambda$ for $\lambda \leq \alpha$, or $M = G_\lambda$ for $\alpha < \lambda < \alpha^*\} = \{M \mid M = H_\lambda$ for $\lambda \leq \alpha\} = \{M \mid M = H_\lambda$ for $\lambda < \alpha^*\} = \mathcal{H}$. $\mathcal{H}_\alpha$ was proved to be a covering of S. Hence $\mathcal{H}$ is the desired open covering of S. If α^* is a limit ordinal, then, again, α^* is not finite. Let $s \in S$. Then since the original open covering $\mathcal{G}$ is locally finite, there exists an ordinal $\gamma < \alpha^*$ such that $s \notin \bigcup_{\gamma<\lambda<\alpha^*} G_\lambda$. Hence, since $\mathcal{H}_\gamma$ is a covering of S, $s \in H_\lambda$ for some $\lambda \leq \gamma$. Thus, again, $\mathcal{H}$ is a covering of S. ▌

33.34 Theorem. *If S is normal and if S has a locally finite open covering $\mathcal{G}$ such that each G in $\mathcal{G}$ is a metrizable space, then S is metrizable.*

Proof: Let $\mathcal{G}$ be a locally finite open covering of S such that each set in $\mathcal{G}$ is a metrizable space in the relative topology. $\mathcal{G}$ can be considered to be well-ordered as in the previous lemma. Let $\mathcal{G} = \{G_1, G_2, \ldots, G_\omega, G_{\omega+1}, \ldots, G_\alpha, \ldots\}$. By theorem 33.24, there exists, then, a Smirnov basis $\mathcal{B}_\alpha$ for each G_α in $\mathcal{G}$. $\mathcal{B}_\alpha$ is then, by definition 33.18, the union of a countable number of locally finite systems. Let $\mathcal{B}_\alpha = \bigcup_{i=1}^\infty \mathfrak{A}_i^\alpha$, where each $\mathfrak{A}_i^\alpha$ is a locally finite system of open sets. Now by the previous lemma (33.33) for each G_α in $\mathcal{G}$ a set H_α is defined such that $\overline{H}_\alpha \subseteq G_\alpha$ and $\mathcal{H} = \{H_\alpha \mid G_\alpha \in \mathcal{G}\}$ is an open covering of S. Now define, for a fixed α, the systems $\mathfrak{M}_1^\alpha, \mathfrak{M}_2^\alpha, \ldots, \mathfrak{M}_i^\alpha, \ldots$, where $\mathfrak{M}_i^\alpha$ is the set of sets formed by intersecting the sets in the locally finite system $\mathfrak{A}_i^\alpha$ with the set H_α. Now consider $\mathfrak{M}_\alpha^* = \bigcup_i \mathfrak{M}_i^\alpha$. Since $\bigcup_{i=1}^\infty \mathfrak{A}_i^\alpha$ is a base for the subspace G_α and since $H_\alpha \subseteq G_\alpha$, $\mathfrak{M}_\alpha^*$, by theorem 9.8, is a base for the relative topology on H_α. Hence, since $\mathcal{H}$ is a covering of S, $\bigcup_\alpha \mathfrak{M}_\alpha^*$ is a base, $\mathcal{B}$, for the topology on S. Now, for n a natural number, let $\mathcal{V}_n = \bigcup_\alpha \mathfrak{M}_n^\alpha$. Then $\mathcal{B} = \bigcup_n \mathcal{V}_n$. Now it must be shown that $\mathcal{V}_n$ for each n is locally finite. Let k^* be any natural number. Let $s \in S$. Since the original open covering $\mathcal{G}$ is locally finite, s has a neighborhood N which intersects, on a non-empty set, at most a finite number of sets in $\mathcal{G}$, say, $G_{\beta_1}, \ldots, G_{\beta_k}$. Since $\overline{H}_{\beta_i} \subseteq G_{\beta_i}$, $N \cap \overline{H}_\alpha = \emptyset$ for $\alpha \neq \beta_1, \ldots, \alpha \neq \beta_k$. Hence, $s \notin \overline{H}_\alpha$ for $\alpha \neq \beta_1, \ldots, \alpha \neq \beta_k$. By lemma 33.4, $\bigcup_{\alpha\neq\beta_i, i=1,\ldots,k} \overline{H}_\alpha$ is closed in S. Let $F = \bigcup_{\alpha\neq\beta_i, i=1,\ldots,k} \overline{H}_\alpha$. $U = S \sim F$ is then an open neighborhood of s. Since $F = \bigcup_{\alpha\neq\beta_i} \overline{H}_\alpha$ and since the sets in $\mathfrak{M}_{k^*}^\alpha$ are subsets of H_α, $U \cap A = \emptyset$ for A in $\mathfrak{M}_{k^*}^\alpha$ and $\alpha \neq \beta_1, \ldots, \alpha \neq \beta_k$. Now, since the set $\mathfrak{A}_{k^*}^\alpha$, by definition, is locally finite and since the sets in $\mathfrak{M}_{k^*}^\alpha$ are subsets of sets in $\mathfrak{A}_{k^*}^\alpha$, $\mathfrak{M}_{k^*}^\alpha$ is locally finite. This means that for each β_i, $i = 1, \ldots, k$, there exists a neighborhood W_i of s such that W_i intersects, on a non-empty set, at most a finite number of the sets in $\mathfrak{M}_{k^*}^{\beta_i}$. Now consider $U \cap W_1 \cap \cdots \cap W_k$. This, as the intersection of a finite number of neighborhoods of s, is a neighborhood of s and, by definition, can intersect, on a non-empty set, at most a finite number of sets in $\bigcup_\alpha \mathfrak{M}_{k^*}^\alpha$. Thus $\mathcal{V}_{k^*}$ is locally finite. This means that the base $\mathcal{B} = \bigcup_n \mathcal{V}_n$ is the union of a countable number of locally finite systems, and hence S is Smirnov countable. By theorem 33.31, S is then metrizable. ▮

33.35 Definition. A space S is called *locally metrizable* if and only if each point s in S has at least one neighborhood which is a metrizable subspace of S.

33.36 Theorem. *A locally metrizable, Hausdorff space is metrizable if and only if S is paracompact.*

Proof: By Stone's theorem (33.20) every metrizable space is paracompact. Conversely, let S be locally metrizable, Hausdorff and paracompact. Now, by the axiom of choice, an open neighborhood U_s can be assigned to each point s of S such that U_s is a metrizable subspace of S. The set of all these open neighborhoods constitutes an open covering $\mathcal{G}$ of S. Since S is paracompact, $\mathcal{G}$ has a locally finite refinement $\mathcal{G}^*$ which also covers S. By theorem 20.9, every subspace of a metrizable space is a metrizable space. Hence, $\mathcal{G}^*$ is an open locally finite covering of S with the property that each set in it is, with the relative topology, a metrizable subspace. By Dieudonné's theorem (33.9), S is normal. Hence, by the previous theorem (33.34), S is metrizable. ▮

EXERCISE 7. Prove or find a counterexample: every locally metrizable space is Hausdorff.

The space $\{W, o\text{-}\mathfrak{J}\}$ of all countable ordinals with the order topology (definition 28.33) is an example of a space which is normal, first countable, locally compact, countably compact, locally metrizable but not paracompact.

33.37 Lemma. *The space $\{W, o\text{-}\mathfrak{J}\}$, where W is the set of all countable ordinals and $o\text{-}\mathfrak{J}$ is the order topology, is normal.*

Proof: Let F_1 and F_2 be two disjoint closed sets in $\{W, o\text{-}\mathfrak{J}\}$. By lemma 31.50, F_1 or F_2 is bounded. Say, F_1 is bounded in $\{W, \leq\}$. There exists, then, a countable ordinal γ^* such that $\alpha \in F_1$ implies that $\alpha \leq \gamma^*$. This means that if $U = \{\alpha \mid \alpha > \gamma^*\}$, then $U \cap F_1 = \emptyset$. U is open by definition of $o\text{-}\mathfrak{J}$. If, again, $S(\gamma^* + 1) = \{\alpha \mid \alpha \leq \gamma^*\}$, then $S(\gamma^* + 1)$ is compact by the proof of theorem 28.35, case II. Hence, $S(\gamma^* + 1)$ is a compact, Hausdorff, and hence normal space. Thus, there exist two open sets V_1 and V_2 such that $F_1 \subseteq V_1$, $F_2 \cap S(\gamma^* + 1) \subseteq V_2$ and $V_1 \cap V_2 = \emptyset$. Consequently, $U \cup V_2 \supseteq F_2$, $V_1 \supseteq F_1$ and $V_1 \cap (U \cup V_2) = \emptyset$. $\{W, o\text{-}\mathfrak{J}\}$ is, then, normal. ▮

33.38 Lemma. *The space $\{W, o\text{-}\mathfrak{J}\}$ of all countable ordinals with the order topology is not paracompact.*

Proof: By lemmas 28.34 and 28.35, $\{W, o\text{-}\mathfrak{J}\}$ is countably compact but not compact. By theorem 30.5, $\{W, o\text{-}\mathfrak{J}\}$ is, then, not metrizable. By lemma 32.10,

$\{W, o\text{-}\mathfrak{I}\}$ is Hausdorff. Now, let γ be any ordinal in W. If γ is a non-limit ordinal, $\{\gamma\}$ is a neighborhood of γ by definition (28.33) of o-$\mathfrak{I}$. $\{\gamma\}$ is metrizable by the metric $\rho(\gamma, \gamma) = 0$. If γ is a non-limit ordinal, consider $S(\gamma + 1) = \{\alpha \mid \alpha \in W \text{ and } \alpha < \gamma + 1\} = \{\alpha \mid \alpha \in W \text{ and } \alpha \leq \gamma\}$. $S(\gamma + 1)$ is a neighborhood of γ. Further, by the proof of theorem 28.35, $S(\gamma + 1)$ is compact and Hausdorff, and hence is normal. $S(\gamma + 1)$ is also second countable, since it is countable and each point has a countable local base, by definition of o-$\mathfrak{I}$. Thus, $S(\gamma + 1)$ is metrizable by Urysohn's metrization theorem. Consequently, $\{W, o\text{-}\mathfrak{I}\}$ is locally metrizable. $\{W, o\text{-}\mathfrak{I}\}$ is, then, a Hausdorff, locally metrizable but not metrizable space. By theorem 33.36, $\{W, o\text{-}\mathfrak{I}\}$ is then not paracompact. ▌

By definition and by lemmas 33.37, 33.38, 28.35 and parts of the proof of the latter, $\{W, o\text{-}\mathfrak{I}\}$ is a first countable, normal, locally compact, countably compact, non-paracompact space. Since $\{W, o\text{-}\mathfrak{I}\}$ is not metrizable, $\{W, o\text{-}\mathfrak{I}\}$ is not Smirnov countable, and hence is also an example of a regular space which is first countable but not Smirnov countable.

Partitions of Unity

One of the most useful properties of paracompact spaces is the existence of certain families of functions—called partitions of unity.

33.39 Definition. Let S be a space. A family $\mathfrak{F}$ of continuous functions from S into the non-negative reals is called *a partition of unity on S* if and only if for each f in $\mathfrak{F}$, $\sum_{f \in \mathfrak{F}} f(s) = 1$. A partition of unity, $\mathfrak{F}$, on S is called *locally finite* if and only if for each s in S there exists a neighborhood U_s such that all but a finite number of the functions in $\mathfrak{F}$ vanish on U_s.

33.40 Definition. Let $\mathfrak{M}$ be any covering of a space S. A partition of unity, $\mathfrak{F}$, is called *subordinated to* $\mathfrak{M}$ if and only if for each function f in $\mathfrak{F}$, there exists a set M in $\mathfrak{M}$ such that $\sim M \subseteq f^{-1}[\{0\}]$.

33.41 Theorem. *Let S be a T_2-space. The following are equivalent:*

(*a*) *S is paracompact;*

(*b*) *every open covering of S has a locally finite partition of unity subordinated to it;*

(*c*) *every open covering of S has a partition of unity subordinated to it.*

Proof: A. Let S be paracompact and let $\mathcal{G}$ be any open covering of S. $\mathcal{G}$ has an open, locally finite refinement, $\mathcal{P}$, which covers S. Further, by lemma 33.8, S is regular, and so, by corollary 33.12, $\mathcal{P}$ has a closed, locally finite refinement $\mathcal{H}$ which covers S. Let $\mathcal{P} = \{P_\alpha \mid \alpha \in \mathfrak{A}$, i.e., $\mathfrak{A}$ indexes $\mathcal{P}$. It can be assumed that for $\alpha \in \mathfrak{A}$, $\mathcal{P}_\alpha \neq \emptyset$. Since $\mathcal{H}$ is a refinement of $\mathcal{P}$, each set H in $\mathcal{H}$ is a subset of some set P_α in $\mathcal{P}$. For each P_α in $\mathcal{P}$ define $L_\alpha = \bigcup_{H_\nu \subseteq P_\alpha} H_\nu \neq \emptyset$. Each set H_ν in $\mathcal{H}$ is closed, and so, by theorem 33.4, each L_α is closed. Thus $\mathfrak{M} = \{L_\alpha \mid \alpha \in \mathfrak{A}$ is a closed refinement of $\mathcal{P}$ which covers S and $L_\alpha \subseteq P_\alpha$. If

$X \in \mathcal{G}$, let $\mathcal{P} = \{X\}$. Then the constant function $f(s) = 1$ is the desired partition of unity. So assume $X \notin \mathcal{G}$. Then $X \notin \mathcal{P}$. By theorem 33.9, S is normal. So, for each α in $\mathfrak{A}$ define g_α from S into $|0, 1|$ as follows: $g_\alpha(s) = 1$ for s in $L_\alpha \neq 0$ and $g_\alpha(s) = 0$ for s in $S \sim P_\alpha \neq \emptyset$. Define $g(s) = \sum_{\alpha \in \mathfrak{A}} g_\alpha(s)$ and define $f_\alpha(s) = g_\alpha(s)/g(s)$. Since $\mathcal{P}$ is locally finite, each s in S lies in at most a finite number of sets in $\mathcal{P}$. Hence g is defined for each s in S. Also, g is continuous, as is f_α for each α. Now consider $\{f_\alpha \mid \alpha \in \mathfrak{A}\}$. f_α vanishes outside P_α in $\mathcal{P}$. Hence $\{f_\alpha \mid \alpha \in \mathfrak{A}\}$ is subordinated to $\mathcal{P}$, and hence to $\mathcal{G}$, the original open covering for which $\mathcal{P}$ is a refinement. Further, since $\mathcal{P}$ is locally finite, each point s in S has a neighborhood N_s which intersects on a non-empty set at most a finite number of sets P_α. Thus, all but a finite number of the functions f_α vanish on N_s. By definition, $\sum_\alpha f_\alpha(s) = 1$, and hence $\{f_\alpha \mid \alpha \in \mathfrak{A}$ is a locally finite partition of unity on S which is subordinated to $\mathcal{G}$.

B. If every open covering of S has a locally finite partition of unity subordinated to it, then every open covering of S has a partition of unity subordinated to it.

C. Let every open covering of S have a partition of unity subordinated to it. Now if p is any point of S and if F is any non-empty closed set not containing p, then since S is T_1, $\{\sim\{p\}, \sim F\}$ is an open covering of S. Hence there exists a partition of unity subordinated to $\{\sim\{p\}, \sim F\}$. By the definition of a partition of unity, not every function vanishes at p. Now if $f(p) \neq 0$, then by subordination, $f[\sim(\sim F)] = \{0\}$. Hence, $f[F] = \{0\}$ and $f(p) \neq 0$. Thus S is completely regular, and so regular. Now let $\mathcal{G}$ be any open covering of S and let $\mathfrak{F}$ be a partition of unity subordinated to it. Now let $A_f^i = \{s \mid f(s) > 1/i\}$ for i a positive integer, and f in $\mathfrak{F}$. Let $\mathfrak{M}_i = \{A_f^i \mid f \text{ is in } \mathfrak{F}\}$, and let $\mathfrak{M}^* = \bigcup_{i=1}^{\infty} \mathfrak{M}_i$. Since $\mathfrak{F}$ is subordinated to $\mathcal{G}$, each f in $\mathfrak{F}$ vanishes outside some set G_f in $\mathcal{G}$. This means that $A_f^i \subseteq G_f$ for all i. Thus $\mathfrak{M}^*$ is an open refinement of $\mathcal{G}$. Now, by definition of a partition of unity, for each s in S there is some f in $\mathfrak{F}$ such that $f(s) \neq 0$. Hence, there exists a positive integer i such that $f(s) > 1/i$. This means that s is in A_f^i and so $\mathfrak{M}^*$ covers S. Now let k be a fixed positive integer and consider $\mathfrak{M}_k$. For a in S, $\sum_{f \in \mathfrak{F}} f(a) = 1$. Hence there is a finite subset $\mathfrak{F}_0$ of $\mathfrak{F}$ such that $\sum_{f \in \mathfrak{F}_0} f(a) > 1 - 1/k$. If $g(s) = \sum_{f \in \mathfrak{F}_0} f(s)$, then g is continuous since each f is. So there exists a neighborhood N_a of a such that if s is in N_a, $g(s) > 1 - 1/k$. Now consider $A_{f_0}^k$ in $\mathfrak{M}_k$. $A_{f_0}^k = \{s \mid f_0(s) > 1/k\}$. Hence if x is in $N_a \cap A_{f_0}^k$, then $\sum_{f \in \mathfrak{F}_0} f(x) > 1 - 1/k$ and $f_0(x) > 1/k$. Since $\sum_{f \in \mathfrak{F}} f(x) = 1$, f_0 must be in $\mathfrak{F}_0$. Since $\mathfrak{F}_0$ is finite, for each k N_a can intersect on a non-empty set at most a finite number of the sets A_f^k. Thus $\mathfrak{M}^k$ is locally finite and $\mathfrak{M}^*$ is the union of a countable number of locally finite systems. By lemma 33.19, S is paracompact. ▮

SUMMARY FOR CHAPTER 6

Compactness is a topological invariant which demands that every open covering of a space contain a finite subcovering. Countable compactness is a topological invariant which is a weaker form of compactness and demands only that every countable open covering of a space contain a finite subcovering. Compactness and countable compactness can also be defined in terms of closed sets. A space is compact if and only if every family of closed sets with the finite intersection property has a non-empty intersection; a space is countably compact if and only if every countable family of closed sets with the finite intersection property has a non-empty intersection.

A T_1-space S is countably compact if and only if every infinite subset of S has a limit point in S.

Compactness can also be defined in terms of convergence. A space is compact if and only if every filter is contained in a converging filter, and analogously, a space is compact if and only if every net contains a converging subnet. These last two definitions can be stated in terms of ultrafilters and universal nets. A space is compact (1) if and only if every ultrafilter converges, and (2) if and only if every universal net converges.

Any product of compact spaces is compact. However, a product of two countably compact spaces need not be countably compact. The continuous image of a compact (countably compact) space is compact (countably compact).

Compactness and connectedness yield some interesting consequences. A compact, connected, T_1-space which has more than one point contains at least two non-cut points. Also, a compact, connected T_1-space is irreducibly connected about its set of non-cut points.

Compactness and the Hausdorff property are also a strong combination. Compact subsets of Hausdorff spaces are closed and any continuous function from a compact space into a Hausdorff space is closed. Any continuous image of a compact space S in a Hausdorff space is homeomorphic to a quotient space of S. Any compact, Hausdorff space is normal. Every completely regular space is a subspace of a compact, Hausdorff, and hence normal space. In any Hausdorff space, disjoint compact sets are contained in disjoint open sets. Any countably compact, regular space is of the second category in itself; this is one generalization of the Baire category theorem for complete metric spaces. In a compact Hausdorff space, quasi-components are components. Any inverse limit of non-empty, compact, Hausdorff spaces is a non-empty compact, Hausdorff space. If S is a compact, Hausdorff space and H is the set of homeomorphisms of S onto S, then H with the compact-open topology and with composition as the operation becomes a topological group.

Compactness and metrizability yield a third deductively fruitful combination. The first striking result is that in metrizable spaces compactness and countable compactness are equivalent. Also any compact metrizable space is second countable. In addition, in a metric space $\{S, \rho\}$, S is compact if and only if $\{S, \rho\}$ is complete and totally bounded. Further, the non-empty, compact, metrizable spaces are exactly those spaces which are the ranges in Hausdorff spaces of continuous functions whose domains are the Cantor ternary space. Thus no compact metrizable space can have cardinality greater than c. It also follows that any continuous function from a compact metric space, $\{S, \rho\}$, into a metric space, $\{T, \xi\}$, is uniformly continuous. Any compact subset in a metric space $\{S, \rho\}$ is closed and bounded with respect to the metric, ρ. In the special case of Euclidean n-space with the usual Euclidean metric, the compact subsets are exactly the closed and bounded subsets.

If S is compact, a significant metric can be defined for the ring $C(S)$ of continuous functions from S into E^1, the usual space of reals. $C(S)$ then becomes a complete metric space. The Stone-Weierstrass theorem establishes that certain subrings of $C(S)$, for S a compact space, are dense in this metrizable space defined on $C(S)$. Thus an algebraic condition for topological density is established.

The theory of compact uniform spaces parallels the theory of compact metric spaces to some extent. Any continuous function from a compact uniform space into a uniform space is uniformly continuous. Further, a uniform space is compact if and only if it is complete and totally bounded. Also, if S is compact, there is at most one uniform structure which determines the topology on S; it is exactly the set of all neighborhoods of the diagonal in the product space $S \times S$. There are, however, some differences between compact metric and compact uniform spaces. Compact uniform spaces need not be second countable.

The property of compactness can be localized to yield "local compactness." A space is locally compact if and only if each point has at least one compact neighborhood. The continuous image of a locally compact space need not be locally compact; however, if f is continuous and open, with domain S, then $f[S]$ is locally compact if S is. A non-empty product space is locally compact if and only if all of the factor spaces are locally compact, and all but a finite number are compact. Any locally compact, regular space is of the second category in itself.

Non-compact spaces can be enlarged to compact spaces in a significant way via the concept of compactification. One-point compactifications and Stone-Čech compactifications are the most important compactifications. A one-point compactification can be defined for any space with at least one non-empty, closed, compact subset. A space has a one-point Hausdorff compactification if and only if it is locally compact and Hausdorff. As a result of this last theorem, any locally compact Hausdorff space is completely regular, and any locally compact, second countable, Hausdorff space is metrizable. A Stone-Čech compactification exists for all completely regular spaces and only for these spaces; it is a subspace of a product space of unit intervals, $[0, 1]$, and is characterized by an extension property for functions. A Stone-Čech compactification βS of a space S has the property that if f is any continuous function from S into a compact Hausdorff space Y, then f, in a certain general sense, has a unique continuous extension f^* from all of βS into Y. The space $W \cup \{W\}$ consisting of all ordinals up to and including the first uncountable ordinal together with the order topology is both a one-point compactification and a Stone-Čech compactification of W.

One of the most useful special types of compact spaces is the curve. A curve is a topological space which is the range of a continuous function whose domain is the unit interval space, $[0, 1]$. The most important types of curves are curves in

Hausdorff spaces. A curve in a Hausdorff space is called a Peano space. A Peano space is a non-empty, compact, connected, locally connected, metrizable space; the Hahn-Mazurkiewicz establishes that these are the only Peano spaces. A special type of curve is an arc. By definition, an arc is the range of a homeomorphism whose domain is the unit interval space, [0, 1]. A space is an arc if and only if it is a compact, connected, metrizable space with exactly two non-cut points. Another important special type of curve is a simple closed curve. A simple closed curve, by definition, is the range of a homeomorphism whose domain is the unit circle subspace of E^2. A space is a simple closed curve if and only if it is a compact, connected, metrizable space with at least two points and with the property that each two-point subset of it is a cut set.

Arcwise connectedness is the analogue, for arcs, of pathwise connectedness for curves. In Hausdorff spaces, arcwise connectedness and pathwise connectedness are equivalent.

The concept of "local finiteness" leads to a generalization of compactness and to a characterization of metrizable spaces. A set $\mathfrak{M}$ of subsets of a space S is called a locally finite system if and only if each point in S has a neighborhood which intersects, on a non-empty set, at most a finite number of sets in $\mathfrak{M}$. Smirnov proved that a space is metrizable if and only if it is regular and has a base which is the union of a countable number of locally finite systems. Dieudonné defined a paracompact space to be a space S with the property that every open covering had a locally finite refinement which also covered S. Dieudonné and A. H. Stone proved that paracompact, Hausdorff spaces are "strictly between" normal spaces and metrizable spaces. Further, a locally metrizable Hausdorff space is metrizable if and only if it is paracompact. Hausdorff, paracompact spaces have partitions of unity subordinate to any given open covering.

CHAPTER 7

Homotopy

An introduction to the fundamental concept of homotopy follows. Homotopy permeates much of modern mathematics and leads to some useful algebraic topological invariants. Modern topology is heavily algebraic, and homotopy—via the homotopy groups—can serve as a bridge between non-algebraic and algebraic topology.

34. THE BASIC HOMOTOPY EQUIVALENCES.

34.1 Definition. Let $C(X, Y)$ denote the set of all continuous functions from the space X into the space Y. Let f and g be in $C(X, Y)$. f is said to be *homotopic* to g *in* Y if and only if there exists a continuous function, H, from the product space $X \times I$, where I is the closed unit interval, $[0, 1]$, with the usual topology, into Y such that $H((x, 0)) = f(x)$ and $H((x, 1)) = g(x)$ for all x in X. H is called a *homotopy between* f and g or *from* f to g.

NOTATION: "f is homotopic to g in Y" will be abbreviated to "f *homt* g in Y."

34.2 Lemma. *homt is an equivalence relation in* $C(X, Y)$.

Proof: A. Let f be in $C(X, Y)$. Define $H((x, t))$, for (x, t) in $X \times I$, to be $f(x)$. Let V be a neighborhood of $H((x, t))$ in Y. V is then a neighborhood of $f(x)$ in Y. Since f is continuous, there is a neighborhood U of x in X such that $f[U] \subseteq V$. Hence if (a, s) is in $U \times I$, $H((a, s))$ is in V, since $H((a, s)) = f(a)$. Thus H is continuous and f *homt* f.

B. Let H be a homotopy between f and g in $C(X, Y)$, where f *homt* g in Y. $H((x, 0)) = f(x)$ and $H((x, 1)) = g(x)$ for all x in X. Define H^* from $X \times I$ into Y as follows: $H^*((x, t)) = H((x, 1 - t))$. $H^*((x, 0)) = H((x, 1)) = g(x)$ and $H^*((x, 1)) = H((x, 0)) = f(x)$. Since H is a homotopy, H is continuous. Let $r: X \times I \to X \times I$ where $r((x, t)) = (x, 1 - t)$. By theorem 11.19,

r is continuous. Since H^* is the composite of the continuous functions r and H, H^* is continuous. H^* is then a homotopy between g and f and f *homt* g implies g *homt* f.

C. Let f, g and m be in $C(X, Y)$. Let H_1 be a homotopy from f to g and let H_2 be a homotopy from g to m. Thus f *homt* g and g *homt* m. Define H^* from $X \times I$ into Y as follows: Let $H^*((x, t)) = H_1((x, 2t))$ for all x in X and $0 \leq t \leq 1/2$, and let $H^*(x, t) = H_2(x, 2t - 1)$ for all x in X and $1/2 \leq t \leq 1$. Now, $H^*((x, 0)) = H_1((x, 0)) = f(x)$ and $H^*((x, 1)) = H_2((x, 1)) = m(x)$. Let S_1 and S_2 denote, respectively, the closed subspaces $S_1 = \{(x, t) \mid 0 \leq t \leq 1/2\}$ and $S_2 = \{(x, t) \mid 1/2 \leq t \leq 1\}$. Again by theorem 11.19 and the same reasoning as in part (2), above, H^* restricted to S_1 and H^* restricted to S_2 are continuous. Also, for $t = 1/2$, H^* is single-valued. Thus, by theorem 9.23, H^* is continuous. Hence f *homt* m. ∎

Thus, for spaces X and Y, the set $C(X, Y)$ of continuous functions from X into Y is divided into equivalence classes by the equivalence relation *homt*. The next definition refers to a special case in which there exists exactly one such equivalence class.

34.3 Definition. A space X is called *contractible* if and only if the equivalence relation *homt* determines exactly one equivalence class in $C(X, X)$, i.e., if and only if all continuous functions from X into X are homotopic in X.

34.4 Lemma. *X is contractible if and only if the identity function is homotopic to some constant function.*

Proof: A. If X is contractible, then the identity function is homotopic to any constant function by definition of contractiblity.

B. If the identity function $i(x) = x$ is homotopic to a constant function $k(x) = c$ for all x in X, then there exists a homotopy $H: X \times I \to X$ such that $H((x, 0)) = x$ and $H((x, 1)) = c$ for all x in X. Let f be in $C(X, X)$. Let f^* be the function from $X \times I$ onto $f[X] \times I$ defined by $f^*((x, t)) = (f(x), t)$. Since f is continuous, f^* is continuous, again by theorem 11.19. The composite function $H \circ f^*$ is then a continuous function from $X \times I$ into X such that $H \circ f^*((x, 0)) = H((f(x), 0)) = f(x)$ and $H \circ f^*((x, 1)) = H((f(x), 1)) = c$. Thus $H \circ f^*$ is a homotopy from f to k, the constant map $k(x) = c$. Since *homt* is an equivalence relation, all continuous functions from X into X are homotopic. ∎

34.5 Example. Euclidean n-space, E^n, for all natural numbers n, is contractible. Define $H(((x_1, \ldots, x_n), t)) = ((1 - t)x_1, (1 - t)x_2, \ldots, (1 - t)x_n)$. By theorem 11.19, H is continuous. Further $H((x_1, x_2, \ldots, x_n), 0) = (x_1, x_2, \ldots, x_n)$ and $H(((x_1, x_2, \ldots, x_n), 1)) = (0, 0, \ldots, 0)$ for all $(x_1, x_2, \ldots, x_n)$ in Euclidean n-space. Thus the identity function is homotopic to a constant function and, by lemma 34.4, E^n is contractible.

Originally a homotopy between a continuous function $f: X \to Y$ and a continuous function $g: X \to Y$ was described intuitively as a "shrinking" of the range of f into the range of g in such a way that the "stages" of the shrinking could be indexed by the real numbers in the closed interval $[0, 1]$ and so that at each "stage" ("instant of time"), the range was contained entirely in Y. Figure 28 below illustrates this "shrinking" with the homotopy $H(((x, y), t)) = ((1 - t)x, (1 - t)y)$, defined from $I^2 \times I \to I^2$, where I^2 is the subspace of the plane determined by $\{(x, y) \mid 0 \leq x \leq 1 \text{ and } 0 \leq y \leq 1\}$.

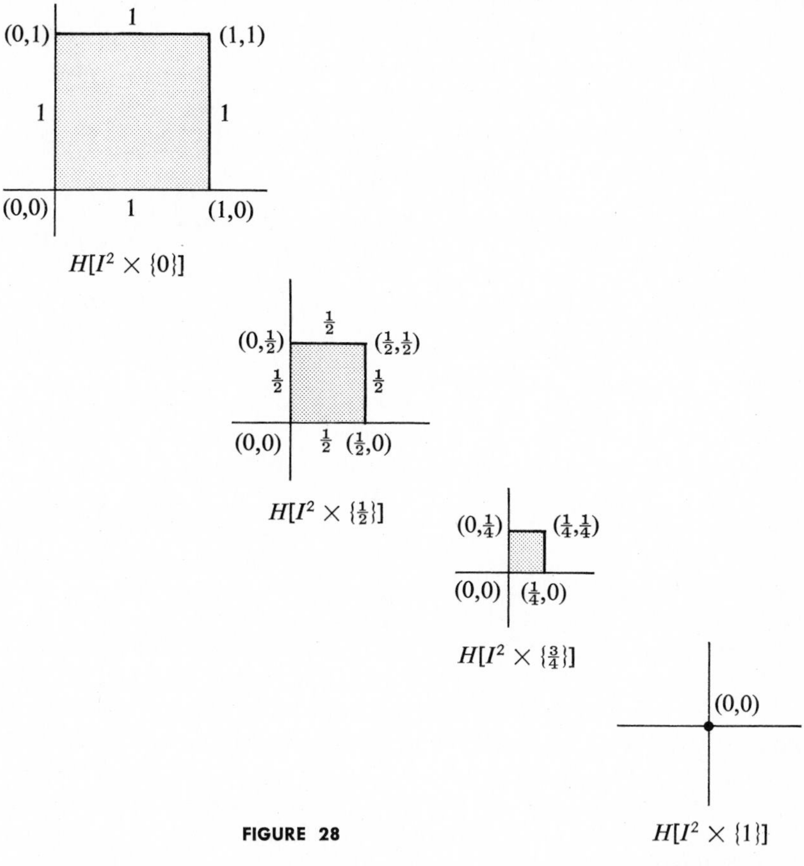

FIGURE 28

The following theorem establishes another situation in which the equivalence relation *homt* determines exactly one equivalence class in the set $C(X, Y)$.

34.6 Theorem. *If Y is a contractible space and X is any space, then homt determines exactly one equivalence class in $C(X, Y)$, i.e., all continuous functions from X into Y are homotopic in Y.*

Proof: Let f and g be continuous functions from X into Y. By lemma

34.4, the identity function $i(y) = y$ of Y onto itself and some constant map $k(y) = c$ of Y onto $\{c\}$ are homotopic in Y. Therefore, there exists a homotopy $H: Y \times I \rightarrow Y$ such that $H((y, 0)) = y$ and $H((y, 1)) = c$. Let H^* denote the function from $X \times I$ into $Y \times I$ defined by $H^*((x, t)) = (f(x), t)$. By theorem 11.19, H^* is continuous. The composite function $H \circ H^*$ is continuous from $X \times I$ into Y. Further, $H \circ H^*((x, 0)) = H((f(x), 0)) = f(x)$ and $H \circ H^*((x, 1)) = H((f(x), 1)) = c$. Thus if k^* is the constant function $k^*(x) = c$ from X into Y, then f *homt* k^*. Similarly, it can be established that g *homt* k^*. Since *homt* is an equivalence relation, f *homt* g. f and g were any continuous functions from X into Y; hence, the theorem is proved. ▮

34.7 Theorem. *Any contractible space is pathwise connected.*

Proof: Let a and b be two points in the contractible space X. By the definition of contractiblity, the constant function $k_1(x) = a$ is homotopic in X to the constant function $k_2(x) = b$. Hence there exists a homotopy $H: X \times I \rightarrow X$ such that $H((x, 0)) = a$ and $H((x, 1)) = b$ for all x in X. Consider the function H restricted to the subspace $\{a\} \times I$. $\{a\} \times I$ is homeomorphic to I by lemma 24.25; hence, $H[\{a\} \times I]$ is a curve in X. $H((a, 0)) = a$ and $H((a, 1)) = b$. Thus X contains a curve between a and b and so is pathwise connected. ▮

The following theorem contains a general statement about a homotopy between two composite functions under certain circumstances. Special cases of this theorem were proved in the proofs of the last theorem and lemma.

34.8 Theorem. *If f and g are continuous functions from a space X into a space Y, if m and n are continuous functions from Y into a space Z and if, further, f homt g in Y and m homt n in Z, then $m \circ f$ homt $n \circ g$ in Z where, of course, $m \circ f$ and $n \circ g$ denote the composite functions.*

Proof: Let H_1 denote the homotopy from f to g in Y and let H_2 denote the homotopy from m to n in Z. Consider, first, the composite function $m \circ H_1$ from $X \times I$ into Z. $m \circ H_1$ is continuous, since it is the composite of two continuous functions. Further, $m \circ H_1((x, 0)) = m(f(x)) = m \circ f(x)$ and $m \circ H_1((x, 1)) = m(g(x)) = m \circ g(x)$. Thus $m \circ H_1$ is a homotopy from $m \circ f$ to $m \circ g$ in Z, and so $m \circ f$ *homt* $m \circ g$ in Z. Next, define H from $X \times I$ into $Y \times I$ as follows. $H((x, t)) = (g(x), t)$. By theorem 11.19, and the continuity of g, H is continuous. Hence, the composite function $H_2 \circ H$, from $X \times I$ into Z, is continuous. Further, $H_2 \circ H((x, 0)) = H_2((g(x), 0)) = m \circ g(x)$ and $H_2 \circ H((x, 1)) = H_2((g(x), 1)) = n \circ g(x)$. Thus $H_2 \circ H$ is a homotopy from $m \circ g$ to $n \circ g$ in Z. Thus $m \circ g$ *homt* $n \circ g$ in Z. Thus since *homt* is an equivalence relation, $m \circ f$ *homt* $n \circ g$ in Z. ▮

EXERCISE 1. Let h be a homeomorphism from X onto Y and let Y be contractible. Prove that X is contractible.

The problem of extending a continuous function defined on a subspace A of a space S to a continuous function defined on all of S occurs in a significant way in many places in modern mathematics. The homotopy equivalence between functions has some bearing on this problem. The next two theorems and the corollary which follows them relate to the problem; in particular, theorem 34.12 and corollary 34.14 illustrate some of the power of the homotopy equivalence for functions. Some definitions and lemmas are needed and also follow.

34.9 Theorem. *A subspace A of a space S is a retract of S if and only if for any space T every continuous function f from A into T has a continuous extension f^* from S into T.*

Proof: If r is a retraction from S onto A and if f is continuous from A into T, then the composite function $f \circ r$ from S into T is a continuous extension of f from S into T. Conversely, if every continuous function g from A into any space T has a continuous extension g^* from S into T, then the identity function i from A onto A has a continuous extension i^* from S onto A and, by definition, i^* is a retraction of S onto A. ▌

34.10 Definition. A subset A of a space S is said to have the *neighborhood extension property in S with respect to the space T* if and only if every continuous function f from A into T has a continuous extension f^* from some open neighborhood U of A into T.

The next definition is not the usual definition of an absolute neighborhood retract but it is equivalent to it and the given form of the definition will be used in what follows.

34.11 Definition. A metrizable space T is *an absolute neighborhood retract* if and only if every closed subset A of an arbitrary metrizable space S has the neighborhood extension property in S with respect to T.

34.12 Theorem (Borsuk). *Let A be a closed subset of a metrizable space S and let f and g be continuous functions from A into a metrizable space T which is an absolute neighborhood retract. Further, let f and g be homotopic and let f have an extension f^* from S into T. Then, g has an extension g^* from S into T.*

Proof: Let H be a homotopy from $A \times I$ into T such that $H((a, 0)) = f(a)$ and $H((a, 1)) = g(a)$ for a in A. Let $A^* = (S \times \{0\}) \cup A \times I$. Define $H^*((s, 0)) = f^*(s)$ for s in S and $H^*((a, t)) = H((a, t))$ for a in A and $0 \leq t \leq 1$. H^* is continuous by theorem 9.23. Now since Y is an absolute neighborhood retract and since A^* is closed in the metrizable space $S \times I$, H^* has a continuous extension H^{**} whose domain is an open neighborhood U of A^* and whose range is in T. Now $U \supseteq A \times I$ and, by lemma 31.37, there is an open set V in S containing A such that $A \times I \subseteq V \times I \subseteq U$. If $V = S$, the theorem is proved. So assume $V \neq S$. $\sim V$ and A are then non-empty disjoint, closed subsets of S and hence, by Urysohn's lemma, there exists a continuous function h from S into the unit interval space, [0, 1], such that $h[\sim V] = \{0\}$ and $h[A] = \{1\}$. A function $\tilde{H}$ can now be defined from $S \times I$ into T as follows. $\tilde{H}((s, t)) = H^{**}((s, t \cdot h(s)))$. If s is in V, $\tilde{H}((s, t))$ is defined since the domain of H^{**} contains $V \times I$; if s is in $\sim V$, $h(s) = 0$, and so $t \cdot h(s) = 0$ for $0 \leq t \leq 1$. Since the domain of H^{**} contains $S \times \{0\}$ also, $\tilde{H}((s, t))$ is again defined. Thus, the domain of $\tilde{H}$ is $S \times I$. Now define $g^*(s) = \tilde{H}((s, 1))$ for s in S. If a is in A, $g^*(a) = \tilde{H}((a, 1)) = H^{**}((a, 1 \cdot h(a))) = H^*((a, 1)) = H((a, 1)) = g(a)$. Thus g^* is a continuous extension of g to all of S. ∎

NOTATION: S^n denotes, as usual, the subspace of Euclidean $n + 1$-space, E^{n+1}, determined by $\{(x_1, x_2, \ldots, x_{n+1}) \mid \sum_{i=1}^{n+1} x_i^2 = 1\}$.

34.13 Lemma. *S^n, for any positive integer n, is an absolute neighborhood retract.*

Proof: Let A be a closed subset of a metrizable space S; let f be a continuous function from A into S^n. For a in A, let $f(a) = (a_1, a_2, \ldots, a_{n+1})$ in S^n. $\sum_{i=1}^{n+1} a_i^2 = 1$ and $|a_i| \leq 1$ for $i = 1, 2, \ldots, n + 1$. By theorem 11.19, the composite functions $p_i \circ f$, where p_i is the i-th projection function, i.e., $p_i((a_1, a_2, \ldots, a_{n+1})) = a_i$ for $i = 1, \ldots, n + 1$, is continuous from A into the interval $[-1, 1]$ of E^1. By Tietze's extension theorem (18.29), each function $p_i \circ f$ can be extended to a continuous function g_i from S into E^1. Since sums and products of continuous functions into E^1 are continuous, $g^* = \sum_{i=1}^{n+1} g_i^2$ is continuous from S into E^1. Let $U = \{s \mid g^*(s) > 0\}$. U is open in S. Since $f[A] \subseteq S^n$, $g^*(a) = 1$ for a in A. Hence, $A \subseteq U$. Now let

$$f^*(s) = \left(\frac{g_1(s)}{\sqrt{g^*(s)}}, \frac{g_2(s)}{\sqrt{g^*(s)}}, \ldots, \frac{g_{n+1}(s)}{\sqrt{g^*(s)}}\right)$$

for s in U. Since each g_i is defined on all of S and since g^* is positive for s in U, f^* is defined and continuous on all of U. Further, for a in A, $g^*(a) = 1$, and so $f^*(a) = (g_1(a), \ldots, g_{n+1}(a)) = (a_1, a_2, \ldots, a_{n+1}) = f(a)$. Thus S^n is an absolute neighborhood retract. ∎

34.14 Corollary. *If S is a metrizable space, if A is a closed subset of S, if f and g are continuous and homotopic from A into S^n and if f has a continuous extension f^* from S into S^n, then g also has a continuous extension from S into S^n.*

Proof: The corollary is a direct result of lemma 34.13 and theorem 34.12. ∎

The existence of a continuous extension for a continuous function can thus depend on the homotopy class in which the function lies.

Of course, the basic question related to the homotopic classification of functions namely "when are two continuous functions f and g from the space X into the space Y homotopic?"—can now be phrased in terms of extensions of functions. Define $H((x, 0)) = f(x)$ and $H((x, 1)) = g(x)$. Then, "does H have a continuous extension H^* from $X \times I$ into Y?" is equivalent to the question posed above.

Thus the study of homotopy for functions becomes the study of continuous extensions for functions defined on a closed subset of $X \times I$.

The Homotopy Equivalence for Spaces

Directly related to the homotopy equivalence between functions is a useful homotopy equivalence between topological spaces which is slightly weaker than the topological equivalence for spaces. This equivalence is introduced now.

34.15 Definition. Let X and Y be topological spaces. X and Y are said to be *homotopically equivalent* or to be *of the same homotopy type* if and only if there exists a continuous function f from X into Y and a continuous function g from Y into X such that $g \circ f$ *homt* i_x and $f \circ g$ *homt* i_y where i_x and i_y are the identity functions on X and Y, respectively. Homotopic equivalence for spaces will also be abbreviated to *homt*. The functions f and g are called *homotopy equivalences*.

34.16 Lemma. *homt is an equivalence relation on any set of topological spaces.*

Proof: Let $\mathcal{S}$ be a set of spaces. The reflexivity and symmetry are immediate. So, let X *homt* Y and Y *homt* Z for X, Y, Z in $\mathcal{S}$. There exist continuous functions $f: X \to Y$, $g: Y \to X$, $m: Y \to Z$ and $n: Z \to Y$, such that $f \circ g$ *homt* i_y, $g \circ f$ *homt* i_x, $m \circ n$ *homt* i_z and $n \circ m$ *homt* i_y. Consider the composite functions $m \circ f: X \to Z$ and $g \circ n: Z \to X$. Since $n \circ m$ *homt* i_y and f *homt* f, $n \circ m \circ f$ *homt* $i_y \circ f$ by theorem 34.8. Further, since g *homt* g, $g \circ n \circ m \circ f$ *homt* $g \circ i_y \circ f$, again by theorem 34.8, $g \circ i_y \circ f = g \circ f$. Hence $g \circ n \circ m \circ f$ *homt* i_x. Similarly $m \circ f \circ g \circ n$ *homt* i_z. Thus X *homt* Z. ∎

34.17 Theorem. *If X and Y are topologically equivalent, X and Y are homotopically equivalent.*

Proof: Let h be a homeomorphism from X onto Y. $h^{-1} \circ h$ is the identity function on X. Hence, $h^{-1} \circ h$ *homt* i_x and $h \circ h^{-1}$ *homt* i_y. ∎

34.18 Theorem. *A space is contractible if and only if it is homotopically equivalent to a space consisting of one point.*

Proof: A. Let X be contractible. Let i denote the identity function on X; let k denote a constant function to which i is homotopic. Then the composite function $i \circ k$ is just the function k, and k is homotopic to i by hypothesis. Similarly, the composite function $k \circ i$ is just the function k. Hence $k \circ i$ and $i \circ k$ are homotopic to i and X is homotopic to $\{c\}$, where $k(x) = c$.

B. Let the space X be homotopic to the point space $\{c\}$. Let f and g be the functions which must exist for X to be homotopic to $\{c\}$. $f: X \to \{c\}$ and $g: \{c\} \to X$. $g \circ f$ *homt* i_x. $g \circ f(x) = g(c)$. Let $g(c) = a$. Hence the constant function $g \circ f(x) = a$ for all x in X is homotopic to the identity and X is contractible. ▌

34.19 Corollary. *Any two contractible spaces are homotopically equivalent.*

The previous theorem implies among other things that the usual space E^1 of real numbers is homotopically equivalent to the trivial space consisting of 0 alone, say. These two spaces, of course, are far from being topologically equivalent.

34.20 Example. Let X be the subspace of the plane, E^2, determined by $\{(x, y) \mid 0 < x^2 + y^2 \leq 1\}$ and let S be the subspace determined by $\{(x, y) \mid x^2 + y^2 = 1\}$. These two spaces are homotopically equivalent. Define the homotopy $H: X \times I \to X$ as follows:

$$H((x, y), t) = \left((1 - t)x + t\frac{x}{\sqrt{x^2 + y^2}}, (1 - t)y + t\frac{y}{\sqrt{x^2 + y^2}}\right).$$

By theorem 11.19, H is continuous. Further, when $t = 0$, $H(((x, y), 0)) = (x, y)$, and when $t = 1$,

$$H(((,x\ y), 1)) = \left(\frac{x}{\sqrt{x^2 + y^2}}, \frac{y}{\sqrt{x^2 + y^2}}\right).$$

Now the function $(x, y) \to H(((x, y), 0))$ from X into X is the identity function, i_x, on X, and the function $(x, y) \to H(((x, y), 1))$ from X into X has as its range the subspace S. Further, $H(((x, y), t)) = (x, y)$ for (x, y) in S and all t, and hence $(x, y) \to H(((x, y), 1))$ restricted to S is the identity function. Thus if f denotes the function $(x, y) \to H(((x, y), 1))$ from X into S, then the composite function $i_s \circ f$ of the identity on S and f is just the function f. This, however, has just been proved above to be homotopic to i_x. Hence $i_s \circ f$ *homt* i_x in X. Also, $f \circ i_s = i_s$. Hence $f \circ i_s$ *homt* i_s in S and so X and S are homotopically equivalent.

34.21 Lemma. *The space* $E^2 \sim \{(0, 0)\}$ *that is the subspace of the plane obtained by deleting the origin* $(0, 0)$ *is homotopically equivalent to the circumference of the unit circle,* $\{(x, y)$ *in* $E^2 \mid x^2 + y^2 = 1\}$.

Proof: Exercise. [*Hint:* The function H in the previous example can be extended to $E^2 \sim \{(0, 0)\}$.]

REMARK: The previous example gives a specific instance of a general situation. The hypothesis, which made possible the proof that the space X was homotopic to the subspace S, was the existence of a continuous function f from X onto S which was homotopic to the identity function on X and whose restriction to S was the identity function on S. The next definition and theorem give a generalization of example 34.20.

34.22 Definition. Let X be a space and let S be a subspace of X. S is called a *deformation retract* of X if and only if there exists a retraction from X onto S which is homotopic to the identity function on X.

34.23 Theorem. *If X is a space and S is any subspace of X which is a deformation retract of X, then X and S are homotopically equivalent.*

Proof: Let f be a continuous function from X onto S which is homotopic to the identity function, i_x, on X and whose restriction to S is the identity function, i_s, on S. Then the composite function $i_s \circ f$ from X onto S is just the function f. Hence $i_s \circ f$ is homotopic to i_x. Further, $f \circ i_s$ from S into X is just i_s. Hence X and S are homotopically equivalent spaces. ∎

EXERCISE 2. Prove that any point, x, in a contractible space, X, determines a subspace $\{x\}$ which is a deformation retract of X.

EXERCISE 3. Prove that contractibility is an invariant of the homotopy type of a space as well as a topological invariant, i.e., prove that if X and Y are homotopically equivalent and if Y is contractible, then X is also contractible.

It has thus been established that *homt* determines exactly one equivalence class in $C(X, Y)$, the set of all continuous functions from X into Y, whenever Y is contractible. It has also been established that any two contractible spaces are homotopically equivalent, and that all contractible spaces are homotopically equivalent to trivial point-spaces. Further, it has been established that any space is homotopically equivalent to any of its deformation retracts.

35. THE FUNDAMENTAL GROUPOID AND THE FUNDAMENTAL GROUP.

In section 22 on completely regular spaces, the set $C(X)$ or $C(X, E^1)$ of all continuous functions from a space X into the usual space E^1 of real numbers was used to define a ring, $\{C(X, E^1), \boxplus, \boxtimes\}$, which is a topological invariant for X in the sense that homeomorphic spaces have isomorphic rings. In a somewhat analogous manner, equivalence classes of functions in $C(I, Y)$ will be used to define two algebraic structures for a space Y, the fundamental groupoid and the fundamental group.

35.1 Definition. The *product*, $f * g$, of paths f and g in a space Y is defined to be the function which assigns to t the image $f(2t)$ if $0 \leq t \leq 1/2$, and

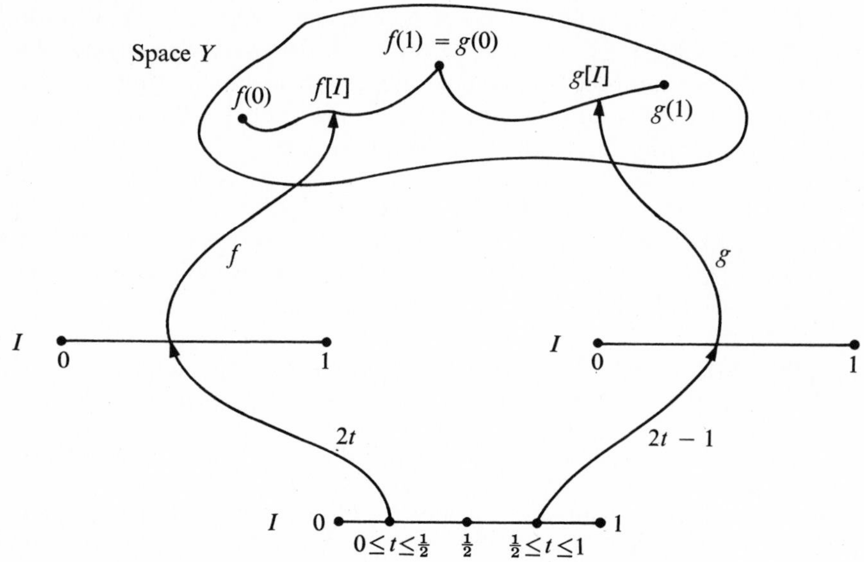

FIGURE 29 An illustration of the product, $f * g$

the image $g(2t - 1)$ if $1/2 \leq t \leq 1$. $f * g$ is defined if and only if $f(1) = g(0)$. By theorems 9.23 and 4.8, $f * g$, when it is defined, is a path in Y.

35.2 Definition. The *inverse*, f^{-1}, of a path, f, in a space Y is defined as follows: $f^{-1}(t) = f(1 - t)$. By theorem 4.8, f^{-1} is a path in Y. It is to be observed that $f(0) = f^{-1}(1)$ and $f(1) = f^{-1}(0)$. Thus, $f * f^{-1}$ and $f^{-1} * f$ are both defined.

EXERCISE 1. Let $f(t) = (t, 1/(t + 1))$ and $g(t) = (t + 1, (t + 1)/2)$ denote two paths in the plane, E^2. Determine $f * g(1/4)$ and $f * g(3/4)$.

EXERCISE 2. Prove or disprove: $f * f^{-1} = f^{-1} * f$.

EXERCISE 3. Let $\tilde{a}$ denote the constant path which assigns the point a in Y as the image for all t in I. Let f be a path in Y such that $f(0) = a$ and $f(1) = b$. Prove or disprove:

(1) $\tilde{a} * f = f = f * \tilde{b}$;

(2) $*$ is associative.

The concept of "relative homotopy" which is a smaller equivalence relation than *homt* must be introduced.

35.3 Definition. Let X and Y be spaces; let $A \subseteq X$ and let f and g be continuous functions from X into Y which agree on A, i.e., $f(a) = g(a)$ for every a in A. f and g are called *homotopic relative to A* if and only if there exists a homotopy H from $X \times I$ into Y such that $H((a, 0)) = H((a, t)) =$

$f(a) = g(a)$ for all a in A and t in I. The existence of this stricter type of homotopy between f and g will be written f *homt*(A) g.

EXERCISE 4. Let $A \subseteq X$. Let f and g be continuous functions from X into Y. Prove that if f *homt* $(A)g$, then f *homt* g.

35.4 Definition. Let "*r-homt*" throughout be an abbreviation of "homotopic relative to the set, $\{0, 1\}$." Two paths f and g in Y are *r-homotopic* if and only if $f(0) = g(0)$, $f(1) = g(1)$ and there exists a homotopy relative to $\{0, 1\}$ between f and g.

EXERCISE 5. Prove that *r-homt* is an equivalence relation on $C(I, Y)$ (see lemma 34.2).

35.5 Theorem. *Let f, g, m and n denote paths in a space Y. Let $f * g$ and f^{-1} be defined as in definitions 35.1 and 35.2. Then*

(*a*) *$f * (g * m)$ r-homt $(f * g) * m$ whenever $f * g$ and $g * m$ are defined;*
(*b*) *$f * f^{-1}$ r-homt λ_f, where $\lambda_f(t) = f(0)$ for $0 \leq t \leq 1$, and $f^{-1} * f$ r-homt ρ_f, where $\rho_f(t) = f(1)$ for $0 \leq t \leq 1$;*
(*c*) *$f * \rho_f$ r-homt f and $\lambda_f * f$ r-homt f;*
(*d*) *if f r-homt m and g r-homt n, then $f * g$ r-homt $m * n$, whenever $f * g$ and $m * n$ are defined.*

Proof: A. By definition of $*$, it follows that $(f * g) * m(s) = f * g(2s)$ for $0 \leq s \leq 1/2$, and $(f * g) * m(s) = m(2s - 1)$ for $1/2 \leq s \leq 1$. $f * g(2s) = f(4s)$ for $0 \leq s \leq 1/4$ and $f * g(2s) = g(4s - 1)$ for $1/4 \leq s \leq 1/2$. Thus $(f * g) * m(s) = f(4s)$ when $0 \leq s \leq 1/4$, $(f * g) * m(s) = g(4s - 1)$ when $1/4 \leq s \leq 1/2$, and $(f * g) * m(s) = m(2s - 1)$ for $1/2 \leq s \leq 1$. $f * (g * m)(s) = f(s)$ when $0 \leq s \leq 1/2$, $f * (g * m)(s) = g(4s - 2)$ when $1/2 \leq s \leq 3/4$ and $f * (g * m)(s) = m(4s - 3)$ when $3/4 \leq s \leq 1$. See figure 30, page 372.

Define $H((s, t))$ from $I \times I$ as follows:

$$H((s,t)) = f\left(\frac{4s}{2-t}\right) \qquad \text{for } 0 \leq s \leq \frac{2-t}{4},$$

$$H((s,t)) = g(4s - 2 + t) \qquad \text{for } \frac{2-t}{4} \leq s \leq \frac{3-t}{4},$$

$$H((s,t)) = m\left(\frac{4s - 3 + t}{1 + t}\right) \qquad \text{for } \frac{3-t}{4} \leq s \leq 1.$$

H is continuous by theorems 9.23 and 4.8. Further,

$$\begin{aligned} H((s,0)) &= f(2s) && \text{for } 0 \leq s \leq 1/2, \\ H((s,0)) &= g(4s-2) && \text{for } 1/2 \leq s \leq 3/4, \\ H((s,0)) &= m(4s-3) && \text{for } 3/4 \leq s \leq 1. \end{aligned}$$

Thus $H((s, 0)) = f * (g * m)(s)$. Also,

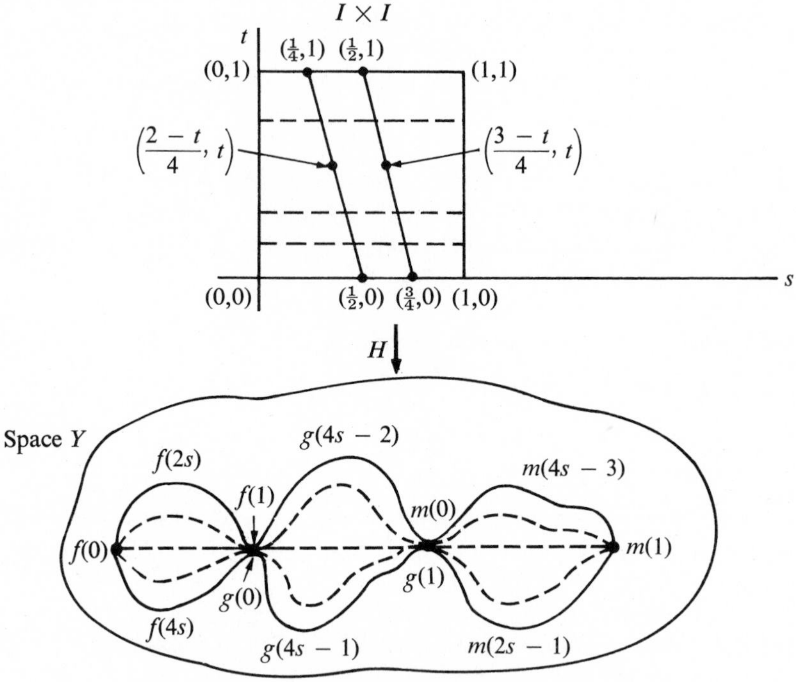

FIGURE 30 Illustration of the r-homotopy from $f * (g * m)$ to $(f * g) * m$

$$H((s, 1)) = f(4s) \quad \text{for } 0 \le s \le 1/4,$$
$$H((s, 1)) = g(4s - 1) \quad \text{for } 1/4 \le s \le 1/2,$$
$$H((s, 1)) = m(2s - 1) \quad \text{for } 1/2 \le s \le 1.$$

Hence $H((s, 1)) = (f * g) * m(s)$. Also $H((0, t)) = f(0)$ and $H((1, t)) = m(1)$. H is then an r-homotopy from $f * (g * m)$ to $(f * g) * m$.

B. Let $H((s, t))$ from $I \times I$ into Y be defined now as follows:

$$H((s, t)) = \lambda_f(s) \quad \text{for } 0 \le s \le t/2,$$
$$H((s, t)) = f(2s - t) \quad \text{for } t/2 \le s \le 1/2,$$
$$H((s, t)) = f^{-1}(2s + t - 1) \quad \text{for } 1/2 \le s \le (2 - t)/2,$$
$$H((s, t)) = \lambda_f(s) \quad \text{for } (2 - t)/2 \le s \le 1.$$

H is continuous by theorems 4.8 and 9.23. Further, $H((s, 0)) = f(2s)$ for $0 \le s \le 1/2$, and $H((s, 0)) = f^{-1}(2s - 1)$ for $1/2 \le s \le 1$. Thus, $H((s, 0)) = f * f^{-1}(s)$. Also, $H((s, 1)) = f(0)$ for $0 \le s \le 1/2$, and $H((s, 1)) = f(0)$ for $1/2 \le s \le 1$. Thus $H((s, 1)) = \lambda_f(s)$. Also, $H((0, t)) = \lambda_f(0) = f(0)$ and $H((1, t)) = \lambda_f(1) = f(0) = f^{-1}(1)$. H is then an r-homotopy between $f * f^{-1}$ and λ_f. The r-homotopy H is illustrated in figure 31. Similarly, H can be interpreted as an r-homotopy from $f^{-1} * f$ to ρ_f since $(f^{-1})^{-1} = f$. $f^{-1} * f$ can

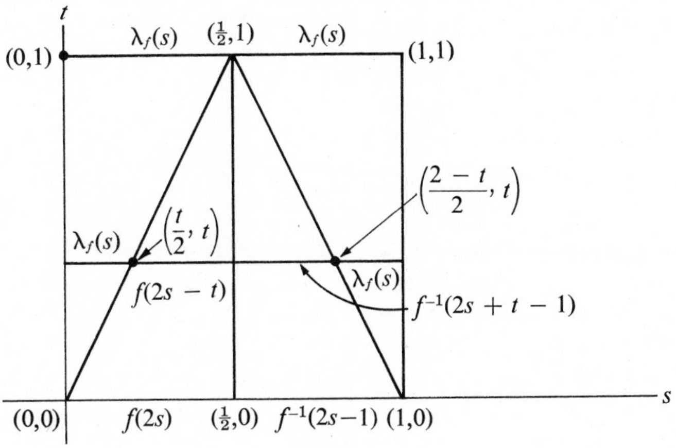

FIGURE 31

be written $f^{-1} * (f^{-1})^{-1}$. So, if $g = f^{-1}$, $f^{-1} * f = g * g^{-1}$ and H is an r-homotopy from $g * g^{-1}$ to ρ_f.

C. Let $A((s, t))$ be defined as follows from $I \times I$ into Y.

$$A((s, t)) = \lambda_f(s) \qquad \text{for } 0 \leq s \leq t/2,$$

$$A((s, t)) = f\left(\frac{2s - t}{2 - t}\right) \qquad \text{for } t/2 \leq s \leq 1.$$

By theorems 4.8 and 9.23, A is continuous. $A((s, 0)) = f(s)$ for $0 \leq s \leq 1$. $A((s, 1)) = \lambda_f(s) = f(0)$ for $0 \leq s \leq 1/2$, and $A((s, 1)) = f(2s - 1)$ for $1/2 \leq s \leq 1$. Thus A is a homotopy from f to $\lambda_f * f$. Further, since $A((0, t)) = \lambda_f(0) = f(0)$ and $A((1, t)) = f(1)$ for all t, A is an r-homotopy from f to $\lambda_f * f$ (see figure 32).

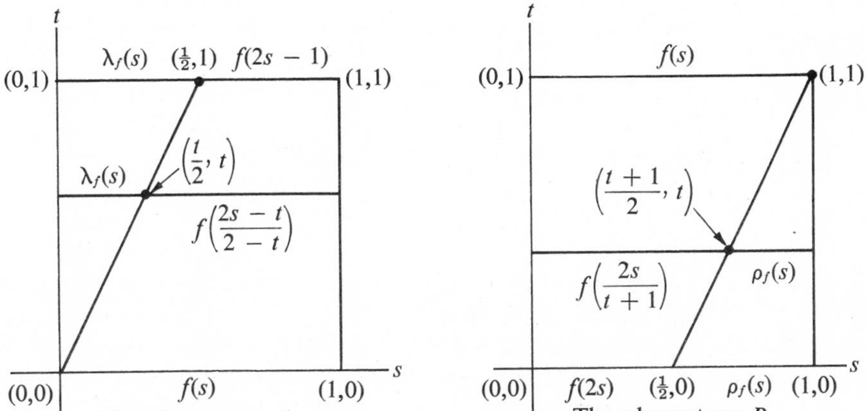

The r-homotopy A The r-homotopy B

FIGURE 32

Similarly the r-homotopy B from $f * \rho_f$ to f is defined as follows:

$$B((s,t)) = f\left(\frac{2s}{t+1}\right) \quad \text{for } 0 \le s \le \frac{t+1}{2},$$
$$B((s,t)) = \rho_f(s) \quad \text{for } \frac{t+1}{2} \le s \le 1.$$

B is continuous by theorems 4.8 and 9.23. $B((s,0)) = f(2s)$ for $0 \le s \le 1/2$ and $B((s,0)) = \rho_f(s) = f(1)$ for $1/2 \le s \le 1$. $B((s,1)) = f(s)$ for $0 \le s \le 1$. Thus B is a homotopy from $f * \rho_f$ to f. Since $B((0,t)) = f(0)$ and $B((1,t)) = \rho_f(1) = f(1)$, B is an r-homotopy.

D. Let f *r-homt* m and g *r-homt* n and let $f * g$ and $m * n$ be defined. Let A_1 denote the r-homotopy from f to m and let A_2 denote the r-homotopy from g to n. Define H from $I \times I$ into Y as follows:

$$H((s,t)) = A_1((2s,t)) \quad \text{for } 0 \le s \le 1/2,$$
$$H((s,t)) = A_2((2s-1,t)) \quad \text{for } 1/2 \le s \le 1.$$

By theorems 4.8 and 9.23, H is continuous. $H((s,0)) = A_1((2s,0)) = f(2s)$ for $0 \le s \le 1/2$ and $H((s,0)) = A_2((2s-1,0)) = g(2s-1)$ for $1/2 \le s \le 1$. Hence $H((s,0)) = f * g(s)$. $H((s,1)) = A_1((2s,1)) = m(2s)$ for $0 \le s \le 1/2$ and $H((s,1)) = A_2((2s-1,1)) = n(2s-1)$. Thus $H((s,1)) = m * n(s)$ and H is a homotopy from $f * g$ to $m * n$. Since $H((0,t)) = A_1((0,t)) = f(0) = m(0)$ and $H((1,t)) = A_2((1,t)) = g(1) = n(1)$ for all t in I, H is also an r-homotopy from $f * g$ to $m * n$. ∎ (See figure 33.)

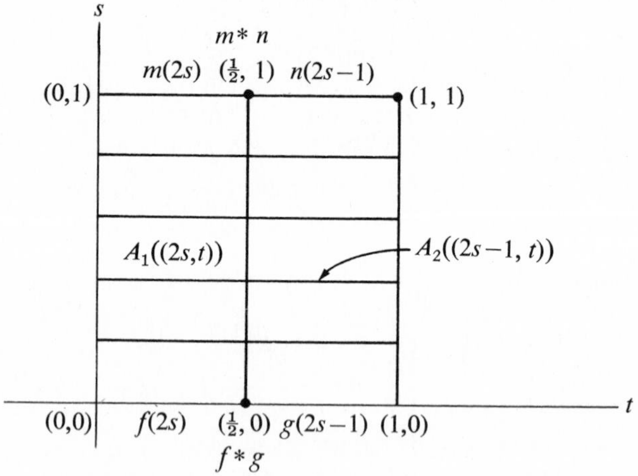

FIGURE 33

The equivalence relation *r-homt* determines, of course, equivalence classes in $C(I, Y)$. These classes are in general smaller than the *homt* classes since *r-homt* $\subseteq$ *homt*, and in general *r-homt* $\neq$ *homt*. Theorem 35.5 establishes properties of $*$ with respect to r-homotopy. Since $f * g$ is not defined for all paths in Y, no induced group structure seems possible on the *r-homt* equivalence classes in $C(I, Y)$. However, a quasi-group-like structure can be defined on this set. The structure, called a groupoid, is useful in modern mathematics.

35.6 Definition. A pair $\{S, \circledast\}$ is called a *groupoid* if and only if S is a set and $\circledast$ is a function from a subset of $S \times S$ into S satisfying the following axioms ($\circledast((x, y))$ is written $x \circledast y$):

1. For each element x in S are defined elements λ_x and ρ_x of S such that $\lambda_x \circledast x = x = x \circledast \rho_x$;
2. $x \circledast y$, for x, y in S, is defined if and only if $\rho_x = \lambda_y$;
3. $\lambda_{\lambda_x} = \lambda_x = \rho_{\lambda_x}$ and $\rho_{\rho_x} = \rho_x = \lambda_{\rho_x}$;
4. $\lambda_x \circledast \lambda_x = \lambda_x$ and $\rho_x \circledast \rho_x = \rho_x$;
5. $\lambda_{x \circledast y} = \lambda_x$ and $\rho_{x \circledast y} = \rho_y$ for x, y in S and $x \circledast y$ defined;
6. $(x \circledast y) \circledast z = x \circledast (y \circledast z)$ for x, y, z in S and for $x \circledast y$ and $y \circledast z$ defined.
7. For each x in S, there exists an element x^{-1} in S such that $\lambda_{x^{-1}} = \rho_x$, $\rho_{x^{-1}} = \lambda_x$, $x \circledast x^{-1} = \lambda_x$ and $x^{-1} \circledast x = \rho_x$.

It is clear that λ_x and ρ_x behave somewhat like left and right identities respectively, x^{-1} is somewhat like an inverse and $\circledast$ is somewhat like an associative operation.

35.7 Theorem. *Let Y be a space and let $\Gamma(Y)$ denote the set of equivalence classes determined by r-homt in $C(I, Y)$. Then $\{\Gamma(Y), \circledast\}$ is a groupoid, where $[f] \circledast [g] = [f * g]$ for $[f]$ and $[g]$ in $\Gamma(Y)$ and $f * g$ as defined in* 35.1.

Proof: For f a path in Y, define $\lambda_{[f]}$ to be the class containing the constant path c_0 defined by $c_0(t) = f(0)$ for $0 \leq t \leq 1$, and define $\rho_{[f]}$ to be the class containing the constant path c_1 defined by $c_1(t) = f(1)$ for $0 \leq t \leq 1$. It follows from theorem 35.5 that $\{\Gamma(Y), \circledast\}$ is a groupoid. ∎

35.8 Definition. For any space Y, the groupoid $\{\Gamma(Y), \circledast\}$ is called the *fundamental groupoid* of Y. $\{\Gamma(Y), \circledast\}$ will be abbreviated to $\Gamma(Y)$ when no confusion seems likely.

35.9 Definition. A function γ from a groupoid $\{\Gamma_1, \circledast\}$ into a groupoid $\{\Gamma_2, \boxed{*}\}$ is called a *homomorphism* if and only if $\gamma(a \circledast b) = \gamma(a) \boxed{*} \gamma(b)$. γ is an *isomorphism* if and only if γ is a 1:1, onto homomorphism.

35.10 Theorem. *Let w be a continuous function from the space X into the space Y. Then w induces a homomorphism w_* from $\Gamma(X)$ into $\Gamma(Y)$ defined by* $w_*([f]) = [w \circ f]$ *for* $[f]$ *in* $\Gamma(X)$.

Proof: If f is a path in X then $w \circ f$ is a path in Y. Further, if f *r-homt* g, then $w \circ f$ *r-homt* $w \circ g$ by the homotopy $w \circ H$, where H is the r-homotopy from f to g. Thus w_* is single-valued. Now, if $f * g$ is defined for paths f and g in X, then $f(1) = g(0)$. Hence $w \circ f(1) = w \circ g(0)$, and so $(w \circ f) * (w \circ g)$ is defined. Further, $w_*([f] \circledast [g]) = w_*([f * g]) = [w \circ (f * g)] = [(w \circ f) * (w \circ g)] = [w \circ f] \circledast [w \circ g] = w_*([f]) \circledast w_*([g])$. Thus, w_* is a homomorphism. ▮

35.11 Theorem. *If w is a continuous function from the space X into the space Y and if v is a continuous function from the space Y into the space Z, then $(v \circ w)_* = v_* \circ w_*$, and if $X = Y$ and w is the identity function on X, then w_* is the identity isomorphism on $\Gamma(X)$.*

Proof: Let f be a path in X. Then $(v \circ w)_*([f]) = [v \circ w \circ f] = v_*([w \circ f]) = v_*(w_*([f])) = v_* \circ w_*([f])$. If $w(x) = x$, then $w \circ f = f$ for f a path in X. Hence $w_*([f]) = [f]$. ▮

35.12 Theorem. *If X and Y are homeomorphic, then $\Gamma(X)$ and $\Gamma(Y)$ are isomorphic.*

Proof: $h \circ h^{-1}$ is the identity on Y and $h^{-1} \circ h$ is the identity on X. Therefore, $(h \circ h^{-1})_*$ and $(h^{-1} \circ h)_*$ are identity isomorphisms on $\Gamma(Y)$ and $\Gamma(X)$ respectively. This means that $h_* \circ h_*^{-1} = i_{\Gamma(Y)}$ and $h_*^{-1} \circ h_* = i_{\Gamma(X)}$. Thus h_* and h_*^{-1} are isomorphisms. ▮

The fundamental groupoid is then, in the sense of definition 18.50, an algebraic topological invariant.

EXERCISE 6. Prove or disprove: the fundamental groupoid is an invariant of the homotopy type of a space; i.e., whenever two spaces are homotopically equivalent their fundamental groupoids are isomorphic.

The fundamental groups of a space are subgroupoids of the fundamental groupoid which also satisfy the axioms for a group.

35.13 Definition. An element e in a groupoid $\{\Gamma, \circledast\}$ is called an *idempotent* if and only if $\lambda_e = e$. It follows immediately from axiom 3 for a groupoid that e is an idempotent if and only if $\lambda_e = e = \rho_e$.

35.14 Lemma. *An element e in a groupoid $\{\Gamma, \circledast\}$ is an idempotent if and only if $e \circledast e = e$ and for each x in $\{\Gamma, \circledast\}$, λ_x and ρ_x are idempotents.*

Proof: Exercise.

35.15 Definition. A groupoid $\{A, \boxplus\}$ is called a *subgroupoid* of a groupoid $\{S, \circledast\}$ if and only if $A \subseteq S$, $a \boxplus b = a \circledast b$ whenever both are defined and, lastly, $a \circledast b$ is in A whenever a and b are in A and $a \circledast b$ is defined.

35.16 Lemma. *Let $\{\Gamma, \circledast\}$ be a groupoid and let e be an idempotent in*

$\{\Gamma, \circledast\}$. *Then if* $A_e = \{x \mid x \text{ is in } \Gamma \text{ and } \lambda_x = e = \rho_x\}$, *then* $\{A_e, \circledast\}$ *is a subgroupoid of* $\{\Gamma, \circledast\}$ *which is also a group.*

Proof: By definition of an idempotent, $\lambda_e = e = \rho_e$. Hence, e is in A_e. Now if x is any element in A_e, $\lambda_x = e = \rho_x$, and so λ_x and ρ_x are in A_e. Further, if x and y are in A, then $\lambda_x = \lambda_y = e = \rho_x = \rho_y$. Hence, if $x \circledast y$ is defined, $\lambda_{x \circledast y} = \lambda_x = e = \rho_y = \rho_{x \circledast y}$ and $x \circledast y$ is in A_e. Now let x be in A_e and consider x^{-1} in Γ. By axiom 7 for a groupoid, $x \circledast x^{-1}$ and $x^{-1} \circledast x$ are defined in $\{\Gamma, \circledast\}$. Hence, $\rho_x = \lambda_{x^{-1}}$ and $\rho_{x^{-1}} = \lambda_x$. Now, since x is in A, $\rho_x = e = \lambda_x$. It then follows that $\lambda_{x^{-1}} = e = \rho_{x^{-1}}$ and that x^{-1} is in A_e. The other axioms for a groupoid follow because $\{\Gamma, \circledast\}$ is a groupoid. Thus $\{A_e, \circledast\}$ is a groupoid. Now, let x and y be in A_e. Then $\lambda_y = e = \rho_x$ and $\lambda_x = e = \rho_y$. Hence, $x \circledast y$ and $y \circledast x$ are both defined, and so by the above are in A_e. Since $\lambda_x = e = \rho_x$ for x in A_e, $e \circledast x = x = x \circledast e$ for all x in A_e. Associativity for $\circledast$ follows from axiom 6 for a groupoid, since $\{\Gamma, \circledast\}$ is a groupoid. Finally if x is in A_e, x^{-1} is in A_e, by the above. Hence, $x \circledast x^{-1} = e = x^{-1} \circledast x$ and $\{A_e, \circledast\}$ is a group. ▌

35.17 Lemma. *Let Y be a space and, again, let $\{\Gamma(Y), \circledast\}$ denote the fundamental groupoid of Y. Let y_0 be a point in Y and let $\tilde{y}_0$ denote the constant path $\tilde{y}_0(t) = y_0$ for $0 \leq t \leq 1$. $[\tilde{y}_0]$, the class containing $\tilde{y}_0$, is an idempotent in $\{\Gamma(Y), \circledast\}$.*

Proof: $[\tilde{y}_0] \circledast [\tilde{y}_0] = [\tilde{y}_0 * \tilde{y}_0] = [\tilde{y}_0]$ by definition of $*$. ▌

35.18 Definition. It follows from lemma 35.17 that each point, y_0, of a space Y determines a subgroupoid, $\pi_1(Y, y_0)$, of the fundamental groupoid $\{\Gamma(Y), \circledast\}$. The groupoid $\pi_1(Y, y_0)$ is also a group and is called the *fundamental group* of Y at y_0.

35.19 Definition. Let Y be a space. A path f in Y is called a *loop* if and only if $f(0) = f(1)$.

35.20 Lemma. *The elements of the fundamental group $\pi_1(Y, y_0)$ of Y at y_0 are r-homotopy equivalence classes of loops f such that $[f]$ is in $\pi_1(Y, y_0)$ if and only if $f(0) = y_0 = f(1)$.*

Proof: Let $[f]$ be in the group $\pi_1(Y, y_0)$. By definition of $\pi_1(Y, y_0)$, $\lambda_{[f]} = [\tilde{y}_0] = \rho_{[f]}$, where again $\tilde{y}_0$ denotes the constant loop $\tilde{y}_0(t) = y_0$ for $0 \leq t \leq 1$. Hence by definition of $\lambda_{[f]}$ and $\rho_{[f]}$ in $\{\Gamma(Y), \circledast\}$, $f(0) = y_0 = f(1)$ and f is a loop in Y. ▌ (See figure 34 on page 376.)

If Y is a pathwise connected space, then all fundamental groups $\pi_1(Y, y_0)$, $\pi_1(Y, z_0)$, etc., are isomorphic. This will be proved below. First, however, a generalization of this statement to groupoids will be proved.

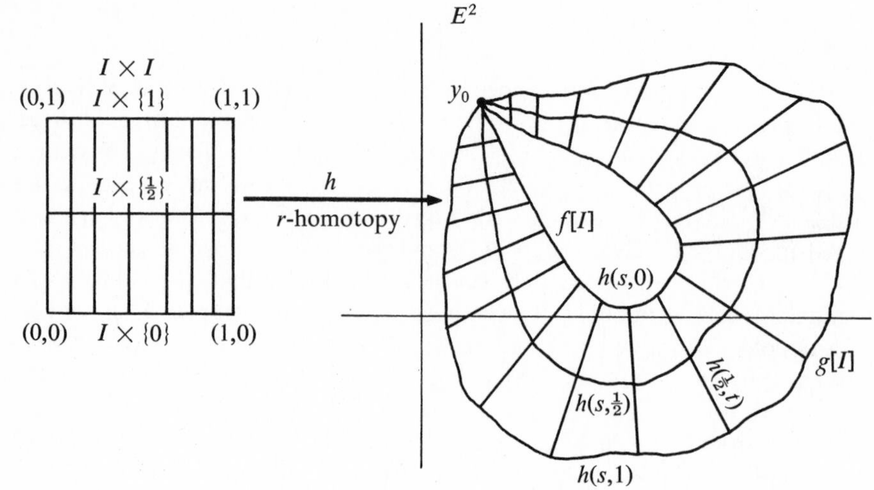

An illustration of an r-homotopy between loops f and g related to $\pi_1(E^2, y_0)$

FIGURE 34

35.21 Theorem. *If $\{\Gamma, \circledast\}$ is any groupoid and if α is in Γ, then the groups $\{A_{\lambda_\alpha}, \circledast\}$ and $\{A_{\rho_\alpha}, \circledast\}$ determined by the idempotents λ_α and ρ_α are isomorphic.*

Proof: For x in A_{λ_α}, let $h(x) = \alpha^{-1} \circledast x \circledast \alpha$. The proof that h is an isomorphism from $\{A_{\lambda_\alpha}, \circledast\}$ onto $\{A_{\rho_\alpha}, \circledast\}$ is left as an exercise. ▮

35.22 Theorem. *If Y is a pathwise connected space and if $\pi_1(Y, y_0)$ and $\pi_1(Y, z_0)$ are fundamental groups, then $\pi_1(Y, y_0)$ is isomorphic to $\pi_1(Y, z_0)$.*

Proof: Since Y is pathwise connected, there exists a path f from y_0 to z_0 in Y, i.e., $f(0) = y_0$ and $f(1) = z_0$. For $[f]$, the path class of f in the fundamental groupoid $\{\Gamma(Y), \circledast\}$, then $\lambda_{[f]} = [\tilde{y}_0]$ and $\rho_{[f]} = [\tilde{z}_0]$, where $\tilde{y}_0$ and $\tilde{z}_0$ are the constant functions $\tilde{y}_0(t) = y_0$ and $\tilde{z}_0(t) = z_0$ for $0 \leq t \leq 1$. By the previous theorem, this means that the groups determined by the idempotents $[\tilde{y}_0]$ and $[\tilde{z}_0]$ are isomorphic. Hence $\pi_1(Y, y_0)$ is isomorphic to $\pi_1(Y, z_0)$. ▮

Thus for each pathwise connected space Y, there is essentially one fundamental group in the sense that all fundamental groups are isomorphic.

It can be established immediately with the help of the next two theorems and lemma that any fundamental group of a pathwise connected space is an algebraic topological invariant in the sense of definition 18.50. This is the analogue of theorem 35.12.

35.23 Theorem. *Let X and Y be pathwise connected spaces and let $w: X \to Y$*

be continuous. Then w induces a homomorphism w_* from $\pi_1(X, x_0)$ into $\pi_1(Y, w(x_0))$.

Proof: A. Let w_* be defined as follows. $w_*([f]) = [w \circ f]$. Since f is a loop in X, the composite function $w \circ f$ is a loop in Y and since $f(0) = f(1) = x_0$, $w \circ f(0) = w \circ f(1) = w(x_0)$. Hence $[w \circ f]$ is a uniquely defined element in $\pi_1(Y, w(x_0))$. Let $[f] = [g]$. Then, f *r-homt* g. Let H be an r-homotopy between f and g in X. The composite function $w \circ H$ is an r-homotopy between $w \circ f$ and $w \circ g$ and so w_* is single-valued.

B. w_* is a homomorphism. Consider $w_*([f] \circledast [g])$. $w_*([f] \circledast [g]) = w_*([f * g]) = [w \circ (f * g)]$. $w \circ (f * g)(s) = w \circ f(2s)$ for $0 \leq s \leq 1/2$ and $w \circ (f * g)(s) = w \circ g(2s - 1)$ for $1/2 \leq s \leq 1$. Hence, $w \circ (f * g) = w \circ f * w \circ g$. Therefore,

$$w_*([f] \circledast [g]) = [w \circ f * w \circ g] = [w \circ f] \circledast [w \circ g] = w_*([f]) \circledast w_*([g]).$$

Hence w_* is a homomorphism. ▮

The next theorem lists the properties of the correspondence $w \to w_*$ established in the previous theorem. w_* is again called the induced homomorphism.

35.24 Theorem. *If w is a continuous function from the pathwise connected space X into the pathwise connected space Y, then the correspondence $w \to w_*$, where $w_*([f]) = [w \circ f]$ for $[f]$ in $\pi_1(X, x_0)$, has the following properties:*

A. if $w = i_x$, then $w_* =$ identity isomorphism;
B. if w r-homt $(x_0)w'$, then $w_* = w'_*$;
C. if v is continuous from Y into Z, then $(v \circ w)_* = v_* \circ w_*$.

Proof: A. If $w(x) = x$, then $w \circ f = f$ and $[w \circ f] = [f]$. Thus $w_*([f]) = [f]$.

B. Let w *r-homt* $(x_0)w'$. $w_*([f]) = [w \circ f]$ and $w'_*([f]) = [w' \circ f]$. Since w and w' are homotopic relative to $\{x_0\}$, $w(x_0) = w'(x_0)$. Hence $w \circ f$ *r-homt* $\{(0, 1)\}\, w' \circ f$ and $[w \circ f] = [w' \circ f]$. Thus $w_*([f]) = w'_*([f])$ for all $[f]$ in $\pi_1(X, x_0)$ and so $w_* = w'_*$.

C. $(v \circ w)_*([f]) = [v \circ w \circ f] = v_*([w \circ f])$ and $v_*([w \circ f]) = v_*(w_*([f]) = v_* \circ w_*([f])$. ▮

This last theorem describes a "transition." The transition goes from topology to algebra in such a way that (1) to spaces are assigned groups, (2) to continuous functions are assigned unique homomorphisms in such a way that

(a) the image of the identity $i_X : X \to X$ is the identity $i_G : G_X \to G_X$;
(b) the image $(v \circ w)_*$ of a composite $v \circ w : X \to Y \to Z$ is the composite $v_* \circ w_*$ of the images; and
(c) the correspondence is constant on certain relative homotopy classes.

35.25 Lemma. *If X and Y are pathwise connected spaces, if w is a continuous* *function from X into Y and if v is a continuous function from Y into X and if, further,* $v \circ w$ *is homotopic to the identity* i_X *relative to* $\{x_0\}$ *and* $w \circ v$ *is homotopic to the identity* i_Y *relative to* $\{f(x_0)\}$, *then* $\pi_1(X, x_0)$ *and* $\pi_1(Y, f(x_0))$ *are isomorphic.*

Proof: Let $w_*:[f] \to [w \circ f]$ and $v_*:[m] \to [v \circ m]$. Since $v \circ w$ is homotopic to i_X relative to $\{x_0\}$, $(v \circ w)_*$ is the identity isomorphism on $\pi_1(X, x_0)$ by theorem 35.24. Hence, again by theorem 35.24, $v_* \circ w_*$ is the identity isomorphism on $\pi_1(X, x_0)$. Similarly $w_* \circ v_*$ is the identity isomorphism on $\pi_1(Y, w(x_0))$. Thus w_* is 1:1 and onto. Hence, $\pi_1(X, x_0)$ is isomorphic to $\pi_1(Y, w(x_0))$. ▮

35.26 Theorem. *If X and Y are homeomorphic, pathwise connected spaces, then any fundamental group of X is isomorphic to any fundamental group of Y.*

Proof: If h is a homeomorphism from X onto Y, then $h^{-1} \circ h$ is the identity on X and $h \circ h^{-1}$ is the identity on Y. Thus, by the previous lemma, $\pi_1(X, x_0)$ is isomorphic to $\pi_1(Y, h(x_0))$ for any point x_0 in X. ▮

The topological invariance of the fundamental group also comes as a result of the homotopical invariance.

The Fundamental Group as an Invariant of the Homotopy Type

Lemma 35.25 comes very close to saying that if two pathwise connected spaces are of the same homotopy type their fundamental groups are isomorphic and, indeed, two pathwise spaces of the same homotopy type do have isomorphic fundamental groups. However, in order to obtain this result the relative nature of the homotopies must be removed. In part B of theorem 35.24, let w and w' be just homotopic and then consider the "induced" homomorphisms w_* and w'_*. $w_*([f]) = [w \circ f]$ and $w'_*([f]) = [w' \circ f]$. Now if x_0 is the base point for the loops in X, $w(x_0)$ may not be equal to $w'(x_0)$, thus $[w \circ f]$ and $[w' \circ f]$ are not necessarily in the same group, so w_* cannot be equal to w'_*. Further, even if $w(x_0) = w'(x_0)$, if there is no homotopy between w and w' which is constant on x_0, then $w \circ f$ is not homotopic to $w' \circ f$ in the required way, and so $[w \circ f] \neq [w' \circ f]$. Thus, no longer is the same homomorphism "induced" by homotopic functions w and w'. This means that $(v \circ w)_*$ may not be the identity isomorphism even though $v \circ w$ is homotopic to the identity function on X. This was a crucial point in the proof that w_* was an isomorphism and hence that the fundamental groups $\pi_1(X, x_0)$ and $\pi_1(Y, y_0)$ were isomorphic. However, there is a relation between the two homomorphisms induced by homotopic functions which makes possible the proof that the fundamental groups of two homotopically equivalent spaces are isomorphic.

35.27 Definition. Let G be a group. An inner *automorphism* of G is an isomorphism ψ_γ where $\psi_\gamma(g) = \gamma g \gamma^{-1}$ for g and γ in G. If ξ_1 and ξ_2 are homomorphisms from a group G into a group G^*, then ξ_1 and ξ_2 are called *conjugates* if and only if $\xi_2 = \psi_\gamma \circ \xi_1$, where ψ_γ is an inner automorphism on G^*.

35.28 Lemma. *If G and G^* are groups and if $Hom(G, G^*)$ denotes the set of homomorphisms from G into G^*, then conjugacy is an equivalence relation on $Hom(G, G^*)$.*

Proof: Exercise.

35.29 Lemma. *If ξ is an isomorphism from the group G onto the group G^*, then any conjugate of ξ is an isomorphism onto.*

Proof: An inner automorphism is 1:1 and onto. ▮

35.30 Lemma. *Let ξ_1 and ξ_2 be conjugate homomorphisms from a group G into a group G^*, and let ζ_1 and ζ_2 be conjugate homomorphisms from G^* into a group G^{**}. Then the composites $\zeta_1 \circ \xi_1$ and $\zeta_2 \circ \xi_2$ are conjugate homomorphisms from G into G^{**}.*

Proof: Exercise.

In theorem 35.22, the fundamental groups $\pi_1(Y, y_0)$ and $\pi_1(Y, z_0)$, where Y is a pathwise connected space, were shown to be isomorphic by using paths from y_0 to z_0. Such paths, of course, determine elements of the fundamental groupoid $\{\Gamma(Y), \circledast\}$.

35.31 Theorem. *The isomorphisms defined from $\pi_1(Y, y_0)$ onto $\pi_1(Y, z_0)$ by paths in Y from y_0 to z_0, where Y is pathwise connected, are all conjugate.*

Proof: Let α and γ be paths from y_0 to z_0 in Y. Let $[\alpha]$ and $[\gamma]$ denote the elements of $\{\Gamma(Y), \circledast\}$ which contain λ and γ respectively. $\alpha * \gamma^{-1}$ is a loop based at y_0. Hence $[\alpha * \gamma^{-1}]$ is an element in $\pi_1(Y, y_0)$. Now the isomorphism induced by $[\alpha]$ is $[g] \to [\alpha] \circledast [g] \circledast [\alpha^{-1}]$ for $[g]$ in $\pi_1(Y, y_0)$. By theorem 35.5, $[\alpha] \circledast [g] \circledast [\alpha^{-1}] = [\alpha] \circledast [\gamma^{-1}] \circledast [\gamma] \circledast [g] \circledast [\gamma^{-1}] \circledast [\gamma] \circledast [\alpha^{-1}] = [\alpha * \gamma^{-1}] \circledast ([\gamma] \circledast [g] \circledast [\gamma^{-1}]) \circledast [\alpha * \gamma^{-1}]^{-1}$. Thus the isomorphism $[g] \to [\gamma] \circledast [g] \circledast [\gamma^{-1}]$ is a conjugate of $[g] \to [\alpha] \circledast [g] \circledast [\alpha^{-1}]$. ▮

35.32 Definition. Let w be a continuous function from a pathwise connected space X into a pathwise connected space Y. Let $\pi_1(X, x)$ and $\pi_1(Y, y)$ be fundamental groups of X and Y respectively. Let w_* be the homomorphism from $\pi_1(X, x)$ into $\pi_1(Y, y)$ induced by w. $w_*([f]) = [w \circ f]$. Let α be a path from y to $w(x)$, i.e., $\alpha(0) = y$ and $\alpha(1) = w(x)$. The homomorphism $w_{*,\alpha}$ defined by $w_{*,\alpha}([f]) = [\alpha] \circledast w_*([f]) \circledast [\alpha^{-1}]$ from $\pi_1(X, x)$ into $\pi_1(Y, y)$ is also said to be *induced* by w.

35.33 Corollary. *Let w be a continuous function from a pathwise connected space X into a pathwise connected space Y. The homomorphisms induced* *by w from any fundamental group $\pi_1(X, x)$ into any fundamental group $\pi_1(Y, y)$ are all conjugates.*

Proof: Let w_* be the homomorphism from $\pi_1(X, x)$ into $\pi_1(Y, w(x))$ induced by w. $w_*([f]) = [w \circ f]$. Let α and γ be paths from y to $w(x)$. $\alpha(0) = y = \gamma(0)$ and $\alpha(1) = w(x) = \gamma(1)$. By theorem 35.31, the isomorphisms $[g] \to [\alpha] \circledast [g] \circledast [\alpha^{-1}]$ and $[g] \to [\gamma] \circledast [g] \circledast [\gamma^{-1}]$ are conjugate. Hence, by lemma 35.30, the composites $[g] \to [\alpha] \circledast w_*([f]) \circledast [\alpha^{-1}]$ and $[g] \to [\gamma] \circledast w_*([f]) \circledast [\gamma^{-1}]$ are conjugates. ∎

All that remains to be shown is that homotopic functions from a pathwise connected space X into a pathwise connected space Y induce conjugate homomorphisms from a fundamental group $\pi_1(X, x)$ into any fundamental group $\pi_1(Y, y)$. From this it will follow easily that pathwise connected spaces of the same homotopy type have isomorphic fundamental groups. First a lemma is needed.

35.34 Lemma. *Let α_0 and α_1 be paths in a pathwise connected space Y. Let H be a homotopy from α_0 to α_1 in Y. Let $\gamma_0(t) = H((0, t))$ and let $\gamma_1(t) = H((1, t))$. Then $[\gamma_0] \circledast [\alpha_1] \circledast [\gamma_1^{-1}]$ is defined in the fundamental groupoid $\{\Gamma(Y), \circledast\}$, and $[\gamma_0] \circledast [\alpha_1] \circledast [\gamma_1^{-1}] = [\alpha_0]$.*

Proof: The domain of H is $I \times I$, where—as usual—I is the unit interval space. The paths $\tilde{\gamma} = (\gamma_0 * \alpha_1) * \gamma_1^{-1}$ and α_0 have the same end points in Y.

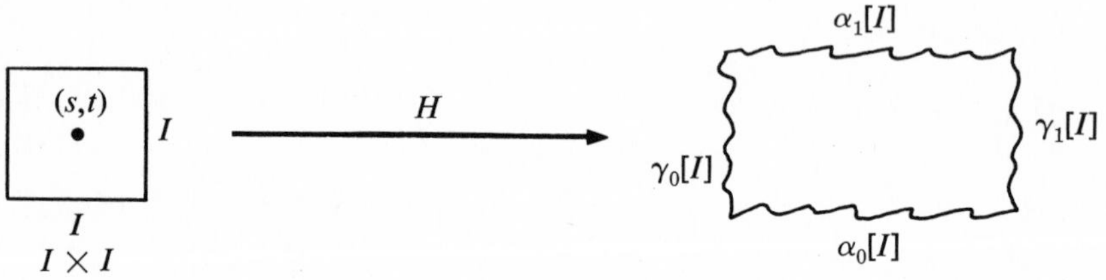

FIGURE 35

A homotopy will be defined from α_0 to $\tilde{\gamma}$ which is constant on $\{0\} \times I$ and $\{1\} \times I$. In order to do this it will be assumed that any non-trivial triangle in the plane is homeomorphic to any other non-trivial triangle. The vertices can be paired and then the sides can be mapped linearly and then this linear map on the perimeter can be extended by barycentric coordinates to the whole triangle. So define the following function F from $I \times I$ onto $I \times I$ as follows. Let $I \times I$ be represented as the union of the triangles in figure 36.

Let $F((0, 0)) = F((0, 1)) = (0, 0)$; $F((1/2, 0)) = (1/2, 0)$; $F((1, 1)) = (1, 0) = F((1, 0))$; $F((1/2, 1)) = (1, 1)$; $F((1/4, 1)) = (0, 1)$. Then extend F linearly to all points of each triangle. The restrictions $F \mid A$ and $F \mid E$ are also restrictions of the projection function from I^2 onto I. By theorem 9.23, F is continuous

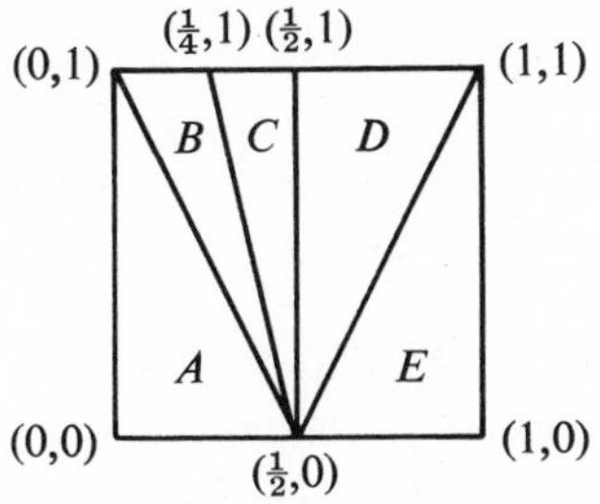

FIGURE 36

from $I \times I$ onto $I \times I$. Define $\tilde{H}$ as the composite $H \circ F$. Then

$$\tilde{H}[I \times \{0\}] = H[I \times \{0\}] = \alpha_0[I]$$

and

$$\tilde{H}[I \times \{1\}] = H[\{0\} \times I] \cup H[I \times \{1\}] \cup H[\{1\} \times I]$$
$$= \gamma_0[I] \cup \alpha_1[I] \cup \gamma_1[I].$$

$$\tilde{H}((s, 0)) = H((s, 0)) = \alpha_0(s) \quad \text{and} \quad \tilde{H}((s, 1)) = (\gamma_0 * \alpha_1) * \gamma_1^{-1}(s).$$

The details of the proof of this last inequality are left as an exercise, i.e., $\tilde{H}((s, 1)) = (0, 4s)$, for $0 \leq s \leq 1/4$, etc. Further $\tilde{H}((0, t)) = H((0, 0)) = \gamma_0(0)$ and $\tilde{H}((1, t)) = H((1, 0)) = \gamma_0(1)$ for all t in $[0, 1]$. Thus $\tilde{H}$ is the desired homotopy from γ_0 to $(\gamma_0 * \alpha_1) * \gamma_1^{-1}$. ∎

35.35 Theorem. *Let X and Y be pathwise connected spaces; let w and w' be continuous from X into Y and homotopic; let $\pi_1(X, x)$ and $\pi_1(Y, y)$ be fundamental groups of X and Y respectively. Then the homomorphisms from $\pi_1(X, x)$ into $\pi_1(Y, y)$ induced by w and w' are all conjugate.*

Proof: Let w_* and w'_* denote the homomorphisms from $\pi_1(X, x)$ into $\pi_1(Y, w(x))$ and $\pi_1(Y, w'(x))$ induced respectively by w and w'. Then for $[f]$ in $\pi_1(X, x)$, $w_*([f]) = [w \circ f]$ in $\pi_1(Y, w(x))$ and $w'_*([f]) = [w' \circ f]$ in $\pi_1(Y, w'(x))$. Then a homomorphism $w_{*,\alpha}$ (definition 35.31) induced by w from $\pi_1(X, x)$ into $\pi_1(Y, y)$ is a composite $[f] \to [\alpha] \circledast [w \circ f] \circledast [\alpha^{-1}]$, where α is a path from y to $w(x)$, and all such homomorphisms are, by corollary 35.32, conjugate. Now let H be a homotopy from w to w'. Define $H^*((s, t)) = H(f(s), t)$ for $[f]$ in $\pi_1(X, x)$ and $0 \leq s \leq 1$ and $0 \leq t \leq 1$. $H^*((s, 0)) = H((f(s), 0)) = w \circ f(s)$ and $H^*((s, 1)) = H((f(s), 1)) = w' \circ f(s)$. Thus H^* is a homotopy from $w \circ f$ to $w' \circ f$. Define $\gamma_0(t) = H^*((0, t))$ and $\gamma_1(t) = H^*((1, t))$. Since $H^*((0, t)) = H((f(0), t))$ and $H^*((1, t)) = H((f(1), t))$ and since $f(0) = f(1)$, $\gamma_0(t) = \gamma_1(t)$ for all t in $[0, 1]$. Let $\gamma(t) = \gamma_0(t) = \gamma_1(t)$. $\gamma(0) = w(x)$ and $\gamma(1) = w'(x)$. Now by lemma 35.34, $w \circ f$ is homotopic to $(\gamma * (w' \circ f)) * \gamma^{-1}$ relative to $\{0, 1\}$. It then follows from theorem 35.5 that $(\alpha * (w \circ f)) * \alpha^{-1}$ is homotopic to $(\alpha * ((\gamma * (w' \circ f)) * \gamma^{-1})) * \alpha^{-1}$ relative to $\{0, 1\}$. Thus $[\alpha] \circledast [w \circ f] \circledast [\alpha^{-1}] = [\alpha] \circledast ([\gamma] \circledast [w' \circ f] \circledast [\gamma^{-1}]) \circledast [\alpha^{-1}]$.

Now, $$w_{*,\alpha}([f]) = [\alpha] \circledast [w \circ f] \circledast [\alpha^{-1}]$$

and $$w'_{*,\gamma}([f]) = [\gamma] \circledast [w' \circ f] \circledast [\gamma^{-1}].$$

Thus $$w_{*,\alpha}([f]) = [\alpha] \circledast w_{*,\gamma}([f]) \circledast [\alpha^{-1}]$$

and the homomorphism $w_{*,\alpha}$, induced by w, from $\pi_1(X, x)$ into $\pi_1(Y, y)$ is conjugate to the homomorphism $w'_{*,\gamma}$, induced by w', from $\pi_1(X, x)$ into $\pi_1(Y, y)$. By corollary 35.33, all homomorphisms induced by w from $\pi_1(X, x)$ into $\pi_1(Y, y)$ are conjugate to each other and all homomorphisms induced by w' from $\pi_1(X, x)$ into $\pi_1(Y, y)$ are conjugate to each other. Thus by lemma 35.28, any homomorphism $w_{*,\alpha}$ induced by w is conjugate to any homomorphism $w'_{*,\gamma}$ induced by w'. ▮

35.36 Theorem. *Let X, Y and Z be pathwise connected spaces and let x, y and z be points of X, Y and Z respectively. Further, let w be a continuous function from X into Y and let v be a continuous function from Y into Z. Let h_1 be a homomorphism from $\pi_1(X, x)$ into $\pi_1(Y, y)$ induced by w and let h_2 be a homomorphism from $\pi_1(Y, y)$ into $\pi_1(Z, z)$ induced by v. Then $h_2 \circ h_1$ is induced by $v \circ w$.*

Proof: If h_1 is induced by w, then, according to definition 35.32, $h_1([f]) = [\alpha] \circledast [w \circ f] \circledast [\alpha^{-1}]$, where $[f]$ is any element in $\pi_1(X, x)$ and α is a path from y to $w(x)$. Similarly, $h_2([g]) = [\gamma] \circledast [(v \circ g)] \circledast [\gamma^{-1}]$, where $[g]$ is any element in $\pi_1(Y, y)$ and γ is a path from z to $v(y)$ in Z. It follows from the definition of $\circledast$ and $*$ that $h_2 \circ h_1([f]) = [\gamma * v \circ \alpha * (v \circ w \circ f) * v \circ \alpha^{-1} * \gamma^{-1}]$. By definition of $*$, $(v \circ \alpha)^{-1}$ and γ^{-1}, $h_2 \circ h_1([f]) = [(\gamma * (v \circ \alpha)) * (v \circ w \circ f) * (\gamma * (v \circ \alpha))^{-1}] = [\gamma * (v \circ \alpha)] \circledast [v \circ w \circ f] \circledast [(\gamma * (v \circ \alpha))^{-1}]$. Now consider $\gamma * (v \circ \alpha)$. γ is a path in Z from z to $v(y)$, while $v \circ \alpha$ is a path in Z from $v(y)$ to $v(w(x))$. Hence $\gamma * (v \circ \alpha)$ is a path from z to $v(w(x))$. This means that the correspondence $[f] \to [\gamma * (v \circ \alpha)] \circledast [v \circ w \circ f] \circledast [(\gamma * (v \circ \alpha))^{-1}]$ is a homomorphism induced by $v \circ w$ according to definition 35.31. Hence $h_2 \circ h_1$ is induced by $v \circ w$. ▮

35.37 Theorem. *If two pathwise connected spaces X and Y are of the same homotopy type, then their fundamental groups are isomorphic.*

Proof: Since X and Y are of the same homotopy type, there exist continuous functions $w: X \to Y$ and $v: Y \to X$ such that $v \circ w$ is homotopic to the identity function on X, and $w \circ v$ is homotopic to the identity function on Y. Let $\pi_1(X, x)$ and $\pi_1(Y, y)$ be fundamental groups of X and Y respectively. Let h_1 be a homomorphism induced by w from $\pi_1(X, x)$ into $\pi_1(Y, y)$ and let h_2 be a homomorphism induced by v from $\pi_1(Y, y)$ into $\pi_1(X, x)$. By the previous theorem (35.36), the composite homomorphism $h_2 \circ h_1$ is induced by $v \circ w$.

Since $v \circ w$ is homotopic to i_X and since, by theorem 35.24, i_X induces the identity isomorphism i on $\pi_1(X, x)$, $h_2 \circ h_1$ is conjugate to the identity isomorphism i on $\pi_1(X, x)$ by theorem 35.35. By lemma 35.29, then, $h_2 \circ h_1$ is an isomorphism from $\pi_1(X, x)$ onto $\pi_1(X, x)$. Similarly, $h_1 \circ h_2$ is an isomorphism from $\pi_1(Y, y)$ onto $\pi_1(Y, y)$. It follows immediately that h_1 is an isomorphism from $\pi_1(X, x)$ onto $\pi_1(Y, y)$ and that h_2 also is an isomorphism from $\pi_1(Y, y)$ onto $\pi_1(X, x)$. ▮

35.38 Corollary. *If A is a deformation retract of the pathwise connected space X, then A and X have isomorphic fundamental groups.*

Proof: By theorem 34.23, A and X are of the same homotopy type. Hence, by theorem 35.37, A and X have isomorphic fundamental groups. ▮

35.39 Definition. If any fundamental group of a pathwise connected space X contains exactly one element, then X is called *simply connected.*

35.40 Theorem. *Any contractible space X is simply connected.*

Proof: By theorem 34.7, X is pathwise connected. By lemma 34.4, theorem 34.23 and corollary 35.38, X has fundamental groups which are all isomorphic to those of $\{x\}$. ▮

35.41 Corollary. *Euclidean n-space, E^n, for each natural number n, is simply connected.*

Proof: In example 34.5, the function $H(((x_1, x_2, \ldots, x_n), t)) = ((1 - t)x_1, (1 - t)x_2, \ldots, (1 - t)x_n)$ from $E^n \times I$ into E^n was used to show that E^n was contractible. Thus E^n is simply connected. ▮

35.42 Corollary. *If T is the subspace of E^2 determined by $\{(x, y) \mid 0 < x^2 + y^2\}$, then T has fundamental groups isomorphic to the fundamental groups of the subspace, S^1, determined by $\{(x, y)$ in $E^2 \mid x^2 + y^2 = 1\}$.*

Proof: The function

$$H(((x, y), t)) = \left((1 - t)x + t \cdot \frac{x}{\sqrt{x^2 + y^2}}, (1 - t)y + t \cdot \frac{y}{\sqrt{x^2 + y^2}}\right)$$

from $T \times I$ into E^2 is continuous by theorem 11.19. Further, if $x^2 + y^2 = 1$, $H(((x, y), t)) = (x, y)$ for all t in I. Also, $H(((x, y), 0)) = (x, y)$ and

$$H(((x, y), 1)) = \left(\frac{x}{\sqrt{x^2 + y^2}}, \frac{y}{\sqrt{x^2 + y^2}}\right).$$

Thus the unit circle space, S^1, is a deformation retract of T; hence, T and S^1 have isomorphic fundamental groups. ▮

The Fundamental Groups of S_1

In general, it is difficult to determine non-trivial fundamental groups. However, there do exist spaces which are not simply connected and non-elementary algebraic machinery to prove smoothly that these spaces are not simply connected. For present purposes, however, only W. Hurewicz's elementary geometric proof that S^1 is not simply connected will be used to establish that non-simply connected spaces do exist. The proof uses some basic geometric facts about the Euclidean plane E^2 and the subspace S^1. The next set of definitions, lemmas and theorems will combine to give this proof.

35.43 Definition. A *triangulation* T of the unit interval $[0, 1]$ is a set of intervals $[0 = a_0, a_1], [a_1, a_2], \ldots, [a_{n-1}, a_n = 1]$, where $0 = a_0 < a_1 < \cdots < a_n = 1$. The points $0 = a_0, a_1, \ldots, a_n = 1$ are called vertices of the triangulation.

35.44 Definition. A function ϕ from the vertices of a triangulation T of $[0, 1]$ into S^1 will be called a *proper vertex loop* if and only if $\phi(0) = \phi(1)$ and the usual Euclidean distance between $\phi(a_i)$ and $\phi(a_{i+1})$, for $0 \leq i \leq n$, is less than 1. With the two directions on S^1—positive (counterclockwise) and negative (clockwise)—given if $\phi(a_i) \neq \phi(a_{i+1})$, $\phi(a_i)$ and $\phi(a_{i+1})$ determine on S^1 two arcs, $A_\phi^+(i, i+1) = \{z \mid \text{the ordering } (\phi(a_i), z, \phi(a_{i+1})) \text{ is positive}\} \cup \{\phi(a_i), \phi(a_{i+1})\}$ and $A_\phi^-(i, i+1) = \{z \mid \text{the ordering } (\phi(a_i), z, \phi(a_{i+1})) \text{ is negative}\} \cup \{\phi(a_i), \phi(a_{i+1})\}$. The requirement that the distance from $\phi(a_i)$ to $\phi(a_{i+1})$ be less than 1 insures that either $A_\phi^+(i, i+1)$ or $A_\phi^-(i, i+1)$ is contained in a semi-circle, and hence is distinguishable as the shorter of the two arcs. The function $\tilde{\phi}$ which assigns to each interval $[a_i, a_{i+1}]$, in the triangulation T on $[0, 1]$, the shorter of the two arcs determined by $\phi(a_i)$ and $\phi(a_{i+1})$ for $\phi(a_i) \neq \phi(a_{i+1})$, and the point $\phi(a_i)$ if $\phi(a_i) = \phi(a_{i+1})$ is called the *quasi-simplical loop* on the triangulation T determined by ϕ.

It follows that if ϕ is a proper vertex loop defined on the vertices of a triangulation T of $[0, 1]$, then the quasi-simplicial loop $\tilde{\phi}$ determined by ϕ sometimes assigns to the interval $[a_i, a_{i+1}]$ the arc $A_\phi^+(i, i+1)$ and sometimes the arc $A_\phi^-(i, i+1)$. It all depends on ϕ.

35.45 Definition. Let T be a triangulation of $[0, 1]$, ϕ a proper vertex loop from T into S^1 and $\tilde{\phi}$ the quasi-simplicial loop determined by ϕ. Define $D(z, T, \tilde{\phi})$, for $z \neq \phi(a_i)$ for all i, to be $p - n$, where p is the number of intervals $[a_i, a_{i+1}]$ such that z is in $\tilde{\phi}([a_i, a_{i+1}])$ and $\tilde{\phi}([a_i, a_{i+1}]) = A_\phi^+(i, i+1)$, and n is the number of intervals $[a_i, a_{i+1}]$ such that z is in $\tilde{\phi}([a_i, a_{i+1}])$ and $\tilde{\phi}([a_i, a_{i+1}]) = A_\phi^-(i, i+1)$. D is called the degree of $\tilde{\phi}$ at p relative to T. It will be established via the next several lemmas, etc., that D depends only on $\tilde{\phi}$.

35.46 Lemma. *Let* $0 = a_0, a_1, \ldots, a_n = 1$ *be the vertices of a triangulation* T *of* $[0, 1]$. *Let* ϕ *be a proper vertex loop from* T *into* S^1 *and* z *a point in* S^1 *such that* $z \neq \phi(a_i)$ *for* $i = 1, \ldots, n$. *Then there exists a positive real number* ϵ *such that if* ψ *is another proper vertex loop from* T *into* S^1 *such that* $\rho(\phi(a_i), \psi(a_i)) < \epsilon$ *for all* $i = 0, \ldots, n$, *where* ρ *denotes Euclidean distance in* E^2, *then* $D(z, T, \tilde{\phi}) = D(z, T, \tilde{\psi})$.

Proof: Since E^2 is Hausdorff, there exists a spherical neighborhood $V_\rho(z, 2\delta)$ of z such that if x is in $V_\rho(z, 2\delta)$, $x \neq \phi(a_i)$, for $i = 0, 1, \ldots, n$. Let $\epsilon = \delta/4$. Then by the triangle inequality for a metric if ψ is any proper vertex loop such that $\rho(\psi(a_i), \phi(a_i)) < \epsilon$, $\psi(a_i)$ is not in $V_\rho(z, \delta)$ for all $i = 0, 1, 2, \ldots, n$. Thus $D(z, T, \tilde{\psi}) = D(z, T, \tilde{\phi})$. ▮

35.47 Lemma. *If* T *is a triangulation of* $[0, 1]$ *with vertices* $0 = a_0, a_1, \ldots, a_n = 1$ *and if* ϕ *is a proper vertex loop from* $\{a_0, a_1, \ldots, a_n\}$ *into* S^1, *then for any positive real number* ϵ *there exists a proper vertex loop* ψ *from* $\{a_0, a_1, \ldots, a_n\}$ *into* S^1 *such that* ψ *is* 1:1 *on* $\{a_0, a_1, \ldots, a_{n-1}\}$, $\rho(\phi(a_i), \psi(a_i)) < \epsilon$ *for all* $i = 0, \ldots, n$, *and whenever* $\phi(a_i) \neq \phi(a_{i+1})$, $\tilde{\phi}([a_i, a_{i+1}])$ *and* $\tilde{\psi}([a_i, a_{i+1}])$ *have the same sign, i.e., if* $\tilde{\phi}([a_i, a_{i+1}]) = A_\phi^+(i, i+1)$, *then* $\tilde{\psi}([a_i, a_{i+1}]) = A_\psi^+(i, i+1)$, *etc.*

Proof: First let $\phi(a_j) = \phi(a_{j+1})$. Define $\psi(a_j) = \phi(a_j)$. If $\phi(a_{j+1}) \neq \phi(a_{j+2})$, let $\psi(a_{j+1}) = z_0$, where z_0 is in the arc $\phi([a_{j+1}, a_{j+2}])$ such that $\rho(\phi(a_{j+1}), z_0) < \epsilon$ and $z_0 \neq \phi(a_j)$. Then $\tilde{\phi}([a_{j+1}, a_{j+2}])$ and $\tilde{\psi}([a_{j+1}, a_{j+2}])$ will have the same sign. If $\phi(a_j) = \phi(a_{j+1}) = \phi(a_{j+2})$, let $\psi(a_j) = \phi(a_j)$ and let $\psi(a_{j+1})$ be any z_0 such that $z_0 \neq \phi(a_i)$ for all $i = 0, 1, \ldots, n$, and $\rho(\phi(a_{j+1}), z_0) < \epsilon$. The above procedure can be repeated as many times as is necessary and yields the result that $\psi(a_i) \neq \psi(a_{i+1})$ for $i = 0, 1, \ldots, n-1$. A similar procedure yields $\psi(a_i) \neq \psi(a_j)$ for $i, j = 0, 1, \ldots, n-1$. ▮

35.48 Corollary. *If* T *is a triangulation of* $[0, 1]$ *with vertices* $0 = a_0, a_1, \ldots, a_n = 1$ *and if* ϕ *is a proper vertex loop from* $\{a_0, a_1, \ldots, a_n\}$ *into* S^1, *then there is a proper vertex loop* ψ *from* $\{a_0, a_1, \ldots, a_n\}$ *into* S^1 *such that* ψ *is* 1:1 *on* $\{a_0, a_1, \ldots, a_{n-1}\}$ *and* $D(x, T, \tilde{\phi}) = D(x, T, \tilde{\psi})$, *whenever* $D(x, T, \tilde{\phi})$ *is defined.*

Proof: The last two lemmas combine to give the desired result. ▮

35.49 Theorem. *If* T *is a triangulation of* $[0, 1]$ *with vertices* $\{a_0, a_1, \ldots, a_n\}$ *and if* ϕ *is a proper vertex loop from the vertices of* T *into* S^1 *which is* 1:1 *on* $\{a_0, a_1, \ldots, a_{n-1}\}$ *then if* $D(x_0, T, \tilde{\phi})$ *and* $D(x_1, T, \tilde{\phi})$ *are both defined for* $\tilde{\phi}$ *the quasi-simplicial loop determined by* ϕ, *then* $D(x_0, T, \tilde{\phi}) = D(x_1, T, \tilde{\phi})$.

Proof: Let $A^+(z_0, z_1)$, for $z_0 \neq z_1$, denote the positive arc on S^1 determined by z_0 and z_1, i.e., $A^+(z_0, z_1) = \{z \mid (z_0, z, z_1)$ is a counterclockwise ordering of the three points$\} \cup \{z_0, z_1\}$. Then the points on $A^+(z_0, z_1)$ are linearly ordered by $\leq$, where $z \leq z'$ if and only if (z_0, z, z') is a counterclockwise ordering for z and z' on $A^+(z_0, z_1)$. As a result there is a first point z^* on $A^+(z_0, z_1)$ such that $z^* = \phi(a_i)$ for a_i a vertex of T. Now if $z_0 < z < z^*$, z is in any arc $\phi([a_j, a_{j+1}])$ that z_0 is in, by definition of z^*, and hence $D(z, T, \tilde{\phi}) = D(z_0, T, \tilde{\phi})$. However if z is "on the other side" of $\phi(a_i)$, i.e., if $z > z^*$, but close enough so that there is no $\phi(a_j)$ between z and z^*, then two cases are possible: (a) $\phi(a_{i-1})$ and $\phi(a_{i+1})$ are on the same side of $z^* = \phi(a_i)$ as z_0 is, i.e., z_0 is in $\tilde{\phi}([a_{i-1}, a_i]) \cap \tilde{\phi}([a_i, a_{i+1}])$ and z is in neither $\tilde{\phi}([a_{i-1}, a_i])$ nor $\tilde{\phi}([a_i, a_{i+1}])$, or vice versa z is in $\tilde{\phi}([a_{i-1}, a_i]) \cap \tilde{\phi}([a_i, a_{i+1}])$ and z_0 is in neither $\tilde{\phi}([a_{i-1}, a_i])$ nor $\tilde{\phi}([a_i, a_{i+1}])$. However, this means that $\tilde{\phi}([a_{i-1}, a_i]) = A^+_\phi(i-1, i)$ and $\tilde{\phi}([a_i, a_{i+1}]) = A^-_\phi(i, i+1)$, or $\tilde{\phi}([a_{i-1}, a_i]) = A^-_\phi(i-1, i)$ and $\tilde{\phi}([a_i, a_{i+1}]) = A^+_\phi(i, i+1)$. Hence, they contribute 0 to the calculation of $D(z_0, T, \tilde{\phi})$ or $D(z, T, \tilde{\phi})$. So $D(z_0, T, \tilde{\phi}) = D(z, T, \tilde{\phi})$. (b) $\phi(a_{i-1})$ and $\phi(a_{i+1})$ are on opposite sides of $z^* = \phi(a_i)$. Then z is in $A^+_\phi(i-1, i)$ and z_0 is in $A^+_\phi(i, i+1)$, or z is in $A^-_\phi(i-1, i)$ and z_0 is in $A^-_\phi(i, i+1)$. Thus, again $D(z, T, \tilde{\phi}) = D(z_0, T, \tilde{\phi})$. Since T has only a finite number of vertices the above procedure can be repeated a finite number of times to prove that $D(z_0, T, \tilde{\phi}) = D(z_1, T, \tilde{\phi})$. ▮

Thus D is a function of T and $\tilde{\phi}$ only. The next step will be to show that it is independent of T.

35.50 Lemma. *If f is a loop from* $[0, 1]$ *into* S^1, *then there exists a triangulation T of* $[0, 1]$ *such that $f|V$—the restriction of f to the set V of vertices of T—is a proper vertex loop.*

Proof: Since $[0, 1]$ is compact, f is uniformly continuous. Hence there is a positive real number δ such that if $\rho_1(a_i, a_{i+1}) < \delta$, $\rho_2(f(a_i), f(a_{i+1})) < 1$, where ρ_1 and ρ_2 are the usual metrics for E^1 and E^2. ▮

35.51 Lemma. *Let f be a loop from* $[0, 1]$ *into S^1 and let T and T' be two triangulations of* $[0, 1]$ *such that the restrictions of f to the sets of vertices of T and T' are proper vertex loops. Then $D(T, \tilde{f}) = D(T', \tilde{f}')$, where $\tilde{f}$ and $\tilde{f}'$ are the quasi-simplicial loops determined by f on T and T'.*

Proof: Let $a_0 = 0, a_1, \ldots, a_n = 1$ be the vertices of T. Let b^* be a vertex of T' which is not in T and let $a_i < b^* < a_{i+1}$. Let T^+ be the triangulation determined by the vertices $a_0 = 1, \ldots, a_i, b^*, a_{i+1}, \ldots, a_n = 1$. Since b^* is in the interval $[a_i, a_{i+1}]$, $f(b^*)$ is in $f[[a_i, a_{i+1}]]$. Since f, restricted to the vertices of T, is a proper vertex loop, there is a point z in S^1 which does not lie in $f[[a_i, a_{i+1}]]$ and which is not the image of a vertex in T. Hence, $D(z, T, \tilde{f}) = D(z, T^+, \tilde{f}^+)$, where $\tilde{f}^+$ is the quasi-simplicial loop determined on T^+ by f. Since T' has only a finite number of vertices, the above procedure can be repeated to obtain that $D(z, T, \tilde{f}) = D(z, T', \tilde{f}')$. Hence, $D(T, \tilde{f}) = D(T', \tilde{f}')$. ▮

Thus D is a function of the loop f only.

35.52 Definition. If f is a loop in S^1, $D(T, \tilde{f})$, for T a triangulation and $\tilde{f}$ the quasi-simplicial loop determined by f on T, is denoted by $D(f)$ and is called the degree of f.

35.53 Theorem. *If f_0 and f_1 are two loops in S^1 and if f_0 and f_1 are homotopic by a homotopy H such that H restricted to $I \times \{t\}$ for each t in $[0, 1] = I$ is a loop, then $D(f_0) = D(f_1)$.*

Proof: Since $I \times I$ is compact and metrizable, H is uniformly continuous from $I \times I$ into S^1. It then follows that for any real ϵ such that $0 < \epsilon < 1$, there exists a real number δ such that if $|s_1 - s_2| < \delta$ and $|t_1 - t_2| < \delta$, then $\rho(H((s_1, t_1)), H((s_2, t_2))) < \epsilon$. Now if T is a triangulation of $[0, 1]$ with vertices $0 = t_0, t_1, \ldots, t_n = 1$ such that $|t_i - t_{i+1}| < \delta$, then $\rho(H((s, t_i)), H((s, t_{i+1}))) < 1$ for any s in $[0, 1]$. Now let $f_t(s) = H((s, t))$. Then if $|t - t'| < \delta$, $\rho(f_t(s), f_{t'}(s)) < \epsilon$ for all s in $[0, 1]$. By lemma 35.46, it follows, since each f_t is a loop, that $D(f_t) = D(f_{t'})$. Since I is compact, there exists a finite set $\{0 = t_0, t_1, \ldots, t_n = 1\}$ such that $|t_i - t_{i+1}| < \delta/2$ for all i. So, $D(f_0) = D(f_1)$. ∎

35.54 Theorem. *The fundamental groups of S^1 are not trivial.*

Proof: Let f_0 denote the loop defined as follows: $f_0(t) = e^{2\pi i t}$, where e as usual denotes the base of the natural logarithm. By definition, f_0 is a homeomorphism from the open interval $(0, 1)$ onto $S^1 \sim \{(1, 0)\}$. Hence $D(f_0) = 1$. Let $f_1(t) = (1, 0)$ for all t in $[0, 1]$. $D(f_1) = 0$. Thus f_0 does not represent the same element of $\pi_1(S^1, (1, 0))$ as does f_1, and so $\pi_1(S^1, (1, 0))$ has more than one element. ∎

35.55 Corollary. *Any fundamental group of S^1 contains at least as many elements as the integers.*

Proof: The loop $f_k(t) = e^{2k\pi i t}$, for k an integer, has degree k. By theorem 35.53 no two of these loops are homotopic. ∎

Every loop actually does have a degree, and if two loops based at $(1, 0)$ have the same degree they are homotopic relative to $\{0, 1\}$. Thus $\pi_1(S^1, (1, 0))$ is actually isomorphic to the additive group of integers. The rest of this proof however will not be included here.

By example 34.20, definition 34.22 and corollary 35.38, it follows that the fundamental groups of $E^2 \sim \{(0, 0)\}$ are also isomorphic to the additive group of integers and hence are non-trivial.

The Brouwer Fixed Point Theorem for the 2-Cell

Many results follow from the fact that the space S^1 is not simply connected. A famous one is that any continuous function, f, from B_2—the 2-cell—into itself has a fixed point, i.e., a point z such that $f(z) = z$.

35.56 Lemma. *A continuous function f_0 from the space S^1 into a space Y is homotopic to a constant function if and only if f_0 has a continuous extension f_0^* to all of B_2, the subspace of E^2 determined by $\{(x, y) \mid x^2 + y^2 \leq 1\}$.*

Proof: A. Let f_0 have a continuous extension f_0^* to all of B_2. Define H from $S^1 \times I$ into Y as follows: $H((z, t)) = f_0^*((1 - t)z)$. H then is a homotopy from f_0 to a constant function, f_1, where $f_1(z) = k$.

B. Let f_0 be homotopic to a constant function, f_1, where $f_1(z) = k$ for all z on S^1. Let H be a homotopy from f_0 to f_1. Define f_0^* from B_2 into Y as follows: $f_0^*(z) = H((z/|z|, 1 - |z|))$ for $|z| \neq 0$, and $f_0^*(z) = k$ for $z = (0, 0)$. Since $z \to z/|z|$ and $z \to 1 - |z|$ for all $z \neq (0, 0)$ are continuous, then by theorems 11.19 and 4.8 f^* is continuous for $z \neq (0, 0)$. The rest of the proof is straightforward. Let W_ϵ be any neighborhood of k in Y. Since $H((z, 1)) = k$ for z in S^1 and since H is continuous, there exists for each point $(z, 1)$ in $S^1 \times I$ a neighborhood $U \times V$ such that $H[U \times V] \subseteq W_\epsilon$. Since $S^1 \times \{1\}$ is compact, a finite number, say, $U_1 \times V_1, \ldots, U_n \times V_n$ cover $S^1 \times \{1\}$. Each V_i is a neighborhood of the point 1 in $[0, 1]$. Hence $V_1 \cap \cdots \cap V_n$ is a neighborhood of 1 in $[0, 1]$; and $S^1 \times (V_1 \cap \cdots \cap V_n)$ is a neighborhood of $S^1 \times \{1\}$. in $S^1 \times I$. Let $U_\delta = (1 - \delta, 1]$ and let $S^1 \times U_\delta \subseteq S^1 \times (V_1 \cap \cdots \cap V_n)$. $H[S^1 \times U_\delta] \subseteq W_\epsilon$. Hence if $0 < |z| < \delta$, $1 - |z| > 1 - \delta$ and $1 - |z|$ is in U_δ. Then $H((z/|z|, 1 - |z|)) \in S^1 \times U_\delta \subseteq W_\epsilon$. Thus $f_0^*(z) \in W_\epsilon$ and f_0^* is continuous at $z = (0, 0)$. ▮

35.57 Theorem. *S^1 is not a retract of B_2.*

Proof: If r is continuous from B_2 onto S^1 such that $r(z) = z$ for all z in S^1, then r is an extension of the identity function i_1 on S^1 to all of B_2. Thus i_1, by the previous lemma, is homotopic to a constant function $\tilde{k}(z) = k$ for all z in S^1. Let H be such a homotopy, i.e., $H: S^1 \times I \to S^1$, $H((z, 0)) = z$ and $H((z, 1)) = k$ for z in S^1. Now define $\tilde{H}$ from $I \times I$ to S^1 as follows: $\tilde{H}((s, t)) = H((e^{2\pi is}, t))$. Now $\tilde{H}((s, 0)) = H((e^{2\pi is}, 0)) = e^{2\pi is}$ and $\tilde{H}((s, 1)) = H((e^{2\pi is}, 1)) = k$. Thus $f(s) = e^{2\pi is}$ and $g(s) = k$, by theorem 35.53, have the same degree. This is a contradiction since $D(f) = 1$ and $D(g) = 0$. Thus no retraction can exist. ▮

35.58 Theorem (Brouwer). *If f is a continuous function from B_2 into B_2, then there exists at least one point z such that $f(z) = z$.*

Proof: Assume that f is continuous and that $f(z) \neq z$ for all z in B_2. Then for each z in B_2, a line L_z is determined by z and $f(z)$. Any such line can be described by a homeomorphism $h_1(t) = f(z) + t(z - f(z))$ from E^1 into E^2, where $+$ and $-$ refer to the usual coordinate addition in E^2. Define $r(z) = h_1(t)$, for $t > 0$ and $h_1(t)$ on S^1. It follows from the geometry of E^2 that such a point exists and that r is continuous. Since for z on S^1, $r(z) = z$, r is then a retraction of B_2 onto S^1. This is a contradiction. Hence, for some z, $f(z) = z$ and f has at least one fixed point. ▮

36. FUNCTION SPACES. PATH SPACES. HIGHER HOMOTOPY GROUPS.

Function Spaces and Their Path Components

In section 29, the compact-open topology $\mathfrak{I}_{c\text{-}o}$ for subsets of Y^X, the set of functions from a space X into a space Y, was defined. Thus the compact-open topology assigned to $C(X, Y)$, the subset of Y^X consisting of all continuous functions from X into Y, yields a function space, $\{C(X, Y), \mathfrak{I}_{c\text{-}o}\}$. The compact-open topology was shown (theorem 29.34) to contain the product topology. As a result $\{C(X, Y), \mathfrak{I}_{c\text{-}o}\}$ is T_i if Y is for $i = 0, 1, 2$. Also, $\{C(X, Y), \mathfrak{I}_{c\text{-}o}\}$ was shown (theorem 29.40) to be metrizable if X was compact and Y was metrizable. It will first be shown that the path components of $\{C(X, Y), \mathfrak{I}_{c\text{-}o}\}$ are exactly the homotopy equivalence classes in $C(X, Y)$ for X first countable or for X locally compact and Hausdorff.

36.1 Lemma. *Let X, Y and T be spaces. There exists a* 1:1 *correspondence, Φ, between the subset of $Y^{X\times T}$ consisting of $\{h \mid h \mid X \times \{t\}$ is continuous for each t in $T\}$ and $(C(X, Y))^T$, defined as follows: $\Phi(h) = h^*$, where $h^*(t) = h_t$ and $h_t(x) = h((x, t))$.*

Proof: Let h be in $Y^{X\times T}$ and let $h \mid X \times \{t\}$ be continuous for each t in T. Define $h_t(x) = h((x, t))$. For any t in T, h_t is then continuous from X into Y since $h \mid X \times \{t\}$ is continuous. Hence, if $h^*(t)$ is defined to be h_t for each t in T, h^* is in $(C(X, Y))^T$. Of course, if $h \neq m$ for h and m in $Y^{X\times T}$, then there exists (x_0, t_0) in $X \times T$ such that $h((x_0, t_0)) \neq m((x_0, t_0))$. Hence $h_{t_0}(x_0) \neq m_{t_0}(x_0)$ and so $h_{t_0} \neq m_{t_0}$ and $h^*(t_0) \neq m^*(t_0)$. This means that $h^* \neq m^*$ and the correspondence $h \to h^*$ is 1:1. Now let g be any function in $(C(X, Y))^T$. For t in T, assume $g(t) = f$ in $C(X, Y)$. Let x be in X and define h_t from X into Y as follows: $h_t(x) = f(x)$. Since f is in $C(X, Y)$, it is continuous. h_t is then continuous. It follows directly then that if $h((x, t)) = h_t(x)$, then $h \mid X \times \{t\}$ is continuous for each t in T. Now consider h^*. $h^*(t)$ is by definition the function from X into Y which assigns to each x in X the point $h((x, t))$ in Y. Thus $h^*(t)$ is h_t as defined above and hence $h^*(t) = f = g(t)$. This proves that the correspondence $h \to h^*$ from $\{h \mid h$ is in $Y^{X\times T}$ and $h \mid X \times \{t\}$ is continuous for each t in $T\}$ into $(C(X, Y))^T$ is 1:1 and onto. ▌

The functions h in the preceding lemma do not need to be continuous on $X \times T$ but, since no topology for $C(X, Y)$ was specifically mentioned, there was no question of continuity for the corresponding functions h^*. The next two theorems however relate the continuity of h on $X \times T$ and the continuity of h^* when $C(X, Y)$ is assigned the compact-open topology.

36.2 Theorem. *If X, Y and T are spaces and if h is a continuous function from the product space $X \times T$ into Y, then h^* is continuous from T into $\{C(X, Y), \mathfrak{I}_{c\text{-}o}\}$, where, as in the previous lemma, $h^*(t) = h_t$, where $h_t = h \mid X \times \{t\}$.*

Proof: For x in X, $h_t(x) = h((x, t))$. Let $G(K, O)$ be a subbasic element in the compact-open topology on $C(X, Y)$. K, then, is a compact subset of X and O is an open subset of Y. Let t_0 be any point in $h^{*-1}[G(K, O)]$. Then $h^*(t_0) = h_{t_0}$ and h_{t_0} is in $G(K, O)$. Therefore, $h_{t_0}[K] \subseteq O$. This means, by definition of h_{t_0}, that $h[K \times \{t_0\}] \subseteq O$. Hence, $K \times \{t_0\} \subseteq h^{-1}[O]$. Since h is continuous, by hypothesis, $h^{-1}[O]$ is open in $X \times T$ and so can be represented as the union of open product sets. Let $h^{-1}[O] = \bigcup_\nu U_\nu \times V_\nu$. Since K is compact, $K \times \{t_0\}$ is compact. Hence, a finite number of these open product sets, say, $U_1 \times V_1, \ldots, U_k \times V_k$ cover $K \times \{t_0\}$. This means, with no loss of generality, that t_0 is in the open set $V_1 \cap \cdots \cap V_k$. Let $V_1 \cap \cdots \cap V_k = W$ and consider $h^*[W]$. If $t \in W$, $t \in V_1 \cap \cdots \cap V_k$. This means that $h[K \times \{t\}] \subseteq O$, and hence that $h_t[K] \subseteq O$. Thus $h_t \in G(K, O)$, and so $h^*[W] \subseteq G(K, O)$. Therefore, $h^{*-1}[G(K, O)]$ is open and h^* is continuous. ∎

36.3 Theorem. *Let X, Y and T be spaces; let X be Hausdorff and locally compact. h from the product space $X \times T$ into Y is, then, continuous if and only if h^* from T into $\{C(X, Y), \mathfrak{J}_{c\text{-}o}\}$ is continuous.*

Proof: By the previous theorem, the continuity of h implies the continuity of h^*. So, let h^* be continuous from T into $\{C(X, Y), \mathfrak{J}_{c\text{-}o}\}$. Let $h^*(t) = f$ in $C(X, Y)$. Then $h_t(x) = f(x)$ for x in X and t in T, and $h((x, t)) = h_t(x)$. Let W be any open set in Y and let (x_0, t_0) be any point in $h^{-1}[W]$, in $X \times T$. Since, for each t in T, $h^*(t)$ is in $C(X, Y)$, $h^*(t)$ is continuous. This means that h_t from X into Y is continuous. Since for every x in S, $h_t(x) = h((x, t))$ it follows immediately that $h \mid X \times \{t\}$ is continuous. Thus $h \mid X \times \{t_0\}$ is continuous. There must exist, then, an open neighborhood U of x_0 in X such that $h[U \times \{t_0\}] \subseteq W$, or $h_{t_0}[U] \subseteq W$. Since X is locally compact and Hausdorff, it is regular by theorem 31.35. U then contains the compact closure $\overline{V}$ of a neighborhood V of x_0 in X. $h_{t_0}[\overline{V}] \subseteq W$ or $h^*(t_0)$ is in the open set $G[\overline{V}, W]$ (definition 29.33 of the compact-open topology). Since h^* is continuous, there exists an open neighborhood B_0 of t_0 in T such that $h^*[B_0] \subseteq G[\overline{V}, W]$. Now, since $G[\overline{V}, W] \subseteq G[V, W]$, $h^*[B_0] \subseteq G[V, W]$. Therefore, if $t \in B_0$, $h^*(t)$ is in $G[V, W]$. This means that $h_t[V] \subseteq W$ or $h[V \times \{t\}] \subseteq W$. Hence, $h[V \times B_0] \subseteq W$. $V \times B_0$ is open in $X \times T$ and contains (x_0, t_0). Thus h is continuous. ∎

The following theorem contains another sufficient condition for the equivalence of the continuity of h and h^*.

36.4 Theorem. *If Y is any space, and if X and T are first countable spaces, then the continuity of h, from the product space $X \times T$ into Y, is equivalent to the continuity of h^* from T into $\{C(X, Y), \mathfrak{J}_{c\text{-}o}\}$.*

Proof: Again by theorem 36.2, the continuity of h implies the continuity of h^*. So, let h^* be continuous and let W be open in Y. Assume $h^{-1}[W]$ is not open in $X \times T$. Then $\sim h^{-1}[W]$, the complement of $h^{-1}[W]$, is not closed in $X \times T$. So, there exists a limit point (x_0, t_0) of $\sim h^{-1}[W]$ and (x_0, t_0) is in $h^{-1}[W]$. Let $\{B_1, B_2, \ldots, B_n, \ldots\}$ be a countable local base at (x_0, t_0) such that $B_{n-1} \supseteq B_n$ for all n. This is possible by theorem 5.5. For each positive integer n, choose a point (x_n, t_n) in the non-empty set $(B_n) \cap (\sim h^{-1}[W])$. The sequence $((x_1, t_1), (x_2, t_2), \ldots, (x_n, t_n), \ldots)$, of course, converges to (x_0, t_0). Now $h^*(t_0)$ is a continuous function from X into Y. $h^*(t_0) = h_{t_0}$, where $h_{t_0}(x_0) = h((x_0, t_0))$. Since h_{t_0} is continuous, there exists an open neighborhood U of x_0 in X such that $h_{t_0}[U] \subseteq W$. Let $A = U \cap \bigcup_{n=0}^{\infty} \{x_n\}$. By theorem 11.17, the sequence $(x_1, x_2, \ldots, x_n, \ldots)$ converges to x_0 in X. Hence, by definition of convergence of a sequence, any subset of $\{x_1, x_2, \ldots, x_n, \ldots\} \cup \{x_0\}$ which contains x_0 is compact. Hence, A is compact and so $G(A, W)$ is in the compact-open topology on $C(X, Y)$. Since $A \subseteq U$ and since $h_{t_0}[U] \subseteq W$, h_{t_0} is in $G(A, W)$. Therefore, $h^*(t_0)$ is in $G(A, W)$, since $h^*(t_0) = h_{t_0}$, and so t_0 is in $h^{*-1}[G(A, W)]$. h^* is, by hypothesis, continuous; hence, $h^{*-1}[G(A, W)]$ is open in T. $U \times h^{*-1}[G(A, W)]$ is then an open neighborhood of (x_0, t_0) in $X \times T$. There exists, then, a positive integer k^* such that if $n > k^*$, (x_n, t_n) is in $U \times h^{*-1}[G(A, W)]$. Since t_n is in $h^{*-1}[G(A, W)]$, $h^*(t_n)$ is in $G(A, W)$. Therefore, $h_{t_n}[A] \subseteq W$. Since, by definition of A, x_n is in A, $h_{t_n}(x_n)$ is in W. This means that $h((x_n, t_n))$ is in W for $n > k^*$. Since, for every positive integer m, (x_m, t_m) is in $\sim h^{-1}[W]$, there is a contradiction. $h^{-1}[W]$ must then be open and h is continuous. ▮

Next, the previous theorems will be applied to homotopies, i.e., cases in which the space T is the unit interval space I.

36.5 Theorem. *Let X be first countable or let X be locally compact and Hausdorff. Let f and g be continuous functions from X into the space Y. Then f and g are homotopic if and only if f and g lie in the same path component of $\{C(X, Y), \mathfrak{J}_{c\text{-}o}\}$.*

Proof: In theorems 36.3 and 36.4, let $T = I$, the unit interval subspace of E^1. Since I is first countable, locally compact and Hausdorff, the conclusions of the theorems hold. Hence, if h is a homotopy between f and g, the corresponding function h^* (lemma 36.1) from I into $\{C(X, Y), \mathfrak{J}_{c\text{-}o}\}$ is continuous. Thus h^* is a path in $\{C(X, Y), \mathfrak{J}_{c\text{-}o}\}$ from $h^*(0) = h_0 = f$ to $h^*(1) = h_1 = g$. Conversely, if α is a path from f to g in $\{C(X, Y), \mathfrak{J}_{c\text{-}o}\}$, then, by definition of path, α is a continuous function from I into $\{C(X, Y), \mathfrak{J}_{c\text{-}o}\}$ such that $\alpha(0) = f$ and $\alpha(1) = g$. By theorems 36.3 and 36.4 and lemma 36.1, α determines a homotopy h from $X \times I$ into Y defined as follows: $\alpha(t)$ is a function in the set $C(X, Y)$. Denote the function $\alpha(t)$ by the symbol f_t. Define h from $X \times I$ into Y as follows. $h((x, t)) = f_t(x)$. For $t = 0$, $h((x, 0)) = f_0(x)$. However, $f_0 = \alpha(0) = f$. Next, $h((x, 1)) = f_1(x)$ but $f_1 = \alpha(1) = g$. Thus, h is a homotopy from f to g. ▮

36.6 Corollary. *Let X be first countable or let X be locally compact and Hausdorff. Then the homotopy equivalence classes in $C(X, Y)$ for any space Y are exactly the path components of the space $\{C(X, Y), \mathfrak{J}_{c\text{-}o}\}$.*

Path Spaces and the Fundamental Group

36.7 Definition. Let Y be any space and I be the unit interval space. $\Omega(Y)$ denotes the space $\{C(I, Y), \mathfrak{J}_{c\text{-}o}\}$, where $C(I, Y)$, as usual, denotes the set of paths in Y. $\Omega(Y)$ is called *the space of paths in* Y. $\Lambda(Y)$ denotes the subspace of $\Omega(Y)$ determined by the subset of loops in Y. $\Lambda(Y)$ is called *the space of loops in* Y. $\Lambda(Y, y_0)$ denotes the subspace of $\Lambda(Y)$ determined by $\{f \mid f \text{ is in } C(I, Y) \text{ and } f(0) = f(1) = y_0\}$. $\Lambda(Y, y_0)$ is called *the space of loops in Y based at* y_0.

By the remarks made at the beginning of this section, $\Omega(Y)$, and hence $\Lambda(Y)$ and $\Lambda(Y, y_0)$, are T_i if Y is for $i = 0, 1, 2$. Also since I is compact, $\Omega(Y)$ and hence $\Lambda(Y)$ and $\Lambda(Y, y_0)$ are metrizable if Y is.

36.8 Corollary. *For any space Y, the homotopy equivalence classes of paths in Y are exactly the path components of $\Omega(Y)$, the space of paths in Y.*

Proof: The corollary is the special case of corollary 36.6 for $X = I$. ▮

In order to apply the previous corollary to $\Lambda(Y, y_0)$, the space of loops based at y_0, and the fundamental group $\pi_1(Y, y_0)$, relative homotopies must be checked.

36.9 Lemma. *Let X be first countable or let X be locally compact and Hausdorff. Let $A \subseteq X$ and let h be a homotopy relative to A in the set $C(X \times I, Y)$. Then h^* has the property that $h_0(a) = h_t(a) = h_1(a)$ for a in A, where h^* is the correspondent in $(C(X, Y))^I$ of h (lemma 36.1) and $h^*(t)$ is denoted by h_t. Conversely, if h^* has this property, h is a homotopy relative to A.*

Proof: Let h be a homotopy relative to A from $X \times I$ into Y. If a is in A, then by definition (35.3) of a relative homotopy, $h((a, 0)) = h((a, t)) = h((a, 1))$. This means that $h_0(a) = h_t(a) = h_1(a)$. Hence, since $h^*(t) = h_t$, h^* has the desired property. Conversely, if h^* has the property that $f_0(a) = f_t(a) = f_1(a)$ for all a in A and for $h^*(t) = f_t$. Then if $h((x, t)) = f_t(x)$ for x in X and $0 \leq t \leq 1$, $h((a, 0)) = f_0(a) = f_t(a) = h((a, t)) = f_1(a) = h((a, 1))$. Thus h is a homotopy relative to A. ▮

36.10 Corollary. *Let $L(Y, y_0)$ denote the subset of $C(I, Y)$ consisting of the set of all loops in Y based at y_0. The homotopy equivalence classes relative to $\{0, 1\}$ in $L(Y, y_0)$ are exactly the path components of $\Lambda(Y, y_0)$.*

Proof: By theorems 36.3, 36.4 and the previous lemma (36.9), if f and g

are two loops in Y which are homotopic relative to $\{0, 1\}$ by a homotopy h, then h^* is a path in $\{C(I, Y), \mathfrak{I}_{c\text{-}o}\}$ with the property that $h_0(0) = h_t(0) = h_1(0)$ and $h_0(1) = h_t(1) = h_1(1)$, where $h^*(t) = h_t$. Since $h_0(0) = h((0, 0)) = f(0) = y_0$ and $h_0(1) = h((1, 0)) = f(1) = y_0$, then $h_0(0) = h_0(1) = y_0$ and so $h_t(0) = h_t(1) = y_0$ for all t. Thus h^* is a path in $\Lambda(Y, y_0)$ from $h_0 = f$ to $h_1 = g$. Thus if f and g are loops in Y based at y_0 which are homotopic relative to $\{0, 1\}$, f and g lie in the same path component of $\Lambda(Y, y_0)$. Conversely, let f and g lie in the same path component of $\Lambda(Y, y_0)$. There is then a path h^* from f to g in $\Lambda(Y, y_0)$. h^* then maps I into $\Lambda(Y, y_0)$ in such a way that $h^*(t)$ is a loop in Y based at y_0 for each t. Further, $h^*(0) = f$ and $h^*(1) = g$. Let $h^*(t)$ be denoted by h_t. If h from $I \times I$ is defined by $h((s, t)) = h_t(s)$, h is continuous by theorem 36.3 or 36.4. Further, $h((s, 0)) = h_0(s)$. Since $h^*(0) = f$ and $h^*(0) = h_0$, $h((s, 0)) = f(s)$. Similarly, $h((s, 1)) = g(s)$. Now since $h_t(0) = h_t(1) = y_0$, i.e., h_t is a loop for all t, $h((0, t)) = h((1, t)) = y_0$ for all t, and so h is the required relative homotopy. ▮

36.11 Corollary. *The elements of the fundamental group $\pi_1(Y, y_0)$ for any space Y and for y_0 any point in Y are exactly the path components of $\Lambda(Y, y_0)$, the space of loops in Y based at y_0.*

The last corollary emphasizes the fact that the pathwise connectedness of a space Y does not imply anything about the pathwise connectedness of $\Lambda(Y, y_0)$ for any point y_0 in Y.

The Exponential Law

The exponential law states that certain useful function spaces are homeomorphic. Let X, Y and T be spaces; let X be locally compact and Hausdorff, and let T be Hausdorff. Then $\{C(X \times T, Y), \mathfrak{I}_{c\text{-}o}\}$ and $\{C(T, C(X, Y)), \mathfrak{I}_{c\text{-}o}\}$ are homeomorphic. This statement can be abbreviated to $Y^{X \times T} \cong (Y^X)^T$, where $Y^{X \times T}$ denotes the space of continuous functions from $X \times T$ into Y with the *c-o* topology, and similarly for Y^X and $(Y^X)^T$. Hence the name of "exponential law." The correspondence Φ of lemma 36.1 will be the desired homeomorphism. First a lemma is needed.

36.12 Lemma. *Let S be a Hausdorff space and let $\mathcal{V} = \{V_\nu \mid \nu \in \mathfrak{N}\}$ be a subbasis for the topology on a space T. Then $\{G(K, V_\nu) \mid K$ is compact in S and V_ν is in $\mathcal{V}\}$ is a subbasis for the compact-open topology on $C(S, T)$, the set of continuous functions from S into T.*

Proof: Let $G(K, O)$ be a subbasic element for the compact-open topology on $C(S, T)$ and let f be in $G(K, O)$. For each s in K, $f(s)$ is in O. Since O is open in T, there exists a base element $V^s_{\nu_1} \cap \cdots \cap V^s_{\nu_k}$ determined by the subbase $\mathcal{V}$ such that $V^s_{\nu_1} \cap \cdots \cap V^s_{\nu_k} \subseteq O$ and $f(s)$ is in $V^s_{\nu_1} \cap \cdots \cap V^s_{\nu_k}$. f is continuous, so $f^{-1}[V^s_{\nu_1} \cap \cdots \cap V^s_{\nu_k}]$ is open in S and contains s. Let $f^{-1}[V^s_{\nu_1} \cap$

$\cdots \cap V^s_{\nu_k}]$ be denoted by B_s. B_s then is an open neighborhood of s and $f[B_s] \subseteq O$. $B_s \cap K$ is an open neighborhood of s in K. Since K is compact and Hausdorff, it is regular; thus there exists an open neighborhood $U_s \cap K$ of s in K such that $Cl_K(U_s \cap K) \subseteq B_s \cap K$, where $Cl_K(U_s \cap K)$ denotes the closure of $U_s \cap K$ in the subspace K. Since K is compact in the Hausdorff space S, K is closed in S (theorem 29.5). Thus the closure of $U_s \cap K$ in the subbase K is the same as $\overline{U_s \cap K}$, its closure in S (exercise 7 after lemma 9.21). Further, $\overline{U_s \cap K}$ as a closed subspace of a compact space K is compact (theorem 29.1). Since $\{U_s \mid s \text{ is in } K\}$ is an open covering of K in S, a finite number of these sets, say, $U_1, U_2, \ldots, U_n$ cover K. Now the sets $\overline{U_1 \cap K}, \ldots, \overline{U_n \cap K}$ are compact subsets of K and $f[\overline{U_i \cap K}] \subseteq f[B_{s_i}] \subseteq V^{s_i}_{\nu_1} \cap \cdots \cap V^{s_i}_{\nu_{k_i}} \subseteq O$ for $i = 1, \ldots, n$, where $V^{s_i}_{\nu_j}$ for $j = 1, \ldots, i$, is a set in the subbase $\mathcal{V}$. Thus f is in $G(\overline{U_i \cap K}, V^{s_i}_{\nu_1} \cap \cdots \cap V^{s_i}_{\nu_{k_i}}) = G(\overline{U_i \cap K}, V^{s_i}_{\nu_1}) \cap G(\overline{U_i \cap K}, V^{s_i}_{\nu_2}) \cap \cdots \cap G(\overline{U_i \cap K}, V^{s_i}_{\nu_{k_i}})$, i.e., f is in $\bigcap_{j=1}^{k_i} G(\overline{U_i \cap K}, V^{s_i}_{\nu_j})$ for $i = 1, \ldots, n$. Consequently, f is in $\bigcap_{i=1}^{n} (\bigcap_{j=1}^{k_i} G(\overline{U_i \cap K}, V^{s_i}_{\nu_j}))$. Now if g is any other function in $\bigcap_{i=1}^{n} (\bigcap_{j=1}^{k_i} G(\overline{U_i \cap K}, V^{s_i}_{\nu_j}))$, and if c is in K, then c is in $\overline{U_i \cap K}$ for some i such that $1 \leq i \leq n$. Hence, $g(c)$ is in $V^{s_i}_{\nu_1} \cap \cdots \cap V^{s_i}_{\nu_{k_i}} \subseteq O$. Hence $g[K] \subseteq O$ or g is in $G(K, O)$. Thus $\bigcap_{i=1}^{n} (\bigcap_{j=1}^{k_i} G(\overline{U_i \cap K}, V^{s_i}_{\nu_j})) \subseteq G(K, O)$ and $\{G(K, V_\nu) \mid V_\nu \in \mathcal{V}\}$ is a subbase for the compact-open topology for $C(S, T)$. ∎

36.13 Theorem (The Exponential Law). *If X is locally compact and Hausdorff and if T is Hausdorff, then*

$$\{C(X \times T, Y), \mathfrak{J}_{c\text{-}o}\} \quad \textit{and} \quad \{C(T, \{C(X, Y), \mathfrak{J}_{c\text{-}o}\}), \mathfrak{J}_{c\text{-}o}\}$$

are homeomorphic.

Proof: A. By lemma 36.1 and theorem 36.3, the correspondence $\Phi(h) = h^*$, where $h^*(t) = h_t$ and $h_t(x) = h((x, t))$, is 1:1 from $C(X \times T, Y)$ onto $C(T, \{C(X, Y), \mathfrak{J}_{c\text{-}o}\})$.

B. Φ is continuous. For, by lemma 36.12, let $G(K^*, G(K, U))$ be a subbasic open set for the compact-open topology on $C(T, \{C(X, Y), \mathfrak{J}_{c\text{-}o}\})$, where K^* is a compact subset of T, K is compact in X and U is open in Y. Then consider $\Phi^{-1}[G(K^*, G(K, U))]$ in $C(X \times T, Y)$. If h is in $\Phi^{-1}[G(K^*, G(K, U))]$, then $h^*[K^*] \subseteq G(K, U)$. Then for t in K^* $h^*(t) = h_t$ is in $G(K, U)$. Thus $h_t[K] \subseteq U$ for t in K^*. Therefore, $h[K \times \{t\}] \subseteq U$ for t in K^*, or $h[K \times K^*] \subseteq U$. Consequently, h is in$[G(K \times K^*, U)$, and so $\Phi^{-1}[G(K^*, G(K, U))] \subseteq G(K \times K^*, U)$. Conversely, if h is in $G(K \times K^*, U)$, then $h[K \times K^*] \subseteq U$, and so $h[K \times \{t\}] \subseteq U$ for t in K^*. This means that $h_t[K] \subseteq U$ for t in K^*, and consequently that $h^*(t)$ is in $G(K, U)$ for t in K^*. Hence, $h^*[K^*] \subseteq G(K, U)$ and h^* is in $G(K^*, G(K, U))$. It follows that h is in $\Phi^{-1}[G(K^*, G(K, U))]$ and that $G(K \times K^*, U) \subseteq \Phi^{-1}[G(K^*, G(K, U))]$. This makes $\Phi^{-1}[G(K^*, G(K, U))]$ open in $C(X \times T, Y)$ and, by theorem 4.10, makes Φ continuous.

C. Φ^{-1} is continuous. $(\Phi^{-1})^{-1} = \Phi$. So let $G(K, U)$ be a subbasic open set for the compact-open topology on $C(X \times T, Y)$ and consider $\Phi[G(K, U)]$. K is compact in $X \times Y$ and U is open in T. Let f^* be in $\Phi[G(K, U)]$. The aim will be to prove that f^* is interior. $f^* = \Phi(f)$ for f in $G(K, U)$. Let (a, t) be in K. Since f is continuous, $f^{-1}[U]$ is open and contains K. Hence there exists an open product set $V_a \times W_t$ such that (a, t) is in $V_a \times W_t$ and $V_a \times W_t \subseteq f^{-1}[U]$. Let $p_X[K] = K_X$ and $p_Y[K] = K_Y$, where p_X and p_Y are the projection functions on $X \times T$. Since p_X and p_Y are continuous, K_X and K_Y are compact subsets of Hausdorff spaces and so are regular. Hence $V_a \cap K_X$ contains $Cl_{K_X}(L_a \cap K_X)$, the closure in K_X of $L_a \cap K_X$, where L_a is open in X, $a \in L_a$, and $L_a \subseteq V_a$. Since K_X is compact and X is Hausdorff, K_X is closed in X. Hence $Cl_{K_X}(L_a \cap K_X) = \overline{L_a \cap K_X}$, the closure of $L_a \cap K_X$ in X. Similarly, there exists an open neighborhood M_t of t in T such that $M_t \subseteq W_t$ and $\overline{M_t \cap K_Y} \subseteq W_t \cap K_Y$. Now, $(\overline{L_a \cap K_X}) \times (\overline{M_t \cap K_Y}) \subseteq (V_a \cap K_X) \times (W_t \cap K_Y) \subseteq V_a \times W_t$. Hence $f[(\overline{L_a \cap K_X}) \times (\overline{M_t \cap K_Y})] \subseteq U$. $\{(L_a \cap K_X) \times (M_t \cap K_Y) \mid (a, t) \text{ is in } K\}$ covers K, and $\{L_a \times M_t \mid (a, t) \text{ is in } K\}$ is an open covering of K. Hence a finite number, say, $L_1 \times M_1, \ldots, L_k \times M_k$ cover the compact set K. Now $(\overline{L_1 \cap K_X}), (\overline{M_1 \cap K_Y}), \ldots, (\overline{L_k \cap K_X}), (\overline{M_k \cap K_X})$ are closed subsets in the compact spaces K_X or K_Y, and hence are compact. Now $f[(\overline{L_i \cap K_X}) \times (\overline{M_i \cap K_Y})] \subseteq U$. So, for t in $\overline{M_i \cap K_Y}$, $f[\overline{L_i \cap K_X} \times \{t\}] \subseteq U$, and therefore $f_t[\overline{L_i \cap K_X}] \subseteq U$. Consequently, $f^*(t)$ is in $G(\overline{L_i \cap K_X}, U)$ for t in $\overline{M_i \cap K_Y}$, and so $f^*[\overline{M_i \cap K_Y}] \subseteq G(\overline{L_i \cap K_X}, U)$ for $i = 1, 2, \ldots, k$. Thus f^* is in the open set $\bigcap_{i=1}^{k} G(\overline{M_i \cap K_Y}, G(\overline{L_i \cap K_X}, U))$. Now let g^* also be in $\bigcap_{i=1}^{k} G(\overline{M_i \cap K_Y}, G(\overline{L_i \cap K_X}, U))$, and let $\Phi^{-1}(g^*) = g$ in $C(X \times T, Y)$. If (a, t) is in K, then (a, t) is in $L_i \times M_i$, say, since $\{L_1 \times M_1, \ldots, L_k \times M_k\}$ covers K. (a, t) is, then, in $(\overline{L_i \cap K_X}) \times (\overline{M_i \cap K_Y})$. Since $g^*[\overline{M_i \cap K_Y}] \subseteq G(\overline{L_i \cap K_X}, U)$, for t in $\overline{M_i \cap K_Y}$, $g_t[\overline{L_i \cap K_X}] \subseteq U$. Hence for t in $\overline{M_i \cap K_Y}$, $g[\overline{L_i \cap K_X} \times \{t\}] \subseteq U$ or $g[(\overline{L_i \cap K_X}) \times (\overline{M_i \cap K_Y})] \subseteq U$. Hence $g((a, t))$ is in U. Since (a, t) was any point in K. $g[K] \subseteq U$ or g is in $G(K, U)$. g^*, then, is in $\Phi[G(K, U)]$ and $\bigcap_{i=1}^{k} G(\overline{M_i \cap K_Y}, G(\overline{L_i \cap K_X}, U)) \subseteq \Phi[G(K, U)]$. This means that every point of $\Phi[G(K, U)]$ is interior, and so $\Phi[G(K, U)]$ is open. Thus, again, by theorem 4.10, Φ^{-1} is continuous. ▮

The Higher Homotopy Groups

The following definition will be convenient for the definitions of the higher dimensional homotopy groups.

36.14 Definition. A continuous function from the n-cube I^n into a space Y will be called an *n-dimensional hyperpath* in Y.

36.15 Definition. Let f and g be n-dimensional hyperpaths in a space Y. The *product of f and g*, denoted by $f * g$, is defined to be the hyperpath p, say, such that $p((t_1, t_2, \ldots, t_n)) = f((2t_1, t_2, \ldots, t_n))$ for $0 \le t_1 \le 1/2$, and $p((t_1, t_2, \ldots, t_n)) = g((2t_1 - 1, t_2, \ldots, t_n))$ for $1/2 \le t_1 \le 1$. $f * g$ is defined, then, as a hyperpath if and only if $f((1, t_2, \ldots, t_n)) = g((0, t_2, \ldots, t_n))$. This follows from theorems 9.23 and 4.8. The *inverse* of a hyperpath f is defined to be the hyperpath f^{-1} defined by $f^{-1}((t_1, t_2,$

$\ldots, t_n)) = f((1 - t_1, t_2, \ldots, t_n))$. Thus $f^{-1}((0, t_2, \ldots, t_n)) = f((1, t_2, \ldots, t_n))$ and $f^{-1}((1, t_2, \ldots, t_n)) = f((0, t_2, \ldots, t_n))$. Hence, $f * f^{-1}$ and $f^{-1} * f$ are both defined. It is obvious that the product and inverse could have been defined in terms of the last coordinate t_n instead of t_1. Then $f \cdot g((t_1, t_2, \ldots, t_n)) = f((t_1, t_2, \ldots, 2t_n))$ for $0 \leq t_n \leq \frac{1}{2}$ etc. The correspondence $f \to \tilde{f}$ where $\tilde{f}((t_1, t_2, \ldots, t_n)) = f((t_n, t_2, \ldots, t_1))$ establishes an isomorphism between the two structures.

36.16 Definition. The boundary, ∂I^n, of the n-cube I^n in Euclidean n-space is $\{(t_1, t_2, \ldots, t_n) \mid t_i = 0 \text{ or } t_i = 1 \text{ for some } i \text{ such that } 1 \leq i \leq n\}$. An n-dimensional hyperpath f in a space Y will be called an *n-dimensional hyperloop based at y_0* in Y if and only if $f[\partial I^n] = \{y_0\}$. Since the boundary, ∂I, of I in E^1 is $\{0, 1\}$, this is a direct generalization of the concept of loop.

36.17 Lemma. *Let f and g be n-dimensional hyperloops based at y_0 in a space Y. $f * g$ is defined as an n-dimensional hyperloop based at y_0 in Y.*

Proof: Exercise.

36.18 Theorem. *Let $L_n(Y, y_0)$ denote the set of all n-dimensional hyperloops based at y_0 and let $\pi_n(Y, y_0)$ denote the set of equivalence classes determined in $L_n(Y, y_0)$ by homotopies relative to ∂I^n. Define $[f] \circledast [g]$ for $[f]$ and $[g]$ in $\pi_n(Y, y_0)$ to be $[f * g]$. Then $\{\pi_n(Y, y_0), \circledast\}$ is a group.*

Proof: The details of the proof are similar to the details of the proof of theorem 35.5 and some will be left as an exercise. First the correspondence $([f], [g]) \to [f * g]$ must be shown to be single-valued. f *homt* $(\partial I^n)m$ and g *homt* $(\partial I^n)k$ must imply that $f * g$ *homt* $(\partial I^n)m * k$. Let H_1 be a homotopy from f to m relative to ∂I^n and let H_2 be a homotopy from g to k relative to ∂I^n. Define $\tilde{H}(((t_1, \ldots, t_n), s)) = H_1(((2t_1, t_2, \ldots, t_n), s))$ for $0 \leq t_1 \leq 1/2$, $\tilde{H}(((t_1, \ldots, t_n), s)) = H_2(((2t_1 - 1, t_2, \ldots, t_n), s))$ for $1/2 \leq t_1 \leq 1$. Since $H_1(((1, t_2, \ldots, t_n), s)) = H_2(((0, t_2, \ldots, t_n), s))$ for each s in I, $\tilde{H}$ is a continuous function from $I^n \times I$ into Y. Further, since H_1 and H_2 are relative (∂I^n) homotopies, $\tilde{H}$ is a relative (∂I^n) homotopy, and since

$$\tilde{H}(((t_1, t_2, \ldots, t_n), 0)) = H_1(((2t_1, t_2, \ldots, t_n), 0)) = f((2t_1, t_2, \ldots, t_n)),$$

for $0 \leq t_1 \leq 1/2$, and

$$\begin{aligned}\tilde{H}(((t_1, t_2, \ldots, t_n), 0)) &= H_2(((2t_1 - 1, t_2, \ldots, t_n), 0)) \\ &= g((2t_1 - 1, t_2, \ldots, t_n)), \text{ for } \tfrac{1}{2} \leq t_1 \leq 1,\end{aligned}$$

then $\tilde{H}(((t_1, t_2, \ldots, t_n), 0)) = f * g((t_1, t_2, \ldots, t_n))$.

Further, $\tilde{H}(((t_1, t_2, \ldots, t_n), 1)) = H_1(((2t_1, t_2, \ldots, t_n), 1))$
$$= m((2t_1, t_2, \ldots, t_n))$$

for $0 \leq t_1 \leq 1/2$ and

$$\tilde{H}(((t_1, t_2, \ldots, t_n), 1)) = H_2(((2t_1 - 1, t_2, \ldots, t_n), 1))$$
$$= k((2t_1 - 1, t_2, \ldots, t_n))$$

for $1/2 \le t_1 \le 1$. Hence $\tilde{H}(((t_1, t_2, \ldots, t_n), 1)) = m * k((t_1, t_2, \ldots, t_n))$ and $\tilde{H}$ is the desired relative (∂I^n) homotopy. The rest of the proof follows in a similar manner, by generalizing the homotopies in the proof of theorem 35.5 to hyperloops, and is left as an exercise. ▮

The same procedure used in the previous proof would apply to the operation · of definition 36.15. Hence it can be stated that $\{\pi_n(Y, y_0), \odot\}$ is a group isomorphic to $\{\pi_n(Y, y_0), \circledast\}$.

36.19 Definition. For any space Y, the group $\{\pi_n(Y, y_0), \circledast\}$ is usually denoted by $\pi_n(Y, y_0)$ and is called the *n-dimensional homotopy group of the pair* (Y, y_0).

The analogue of corollary 36.8 for higher dimensions is now stated.

36.20 Theorem. *The homotopy equivalence classes in $C(I^n, Y)$ for any space Y are exactly the path components of the space $\{C(I^n, Y), \mathfrak{Z}_{c\text{-}o}\}$.*

Proof: Since I^n is first countable, compact and Hausdorff, the theorem follows from corollary 36.6. ▮

36.21 Theorem. *Let $L_n(Y, y_0)$ denote the subset of $C(I^n, Y)$ consisting of the set of all n-dimensional hyperloops based at y_0. The homotopy equivalence classes relative to ∂I^n are exactly the path components of $\{L_n(Y, y_0), \mathfrak{Z}_{c\text{-}o}\}$.*

Proof: By theorem 36.3 and lemma 36.9, if f and g are two n-dimensional hyperloops in Y based at y_0 and if f and g are homotopic relative to ∂I^n by a homotopy h, then h^* is a path in $\{C(I^n, Y), \mathfrak{Z}_{c\text{-}o}\}$. Now consider $h^*(0)$ and $h^*(1)$ denoted by h_0 and h_1 respectively. $h_0((t_1, \ldots, t_n)) = h(((t_1, \ldots, t_n), 0)) = f((t_1, \ldots, t_n))$ and $h_1((t_1, \ldots, t_n)) = h(((t_1, \ldots, t_n), 1)) = g((t_1, \ldots, t_n))$. Next, for b in ∂I^n, $h_s(b) = h((b, s)) = y_0$. Hence $h_0(b) = h_s(b) = h_1(b) = y_0$ and h^* is a path in $\{L_n(Y, y_0), \mathfrak{Z}_{c\text{-}o}\}$ with the desired property. Conversely, let h^* be a path in $\{L_n(Y, y_0), \mathfrak{Z}_{c\text{-}o}\}$ from f to g with the property that for b in ∂I^n, $h_0(b) = h_s(b) = h_1(b) = y_0$ where $h^*(s) = h_s$. Then the homotopy h established in theorem 36.3 and defined by $h(((t_1, \ldots, t_n), s)) = h_s((t_1, \ldots, t_n))$ has the following properties. $h(((t_1, \ldots, t_n), 0)) = h_0((t_1, \ldots, t_n)) = f((t_0, \ldots, t_n))$ and $h(((t_1, \ldots, t_n), 1)) = h_1((t_1, \ldots, t_n)) = g((t_1, \ldots, t_n))$. Thus h is a homotopy from f to g. Further, if b is in ∂I^n, $h((b, s)) = h_s(b) = y_0$. Thus h is a relative (∂I^n) homotopy. ▮

From the last theorem then it follows that the elements of the n-dimensional homotopy group $\pi_n(Y, y_0)$ are exactly the path components in the subspace $\{L_n(Y, y_0), \mathfrak{Z}_{c\text{-}o}\}$ of n-dimensional hyperloops based at y_0.

REDUCTION FORMULAS

The exponential law, theorem 36.13, yields two reduction formulas for homotopy groups. Since I^n is homeomorphic to $I^{n-1} \times I$ and also to $I \times I^{n-1}$, the exponential law states that $\{C(I^n, Y), \mathfrak{J}_{c\text{-}o}\}$ is homeomorphic to both $\{C(I, \{C(I^{n-1}, Y), \mathfrak{J}_{c\text{-}o}\}), \mathfrak{J}_{c\text{-}o}\}$ and to $\{C(I^{n-1}, \{C(I, Y), \mathfrak{J}_{c\text{-}o}\}), \mathfrak{J}_{c\text{-}o}\}$. These two homeomorphisms yield two isomorphisms between certain homotopy groups of different dimensions.

36.22 Theorem. *Let Y be any space and let y_0 be a point in Y. The space $\{L_n(Y, y_0), \mathfrak{J}_{c\text{-}o}\}$ of n-dimensional hyperloops based at y_0 is homeomorphic to $\Lambda(\{L_{n-1}(Y, y_0), \mathfrak{J}_{c\text{-}o}\}, \tilde{y}_0^{(n-1)})$, the space of (one-dimensional) loops based at the constant $(n-1)$-dimensional hyperloop $\tilde{y}_0^{(n-1)}$ in $\{L_{n-1}(Y, y_0), \mathfrak{J}_{c\text{-}o}\}$.*

Proof: By theorem 36.13 (the exponential law), the space $\{C(I^{n-1} \times I, Y), \mathfrak{J}_{c\text{-}o}\}$ for $n \geq 1$ is homeomorphic to $\{C(I, \{C(I^{n-1}, Y), \mathfrak{J}_{c\text{-}o}\}), \mathfrak{J}_{c\text{-}o}\}$. Hence, the space $\{C(I^n, Y), \mathfrak{J}_{c\text{-}o}\}$ is homeomorphic to $\{C(I, C(I^{n-1}, Y)), \mathfrak{J}_{c\text{-}o}\}$. Now let f be an n-dimensional hyperloop in Y based at y_0. $f: I^n \to Y$ and $f[\partial I^n] = \{y_0\}$. i.e., $f \in L_n(Y, y_0)$. f then identifies a homotopy $\tilde{f}$ from $I^{n-1} \times I \to Y$, where

$$\tilde{f}(((t_1, t_2, \ldots, t_{n-1}), s)) = f((t_1, t_2, \ldots, t_{n-1}, s)).$$

Let $\xi(f) = \tilde{f}$. ξ is the homeomorphism from $\{C(I^n, Y), \mathfrak{J}_{c\text{-}o}\}$ onto $\{C(I^{n-1} \times I, Y), \mathfrak{J}_{c\text{-}o}\}$ induced by the natural homeomorphism from I^n onto $I^{n-1} \times I$. Now the homeomorphism Φ defined in theorem 36.12 assigns to $\tilde{f}$ a function $\tilde{f}^*$ from I into $\{C(I^{n-1}, Y), \mathfrak{J}_{c\text{-}o}\}$ such that if $\tilde{f}^*(s)$ is denoted by $\tilde{f}_s$, then

$$\tilde{f}_s((t_1, t_2, \ldots, t_{n-1})) = \tilde{f}(((t_1, t_2, \ldots, t_{n-1}), s)).$$

Now

$$\tilde{f}(((t_1, t_2, \ldots, t_{n-1}), 0)) = f((t_1, t_2, \ldots, t_{n-1}, 0)) = y_0.$$

Thus $\tilde{f}_0 = \tilde{y}_0$, the constant function $\tilde{y}_0((t_1, t_2, \ldots, t_{n-1})) = y_0$ from I^{n-1} into Y. Similarly,

$$\begin{aligned}\tilde{f}_1((t_1, t_2, \ldots, t_{n-1})) &= \tilde{f}(((t_1, t_2, \ldots, t_{n-1}), 1)) \\ &= f((t_1, t_2, \ldots, t_{n-1}, 1)) = y_0.\end{aligned}$$

Thus $\tilde{f}_1 = \tilde{y}_0$ and $\tilde{f}^*$ is a loop in $\{C(I^{n-1}, Y), \mathfrak{J}_{c\text{-}o}\}$ based at $\tilde{y}_0$. Further, since for any s in I,

$$\tilde{f}_s((t_1, t_2, \ldots, t_{n-1})) = \tilde{f}(((t_1, t_2, \ldots, t_{n-1}), s)) = f((t_1, t_2, \ldots, t_{n-1}, s))$$

and since for b in ∂I^n, $f(b) = y_0$, then if $t_i = 0$ or $t_i = 1$ for at least one i such that $1 \leq i \leq n-1$,

$$\tilde{f}_s((t_1, t_2, \ldots, t_i, \ldots, t_{n-1})) = y_0.$$

Thus for each s, $\tilde{f}_s$ is an $(n-1)$-dimensional hyperloop. Consequently, for each s, $\tilde{f}^*(s)$ is in $L_{n-1}(Y, y_0)$. Thus $\Phi \circ \xi(f)$ has the required properties. Conversely, let g^* be a (1-dimensional) loop based at the constant $(n-1)$-dimensional hyperloop $\tilde{y}_0^{(n-1)}$ in $\{L_{n-1}(Y, y_0), \mathfrak{I}_{c\text{-}o}\}$ and let $g^*(s)$ again be denoted by g_s. g_s is a continuous function which is in $\{L_{n-1}(Y, y_0), \mathfrak{I}_{c\text{-}o}\}$. Hence for each s, $0 \leq s \leq 1$, g_s is an $(n-1)$-dimensional hyperloop based at y_0 in Y. Consider $\Phi^{-1}(g^*) = h$.

$$h(((t_1, t_2, \ldots, t_{n-1}), s)) = g_s((t_1, t_2, \ldots, t_{n-1})),$$
$$h(((t_1, t_2, \ldots, t_{n-1}), 0)) = g_0((t_1, t_2, \ldots, t_{n-1})),$$

and since $g^*(0)$ is the constant $(n-1)$-dimensional hyperloop $\tilde{y}_0^{(n-1)}$

$$g_0((t_1, t_2, \ldots, t_{n-1})) = y_0.$$

Similarly,

$$h(((t_1, t_2, \ldots, t_{n-1}), 1)) = g_1((t_1, t_2, \ldots, t_{n-1})) = y_0.$$

Now, let $t_i = 0$ or $t_i = 1$ for some i such that $0 \leq i \leq n-1$. Since

$$h(((t_1, \ldots, 0, \ldots, t_{n-1}), s)) = g_s((t_1, \ldots, 0, \ldots, t_{n-1}))$$

and

$$h(((t_1, \ldots, 1, \ldots, t_{n-1}), s)) = g_s((t_1, \ldots, 1, \ldots, t_{n-1}))$$

and since g_s is an $(n-1)$-dimensional hyperloop in Y (definition 36.16),

$$g_s((t_1, \ldots, 0, \ldots, t_{n-1})) = g_s((t_1, \ldots, 1, \ldots, t_{n-1})) = y_0.$$

Hence if $\bar{h} = \xi^{-1}(h)$, $\bar{h}((t_1, t_2, \ldots, t_{n-1}, t_n))$ is defined to be $h(((t_0, \ldots, t_{n-1}), t_n))$. $\bar{h}$ then is a hyperpath in Y such that $\bar{h}[\partial I^n] = \{y_0\}$. Hence, $\bar{h}$ is an n-dimensional hyperloop based at y_0 in Y and the desired correspondence has been established. ∎

36.23 Theorem. *If Y is any space, then $\pi_n(Y, y_0)$ is isomorphic to $\pi_1(\{L_{n-1}(Y, y_0), \mathfrak{I}_{c\text{-}o}\}, \tilde{y}_0^{(n-1)})$, where $\tilde{y}_0^{(n-1)}$ denotes the constant $(n-1)$-dimensional hyperloop whose range is $\{y_0\}$ in Y, and so every higher dimensional homotopy group is essentially a fundamental group.*

Proof: By the previous theorem, there exists a homeomorphism, say ψ, from the space $\{L_n(Y, y_0), \mathfrak{I}_{c\text{-}o}\}$ onto the space $\{L_1(\{L_{n-1}(Y, y_0), \mathfrak{I}_{c\text{-}o}\}, \tilde{y}_0^{(n-1)}), \mathfrak{I}_{c\text{-}o}\}$. ψ is defined as a composite of a restriction of the homeomorphism Φ, of theorem 36.13. By theorem 36.21, if f and g are in $L_n(Y, y_0)$ and are homotopic relative to ∂I^n, then they lie in the same path component of $\{L_n(Y, y_0), \mathfrak{I}_{c\text{-}o}\}$. Hence the images $\psi(f)$ and $\psi(g)$ must lie in the same path component of $\{L_1(\{L_{n-1}(Y, y_0), \mathfrak{I}_{c\text{-}o}\}, \tilde{y}_0^{(n-1)}), \mathfrak{I}_{c\text{-}o}\}$. $\{L_1(\{L_{n-1}(Y, y_0), \mathfrak{I}_{c\text{-}o}\}, \tilde{y}_0^{(n-1)}), \mathfrak{I}_{c\text{-}o}\}$ is actually $\Lambda(\{L_{n-1}(Y, y_0), \mathfrak{I}_{c\text{-}o}\}, \tilde{y}_0^{(n-1)})$ (definition 36.7). It then follows, by corollary 36.10, that $\psi(f)$ and $\psi(g)$ are homotopic relative to $\{0, 1\}$. The above reasoning is reversible, and so if $\psi(f)$ and $\psi(g)$ are homotopic relative to $\{0, 1\}$, then f and g are homotopic relative to ∂I^n. Thus there is a 1:1 correspondence between the elements of $\pi_n(Y, y_0)$ and those of $\pi_1(\{L_{n-1}(Y, y_0), \mathfrak{J}_{c\text{-}o}\}, \tilde{y}_0^{(n-1)})$. Now define $\tilde{\psi}([f])$ to be $[\psi(f)]$, where $[f]$ is an element in $\pi_n(Y, y_0)$ and $[\psi(f)]$ is in $\pi_1(\{L_{n-1}(Y, y_0), \mathfrak{J}_{c\text{-}o}\}, \tilde{y}_0^{(n-1)})$. $\tilde{\psi}([f \cdot m]) = [\psi(f \cdot m)]$. Now consider $\psi(f \cdot m)$. By the definition of the homeomorphism ψ, $\psi(f)$ is a loop f^* such that $f^*(s)$ is the $(n - 1)$-dimensional hyperloop f_s, where

$$f_s((t_1, \ldots, t_{n-1})) = f((t_1, \ldots, t_{n-1}, s))$$

and $\psi(m)$ is a loop m^* such that $m^*(s)$ is the $(n - 1)$-dimensional hyperloop m_s, where

$$m_s((t_1, \ldots, t_{n-1})) = m((t_1, \ldots, t_{n-1}, s)).$$

Hence let the product $f^* * m^* = \psi(f) * \psi(m)$ be denoted by p^* and, again, let $p^*(s)$ be denoted by p_s.

$$p_s((t_1, t_2, \ldots, t_{n-1})) = f_{2s}((t_1, \ldots, t_{n-1})) \qquad \text{for } 0 \le s \le 1/2,$$

and

$$p_s((t_1, \ldots, t_{n-1})) = m_{2s-1}((t_1, t_2, \ldots, t_{n-1})) \qquad \text{for } 1/2 \le s \le 1.$$

Thus

$$p_s((t_1, \ldots, t_{n-1})) = f((t_1, \ldots, t_{n-1}, 2s)) \qquad \text{for } 0 \le s \le 1/2,$$

and

$$p_s((t_1, \ldots, t_{n-1})) = m((t_1, \ldots, t_{n-1}, 2s - 1)) \qquad \text{for } 1/2 \le s \le 1.$$

Now if $\psi^{-1}(p^*)$ is, as usual, denoted by p,

$$p((t_1, \ldots, t_{n-1}, s)) = f((t_1, \ldots, t_{n-1}, 2s)) \qquad \text{for } 0 \le s \le 1/2$$

and

$$p((t_1, \ldots, t_{n-1}, s)) = m((t_1, \ldots, t_{n-1}, 2s - 1)) \qquad \text{for } 1/2 \le s \le 1.$$

Hence $p = f \cdot m$ (see definition 36.15). Thus $p^* = (f \cdot m)^*$ or $\psi(f) * \psi(m) = \psi(f \cdot m)$, and so $\tilde{\psi}$ is an isomorphism. (See remark after theorem 36.18). ▮

The previous theorem establishes every homotopy group as essentially a fundamental group, and underwrites the usefulness of the space of loops for any space, Y. In addition to the previous result, the exponential law, theorem 36.13, yields another reduction formula.

36.24 Theorem. *If Y is any space, then the space $\{C(I^n, Y), \mathfrak{J}_{c\text{-}o}\}$ is homeomorphic to $\{C(I^{n-1}, \{C(I, Y), \mathfrak{J}_{c\text{-}o}\}), \mathfrak{J}_{c\text{-}o}\}$.*

Proof: The space I^n is homeomorphic to $I \times I^{n-1}$. Hence $\{C(I^n, Y), \mathfrak{J}_{c\text{-}o}\}$ is homeomorphic to $\{C(I \times I^{n-1}, Y), \mathfrak{J}_{c\text{-}o}\}$. By theorem 36.13, the exponential law, $\{C(I \times I^{n-1}, Y), \mathfrak{J}_{c\text{-}o}\}$ is homeomorphic to

$$\{C(I^{n-1}, \{C(I, Y), \mathfrak{J}_{c\text{-}o}\}), \mathfrak{J}_{c\text{-}o}\}. \blacksquare$$

The next theorem will be the analogue of theorem 36.21 and will establish that the subspace $\{L_n(Y, y_0), \mathfrak{J}_{c\text{-}o}\}$ of $\{C(I^n, Y), \mathfrak{J}_{c\text{-}o}\}$ is homeomorphic to the subspace $\{L_{n-1}(\Lambda(Y, y_0)), \mathfrak{J}_{c\text{-}o}\}$ of $\{C(I^{n-1}, \{C(I, Y), \mathfrak{J}_{c\text{-}o}\}), \mathfrak{J}_{c\text{-}o}\}$. This will relate $\pi_n(Y, y_0)$ to $\pi_{n-1}(\Lambda(Y, y_0))$.

36.25 Theorem. *Let Y be any space and y_0 a point in Y. The space $\{L_n(Y, y_0), \mathfrak{J}_{c\text{-}o}\}$ of n-dimensional hyperloops in Y based at y_0 with the compact-open topology is homeomorphic to the space $\{L_{n-1}(\Lambda(Y, y_0), \tilde{y}_0), \mathfrak{J}_{c\text{-}o}\}$ of $(n-1)$-dimensional hyperloops in $\Lambda(Y, y_0)$ based at $\tilde{y}_0$—the constant loop—with the compact-open topology.*

Proof: Let f be an n-dimensional hyperloop based at y_0 in Y. Consider $\psi(f)$ in $\{C(I^{n-1}, \{C(I, Y), \mathfrak{J}_{c\text{-}o}\}), \mathfrak{J}_{c\text{-}o}\}$, where ψ is the homeomorphism $\Phi \circ \xi$ for Φ from theorem 36.13 (the exponential law) and $\xi((t_1, t_2, \ldots, t_n)) = (t_1, (t_2, \ldots, t_n))$. $\psi(f)$, denoted by f^*, is an $(n-1)$-dimensional path in $\Omega(Y)$, the space of paths in Y. $f^*((t_1, t_2, \ldots, t_{n-1}))$ is a path in Y. Let $f^*((t_1, t_2, \ldots, t_{n-1}))$ be denoted by $f_{(t_1, t_2, \ldots, t_{n-1})}$.

$$f_{(t_1, \ldots, t_{n-1})}(s) = f((s, t_1, \ldots, t_{n-1})).$$

Now since f is a hyperloop,

$$f((0, t_1, \ldots, t_{n-1})) = f((1, t_1, \ldots, t_{n-1})) = y_0.$$

Hence, $f_{(t_1, \ldots, t_{n-1})}$ is a (one-dimensional) loop based at y_0 in Y. Thus f^* has as its domain I^{n-1} and as its range a subspace of $\Lambda(Y, y_0)$—the space of (one-dimensional) loops based at y_0 in Y. Further, since f is a hyperloop, if $t_i = 0$ or $t_i = 1$ for some i such that $0 \leq i \leq n-1$, then for every s in I,

$$\begin{aligned} f_{(t_1, \ldots, 0, \ldots, t_{n-1})}(s) &= f((s, t_1, \ldots, 0, \ldots, t_{n-1})) = y_0 \\ &= f((s, t_1, \ldots, 1, \ldots, t_{n-1})) \\ &= f_{(t_1, \ldots, 1, \ldots, t_{n-1})}(s). \end{aligned}$$

Hence for each boundary point b in ∂I^{n-1}, $f^*(b) = \tilde{y}_0$, the constant (one-dimensional) loop at y_0. Thus f^* is an $(n-1)$-dimensional hyperloop in $\Lambda(Y, y_0)$, based at $\tilde{y}_0$ in $\Lambda(Y, y_0)$. Thus $\psi[L_n(Y, y_0)] \subseteq L_{n-1}(\Lambda(Y, y_0), \tilde{y}_0)$. The above reasoning is reversible, and so if f^* is an $(n-1)$-dimensional hyperloop based at $\tilde{y}_0$ in $\Lambda(Y, y_0)$, then $\psi^{-1}(f^*) = f$ is an n-dimensional hyperloop based at y_0 in Y. Thus $\psi[L_n(Y, y_0)] = L_{n-1}(\Lambda(Y, y_0), \tilde{y}_0)$ and the two subspaces these sets determine are homeomorphic. $\blacksquare$

36.26 Theorem. *Let Y be any space and y_0 a point in Y. Then for $n > 1$, $\pi_n(Y, y_0)$ is isomorphic to $\pi_{n-1}(\Lambda(Y, y_0), \tilde{y}_0)$, where $\tilde{y}_0$ is the constant loop based at y_0 in Y.*

Proof: It must be shown that if f and g are two n-dimensional hyperloops based at y_0 in Y which are homotopic relative to ∂I^n, then the images $\psi(f) = f^*$ and $\psi(g) = g^*$ are homotopic relative to ∂I^{n-1}, where ψ is the homeomorphism of the previous theorem. Let f and g be homotopic relative to ∂I^n. By theorem 36.21, f and g are homotopic relative to ∂I^n if and only if they lie in the same path component of $\{L_n(Y, y_0), \mathfrak{J}_{c\text{-}o}\}$. Thus since ψ is a homeomorphism, $\psi(f) = f^*$ and $\psi(g) = g^*$ lie in the same path component of $\psi[L_n(Y, y_0), \mathfrak{J}_{c\text{-}o}] = \{L_{n-1}(\Lambda(Y, y_0), \tilde{y}_0), \mathfrak{J}_{c\text{-}o}\}$. Now again by theorem 36.21, the path components of $\{L_{n-1}(\Lambda(Y, y_0), \tilde{y}_0), \mathfrak{J}_{c\text{-}o}\}$ are exactly the relative (∂I^{n-1}) homotopy classes. Thus f^* and g^* are homotopic relative to ∂I^{n-1}. The above reasoning is reversible. Hence, f and g are homotopic relative to ∂I^n if and only if f^* and g^* are homotopic relative to ∂I^{n-1}. Thus ψ determines a 1:1 correspondence $\tilde{\psi}$ between the elements of $\pi_n(Y, y_0)$ and the elements of $\pi_{n-1}(\Lambda(Y, y_0), \tilde{y}_0)$. Now consider $\tilde{\psi}([f] \odot [g]) = \tilde{\psi}([f \cdot g]) = [\psi(f \cdot g)]$. Let p denote the product hyperloop $f \cdot g$.

$$p((t_1, \ldots, t_n)) = f((t_1, \ldots, 2t_n)) \qquad \text{for } 0 \le t_n \le 1/2,$$

and

$$p((t_1, \ldots, t_n)) = g((t_1, \ldots, 2t_n - 1)) \quad \text{for } 1/2 \le t_n \le 1.$$

Therefore $\psi(p) = p^*$ is defined as follows. $p^*((t_1, \ldots, t_{n-1})) = p_{(t_1, \ldots, t_{n-1})}$.

$$p_{(t_1, \ldots, t_{n-1})}(s) = p((s, t_1, \ldots, t_{n-1})) = f((s, t_1, \ldots, 2t_{n-1})) \text{ for } 0 \le t_{n-1} \le 1/2$$

and

$$p((s, t_1, \ldots, t_{n-1})) = g((s, t_1, \ldots, 2t_{n-1} - 1)) \text{ for } \tfrac{1}{2} \le t_{n-1} \le 1.$$

Now consider $f^* \cdot g^*((t_1, \ldots, t_{n-1}))$.

$$f^* \cdot g^*((t_1, \ldots, t_{n-1})) = f'^*((t_1, \ldots, 2t_{n-1})) = f_{(t_1, \ldots, 2t_{n-1})} \text{ for } 0 \le t_{n-1} \le \tfrac{1}{2}$$

and

$$f^* \cdot g^*((t_1, \ldots, t_{n-1})) = g^*((t_1, \ldots, 2t_{n-1} - 1)) = g_{(t_1, \ldots, 2t_{n-1})}$$

for

$$\tfrac{1}{2} \le t_n - 1 \le 1.$$

So $p^* = f^* \cdot g^*$ and $\tilde{\psi}$ is a homomorphism. ∎

36.27 Corollary. *Let Y be any space and y_0 a point in Y. $\pi_n(Y, y_0)$ is isomorphic to $\pi_1(\Lambda(\cdots(\Lambda(\Lambda(Y, y_0), \tilde{y}_0), \tilde{y}_0^{(2)})\cdots), \tilde{y}_0^{(n-1)})$, where $\tilde{y}_0^{(i)}$ is the function $\{y_0\}^{I \cdots I\} i \text{ times}}$.*

Induced Homomorphisms and Invariance

By the last corollary and corollary 36.11, it follows that the higher homotopy groups depend on a pair (Y, y_0) rather than a space Y, even in the case that Y is pathwise connected. For, the fundamental group depends essentially on a base point, unless the space Y is pathwise connected. However, even if Y is pathwise connected, $\Lambda(Y, y_0)$ is not pathwise connected except in the case that Y is a simply connected space. Thus an n-dimensional homotopy group is assigned to a pair (Y, y_0).

NOTATION: $f:(X, x_0) \to (Y, y_0)$ will denote a function f from X into Y such that $f(x_0) = y_0$. f will be called a function from the pair (X, x_0) into the pair (Y, y_0).

36.28 Theorem. *Let (X, x_0) and (Y, y_0) be pairs; let f be continuous from (X, x_0) into (Y, y_0). Then f induces a homomorphism f_* from $\pi_n(X, x_0)$ into $\pi_n(Y, y_0)$, for $n = 1, 2, \ldots$, defined by $f_*([\alpha]) = [f \circ \alpha]$ where $[\alpha] \in \pi_n(X, x_0)$.*

Proof: Since α is an n-dimensional hyperloop based at x_0 in X, $f \circ \alpha$ is an n-dimensional hyperloop based at $y_0 = f(x_0)$ in Y. Further, if $[\alpha] = [\beta]$, then α is homotopic to β relative to ∂I^n. Let H be a homotopy from α to β. $f \circ H$ is then a homotopy from $f \circ \alpha$ to $f \circ \beta$, and f_* is single-valued. Next consider $f_*([\alpha] \circledast [\gamma])$. $f_*([\alpha] \circledast [\gamma]) = f_*([\alpha * \gamma]) = [f \circ (\alpha * \gamma)]$. By definition of $\alpha * \gamma$ $f \circ (\alpha * \gamma) = (f \circ \alpha) * (f \circ \gamma)$. However, $[(f \circ \alpha) * (f \circ \gamma)] = [f \circ \alpha] \circledast [f \circ \gamma] =$, $f_*([\alpha]) \circledast f_*([\gamma])$ and f_* is a homomorphism. ∎

36.29 Theorem. *If i is the identity homeomorphism from (X, x_0) onto (X, x_0), then i_* from $\pi_n(X, x_0)$ into $\pi_n(X, x_0)$, for $n = 1, 2, \ldots$, is the identity isomorphism.*

Proof: Exercise.

36.30 Theorem. *Let f be a continuous function from the pair (X, x_0) into the pair (Y, y_0) and let g be a continuous function from the pair (Y, y_0) into the pair (Z, z_0). Then the induced homomorphisms on the homotopy groups satisfy $(g \circ f)_* = g_* \circ f_*$ for $n = 1, 2, \ldots$.*

Proof: Let $[\alpha]$ be in $\pi_n(X, x_0)$, then

$$g_* \circ f_*([\alpha]) = g_*([f \circ \alpha]) = [g \circ (f \circ \alpha)] = [(g \circ f) \circ \alpha] = (g \circ f)_*([\alpha]). \ ∎$$

36.31 Theorem. *If f and g are homotopic from (X, x_0) into (Y, y_0) relative to $\{x_0\}$ in X, then the induced homomorphisms f_* and g_* are equal.*

Proof: Let $[\alpha]$ be an element of $\pi_n(X, x_0)$. Since α is an n-dimensional hyperloop based at x_0, $g \circ \alpha$ and $f \circ \alpha$ are n-dimensional hyperloops based at

y_0 in Y. Further, let H be a homotopy from f to g relative to $\{x_0\}$; let $\tilde{H}(((t_1, \ldots, t_n), s)) = \alpha((t_1, \ldots, t_n))$. Then $H \circ \tilde{H}$ is a homotopy from $f \circ \alpha$ to $g \circ \alpha$ relative to ∂I^n. Hence $f_*([\alpha]) = [f \circ \alpha] = [g \circ \alpha] = g_*([\alpha])$ and $f_* = g_*$. ∎

36.32 Theorem. *If (X, x_0) and (Y, y_0) are homotopically equivalent, then $\pi_n(X, x_0)$ is isomorphic to $\pi_n(Y, y_0)$ for $n = 1, 2, \ldots$.*

Proof: Let f be a homotopy equivalence from (X, x_0) into (Y, y_0) and let g be a homotopy equivalence from (Y, y_0) into (X, x_0) such that $f \circ g$ is homotopic relative to $\{y_0\}$ to i_Y and $g \circ f$ is homotopic relative to $\{x_0\}$ to i_X. Then since $(i_X)_*$ is the identity isomorphism, $(g \circ f)_*$ is also. By theorem 36.30, $(g \circ f)_* = g_* \circ f_*$ and so $g_* \circ f_*$ is the identity isomorphism. Similarly $f_* \circ g_*$ is the identity isomorphism. Hence f_* is an isomorphism from $\pi_n(X, x_0)$ onto $\pi_n(Y, y_0)$. ∎

H-SPACES AND COMMUTATIVITY

The operation $*$ in $\Lambda(Y, y_0)$, the space of loops based at y_0 in Y with the compact-open topology, is continuous and puts a "weak" algebraic structure on the space. This combination of algebra and topology is called a Hopf space or an H-space. The properties of such a structure will establish commutativity for all higher homotopy groups, i.e., for $n > 1$, and will close the chapter and the book.

36.33 Definition. A pair $\{Z, \cdot\}$ is called a *Hopf space* or and *H-space* if and only if (1) Z is a space and $\cdot$ is a continuous function from $Z \times Z$ into Z; (2) there is an element z_0 in Z such that $z_0 \cdot z_0 = z_0$; and (3) λz_0 and ρz_0 are both homotopic relative to $\{z_0\}$ to the identity function i_z on Z, where $\lambda_{z_0}(z) = z_0 \cdot z$ and $\rho_{z_0}(z) = z \cdot z_0$. z_0 is called a *homotopy unit*.

36.34 Theorem. *If Y is any space, the pair $\{\Lambda(Y, y_0), *\}$ consisting of the space of loops based at y_0 in Y with the compact-open topology and the usual path composition (definition 35.1) is an H-space.*

Proof: Let $m((f, g)) = f * g$. Let $G(K, U)$ be a subbasic open set in $\Lambda(Y, y_0)$ which contains $f * g$. K is then a compact subset of I and U is open in Y and $f * g[K] \subseteq U$. $f * g$ is defined one way on $[0, 1/2]$ and another way on $[1/2, 1]$. So consider $K_0 = K \cap [0, 1/2]$ and $K_1 = K \cap [1/2, 1]$. K_0 and K_1 are compact subsets of I. For k in K_0, $f * g(k) = f(2k)$ and for k in K_1, $f * g(k) = g(2k - 1)$. So let $M_0 = \{t \mid t = 2k \text{ for } k \text{ in } K_0\}$ and let $M_1 = \{t \mid t = 2k - 1 \text{ for } k \text{ in } K_1\}$. Then if m is in $G(M_0, U)$ and n is in $G(M_1, U)$, (m, n) is in $G(M_0, U) \times G(M_1, U)$ and $m * n$ is in $G(K, U)$. Thus $*$ is continuous. Now consider the constant loop $\tilde{y}_0$ based at y_0. $\tilde{y}_0 * \tilde{y}_0 = y_0$. Further, $L_{\tilde{y}_0}(f) = \tilde{y}_0 * f$ and $R_{\tilde{y}_0}(f) = f * \tilde{y}_0$, by theorem 35.5 part C, are homotopic relative to $\{y_0\}$ to f. The homotopies, involved in theorem 35.5, are illustrated in figure 32 and lead to the desired homotopies between $L_{\tilde{y}_0}$ and the identity on $\Lambda(Y, y_0)$ and between $R_{\tilde{y}_0}$ and the identity on $\Lambda(Y, y_0)$. First, the fact that the following spaces are homeomorphic will be used: $I \times (\Lambda(Y, y_0) \times I)$; $I \times \Lambda(Y, y_0) \times I$, and $(I \times I) \times \Lambda(Y, y_0)$. Then if $F_1((s, (f, t))) = (s, f, t)$ and $F_2((s, f, t)) = ((s, t), f)$, then $F_2 \circ F_1$ is a homeomorphism from $I \times (\Lambda(Y, y_0) \times I)$ onto $(I \times I) \times \Lambda(Y, y_0)$. Now if

$$G_1(((s, t), f)) = \left(\frac{2s}{1 + t}, f\right),$$

then, by theorem 11.19, G_1 is continuous. Hence $G_1 \circ F_2 \circ F_1$ from $I \times (\Lambda(Y, y_0) \times I)$ into $I \times \Lambda(Y, y_0)$ is continuous. Now the evaluation function

$$\varepsilon\left(\left(\frac{2s}{1 + t}, f\right)\right) = f\left(\frac{2s}{1 + t}\right)$$

is continuous by theorem 31.38. Hence, if

$$\Phi((s, (f, t))) = \varepsilon \circ G_1 \circ F_2 \circ F_1((s, (f, t))) = f\left(\frac{2s}{1 + t}\right) \quad \text{for } 0 \leq s \leq \frac{t + 1}{2}$$

and if

$$\Phi((s, (f, t))) = y_0 \quad \text{for } \frac{t + 1}{2} \leq s \leq 1,$$

then Φ, by theorem 9.23, is continuous from $I \times (\Lambda(Y, y_0) \times I)$ into Y. This means, by theorem 36.2, that the function Φ^* from $\Lambda(Y, y_0) \times I$ into $\Lambda(Y, y_0)$ defined by $\Phi^*((f, t)) = \Phi_{(f,t)}$, where $\Phi_{(f,t)}(s) = \Phi((s, (f, t)))$ is continuous. Φ^* is then a homotopy from $\Lambda(Y, y_0) \times I$ into $\Lambda(Y, y_0)$. Further, if $t = 0$, $\Phi^*((f, 0)) = \Phi_{(f,0)}$ and $\Phi_{(f,0)}(s) = f(2s/(1 + 0)) = f(2s)$ for $0 \leq s \leq 1/2$ and $\Phi_{(f,0)}(s) = y_0$ for $1/2 \leq s \leq 1$. Hence $\Phi^*((f, 0)) = R_{\tilde{y}_0}(f)$. Also, for $t = 1$, $\Phi^*((f, 1)) = \Phi_{(f,1)}$ and $\Phi_{(f,1)}(s) = \Phi((s, (f, 1))) = f(2s/2) = f(s)$. Hence, $\Phi^*((f, 1)) = f$ for all f in $\Lambda(Y, y_0)$. Now let f be the constant loop $\tilde{y}_0$. $\Phi_{(\tilde{y}_0,t)}(s) = \tilde{y}_0$ for all s. Hence, Φ^* is a homotopy from $R_{\tilde{y}_0}$ to the identity function on $\Lambda(Y, y_0)$ relative to $\tilde{y}_0$. Similarly, by using

$$G_2((s, t), f) = \left(\frac{2s - t}{2 - t}, f\right)$$

instead of G_1, the function

$$\psi((s, (f, t))) = f\left(\frac{2s - t}{2 - t}\right),$$

from the homotopy in figure 32 from f to $\lambda_{\tilde{y}_0} * f$, is continuous from $I \times (\Lambda(Y, y_0) \times I)$ into Y. Hence, again by theorem 36.2, the function ψ^* from $\Lambda(Y, y_0) \times I$ into $\Lambda(Y, y_0)$ defined by $\psi^*((f, t)) = \psi_{(f,t)}$, where $\psi_{(f,t)}(s) = \psi((s, (f, t)))$ is continuous. ψ^* is then a homotopy from $\Lambda(Y, y_0) \times I$ into $\Lambda(Y, y_0)$. The details are similar to those for Φ^*, above, and are omitted. ▌

The next several lemmas and theorem will establish that if $\{Z, \cdot\}$ is an H-space with homotopy unit z_0, then $\pi_1(Z, z_0)$ is abelian.

36.35 Lemma. *If $\{Z, \cdot\}$ is an H-space with z_0 as homotopy unit, then for loops f and g based at z_0 in Z, h, defined by $h(s) = f(s) \cdot g(s)$, is also a loop based at z_0 in Z. h will be denoted by $f \# g$.*

Proof: In order to show that $f \# g$ is a loop based at z_0 in Z the function $s \to f(s) \cdot g(s)$ will be exhibited as a composite of continuous functions. Consider $s \xrightarrow{F_1} (f, g, s) \xrightarrow{F_2} (f(s), g(s)) \xrightarrow{F_3} f(s) \cdot g(s)$, i.e., $F_3 \circ F_2 \circ F_1$. F_1 is continuous by theorem 11.19. Consider $(f, g, s) \xrightarrow{G_0} ((f, s), g) \xrightarrow{G_1} (f, s) \xrightarrow{\mathcal{E}} f(s)$. G_0 is a homeomorphism, G_1 is a projection function, and $\mathcal{E}$ is an evaluation function which is continuous by theorem 31.38. Similarly, $(f, g, s) \to (f, (g, s)) \to (g, s) \to g(s)$ is continuous. Hence $F_2 \circ F_1$ is continuous by theorem 11.19. F_3 is continuous by the definition of an H-space. Thus $s \to f(s) \cdot g(s)$ is continuous and $f \# g$ is a path. Since $f(0) = g(0) = f(1) = g(1) = z_0, f \# g$ is a loop based at z_0 in Z. ∎

36.36 Lemma. *Let $\{Z, \cdot\}$ again be an H-space with homotopy unit z_0. Let $f_\rho(t) = f(t) \cdot z_0$ and let $f_\lambda(t) = z_0 \cdot f(t)$, where f is a loop based at z_0 in Z. Now if $R(f) = f_\rho$ and $L(f) = f_\lambda$, then R and L are functions from $\Lambda(Z, z_0)$ into $\Lambda(Z, z_0)$ which are homotopic to the identity, i_Λ, on $\Lambda(Z, z_0)$.*

Proof: By definition of an H-space, there exist homotopies ϕ and ψ from $Z \times I$ into Z such that $\phi((z, 0)) = z$, $\phi((z, 1)) = z \cdot z_0$ and $\phi((z_0, t)) = z_0$ for $0 \leq t \leq 1$; and $\psi((z, 0)) = z$, $\psi((z, 1)) = z_0 \cdot z$, and $\psi((z_0, t)) = z_0$ for $0 \leq t \leq 1$. Now define $H^*: \Lambda(Z, z_0) \times I \to \Lambda(Z, z_0)$ by $H^*((f, t)) = h_{(f,t)}$, where $h_{(f,t)}(s) = \phi(f(s), t)$. Since $H^*((f, 0)) = h_{(f,0)}$ and $\phi((f(s), 0)) = f(s)$, $h_{(f,0)} = f$. Also since $H^*((f, 1)) = h_{(f,1)}$ and $\phi((f(s), 1)) = f(s) \cdot z_0$, $H^*((f, 1)) = R(f)$. Further, if $s = 0$ or $s = 1$, then for any pair (f, t), $H^*((f, t)) = h_{(f,t)}$, where $h_{(f,t)}(s) = \phi(f(s), t) = \phi((z_0, t)) = z_0$. Also, with f and t fixed, $\phi((f(s), t))$ is a composite of $s \xrightarrow{①} (f(s), t) \xrightarrow{②} \phi((f(s), t))$. ① is continuous by theorem 11.19 and ② is just ϕ. Hence $h_{(f,t)}$ is a loop based at z_0 in Z. In addition, if f is the constant loop $\tilde{z}_0$, then $H^*((z_0, t)) = h_{(\tilde{z}_0,t)}$ and, for $0 \leq s \leq 1$, $h_{(\tilde{z}_0,t)}(s) = \phi(\tilde{z}_0(s), t) = \phi((z_0, t)) = z_0$. Thus $H^*((\tilde{z}_0, t))$, for $0 \leq t \leq 1$, is the constant loop $\tilde{z}_0$. Thus if H^* is continuous, then it is a homotopy relative to $\tilde{z}_0$ between the identity function i_Λ on $\Lambda(Z, z_0)$ and the function R on $\Lambda(Z, z_0)$. So consider H^* and apply theorem 36.3 with $X = I$, $Y = \Lambda(Z, z_0)$ and $T = \Lambda(Z, z_0) \times I$. H^* will be continuous, where $H((s, (f, t))) = \phi((f(s), t))$ for $(s, (f, t))$ in $I \times (\Lambda(Z, z_0) \times I)$. Consider, then, the composite function identified by $(s, (f, t)) \xrightarrow{①} (s, f, t) \xrightarrow{②} (f, s, t) \xrightarrow{③} ((f, s), t) \xrightarrow{④} (f, s) \xrightarrow{⑤} f(s)$. Since ①, ② and ③ are homeomorphisms and ④ is a projection function, ④ ∘ ③ ∘ ② ∘ ① is continuous. Since ⑤ is an evaluation function, by theorem 31.38, it is continuous. Hence, ⑤ ∘ ④ ∘ ③ ∘ ② ∘ ① is continuous. Similarly $(s, (f, t)) \to (s, f, t) \to t$ is continuous, and so, by theorem 11.19, $(s, (f, t)) \to (f(s), t)$ is continuous. Since ϕ is continuous, H is then continuous. Again, this implies the continuity of H^* and H^* is the desired homotopy. Analogously, a homotopy H^{**} can be defined from the homotopy ψ, and H^{**} establishes that the identity function i_Λ on $\Lambda(Z, z_0)$ is homotopic relative to $\tilde{z}_0$ to the function L on $\Lambda(Z, z_0)$. ▌

36.37 Lemma. *If $\{Z, \cdot\}$ is an H-space with z_0 as homotopy unit, then the following functions from $\Lambda(Z, z_0) \times \Lambda(Z, z_0)$ into $\Lambda(Z, z_0)$ are homotopic: $(f, g) \to f * g$; $(f, g) \to f \# g$ and $(f, g) \to g * f$.*

Proof: A. First a function from $(\Lambda(Z, z_0) \times \Lambda(Z, z_0)) \times I$ into $\Lambda(Z, z_0)$ is defined. Let $((f, g), t)$ be an element of $(\Lambda(Z, z_0) \times \Lambda(Z, z_0)) \times I$. The following complicated function will show that $(f, g) \to f \# g$ is homotopic to both $(f, g) \to f_\rho * g_\lambda$ and $(f, g) \to g_\lambda * f_\rho$, where $f_\rho(t) = f(t) \cdot z_0$ and $f_\lambda(t) = z_0 \cdot f(t)$. Let $H^*(((f, g), t)) = h_{((f,g),t)}$, where $h_{((f,g),t)}(s) = f(2s(1-t)) \cdot g(2st)$ for $0 \le s \le 1/2$, and $h_{((f,g),t)}(s) = f(1 - 2t(1-s)) \cdot g(2(s + t - st) - 1)$ for $1/2 \le s \le 1$. First, by substitution, it is checked immediately that $h_{((f,g),t)}$ is single-valued at 1/2. Next, $h_{((f,g),t)}(0) = f(0) \cdot g(0) = z_0 = f(1) \cdot g(1) = h_{((f,g),t)}(1)$. Also, since f and g are continuous, $h_{((f,g),t)}$ is continuous. Thus for each $((f, g), t)$, $H^*(((f, g), t))$ is a loop based at z_0 in Z. $H^*: (\Lambda(Z, z_0) \times \Lambda(Z, z_0)) \times I \to \Lambda(Z, z_0)$.

B. H^* is continuous. Consider H from $I \times (\Lambda(Z, z_0) \times \Lambda(Z, z_0) \times I)$ into $\Lambda(Z, z_0)$ defined by $H((t, (f, g, s))) = f(2s(1-t)) \cdot g(2st)$ for $0 \le s \le 1/2$ and $H((t, (f, g, s))) = f(1 - 2t(1-s)) \cdot g(2(s + t - st) - 1)$ for $1/2 \le s \le 1$. Again, by theorem 36.3, with $X = I$, $Y = \Lambda(Z, z_0)$ and $T = \Lambda(Z, z_0) \times \Lambda(Z, z_0) \times I$, H^* will be continuous if H is. H, however, can be obtained as a composite. Consider the composite function defined by $(t, (f, g, s)) \xrightarrow{①} (t, f, g, s) \xrightarrow{②} (f, t, s, g) \xrightarrow{③} ((f, t, s), g) \xrightarrow{④} (f, t, s) \xrightarrow{⑤} (f, (t, s)) \xrightarrow{⑥} (f, 2s(1-t)) \xrightarrow{⑦} f(2s(1-t))$. ①, ② and ③ are homeomorphisms; ④ is a projection function; ⑤ is a homeomorphism; ⑥ is continuous by theorem 11.19, since $(s, t) \to 2s(1-t)$ is continuous; and further, for $0 \le s \le 1/2$, $0 \le 2s(1-t) \le 1$. ⑦ is an evaluation function which by theorem 31.38 is continuous. Thus ⑦ ∘ ⑥ ∘ ⑤ ∘ ④ ∘ ③ ∘ ② ∘ ① is continuous. Similarly, the composite $(t, (f, g, s)) \to (t, f, g, s) \to ((g, t, s), f) \to (g, t, s) \to (g, 2st) \to g(2st)$ is continuous. Hence, the function $(t, (f, g, s)) \to (f(2s(1-t)), g(2st))$ is continuous, again by theorem 11.19. Now, since the function $\cdot$ is continuous from $Z \times Z$ into Z, the composite $(t, (f, g, s)) \to (f(2s(1-t)), g(2st)) \to f(2s(1-\mathrm{t})) \cdot g(2\mathrm{st})$ for $0 \le s \le 1/2$ is continuous. An exactly analogous procedure establishes that $(t, (f, g, s)) \to f(1 - 2t(1-s)) \cdot g(2(s + t - st) - 1)$, for $1/2 \le s \le 1$ is continuous. Hence, H is continuous by theorem 9.23, and so H^* is continuous.

C. H^* is a homotopy between $(f, g) \to f_\rho * g_\lambda$ and $(f, g) \to g_\lambda * f_\rho$. For let $t = 0$. $H^*(((f, g), 0)) = h_{((f,g),0)}$ and $h_{((f,g),0)}(s) = f(2s) \cdot g(0) = f_\rho(2s)$ for $0 \le s \le 1/2$, and $h_{((f,g),0)}(s) = f(1) \cdot g(2s - 1) = g_\lambda(2s - 1)$ for $1/2 \le s \le 1$. Hence, $H^*(((f, g), 0)) = f_\rho * g_\lambda$. Next consider $H^*(((f, g), 1))$. $h_{((f,g),1)}(s) = f(0) \cdot g(2s) = g_\lambda(2s)$ for $0 \le s \le 1/2$, and $h_{((f,g),1)}(s) = f(2s - 1) \cdot g(1) = f_\rho(2s - 1)$ for $1/2 \le s \le 1$. Thus $H^*(((f, g), 1)) = g_\lambda * f_\rho$ and the functions $(f, g) \to f_\rho * g_\lambda$ and $(f, g) \to g_\lambda * f_\rho$ are homotopic.

D. H^* also yields homotopies between $(f, g) \to f_\rho * g_\lambda$ and $(f, g) \to f \# g$, and between $(f, g) \to f \# g$ and $(f, g) \to g_\lambda * f_\rho$. For, consider $H^*(((f, g), 1/2))$. $h_{((f,g),1/2)}(s) = f(s) \cdot g(s)$ for $0 \le s \le 1/2$, and $h_{((f,g),1/2)}(s) = f(s) \cdot g(s)$ for $1/2 \le s \le 1$. Thus $H^*(((f, g), 1/2)) = f \# g$. This means that $(f, g) \to f \# g$ is homotopic to $(f, g) \to f_\rho * g_\lambda$ and to $(f, g) \to g_\lambda * f_\rho$, i.e., if $\tilde{H}(((f, g), t)) = ((f, g), 1/2t)$, then $H^* \circ \tilde{H}$ is a homotopy between $(f, g) \to f_\rho * g_\lambda$ and $(f, g) \to f \# g$, and if

$$\tilde{\tilde{H}}(((f, g), t)) = \left((f, g), \frac{t+1}{2}\right),$$

then $H^* \circ \tilde{\tilde{H}}$ is a homotopy between $(f, g) \to f \# g$ and $(f, g) \to g_\lambda * f_\rho$.

E. Lastly, $(f, g) \to f * g$ is homotopic to $(f, g) \to g_\lambda * f_\rho$. For, by the previous lemma (36.36), there exists a homotopy Φ between the identity function i_Λ on $\Lambda(Z, z_0)$ and the function R where $R(f) = f_\rho$, and there exists a homotopy Ψ between the identity function i_Λ and the function L where $L(f) = f_\lambda$. $\Phi : \Lambda(Z, z_0) \times I \to \Lambda(Z, z_0)$ and $\Psi : \Lambda(Z, z_0) \times I \to \Lambda(Z, z_0)$. Also, $\Phi((f, 0)) = f$, $\Phi((f, 1)) = f_\rho$, $\Psi((f, 0)) = f$ and $\Psi((f, 1)) = f_\lambda$. On the basis of these homotopies define $H(((f, g), t)) = \Phi((f, t)) * \Psi((g, t))$. H can be represented as a composite as follows. Consider $((f, g), t) \xrightarrow{①} (f, g, t) \xrightarrow{②} ((f, t), g) \xrightarrow{③} (f, t) \xrightarrow{④} \Phi((f, t))$ and $((f, g), t) \xrightarrow{①'} (f, g, t) \xrightarrow{②'} ((g, t), f) \xrightarrow{③'} (g, t) \xrightarrow{④'} \Psi((g, t))$. ①, ②, ①′ and ②′ are homeomorphisms; ③ and ③′ are projection functions, and ④ and ④′ are Φ and Ψ, respectively. Thus, by theorem 11.19, $((f, g), t) \to (\Phi((f, t)), \Psi((g, t)))$ is continuous. Lastly, since the function $*$ is continuous, by theorem 36.2, the composite $((f, g), t) \to (\Phi((f, t)), \Phi((g, t))) \to \Phi((f, t)) * \Psi((g, t))$ is continuous. Thus H is continuous. In an exactly analogous manner, it can be shown that H' is continuous, where $H'(((f, g), t)) = \Psi((g, t)) * \Phi((f, t))$. $H((f, g), 0) = \Phi((f, 0)) * \Psi((g, 0)) = f * g$; $H((f, g), 1) = \Phi((f, 1)) * \Psi((g, 1)) = f_\rho * g_\lambda$. Similarly, H' is a homotopy between $(f, g) \to g * f$ and $(f, g) \to g_\lambda * f_\rho$. Now, it was previously shown in part C, above, that $(f, g) \to f_\rho * g_\lambda$ and $(f, g) \to g_\lambda * f_\rho$ are homotopic. Hence, it follows, by the transitivity of the homotopy relation, that $(f, g) \to f * g$ and $(f, g) \to g * f$ are homotopic. Also, by part D, both of these functions are homotopic to $(f, g) \to f \# g$. ▌

36.38 Theorem. *Let $\{Z, \cdot\}$ be an H-space with homotopy unit z_0. Further, let $[f]$ and $[g]$ be elements in $\pi_1(Z, z_0)$. Then $[f] * [g] = [g] * [f]$.*

Proof: The composite function, defined by the following, yields a homotopy between the loops $f * g$ and $f_\rho * g_\lambda$. Consider $(s, t) \xrightarrow{①} ((f, g), t, s) \xrightarrow{②} (((f, g), t), s) \xrightarrow{③} (H(((f, g), t)), s) \xrightarrow{④} H(((f, g), t))(s)$, where H is the homotopy established in the previous theorem between $(f, g) \to f * g$ and $(f, g) \to f_\rho * g_\lambda$. ① and ② are homeomorphisms; ③ is continuous by theorem 11.19; and ④ is an evaluation function, and, by theorem 31.38, is continuous. Thus if $h((s, t)) = H(((f, g), t))(s)$, h is a homotopy. Now, consider $h((s, 0))$. $h((s, 0)) = H(((f, g), 0))(s) = f * g(s)$. Also, $h((s, 1)) = H(((f, g), 1))(s) = f_\rho * g_\lambda(s)$.

Thus $f * g$ is homotopic to $f_\rho * g_\lambda$. In an exactly analogous manner from the homotopies of the previous theorem, $f_\rho * g_\lambda$ can be shown to be homotopic to $g_\lambda * f_\rho$, and $g_\lambda * f_\rho$ in turn can be shown to be homotopic to $g * f$. By transitivity, then, $f * g$ is homotopic to $g * f$. In addition, if $s = 0$, then $h((0, t)) = H(((f, g), t))(0) = \Phi((f, t)) * \Psi((g, t))(0)$. Since Φ and Ψ are functions from $\Lambda(Z, z_0) \times I$ into $\Lambda(Z, z_0)$, $\Phi((f, t))$ and $\Psi((g, t))$, for $0 \leq t \leq 1$, are loops based at z_0 in Z. Hence $\Phi((f, t)) * \Psi((g, t))(0) = z_0 = \Phi((f, t)) * \Psi((g, t))(1)$. Thus $h((0, t)) = z_0 = h((1, t))$ for $0 \leq t \leq 1$, and so the homotopy h is a homotopy relative to $\{0, 1\}$. The reasoning is similar for the other homotopies from $f_\rho * g_\lambda$ to $g_\lambda * f_\rho$, and from $g_\lambda * f_\rho$ to $g * f$. Thus $[f * g] = [g * f]$ or $[f] \circledast [g] = [g] \circledast [f]$, and so $\pi_1(Z, z_0)$ is abelian. ▮

36.39 Theorem. *For any pair* $\{Y, y_0\}$, $\pi_n(Y, y_0)$ *is abelian for* $n > 1$.

Proof: By corollary 36.27, $\pi_n(Y, y_0)$ is isomorphic to

$$\pi_1(\Lambda(\Lambda(\ldots \Lambda(\Lambda(Y, y_0), \tilde{y}_0), \ldots), \tilde{y}_0^{(n-1)})).$$

Hence, if $n > 1$, $\pi_n(Y, y_0)$ is isomorphic to the fundamental group of a space of loops based at some fixed point. Hence, by theorem 36.34, for $n > 1$, $\pi_n(Y, y_0)$ is isomorphic to the fundamental group of an H-space. By the previous theorem, $\pi_n(Y, y_0)$, for $n > 1$, must then be abelian. ▮

Algebraic invariants, concepts, and structures permeate almost all parts of modern topology. It is hoped that this introduction to homotopy from the basic concepts through to the definition and basic facts about the homotopy groups, along with the introduction to the ring $\{C(X), \boxplus, \boxtimes\}$ in sections 18 and 30, will serve as a sort of bridge between the non-algebraic, "internal" topology, i.e., connectedness, compactness, separability, first and second countability, etc., and the algebraic, "external" topology concerned with algebraic structures which are "attached" to the space "from the outside" in a certain sense.

SUMMARY FOR CHAPTER 7

A homotopy, H, is a continuous function from a product space $X \times I$, where I is the unit interval space, into a space Y. Homotopies determine an equivalence relation on the set $C(X, Y)$ of continuous functions from X into Y. f is homotopically equivalent to g in $C(X, Y)$ if and only if there exists a homotopy, H, from $X \times I$ into Y such that $H((x, 0)) = f(x)$ and $H((x, 1)) = g(x)$ for all x in X. A space X is contractible if and only if homotopies determine one equivalence class, namely, $C(X, X)$, on $C(X, X)$—then any function in $C(X, X)$ is homotopically equivalent to any other. Such spaces are pathwise connected. The existence of homotopies between functions is related to the existence of continuous extensions of functions defined on closed subsets. Under certain circumstances, a function, f, defined on a closed subset A of a metrizable space

X has a continuous extension to all of X if and only if every function which is homotopically equivalent to f on A has a continuous extension to all of X.

In addition to the homotopy equivalence for functions, there is a homotopy equivalence for spaces which is "slightly" weaker than the topological equivalence for spaces. Two spaces X and Y are topologically equivalent if and only if there exist continuous functions $f: X \to Y$ and $g: Y \to X$ such that $g \circ f = i_X$, the identity function on X, and $f \circ g = i_Y$, the identity function on Y. It is a generalization of this definition which leads to homotopically equivalent spaces. Two spaces X and Y are homotopically equivalent or of the same homotopy type if and only if there exist continuous functions $f: X \to Y$ and $g: Y \to X$ such that $g \circ f$ is homotopic to i_X and $f \circ g$ is homotopic to i_Y. f and g are then called homotopy equivalences between X and Y. Homotopy invariants are properties of spaces which if possessed by a space X must be possessed by all spaces Y which are homotopically equivalent to X. For pathwise connected spaces, the fundamental group is an algebraic homotopy invariant in the sense that homotopically equivalent spaces have isomorphic fundamental groups. Simply connected spaces are pathwise connected spaces with trivial (i.e., one element) fundamental groups. Euclidean n-space, E^n, for $n = 1, 2, \ldots$ is simply connected; S^1, the circumference of the unit circle, as a space, is not simply connected. This fact leads to the result that S^1 is not a retract of the 2-cell B_2—the subspace $\{(x, y) \mid x^2 + y^2 \leq 1\}$ of E^2—and to the result that every continuous function from B_2 into itself has a fixed point (Brouwer fixed point theorem).

The set of loops in a space Y based at y_0 with the compact-open topology yields a space $\Lambda(Y, y_0)$ which is related to the fundamental group $\pi_1(Y, y_0)$. The path components of $\Lambda(Y, y_0)$ are the elements of $\pi_1(Y, y_0)$. A generalization of this fact states that the path components of the space $\{C(X, Y), \mathfrak{I}_{c\text{-}o}\}$ are exactly the homotopy equivalence classes in $C(X, Y)$ whenever X is first countable or X is locally compact and Hausdorff.

The higher homotopy group $\pi_n(Y, y_0)$, for $n > 1$, is a generalization of the fundamental group $\pi_1(Y, y_0)$ with I replaced by the product I^n. Reduction formulas reduce the higher homotopy group $\pi_n(Y, y_0)$ to a fundamental group of a space of loops. The combined topological-algebraic structure on the space $\Lambda(Y, y_0)$ is called a Hopf structure (or H-structure) and such spaces are called Hopf spaces (or H-spaces). The fundamental group $\pi_1(Z, z_0)$ of any H-space Z with homotopy unit z_0 is abelian; hence the fundamental group $\pi_1(\Lambda(Y, y_0), \tilde{y}_0)$, where $\tilde{y}_0$ is the constant loop $f(t) = y_0$ for $0 \leq t \leq 1$, is abelian. Since $\pi_n(Y, y_0)$, for $n > 1$, is isomorphic to a fundamental group of a space of paths, $\pi_n(Y, y_0)$, for $n > 1$, is abelian.

Notations and Conventions

For the most part the terminology and notation are standard.

1. $\{p, q, r\}$: Braces denote a *set*. Between the braces are listed or denoted the elements of the set.

2. $\{x \mid Q(x)\}$: The *classifier* from set theory is used in the usual way, e.g., $\{x \mid x \text{ is real and } 0 \leq x \leq 1\}$ denotes the set of all real numbers between 0 and 1.

3. $x \in A$: A is a set and x is an element of A. A is said to "contain" x, if $x \in A$. $x \notin A$ means x is not in A.

4. $(\exists x)$ and $(\forall x)$: The usual *quantifiers* from set theory, "there exists x" and "for every x," respectively.

5. $\subseteq$: $A \subseteq B$ means A and B are sets and $(\forall x)(x \in A$ implies $x \in B)$. A is called a *subset* of B if and only if $A \subseteq B$ is true. $A \not\subseteq B$ means A is not a subset of B. If $A \subseteq B$, B is said to contain A. Thus "contain" is used ambiguously. $A \subsetneq B$ means $A \subseteq B$ and $A \neq B$. If $A \subsetneq B$, A is called a *proper subset* of B.

6. $\emptyset$: The *null set*, $\{x \mid x \neq x\}$. It follows that $(\forall A)$ (A a set $\Rightarrow \emptyset \subseteq A$).

7. $\bigcup \mathcal{B}$ and $\bigcap \mathcal{B}$: $\mathcal{B}$ is a set of subsets of a set X.

$$\bigcup \mathcal{B} = \{x \mid (\exists A)\,(A \in \mathcal{B} \text{ and } x \in A)\}$$

and

$$\bigcap \mathcal{B} = \{x \mid (\forall A)\,(A \in \mathcal{B} \text{ implies } x \in A)\}.$$

$\bigcup \mathcal{B}$ is called the *union* of the sets in $\mathcal{B}$ and $\bigcap \mathcal{B}$ is called the *intersection* of the sets in $\mathcal{B}$.

8. $X \sim A$ or $\sim A$: The *complement* of A, where $A \subseteq X$, and $X \sim A = \sim A = \{x \mid x \in X \text{ and } x \notin A\}$. It follows that $\sim(\sim A) = A$.

9. $P(X)$: The *power set* of a set X is $\{A \mid A \subseteq X\}$.

10. (x, y): An *ordered pair*, $\{x, \{x, y\}\}$.

11. Relations and functions: A *relation*, f, is a set of ordered pairs; a *function*, f, is a relation with the additional property that if (a, b) and (a, d) are both in f, then $b = d$. If, also, (a, b) and (c, b) being in the function f implies that $a = c$, f is called *1:1* (one-to-one) or a 1:1 correspondence or an injection or injective. If (a, b) is in f, b is called an *image* of a and a is called a *pre-image* of b. If f is a function, b is called *the image* of a assigned by f and is denoted by $f(a)$. If f is 1:1, a is called *the pre-image* of b and is denoted by $f^{-1}(a)$. The *domain* of a relation f is

$$\{x \mid (\exists y)\ ((x, y) \in f)\};$$

the *range* of a relation f is

$$\{y \mid (\exists x)\ ((x, y) \in f)\}.$$

The range is the set of images. If A is a subset of the domain of f, then

$$f[A] = \{y \mid (\exists a)\ (a \in A \text{ and } (a, y) \in f)\}.$$

If B is a subset of the range of f, then

$$f^{-1}[B] = \{x \mid (\exists b)\ (b \in B \text{ and } (x, b) \in f)\}.$$

Thus the symbol $f(\ )$ is used only for functions and is completed by a symbol denoting an element of the domain of f; e.g., if the ordered pair (α, β) is in the domain of f, $f((\alpha, \beta))$ denotes its image. The symbol $f[\ ]$ is completed by a symbol denoting a subset of the domain of f and may be used for any relation f. The verb "to map" is used with respect to a function f. f is said to *map* its domain *onto* its range or to *map* its domain *into* a set which contains its range. f is said to be surjective with respect to its range. The symbol $f: X \to Y$ is also used to indicate that f is a function, X is its domain and Y contains, as a subset, its range.

12. Indexing set: The domain of a function is sometimes called an indexing set.

13. $(x_1, x_2, \ldots, x_n)$: An *ordered n-tuple*.

14. $\bigcup_{\alpha \in \mathfrak{A}} A_\alpha$ and $\bigcap_{\alpha \in \mathfrak{A}} A_\alpha$: $\mathfrak{A}$ is an indexing set, A_α is a set and A_α is the image of α. $\bigcup_{\alpha \in \mathfrak{A}} A_\alpha = \bigcup \mathfrak{B}$ and $\bigcap_{\alpha \in \mathfrak{A}} A_\alpha = \bigcap \mathfrak{B}$, where $\mathfrak{B}$ is the range of the indexing function with domain $\mathfrak{A}$.

15. $g \circ f$: *Composition* of relations. $g \circ f = \{(x, z) \mid (\exists y)\ ((x, y) \in f \text{ and } (y, z) \in g)\}$. $g \circ f$ is always a relation but it may be the null set (relation).

16. $A \times B$: The *cross product* or *Cartesian product* of sets A and B is $\{(a, b) \mid a \in A \text{ and } b \in B\}$.

17. E^n: *Euclidean n-space*.

18. (a, b): This symbol is used ambiguously for the ordered pair, as stated above, and for $\{x \mid a < x < b\} \subseteq E^1$.

19. $[a, b]$: The subset of E^1 consisting of $\{x \mid a \leq x \leq b\}$.

20. Equivalence Relation: An *equivalence relation*, Q, on a set S is a subset of $S \times S$ satisfying (1) $s \in S$ implies $(s, s) \in Q$, (2) $(s, t) \in Q$ implies $(t, s) \in Q$, and (3) $(s, t) \in Q$ and $(t, r) \in Q$ imply $(s, r) \in Q$. $(s, t) \in Q$ is sometimes written sQt.

21. Equivalence Classes: Any equivalence relation, Q, on a set S determines subsets of S, called *equivalence classes*. Let $s \in S$ and let $C_s = \{t \mid (s, t) \in Q\}$. C_s is called the equivalence class containing s and is exactly the set of images of s assigned by Q. It can easily be shown that (1) $\bigcup_{s \in S} C_s = S$, and (2) for s and t in S, $C_s = C_t$ or $C_s \cap C_t = \emptyset$.

22. De Morgan's Laws: Let $A \subseteq S$ and $B \subseteq S$. Then (1) $\sim(A \cup B) = \sim A \cap \sim B$ and (2) $\sim(A \cap B) = \sim A \cup \sim B$. These laws are generalized to any union and intersection. $\sim \bigcup_{\alpha \in \mathfrak{A}} A_\alpha = \bigcap_{\alpha \in \mathfrak{A}} \sim A_\alpha$ and $\sim \bigcap_{\alpha \in \mathfrak{A}} A_\alpha = \bigcup_{\alpha \in \mathfrak{A}} \sim A_\alpha$, where $A_\alpha \subseteq S$ for every α. $\bigcup_{\alpha \in \emptyset} A_\alpha$

is defined to be $\emptyset \subseteq S$. It then follows that $\sim\bigcup_{\alpha\in\emptyset} A_\alpha = S$. Hence, if De Morgan's generalized laws are to apply, $\bigcap_{\alpha\in\emptyset} \sim A_\alpha = S$. Since any set can be considered to be a complement, $(A = \sim(\sim A))$, it follows that $\bigcap_{\alpha\in\emptyset} B_\alpha = S$ for $B_\alpha \subseteq S$.

23. 2^s: 2^s denotes the set of all functions from the set S into the two-element set $\{0, 1\}$. If $A \subseteq S$ and if Φ_A is the function from S into $\{0, 1\}$ defined by $\Phi_A(s) = 1$ if $s \in A$ and $\Phi_A(s) = 0$ if $s \notin A$, then the correspondence $A \to \Phi_A$ from $P(S)$ into 2^s is 1:1 and onto, i.e., 2^s is the range. The proof is left as an exercise. Because of the above 1:1 correspondence, 2^s is also used to denote $P(S)$ by many authors.

24. Y^X The set of all functions which have X as domain and whose ranges are subsets of Y where X and Y are sets. X is called the *domain* and Y is called the *codomain* for the set.

25. $C(X, Y)$: The set of all continuous functions which have X as domain and whose ranges are subspaces of Y where X and Y are topological spaces. Again X is called the *domain* and Y is called the *codomain* for the set.

Bibliography

ALEXANDROFF, P.

[1] "Combinatorial Topology," vol. I., Rochester, Graylock Press, 1956.

ALEXANDROFF, P. and HOPF, H.

[1] *Topologie*, Berlin, Springer-Verlag, 1935.

APOSTOL, T.

[1] *Mathematical Analysis*, Reading, Mass., Addison-Wesley, 1957.

ARENS, R. and DUGUNDJI, J.

[1] "Topologies for Function Spaces," *Pacific Journal of Math.*, **1** (1951), pp. 5–31.

BING, R. H.

[1] "Extending a Metric," *Duke Math. Journal*, **14** (1947), pp. 511–519.

[2] "Some Characterizations of Arcs and Simple Closed Curves," *American Journal of Math.*, **70** (1948), pp. 497–506.

[3] "Metrization of Topological Spaces," *Canadian Journal of Math.*, **3** (1951), pp. 175–186.

[4] "Summary of Lectures and Seminars of the Summer Institute on Set Theoretic Topology," Madison, Wisconsin, 1957.

BIRKHOFF, G.

[1] *Lattice Theory*, Providence, R.I., A.M.S. Colloquium Publication No. 25, 1948.

BOURBAKI, N.

[1] *Topologie Générale*, 2nd Ed., Chap. 1 and 2, Paris, Hermann et Cie., 1951.

BUCK, R. C.

[1] *Advanced Calculus*, 2nd Ed., New York, McGraw-Hill, 1965.

DIEUDONNÉ, J.

[1] "Un exemple d'Espace Normal Non-Susceptible d'une Structure Uniforme d'Espace Complet," *Comptes Rend. Acad. Sci.*, Paris, **209** (1939), pp. 145–147.

[2] "Sur les Espaces Uniforms Complets," *Ann. Sci. École Norm. Sup.* **56** (1939), pp. 227–291.

[3] "Une Généralisation des Espaces Compacts," *J. Math. Pures et Appl.*, **23** (1944), pp. 65–76.

[4] *Foundations of Modern Analysis*, New York, Academic Press, 1960.

DUGUNDJI, J.

[1] *Topology*, Boston, Allyn and Bacon, 1966.

EILENBERG, S. and STEENROD, N.

[1] *Foundations of Algebraic Topology*, Princeton, Princeton Univ. Press, 1952.

FOX, R. H.

[1] "On Topologies for Function Spaces," *Bull. A.M.S.*, **51** (1945), pp. 429–432.

GILLMAN, L. and JERISON, M.

[1] *Rings of Continuous Functions*, Princeton, Van Nostrand, 1960.

HALL, D. W. and SPENCER, G. L.

[1] *Elementary Topology*, New York, J. Wiley, 1955.

HAUSDORFF, F.

[1] *Set Theory*, 3rd Ed. (Transl.), New York, Chelsea, 1957.

HERRLICH, H.

[1] "Wann sind alle stetigen Abbildungen in *Y* konstant?" *Math. Z.*, **90** (1965), pp. 152–154.

HEWITT, E.

[1] "On Two Problems of Urysohn," *Ann. of Math.* (2), **47** (1946), pp. 503–509.

[2] "Rings of Real-Valued Continuous Functions," *Trans. A.M.S.*, **64** (1948), pp. 45–99.

[3] "The Role of Compactness in Analysis," *American Math. Monthly*, **67** (1960), pp. 499–516.

HILTON, P. J.

[1] *An Introduction to Homotopy Theory*, Cambridge, Cambridge Univ. Press, 1953.

HOCKING, J. G. and YOUNG, G. S.

[1] *Topology*, Reading, Mass., Addison-Wesley, 1961.

HU, S. T.

[1] *Homotopy Theory*, New York, Academic Press, 1959.

[2] "Homotopy and Isotopy Properties of Topological Spaces," *Canadian Journal of Math.*, **13** (1961), pp. 167–176.

[3] *Elements of General Topology*, San Francisco, Holden-Day, 1964.

HUREWICZ, W.

[1] "Über oberhalb-stetige Zerlegungen von Punktmengen in Kontinua," *Fund. Math.*, **15** (1930), pp. 57–60.

HUREWICZ, W. and WALLMAN, H.

[1] *Dimension Theory*, Princeton, Princeton Univ. Press, 1941.

ISBELL, J. R.

[1] *Uniform Spaces*, Providence, R.I., A.M.S., 1964.

JONES, F. B.

[1] "Concerning the Separability of Certain Locally Connected Metric Spaces," *Bull. A.M.S.*, **52** (1946), pp. 303–306.

KAPLAN, W.

[1] *Advanced Calculus*, Reading, Mass., Addison-Wesley, 1952.

KELLEY, J. L.

[1] "Convergence in Topology," *Duke Math. Journal*, **17** (1950), pp. 277–283.

[2] "The Tychonoff Product Theorem Implies the Axiom of Choice," *Fund. Math.* **37** (1950), pp. 75–76.

[3] *General Topology*, Princeton, Van Nostrand, 1955.

KNASTER, B.

[1] "Un Continu dont Tout Sous-Continu est Indécomposable," *Fund. Math.* **3** (1922), p. 247.

KOWALSKI, H. J.

[1] *Topologische Räume*, Birkhäuser Verlag, Basel, 1961.

KURATOWSKI, C.

[1] *Topologie I*, 4th Ed., Warsaw, Panst. Wydaw. Nauk., 1958.

[2] *Topologie II*, 3rd Ed., Warsaw, Panst. Wydaw. Nauk., 1961.

MACLANE, S.

[1] "Algebraic Topology," Univ. of Chicago Lecture Notes, 1951.

[2] "Point Set Topology," Univ. of Chicago Lecture Notes, 1955.

MARCZEWSKI, E.
[1] "Séparabilité et Multiplication Cartésienne des Espaces Topologiques," *Fund. Math.*, **34** (1947), pp. 127–143.

MENDELSON, B.
[1] *Introduction to Topology*, Boston, Allyn and Bacon, 1962.

MICHAEL, E.
[1] "A Note on Paracompact Spaces," *Proc. A.M.S.*, 1953, pp. 831–838.

MOORE, R. L.
[1] *Foundations of Point Set Topology*, Rev. Ed., Providence, A.M.S. Colloquium Publication No. 13, 1962.

MOORE, T. O.
[1] *Elementary General Topology*, Englewood Cliffs, N.J., Prentice-Hall, 1964.

NEWMAN, M. H. A.
[1] *Elements of the Topology of Plane Sets of Points*, 2nd Ed., Cambridge, Cambridge Univ. Press, 1951.

NOVAK, J.
[1] "Regular Spaces on Which Every Continuous Function Is Constant," *Casopis Pest. Mat. Fys.* **73** (1948), pp. 58–68.
[2] "On the Cartesian Product of Two Compact Spaces," *Fund. Math.* **40** (1953), pp. 106–112.
[3] *General Topology and Its Relations to Modern Analysis and Algebra*, Proceedings of the Symposium Held in Prague in Sept. 1961, New York, Academic Press, 1962.

PONTRJAGIN, L. S.
[1] *Topological Groups*, Princeton, Princeton Univ. Press, 1939.

SIERPINSKI, W.
[1] *General Topology*, 2nd Ed. (Transl.), Toronto, Univ. of Toronto Press, 1956.
[2] *Cardinal and Ordinal Numbers*, Rev. Ed., Hafner, 1965.

SIMMONS, G. F.
[1] *Introduction to Topology and Modern Analysis*, New York, McGraw-Hill, 1963.

SMIRNOV, Y. M.
[1] "On Metrization of Topological Spaces," *Uspekhi Matem. Nauk*, **6** (1951), pp. 100–111.
[2] "A Necessary and Sufficient Condition for Metrizability of a Topological Space," *Doklady Akad. Nauk SSSR*, **77** (1951), pp. 197–200.

SPANIER, E. H.
[1] "Set Theory and Metric Spaces," Lecture Notes, Univ. of Chicago, 1955.
[2] "Algebraic Topology, I," Lecture Notes, Univ. of Chicago, 1954.
[3] "Quasi-Topologies," *Duke Math. Journal*, **30** (1963), pp. 1–14.

STONE, A. H.
[1] "Paracompactness and Product Spaces," *Bull. A.M.S.*, **54** (1948), pp. 977–982.

STONE, M. H.
[1] "On the Compactification of Topological Spaces," *Ann. Soc. Polon. Math.*, **21** (1948), pp. 153–160.
[2] "The Generalized Weierstrass Approximation Theorem," *Math. Mag.*, **21** (1948), pp. 167–184, 237–254.

SUPPES, P.
[1] *Axiomatic Set Theory*, Princeton, Van Nostrand, 1960.

TUKEY, J. W.
[1] *Convergence and Uniformity in Topology*, Princeton, Princeton Univ. Press, Annals of Math. Studies #2, 1940.

VAIDYANATHASWAMY, R.
[1] *Set Topology*, 2nd Ed., New York, Chelsea, 1960.

WEIL, A.
[1] *Sur les Espaces à Structure Uniforme et sur la Topologie Générale*, Paris, Hermann et Cie, 1937.
WHITEHEAD, G.
[1] *Homotopy Theory*, Cambridge, Mass., M.I.T. Press, 1966.
WHYBURN, G. T.
[1] *Analytic Topology*, Providence, R.I., A.M.S. Colloquium Publication No. 28, 1942.
[2] *Open Mappings on Locally Compact Spaces*, Providence, A.M.S. Memoirs #1, 1950.
[3] *Topological Analysis*, Rev. Ed., Princeton, Princeton Univ. Press, 1964.
WILDER, R. L.
[1] *Topology of Manifolds*, Rev. Ed., Providence, R.I., A.M.S. Colloquium Publication #32, 1949.
[2] *Introduction to the Foundations of Mathematics*, New York, John Wiley, 1952.

INDEX

123567890